NUMERICAL MATHEMATICS

Calculus Explained in Numbers

NUMERICAL MATHEMATICS

JEROME C. R. LI

Professor Emeritus of Statistics

Oregon State University

Corvallis, Oregon

Distributed by

EDWARDS BROTHERS, INC.

2500 South State Street

Ann Arbor, Michigan 48104

TO

W. E. MILNE

PREFACE

Numerical Mathematics is essentially a book on elementary calculus. Its characteristic is that numbers and arithmetic operations are used as a means of communication. Its main objective is to explain the meaning of differentiation and integration.

The meaning of the formulas is demonstrated numerically. For example, the integral

$$\int \cos x \, dx \; = \; \sin x \, + \, C$$

is demonstrated through the trigonometry table. The mathematical proof is not emphasized.

The book is not oriented towards a particular group of students. Right now I cannot tell which group or groups will find it useful. However, while I was writing the book, I did have graduate students of social and biological sciences in mind. Many of these people have had little or no college mathematics in their undergraduate days, and suddenly in their graduate work they are confronted with the need of matrix and calculus. At this stage, many of them face the dilemma of being unable to acquire the necessary mathematical knowledge and unwilling to give up graduate work. Now I am trying to solve their problem with this text. It is my belief that most of them can read and understand the book without the help of a teacher. This is the reason why the book is so wordy and repetitious.

The only mathematical background required of the reader is high-school algebra. Trigonometry and analytic geometry are not prerequisites. These topics are included in the text.

A chapter on matrix algebra is included. This is done because matrix has become an increasingly popular tool in so many fields of learning. That chapter, however, may be omitted without interrupting the continuity of the book.

Traditional applications of calculus to physics and engineering are not discussed in this text. In their place, non-technical illustrations from daily life are substituted.

Despite its title, *Numerical Mathematics* is not a book on numerical calculus. The methods presented in the text do not go beyond the trapezoidal rule and Simpson's rule.

The book consists of fifteen chapters, each of which is divided into a number of sections. Every section is numbered. For example, the fourth section of chapter 12 is called section 12.4.

Many cross references are used in this book. The reader's attention is frequently directed to a certain equation, table or figure. For ready reference, indexes of tables and figures are given at the end of the book.

Important equations are numbered. The number starts anew in each section. In the section where an equation appears, the equation is simply referred to by its number such as "equation (2)". If the same equation is referred to in another section, it is further identified by the section number such as "equation (2) of section 12.4".

The number given to a table or a figure is the same as that given to the section in which it appears. If several tables or figures appear in the same section, they are further identified by letters. For example, tables 12.4a and 12.4b are the first and second tables given in section 12.4.

The reader should have access to a desk calculator if he wants to work through the examples and the exercises. A computer is not necessary. However, if one is available, it would be a good experience to work the problems on a modern computing tool.

The solutions to the problems are listed at the end of the book. All the problems are of a routine nature. They are designed to test the reader's mastery of the subject matter rather than his imagination. When the reader finds himself unable to work a problem, he should further study the book rather than ponder over the problem.

Jerome C. R. Li

July 1965

CONTENTS

CHAPTER 3. MATRIX

CHAPTER 4. FUNCTIONAL RELATION

CHAPTER 5 DIFFERENTIATION—FINITE INTERVAL

CHAPTER 6. DIFFERENTIATION——INFINITESIMAL INTERVAL

CHAPTER 7. INTEGRATION——FINITE INTERVAL

CHAPTER 8. INTEGRATION——INFINITESIMAL INTERVAL

CHAPTER 12. CALCULUS OF TRIGONOMETRIC FUNCTIONS

CHAPTER 13. SERIES

CHAPTER 14. PARTIAL DIFFERENTIATION

CONTENTS

CHAPTER 15.   MULTIPLE INTEGRATION

APPENDIX

SOLUTION TO PROBLEMS

INDEXES

INTRODUCTION

This text explains elementary mathematics in terms of numbers and arithmetic operations. Before specific topics are brought up, some notions of numbers and operations are discussed in this introductory chapter.

1.1 Deduction

Mathematics is a tool of deduction. From given conditions, one can derive their consequences without experimentation. For example, a boy doing odd jobs earned $3.50 in one day and $4.50 the next. Without asking him, one can tell that the boy earned $8.00 in two days. With the earnings of two separate days known, one can deduce the combined earning of the two days.

This simple example illustrates the usefulness of mathematics and also its limitations. With the earnings of the separate days known, it does not take much a mathematician to figure out the combined earning for the two days. However, if no information is given, a mathematician—no matter how smart he is—cannot tell how much the boy has earned.

A mathematician's job is to deduce, that is, to derive the consequences from *given* conditions. He does not produce something from nothing. The answer he produces is what he can squeeze out of the question itself.

Solving an equation can be used as an illustration of this point. The equation.

$$3x - 6 = 0$$

is a question. The solution

$$x = 2$$

is the answer. The question asked is: Subtract six from three times of what number is equal to zero? To obtain the answer, one has to manipulate the question. Adding 6 to both sides of the equation, one obtains

1

$$3x = 6 .$$

Dividing both sides of the above equation by 3, one obtains the solution

$$x = 2$$

which says that three times *two* then minus six is equal to zero.

The above example illustrates the fact that through mathematics one can only answer the questions which contain their answers. The problem is not to find the answers elsewhere but to reveal or derive them from the questions themselves.

Questions which do not contain their own answers connot be answered by mathematics. For example, the question "Where is the capital of Oregon?" cannot be answered through mathematics. The answer Salem cannot be obtained by manipulating the letters O R E G O N.

One should not get the impression that mathematics is sterile because it can only deduce consequences from known facts. In reality, numerous results can be derived from very little known fact. The limitation is one's imagination. This is not unlike the situation that infinitely many ideas can be expressed by the 26 letters of the alphabet. A creative author does not invent new letters. He only rearranges the old ones.

1.2　Uses of Numbers

The major uses of numbers are count, order, measure and identification. To count the number of objects, such as 1, 2 and 3, is a familiar use of numbers. To order the objects, such as the first, second and third, is another use. To measure an object, such as six feet tall, is the third use. A more recent use of numbers is identification, such as the telephone number and ZIP code.

Two different systems of order are being used—one starts with the first and the other with the zeroth. In the United States the floors of a building are called first floor, second floor and third floor. But the same floors are called ground floor, first floor and second floor in England, where the ground floor is the zeroth floor. Here one may feel that the English are strange and any one with sense would naturally start with the first. Who has ever heard of zeroth? But now look at the way the Americans order the birthdays. The day on which a baby is one year old is called his first birthday. The day on which the baby was actually born somehow does not even count as his birthday. This day is unconsciously designated as the zeroth birthday. At this point, one might think that this is the natural way to order the birthdays. But this way, natural or not, is by no means universal. The Chinese order their birthdays by first, second, third and so forth just like the Americans order their floors. The day on which a Chinese baby is born is his first birthday. The day on which he is one year old is called his second birthday. When a Chinese celebrates his fiftieth birthday, he is only forty-nine years old.

The two systems of order are equally effective. The important thing is to use one consistently in a country for a particular purpose. However, translators of foreign languages should be aware of the different systems being used.

Both systems of order are used in this text. The four terms of the sequence

$$a_0 \qquad a_1 \qquad a_2 \qquad a_3$$

are called the zeroth, first, second and third terms respectively. On the other hand, the four terms of the sequence

$$b_1 \qquad b_2 \qquad b_3 \qquad b_4$$

are called the first, second, third and fourth terms respectively. By using two systems, the order can be made to agree with the subscript of a letter.

The invention of instruments enables one to measure or to associate numbers with phenomena. A man is not just described as tall or short but associated with a numerical height such as six feet. The weather is not just described as hot or cold but associated with a numerical temperature such as eighty degrees. It is this quantification of phenomena that enables scientists to formulate their laws.

Identification is an expanding use of numbers. Not very long ago, only prison inmates are identified by numbers. Now most adults are identified by numbers in one place or another. A person is identified by an employee number where he works, and by another number where he pays his income tax. The house he lives in, the telephone he uses, the car he drives, the road he drives on, the bank account he keeps, and the checks he writes are all identified by numbers. These seem to be not enough. Now the neighborhood in which he lives is also identified by a number, the ZIP code. Some people hate these numbers, but this trend of using numbers for identification is unavoidable as long as machines are being used to replace clerks.

1.3 Point and Interval

A number may be interpreted geometrically as a *point* on a horizontal line. All the numbers between any two points are represented by an *interval* on that line. In figure 1.3 the numbers 1, 2, 3, 4 and 5 beneath the horizontal line are the five points. The numbers 1, 2, 3 and 4 above the line designate the non-overlapping intervals 1 to 2, 2 to 3, 3 to 4, and 4 to 5. The combined interval, from point 1 to point 5, is called the *range*. The terms point, interval and range are frequently used in later chapters.

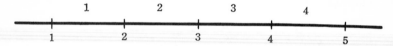

Fig. 1.3. Four intervals bounded by five points.

In pure mathematics it is usually claimed that infinitely many numbers exist between any two distinct points. However, in reality, the number of numbers is always finite. Between points 1 and 2, there are only nine distinct numbers such as

$$1.1 \quad 1.2 \quad 1.3 \quad 1.4 \quad 1.5 \quad 1.6 \quad 1.7 \quad 1.8 \quad 1.9$$

if all the numbers between the two points are rounded off to two significant figures. Within the same interval, there are 99 distinct numbers such as

$$1.01 \quad 1.02 \quad 1.03 \quad 1.04 \quad \cdots \quad 1.98 \quad 1.99$$

if all the numbers are rounded off to three significant figures. As long as the number of significant figures is finite, the number of distinct numbers between any two given points is also finite. In the real world, the number of digits of a value is always finite.

In one's daily life the distinction between a point and an interval is not always clear. For example, the age 21 appears to be a point.

Yet it is the interval of time between one's 21st and 22nd birthdays. The height 72 inches of a person appears to be a point, but it is the interval between 71.5 and 72.5 inches if the height is measured to the nearest inch. The measurement 72 inches merely indicates that one's height is closer to 72 than to 71 and 73 inches. In fact, any rounded-off number is an interval.

1.4 Zero and One

Two simple numbers 0 and 1 frequently cause confusion on the mind of a beginner in mathematics. It is not at all unusual for a college freshman to make a mistake such as

$$\frac{1250}{1250} = 0$$

even though he could change the 0 into 1 himself if he were told that a mistake had been made. Such a mistake is frequently dismissed as a careless one and let it go at that. But this confusion has its reasons.

The two systems of order help the confusion. One may start from the zeroth in ordering one set of items and from the first in another without knowing that two different systems are being used. Such indifference to 0 and 1 carries over to one's arithmetic.

The numbers 0 and 1 has another superficial similarity. If 0 is added to or subtracted from a number n, the sum or the difference is equal to n itself or

$$n + 0 = n$$

and.

$$n - 0 = n.$$

But when the number n is multiplied or divided by 1, the product or quotient is equal to n itself or.

$$n \times 1 = n(1) = n$$

and

$$n \div 1 = n/1 = n.$$

The fact that 0 and 1 do not change the number n when some operation is performed may have created the wrong impression that 0 and 1 can be used interchangeably. One should realize that the number 0 does not change n when addition or subtraction is performed and the number 1 does not change n when multiplication or division is performed.

Two ways of comparing a pair of numbers also help the confusion between 0 and 1. When the enrollment of a college changes from 1,250 to 1,500, the increase can be expressed in one of two ways. One is the difference

$$1{,}500 - 1{,}250 \; = \; 250$$

and the other is the quotient

$$1{,}500/1{,}250 \; = \; 1.20 \,.$$

The former method gives the result that the increase is 250 students, while the latter says that the increase is 20 per cent. However, if the enrollment is not changed at all, the difference method gives the result

$$1{,}250 - 1{,}250 \; = \; 0$$

and the quotient method gives

$$1{,}250/1{,}250 \; = \; 1.00 \,.$$

Here 0 and 1 say the same thing—no increase in enrollment. No wonder some college freshmen make the mistake

$$1{,}250/1{,}250 \; = \; 0 \,.$$

However, one should realize that 0 is the difference between two like numbers and 1 is the quotient of two like numbers.

The reasons for confusion between 0 and 1 given above are the author's speculation. He has no proof that these are the real causes. But it is the author's experience that the confusion mysteriously disappeared among his students after these reasons were given to them.

1.5 Number-Processing Tools

While the uses of numbers are many, the tools of processing numbers are no less. Fingers, pencils, abaci, slide rules, adding machines, desk calculators, punch-card machines and computers are all tools of processing numbers. More sophisticated is a machine; more skill is required of the operator. Indeed, to handle huge quantities of numbers is a highly technical job.

Such skills are not taught in schools and colleges except in specialized courses. In mathematics courses, however, one does incidentally learn some elementary skills in handling numbers with primitive tools such as pencil and paper. Even though ordinary mathematics courses do not offer the skills of handling large amount of computing work, they do offer many ingenious devices in reducing the amount of work. Some of such devices are discussed in later chapters.

This text does not go into number-processing as such. Here the numbers are used as a medium through which elementary mathematics is explained. The computing procedures given here are purely incidental. Even so, the reader needs a desk calculator to work through the examples.

1.6 Symbols

Symbols are an indispensable part of mathematics. They are used in indicating numbers or operations on the numbers. In the identity

$$ax + bx = (a + b)x,$$

a, b and x are numbers. But they are *generalized numbers* rather than specific ones. When $a = 2$, $b = 3$, $x = 10$, the left-hand side is

$$ax + bx = 2 \times 10 + 3 \times 10 = 20 + 30 = 50$$

and the right-hand side is

$$(a + b)x = (2 + 3)10 = 5 \times 10 = 50.$$

When other values are assigned to a, b and x, the identity still holds. If these symbols are not used, one has to use an extremely long list of numerical values to express the same idea. Even then, the list is never long enough to express the whole idea.

Another reason of using symbols is to save space. The idea is not to save paper, but to enable a person to see a lot of relations among many numbers at a glance. In this respect, the use of symbols is a lot like map-making. Most maps are small enough to be put on the top of a desk, regardless of the sizes of the regions covered by them. The maps of the United States, Oregon state and Benton county are frequently made the same size by changing the scale and the symbols. This is done for the convenience of the reader. In mathematics, similar things happen. It is not at all unusual that symbols are repeatedly condensed so that a lot of relations among many numbers are shown in a small space.

The power of a quantity such as

$$xxxxxxxxxx = x^{10}$$

is an example of condensation of symbols. The simplified notation x^{10} occupies far less room and also eliminates the need of counting the x's. However, one should realize that a *simplified notation does not necessarily lead to a simplified computation.* The streamlined x^{10} requires the same amount of time and effort to compute as the cumbersome $xxxxxxxxxx$.

1.7 Mathematical Operations

The basic operation in mathematics is addition. By skillful use of this single operation many complicated ones can be performed.

Count is a special case of addition. Each object to be counted is associated with the number 1. By adding the 1's together, one obtains the number of objects. For example, when one counts a group of people the number 1 is associated with each person as follows:

$$1 \qquad 1 \qquad 1 \qquad 1 \qquad 1$$

To obtain the number of persons, one simply adds these 1's together as

$$1 + 1 + 1 + 1 + 1 = 5.$$

This resulting sum becomes the number of persons counted.

A subtraction is the addition of a negative number, and a negative number is a number obtained by counting the objects backwards. For example, the operation

$$5 - 3 = 2$$

may be visualized as the counting operation

$$\rightarrow \quad 1 \quad 1 \quad 1 \quad 1 \quad 1 \quad \rightarrow$$

followed by a second operation

$$\leftarrow \qquad 1 \quad 1 \quad 1 \quad \leftarrow$$

which leaves 2 as the difference. This is essentially what one does when fingers are used as a computing tool.

Multiplication is a series of repeated additions of the same number. The multiplication

$$5 \times 3 = 15$$

is the addition of 5 three times

$$5 + 5 + 5 = 15$$

or the addition of 3 five times

$$3 + 3 + 3 + 3 + 3 = 15.$$

From this point of view, a multiplication is a short-cut device of adding the same number repeatedly.

Division is a series of repeated subtractions. To divide the number a by b is to subtract b from a repeatedly until the remainder is less than the divisor b. The number of subtractions performed is the quotient. For example, to divide 15 by 5 one can keep subtracting 5 from 15 and keep counting the number of subtractions performed as follow:

$$1 \qquad 15 - 5 = 10$$

$$2 \qquad\qquad 10 - 5 = 5$$

$$3 \qquad\qquad\qquad 5 - 5 = 0$$

The final count 3 is the quotient of 15/5.

The above examples illustrate the point that all arithmetic operations are ramifications of the basic operation addition. However, these simple operations are not just ends by themselves; they are also ingredients of more complicated operations. This is the reason why a machine can solve difficult mathematical problems. To use a machine, every problem has to be broken down into a series of simple operations—so simple that even a machine can carry them out. The chief advantage of a computer is not that it is so smart but it is so fast in doing the routine work. The smart ones are the designers, manufacturers and users of the computers. One need not fear that machines may become the masters of the human race. Instead, one should be glad that such efficient slaves are at his service.

Efficient tools are two-edged swords. They can be indeed dangerous if they fall in the wrong hands. This danger, however, is not limited to computers. Even an automobile can be used as a murder weapon. If one wants to worry, he should worry about the people who may use these machines and not the machines themselves.

The capacity of seeing a complicated mathematical problem in simple terms is essential to a successful user of computers. To be able to do the four arithmetical operations is not considered much a skill, but the ability to make something out of these simple operations is what separates the men from the boys. This situation is not unlike that of using a language. Almost every body in this world can learn the twenty-six letters of the alphabet, but much fewer people can make something out of them. A freshman who failed in English composition and an author who won the Nobel prize used the same twenty-six letters. The difference is in the way they combined and arranged the letters.

CHAPTER 2

ALGEBRA

The first part of this chapter reviews such familiar algebraic topics as common factor and collecting terms to demonstrate that a substantial part of high-school algebra deals with short cuts of computation. While these topics are being discussed, the tabular arrangement of computational work is introduced. Then later in the chapter these same topics are used to introduce the subscripts and the summation sign which are so commonly used in the literature of science and technology.

2.1 Common Factor

The identity

$$ax + bx + cx = (a + b + c)x$$

is a computing short cut. When $a = 3$, $b = 4$, $c = 5$, and $x = 10$, the left-hand side is equal to

$$ax + bx + cx = (3 \times 10) + (4 \times 10) + (5 \times 10) = 30 + 40 + 50 = 120$$

and the right-hand side is also equal to

$$(a + b + c)x = (3 + 4 + 5)10 = 12 \times 10 = 120$$

as it should be. But the former method requires *three* multiplications and two additions; while the latter requires only *one* multiplication and the same number of additions.

This method of common factor shows its advantage more clearly when the number of terms in that identity is large. In the above example, the number of multiplications saved is 2. If the number of terms were 100, the number of multiplications saved would be 99. In general, $(m-1)$ multiplications can be eliminated if the number of terms is m.

The usefulness of common factor can be illustrated by the example given in table 2.1 which shows the floor space of nine rooms in square feet. The problem is to compute the total floor space in square meters. Here one can convert the floor space of each room from a

11

number of square feet into that of square meters by multiplying the number of square feet by 0.0929 such as

$$168 \times 0.0929 = 15.6072$$

as shown in table 2.1. Then the nine numbers of square meters can be added together to yield the total floor space of 184.9639 square meters as shown in the table. However, this process can be simplified by first finding the total floor space in square feet, which is 1,991, and then multiplying that total by 0.0929. The resulting product is

$$1,991 \times 0.0929 = 184.9639$$

which is the same number obtained by the long method.

TABLE 2.1

FLOOR SPACE OF NINE ROOMS

Room No.	Floor Space	
	sq. ft.	sq. m.
1	168	15.6072
2	360	33.4440
3	126	11.7054
4	180	16.7220
5	72	6.6888
6	224	20.8096
7	306	28.4274
8	270	25.0830
9	285	26.4765
Total	1,991	184.9639

This numerical example is an illustration of the identity

$$ax + bx + cx = (a + b + c)x .$$

Here a, b, c and so forth are the numbers of square feet of the rooms, and x is the conversion factor 0.0929. One can see from this example how much computing time can be saved by this simple device of common factor.

Purely as a side light, table 2.1 also demonstrates how computational work can be arranged in a tabular form. The advantage of this table is that every number in it is identified. For example, the number 1,991 is identified as the total on the left and as the floor space in square feet at the top of the table. These labels—total, floor space, and square feet—jointly identify 1,991 as the total floor space in square feet. In addition, the tabular arrangement also facilitates the computation regardless of the tool being used. In a large-scale computation the tables are indispensable.

2.2 Collecting Terms

The process of collecting terms such as

$$ax + by + cx + dy = (a + c)x + (b + d)y$$

is a computing short cut. The left-hand side requires *four* multiplications and three additions

$$ax + by + cx + dy$$
$$\times + \times + \times + \times ;$$

while the right-hand side requires *two* multiplications and the same number of additions

$$(a + c)x + (b + d)y$$
$$+ \times + \quad + \times .$$

A simple device like this can eliminate two multiplications without paying any price.

Collecting terms is a more complicated version of common factor which is discussed in the preceding section. A numerical example should clarify the meaning of this device. An airline maintains a daily flight between cities A and C making an intermediate stop at city B. The numbers of passengers aboard for every day of a week are given in table 2.2. The distance between cities A and B is 980 miles, and that between B and C is 2,100 miles. The problem is to find the number of passenger-miles for the whole week. One way of finding this number is to find the passenger-miles for each of the seven days. For Sunday the number is

$$45 \times 980 + 24 \times 2,100 = 94,500 ,$$

and for Monday it is

$$89 \times 980 + 86 \times 2,100 = 267,820$$

and so forth. Then these daily numbers of passenger-miles are added
together to give the weekly figure of 1,491,140 as shown in table 2.2.

TABLE 2.2

NUMBERS OF PASSENGERS

Day of Week	A to B 980 miles	B to C 2,100 miles	Passenger- Miles
Sunday	45	24	94,500
Monday	89	86	267,820
Tuesday	93	97	294,840
Wednesday	86	83	258,580
Thursday	74	62	202,720
Friday	80	82	250,600
Saturday	41	39	122,080
Total	508	473	1,491,140

This method of computation requires 14 multiplications and 13
additions. It takes two multiplications and one addition to obtain
each daily figure. Then it requires six additional additions to add
the seven daily figures together.

Another way of computing the same number of passenger-miles
is to add the numbers of passengers for each of the two legs of the
flight, which are 508 and 473 as shown in table 2.2. Then the weekly
number of passenger-miles is

$$508 \times 980 + 473 \times 2,100 = 1,491,140$$

which is the same number obtained before.

The latter method requires 13 additions and two multiplications.
To obtain the two total numbers of passengers requires 12 additions.
The final step of computation requires two multiplications and one
addition.

The latter method uses 12 less multiplications than the former
one. This is indeed a short cut. However, the catch here is that
the daily numbers of passenger-miles are not needed. If they were,
the short cut could not be used except as a checking device.

Now connecting the numerical example with the identity

$$ax + by + cx + dy = (a + c)x + (b + d)y,$$

one should realize that the two distances 980 and 2,100 are the values of x and y respectively. The daily numbers of passengers for the segment A to B are the values of a and c except that there are seven numbers in the table and only two letters in the equation. Similarly, the daily numbers of passengers for the segment B to C are the values of b and d.

2.3 Common Denominator

The common denominator is a device of reducing the number of divisions. Before computing tools were invented, people had division phobia because division was such a painful operation to perform. Even now this fear is still being passed from one generation to another.

The addition of fractions through a common denominator such as

$$\frac{a}{b} + \frac{c}{d} + \frac{e}{f} = \frac{adf + bcf + bde}{bdf}$$

is an outstanding example of the phobia. To compute a numerical value, the left-hand side requires five operations

$$\div \quad + \quad \div \quad + \quad \div$$

and the right-side requires 11 operations

$$\times \times + \times \times + \times \times \div \times \times .$$

Despite the fact that six extra operations are needed, the latter method is frequently preferred because it reduces the number of divisions from three to one. This is understandable when pencil and paper are used as the computing tool. It is doubtful whether any one ever use the common denominator in adding fractions when more advanced tools are used.

The reader can try the example

$$\frac{7}{37} + \frac{17}{19} + \frac{41}{29} = \frac{3,857 + 18,241 + 28,823}{20,387} = \frac{50,921}{20,387}$$

on a calculator, and see which method takes less time. The values of the three original fractions are

$$0.189189189$$
$$0.894736842$$
$$1.413793103$$

whose sum is equal to

$$2.497719134 \, .$$

The value obtained from the one-division method is

$$\frac{50{,}921}{20{,}387} = 2.4977191347 \, .$$

Thus the results of the two method agree up to eight decimal places.

The discrepancy between these two results frequently leads people to defend the common denominator on the ground that it provides an exact quotient. There is no doubt that the fraction 50,921/20,387 is more exact than either one of the two results. If the objective is to reduce the sum of three fractions to one fraction, the common denominator is indeed the method to use. However, if one is after a value in decimal form, one method can give a result just as exact as the other. Then the exactness of the fraction becomes irrelevant, because it is only an intermediate step. If one is interested in exactness rather than the numerical value in decimal form, he could very well leave the three fractions as they are without reducing their sum to one fraction. After all,

$$\frac{7}{37} + \frac{17}{19} + \frac{41}{29}$$

is just as exact as 50,921/20,387.

2.4 Difference between Squares

The familiar formula

$$a^2 - b^2 = (a - b)(a + b)$$

is a computing short cut. This identity says that the difference between the squares of two numbers a and b is equal to the product of their difference and their sum. When $a = 3$ and $b = 2$, the difference between their squares is

$$a^2 - b^2 = 3^2 - 2^2 = 9 - 4 = 5 \, ,$$

and the product of their difference and their sum is also equal to

$$(a - b)(a + b) = (3 - 2)(3 + 2) = 5 \, .$$

From the above example, one can see that the latter method is a short cut. The method

$$a^2 - b^2$$

requires three operations

$$\times \;-\; \times$$

and the method

$$(a - b)(a + b)$$

also requires three operations

$$-\;\times\;+ \;.$$

However, the latter method substitutes an addition for a multiplication. Thus it is considered a simplified method, because an addition is simpler to perform than a multiplication.

The advantage of the identity still exists when it is expressed in a more complicated form such as

$$a^2x^2 - b^2y^2 \;=\; (ax - by)(ax + by)\,.$$

Here the left-hand side requires seven operations

$$a^2 \times x^2 \quad - \quad b^2 \times y^2$$
$$\times\;\times\;\times \quad - \quad \times\;\times\;\times\;;$$

while the right-hand side requires the same number of operations

$$(ax - by) \;\times\; (ax + by)$$
$$\times \;-\; \times \;\;\times\;\;\times \;+\;\times\;.$$

The advantage again is a substitution of an addition for a multiplication.

A simpler way of computing the same quantity is to find ax and by first. By this method, the left-hand side requires five operations

$$(ax)^2 \;-\; (by)^2$$
$$\times\;\times \;-\; \times\;\times\;;$$

while the right-hand side also requires five operations as follows:

$$ax \qquad by$$
$$\times \;-\; \times$$
$$+$$
$$\times$$

Here again a multiplication is replaced by an addition.

The above discussion of various ways of computing the quantity

$$z = a^2x^2 - b^2y^2$$

illustrates how algebra can be used in reducing the amount of computing work. As long as the quantities a, b, x and y are one-digit numbers and only one value of z is needed, it is almost irrelevant which method is used. However, if one million set of ten-digit numbers are assigned to a, b, x and y to compute the corresponding values of z, the problem changes its nature. It then becomes very important to consider various methods before one embarks on the computing project. Here one multiplication saved for each value of z means one million multiplications saved altogether.

2.5 Factoring

Factoring such as

$$x^2 + 5x + 6 = (x + 2)(x + 3)$$

is a computing short cut. The left-hand side requires four operations

$$\times \quad + \quad \times \quad + ;$$

while the right-hand side requires only three operations

$$+ \quad \times \quad + .$$

Thus one multiplication is saved for each value of x. However, this is a device one cannot always depend on. Such neat factors do not occur very often in real problems. Who would try to find the factors of

$$x^2 + 1{,}678.9321\,x + 6{,}543.2178$$

for the sake of saving one multiplication?

To save one multiplication one can depend on the method of collecting terms (section 2.2). By the identity

$$y = x^2 + 5x + 6 = (x + 5)x + 6$$

one can compute a value of y by the same three operations

$$+ \quad \times \quad +$$

as in the method of factoring. To find the value of

$$x^2 + 1{,}678.9321\,x + 6{,}543.2178$$

at $x = 123$, one can find the value of

$$(123 + 1{,}678.9321)123 + 6{,}543.2178$$

which is equal to 228,180.8661.

2.6 Cancellation

Cancellation is not a mathematical term but very commonly used to describe the operation of dividing both the numerator and denominator of a fraction by the same number. For example, the fraction 15/25 can be expressed as 3/5. The idea is to reduce both numerator and denominator to smaller numbers so that the division can be carried out more readily with pencil and paper or even in one's head. This is undoubtedly a neat trick in working out textbook problems but a very burdensome one in real ones. To compute the value

$$\frac{894{,}146}{958{,}069} = 0.933279\,,$$

how many people can tell that 97 is a common factor of the numerator and the denominator? Even if one could, he only makes three divisions

$$\frac{894{,}146}{97} = 9{,}218$$

$$\frac{958{,}069}{97} = 9{,}877$$

and

$$\frac{9{,}218}{9{,}877} = 0.933279$$

out of the original one division.

However, the knowledge that the numerator and the denominator of a fraction can be divided by the same number without changing the value of the fraction may be used as a computing short cut. Performing the operation

$$\frac{ax}{ay} = \frac{x}{y}\,,$$

one can save two multiplications. In evaluating the fraction

$$\frac{144 \times 57.61}{144 \times 38.49} = \frac{8{,}295.84}{5{,}542.56} = 1.49675\,,$$

one can simply ignore the multiplier 144 and carry out the division

$$\frac{57.61}{38.49} = 1.49675 .$$

Thus two multiplications are eliminated.

2.7 Short Cut

The examples given in the preceding sections demonstrate that a short cut is a computing method which involves a smaller number of the same kind of operations or the same number of simpler operations than the long method. Addition and subtraction are the simplest kinds of operations; multiplication is more complicated; and division is considered the most complicated of the four operations. A device involves one multiplication, one subtraction and one addition such as

$$(a - b)(a + b)$$

is considered a short cut in comparison with

$$a^2 - b^2$$

which requires two multiplications and one subtraction. However, these criteria of selecting a short cut are not absolute. They are frequently violated because of the tool being used. Even though the right-hand side of the identity

$$a^2 - b^2 = (a - b)(a + b)$$

is considered a short cut when pencil and paper are used, the left-hand side is definitely preferred if an automatic desk-calculator is used because it saves time.

In most elementary algebra textbooks, one usually operates on one-digit numbers. It is also taken for granted that only pencil and paper are available as a computing tool. As a result, some of the devices suggested such as factoring and solution of an equation by inspection do not have much use in real life.

Tools of computation are very much like those of transportation Many kinds can exist side by side, and each can be used for a different purpose. Despite all the modern means of transportation, human legs are still extremely important. Travelling from one's living room to his kitchen, the legs are more efficient than a jet airplane or an automobile. Of course, for intercontinental travel, the jet airplane is hard to beat.

It is senseless to compare the speed of human legs with that of a jet airplane. There should be no doubt on any body's mind which one can travel faster. Yet demonstration can be made that a human being can run faster than a plane. To accomplish this, all one has to do is set the race course only one foot long. A man can step across the finishing line before the clumsy plane can even begin to move. This is essentially the trick used in demonstrating that an abacus can compute faster than a calculator. In these demonstrations staged on television, each tool was allowed to operate for only a few seconds. If they were allowed to operate for ten hours, there should be no question that a calculator can do a lot more work than an abacus.

Similarly, multiplication table and electronic computer can exist side by side. School children are made to memorize the multiplication table. It seems cruel to make coding and decoding machines out of them at such a tender age. Yet the time devoted to memorizing the multiplication table is very well spent considering the use they can make out of it later in life. Consciously and unconsciously an adult quotes the multiplication table from his memory many times a day. Possibly people who have access to computers use the multiplication table even more frequently than those who do not.

2.8 Checking Device

Algebra, and even elementary algebra, can be very useful in developing checking devices in computation. Alternative ways of computing the same quantities are discussed in the preceding sections. Now they may be looked upon as checking devices. It is not at all unusual that two different methods are used to compute the same quantity to insure the accuracy of the result.

Mistakes in computation do occur, but they must be combed out before the final result can be presented. Mistakes are not laughing matters. Large sums of money or even human lives may be at stake. Ways must be found to eliminate them. Classroom excuses, such as carelessness, method being correct, pressure of examination, or lack of sleep the night before, cannot explain the mistakes away. Neither can these excuses remedy the damages done by the mistakes.

2.9 Subscript

Different numbers, which are hitherto represented by different letters such as a, b and c, can also be denoted by one letter with different numerical subscripts such as a_1, a_2 and a_3. In terms of the new symbols, the identity of common factor

$$ax + bx + cx = (a + b + c)x$$

may be written as

$$a_1x + a_2x + a_3x = (a_1 + a_2 + a_3)x$$

where a_1, a_2 and a_3 are merely new symbols to replace a, b and c. The advantage of the new symbols is that one can have as many terms as needed in the identity and is not limited by the number of letters in the alphabet.

Another advantage of the new symbols is that they are more meaningful than the old ones. This can be seen from the identity of collecting terms

$$ax + by + cx + dy = (a + c)x + (b + d)y$$

which can be written in the subscript form as

$$a_1x + b_1y + a_2x + b_2y = (a_1 + a_2)x + (b_1 + b_2)y \qquad (1)$$

with a_1 and a_2 replacing a and c, and b_1 and b_2 replacing b and d. Now the a's become the coefficients of x and the b's the coefficients of y. The symbol a_1 is the first coefficient of x, and a_2 the second coefficient of the same factor. At a glance one can tell that the symbol

$$(a_1 + a_2)x$$

is the common factor x multiplied by the sum of its two coefficients.

The meaningfulness of the new symbols can also be demonstrated by the identity of common denominator

$$\frac{a}{b} + \frac{c}{d} + \frac{e}{f} = \frac{adf + bcf + bde}{bdf} .$$

This equation may be written in the subscript form as

$$\frac{a_1}{b_1} + \frac{a_2}{b_2} + \frac{a_3}{b_3} = \frac{a_1b_2b_3 + b_1a_2b_3 + b_1b_2a_3}{b_1b_2b_3}$$

with all the numerators represented by a's and denominators by b's. The subscripts 1, 2 and 3 indicate the first, second and third fractions. Then the new symbols clearly indicate the meaning of the terms

$$b_1b_2b_3 \qquad a_1b_2b_3 \qquad b_1a_2b_3 \qquad b_1b_2a_3 \,.$$

The first term is the product of the denominators of the three fractions; the second one is the product of the numerator of the first fraction and the denominators of the other two fractions; and so forth. The fact that each of the four terms contains all the subscripts 1, 2 and 3 indicates that every term is a product of three elements, each of which comes from a different fraction.

In addition to making the symbols more meaningful, the subscripts can also be used to generalize the relations among numbers. The identity of common factor

$$a_1x + a_2x + a_3x = (a_1 + a_2 + a_3)x$$

holds not only for the sum of three terms. It is true for any number of terms. To indicate this fact, the identity can be written as

$$a_1x + a_2x + \cdots + a_mx = (a_1 + a_2 + \cdots + a_m)x \qquad (2)$$

where m may be any positive integer such as 1, 2, 3 and so forth. The three dots used in the above equation stand for all the terms in between. Now the new symbols state that the identity holds for any number of terms.

The subscript with a changing value is frequently represented by the letter i. For example, the three symbols

$$a_1 \qquad a_2 \qquad a_3$$

may be written as

$$a_i \qquad i = 1, 2, 3.$$

In general, the m symbols

$$a_1 \qquad a_2 \qquad \cdots \qquad a_m$$

may be represented by

$$a_i \qquad i = 1, 2, \cdots, m.$$

These are shorthand symbols.

2.10 Summation

As a shorthand the Greek letter sigma Σ is used to indicate the sum of many numbers. The sum

$$a_1 + a_2 + a_3 + a_4 + a_5 + a_6 + a_7 + a_8$$

may be written as

$$\Sigma a_i \qquad i = 1, 2, \cdots, 8,$$

or as

$$\sum_{i=1}^{8} a_i$$

with the upper and lower limits of the value of the subscript i placed above and below the summation sign, or simply as Σa_i with the limits of the subscript i omitted if no possibility of ambiguity exists. In any form the summation sign Σ is a device of condensing an algebraic expression. For the general case of m terms, the sum is condensed into

$$a_1 + a_2 + \cdots + a_m = \sum_{i=1}^{m} a_i .$$

In terms of the summation sign, the identity of common factor

$$a_1 x + a_2 x + \cdots + a_m x = x(a_1 + a_2 + \cdots + a_m)$$

may be written as

$$\Sigma a_i x = x \Sigma a_i \qquad i = 1, 2, \cdots, m \tag{1}$$

or, in an alternative form, as

$$\sum_{i=1}^{m} a_i x = x \sum_{i=1}^{m} a_i \tag{2}$$

which is a very compact equation. However, despite its appearance, equation (2) still represents the plain old principle of common factor.

Such compact notations frequently frighten beginners in mathematics. However, when one finds condensed symbols hard to comprehend, all he has to do is write the symbols in longhand such as

$$\sum_{i=1}^{m} a_i x = a_1 x + a_2 x + \cdots + a_m x$$

and

$$\sum_{i=1}^{m} a_i = a_1 + a_2 + \cdots + a_m$$

to clarify their meaning. For $m = 3$, equation (2) is simply

$$a_1 x + a_2 x + a_3 x = x(a_1 + a_2 + a_3)$$

which is just another way of writing the familiar equation

$$ax + bx + cx = x(a + b + c).$$

To further clarify the meaning of equation (2), the identity is expressed in a tabular form as shown in table 2.10a. Comparing this table with the numerical example given in table 2.1, one can see that x is the conversion factor 0.0929 and the a's are the numbers of square feet.

TABLE 2.10a

IDENTITY OF COMMON FACTOR

i	a_i	$a_i x$
1	a_1	$a_1 x$
2	a_2	$a_2 x$
...	...	...
m	a_m	$a_m x$
Total	$\sum_{i=1}^{m} a_i$	$\sum_{i=1}^{m} a_i x$
Identity	$x \sum_{i=1}^{m} a_i$	$= \sum_{i=1}^{m} a_i x$

Through the use of the summation sign Σ, the identity of collecting terms

$$a_1 x + b_1 y + a_2 x + b_2 y = (a_1 + a_2)x + (b_1 + b_2)y$$

given in equation (1) of section 2.9 may be generalized. The number of terms involving x or y in the above equation does not have to be two. The identity holds for any number of terms. To generalize this aspect of the identity, the number of terms involving x or y is designated by m which can be any positive integer such as 1, 2, 3 and so forth. Then the identity becomes

$$(a_1x + b_1y) + (a_2x + b_2y) + \cdots + (a_mx + b_my)$$
$$= (a_1 + a_2 + \cdots + a_m)x + (b_1 + b_2 + \cdots + b_m)y$$

and, in shorthand, it becomes

$$\sum_{i=1}^{m}(a_ix+b_iy) = x\sum_{i=1}^{m}a_i + y\sum_{i=1}^{m}b_i \tag{3}$$

which is a very compact equation.

To clarify its meaning, equation (3) is presented in a tabular form as shown in table 2.10b. Comparing this table with the numerical example given in table 2.2, one should be able to grasp the physical meaning of equation (3). The a's are the numbers of passengers travelled 980 miles from A to B, and the b's are those traveled 2,100 miles from B to C. The expression $a_ix + b_iy$ is the number of passenger-miles of the ith day of the week, with x and y being the two distances.

TABLE 2.10b

IDENTITY OF COLLECTING TERMS

i	a_i	b_i	a_ix+b_iy
1	a_1	b_1	$a_1x + b_1y$
2	a_2	b_2	$a_2x + b_2y$
...	...	...	...
m	a_m	b_m	$a_mx + b_my$
Total	$\sum_{i=1}^{m}a_i$	$\sum_{i=1}^{m}b_i$	$\sum_{i=1}^{m}(a_ix + b_iy)$
Identity	$x\sum_{i=1}^{m}a_i$	$+ \quad y\sum_{i=1}^{m}b_i$	$= \quad \sum_{i=1}^{m}(a_ix + b_iy)$

2.11 Double Summation

An algebraic expression may have more than one summation sign. To demonstrate the use of double summation signs, the identity of collecting terms

$$\sum_{i=1}^{m}(a_ix + b_iy) = x\sum_{i=1}^{m}a_i + y\sum_{i=1}^{m}b_i$$

given in equation (3) of section 2.10 may be further generalized. The number of common factors such as x and y does not have to be two. The identity holds for any number of common factors. Here this number is designated by n which is a positive integer such as $1, 2, 3$, and the factors themselves are represented by

$$x_1 \qquad x_2 \qquad \cdots \qquad x_n$$

to replace x and y. Their coefficients are designated by

$$c_{i1} \qquad c_{i2} \qquad \cdots \qquad c_{in} \qquad i = 1, 2, \cdots, m$$

to replace the original symbols a_i and b_i. Here the first subscript i of the symbol c still represents the values $1, 2, \cdots, m$, and the second subscript is introduced to distinguish the common factors $x_1, x_2, \cdots, x_n$. Thus the old symbols

$$a_1 \qquad b_1$$
$$a_2 \qquad b_2$$
$$\cdots \qquad \cdots$$
$$a_m \qquad b_m$$

given in table 2.10b are replaced by the new symbols

$$c_{11} \qquad c_{12}$$
$$c_{21} \qquad c_{22}$$
$$\cdots \qquad \cdots$$
$$c_{m1} \qquad c_{m2} .$$

The two subscripts of each coefficient c_{ij} denote two different things. The subscript i identifies a particular one out of m such coefficients of a particular common factor, and the subscript j identifies that particular x_j out of n common factors. Then c_{12} is the first coefficient of the common factor x_2, and c_{21} the second coefficient of x_1. In general, the symbol c_{ij} represents the ith coefficient of the jth common factor.

Now the generalized identity of collecting terms becomes

$$c_{11}x_1 + c_{12}x_2 + \cdots + c_{1n}x_n$$

$$+ c_{21}x_1 + c_{22}x_2 + \cdots + c_{2n}x_n$$

$$\cdots$$

$$+ c_{m1}x_1 + c_{m2}x_2 + \cdots + c_{mn}x_n$$

$$= \tag{1}$$

$$x_1(c_{11} + c_{21} + \cdots + c_{m1})$$

$$+ x_2(c_{12} + c_{22} + \cdots + c_{m2})$$

$$\cdots$$

$$+ x_n(c_{1n} + c_{2n} + \cdots + c_{mn}) \,.$$

The way in which the terms of the above identity are arranged should make the meaning of the identity clear. It is simply a more generalized form of a familar equation such as

$$3x - 2y + 2z$$

$$+ x \qquad - 3z$$

$$- x + y + 5z$$

$$=$$

$$x(3 + 1 - 1)$$

$$+ y(-2 + 0 + 1)$$

$$+ z(2 - 3 + 5)$$

which is equal to $3x - y + 4z$.

Through the use of the summation sign Σ, equation (1) can be written in a shorthand form as

$$\sum_{j=1}^{n} c_{1j}x_j + \sum_{j=1}^{n} c_{2j}x_j + \cdots + \sum_{j=1}^{n} c_{mj}x_j$$

$$= x_1 \sum_{i=1}^{m} c_{i1} + x_2 \sum_{i=1}^{m} c_{i2} + \cdots + x_n \sum_{i=1}^{m} c_{in}$$

which can be further condensed into

$$\sum_{i=1}^{m} \sum_{j=1}^{n} c_{ij}x_j = \sum_{j=1}^{n} x_j \sum_{i=1}^{m} c_{ij} \tag{2}$$

which is a formidable-looking equation. However, despite its looks, the equation still expresses the same old principle of collecting terms which bothers few people in high school. When some one claims that he does not understand equation (2), the chances are that he does know the idea behind it but not the language in which the idea is expressed. Those who do not know the principle of collecting terms seldom have a chance of encountering such an equation.

Whenever one is bewildered by subscripts and summation signs, he should not give up easily. Once the condensed expressions are written out in longhand step by step, more often than not the meaning reveals itself.

2.12 Tabular Form of Double Summation

The meaning of double summation is further explained in this section in a tabular form. The example used here is still the identity of collecting terms

$$\sum_{i=1}^{m} \sum_{j=1}^{n} c_{ij} x_j = \sum_{j=1}^{n} x_j \sum_{i=1}^{m} c_{ij} \tag{1}$$

given in equation (2) of section 2.11. For this example, table 2.12 with m rows and n columns is made. Within each of the mn cells is the product $c_{ij} x_j$. In each of the n columns, x_j is the common factor of the m products. In order to find the grand total

$$\sum_{i=1}^{m} \sum_{j=1}^{n} c_{ij} x_j$$

TABLE 2.12

GENERALIZED IDENTITY OF COLLECTING TERMS

i \ j	1	2	$\cdots$	n
1	$c_{11} x_1$	$c_{12} x_2$	$\cdots$	$c_{1n} x_n$
2	$c_{21} x_1$	$c_{22} x_2$	$\cdots$	$c_{2n} x_n$
$\cdots$	$\cdots$	$\cdots$	$\cdots$	$\cdots$
m	$c_{m1} x_1$	$c_{m2} x_2$	$\cdots$	$c_{mn} x_n$
Total	$x_1 \sum_{i=1}^{m} c_{i1}$	$x_2 \sum_{i=1}^{m} c_{i2}$	$\cdots$	$x_n \sum_{i=1}^{m} c_{in}$

of the mn products, equation (1) says that one can take advantage of the common factors and first find the n column totals (table 2.12)

$$x_j \sum_{i=1}^{m} c_{ij} \qquad j = 1, 2, \cdots, n$$

and then add these n column totals together to obtain the grand total

$$\sum_{j=1}^{n} x_j \sum_{i=1}^{m} c_{ij}.$$

This is obviously a sensible way of doing the job.

Table 2.12 is indeed a generalized identity of collecting terms because some of the c's can be equal to 0 and some of the x's can be equal to 1. For example, the identity

$$(2x_1 + 3x_2 + 4) + (x_1 + 5) = 3x_1 + 3x_2 + 9,$$

does not seem to fit into the pattern of the table. However, once the coefficients

2	3	4
1	0	5

are associated with the symbols

c_{11}	c_{12}	c_{13}
c_{21}	c_{22}	c_{23}

and x_3 is assigned the value 1, one can see that table 2.12 does cover this special case.

The purpose of the identity given in equation (1) is to eliminate a number of multiplications. The original m multiplications in each column is replaced by the only one in the column total. Thus $m-1$ multiplications are saved for each of the n columns, and a total of $n(m-1)$ multiplications are saved in the whole operation.

Whenever one is bewildered by an algebraic expression involving double summation signs and double subscripts, he can usually solve the riddle by writing out all the terms in a tabular form such as table 2.12. After some practice, one can gradually see the meaning of an algebraic expression by merely visualizing a table without actually making one. In time one can instinctly see what does an expression stand for without even visualizing a table. These things need practice. One has no right to expect to have the command of a new language without practicing on it.

2.13 Example of Double Summation

The numerical example given in table 2.13 is used in this section as an illustration of the identity of collecting terms

$$\sum_{i=1}^{m} \sum_{j=1}^{n} c_{ij} x_j = \sum_{j=1}^{n} x_j \sum_{i=1}^{m} c_{ij} \tag{1}$$

given in equation (2) of section 2.11. A motel has three kinds of rooms renting for six, eight and ten dollars a day. The numbers of the three kinds of rooms occupied are listed for each of the seven days of a week. The problem is to find the total receipt of the week.

TABLE 2.13

NUMBERS OF ROOMS OCCUPIED IN A MOTEL

(1)	(2)	(3)	(4)	(5)
Day of Week	$ 6 Room	$ 8 Room	$ 10 Room	Daily Receipt
Sunday	7	8	4	$ 146
Monday	10	12	6	$ 216
Tuesday	15	14	10	$ 302
Wednesday	14	13	9	$ 278
Thursday	13	15	8	$ 278
Friday	12	14	9	$ 274
Saturday	6	5	3	$ 106
Total	77	81	49	$ 1,600

This problem, like many textbook problems, is unrealistic. The most likely way of obtaining a weekly receipt is to add up the seven daily receipts. A daily receipt can be obtained by simply counting the money received without computation and certainly without algebra. This may be so, but the objective of this example here is to illustrate the identity of collecting terms given in equation (1) and not to find a practical way of obtaining the weekly receipt.

One way of finding the weekly receipt from table 2.13 is to find the sum of the seven daily receipts. A daily receipt is the sum of the products of the numbers of rooms occupied and the room rates. For Sunday the receipt is

$$7(\$\,6) + 8(\$\,8) + 4(\$\,10) \;=\; \$\,146\;.$$

For Monday the receipt is

$$10(\$\,6) + 12(\$\,8) + 6(\$\,10) \;=\; \$\,216\;.$$

These two and the other five daily receipts are listed in column 5 of table 2.13. The weekly receipt $\$\,1,600$, which is the sum of the seven daily receipts, is given at the lower-right corner of that table.

Another way of finding the weekly receipt is to find the total number of rooms occupied for each of the three kinds of rooms. These three totals 77, 81 and 49 are given in the bottom row of tables 2.13. Then the weekly receipt is simply

$$77(\$\,6) + 81(\$\,8) + 49(\$\,10) \;=\; \$\,1,600$$

which is the same amount obtained by the former method.

This example is so simple that the reader may feel that his intelligence is being insulted. Yet the formidable-looking equation (1) says no more than this simple fact. Comparing tables 2.12 and 2.13, one can see that m is equal to 7—the number of days in a week—and n is equal to 3—the three kinds of rooms. The symbols c_{ij}—all 21 of them—are the numbers of rooms occupied. The subscript i indicates the day of week and j the kind of room occupied. The common factors x_1, x_2 and x_3 are the room rates which are six, eight and ten dollars a day.

Now the weekly receipt can be expressed in terms of the symbols just identified. A daily receipt is

$$c_{i1}x_1 + c_{i2}x_2 + c_{i3}x_3 \;=\; \sum_{j=1}^{3} c_{ij}x_j \qquad i = 1, 2, \cdots, 7\;.$$

Consequently, the weekly receipt is

$$\sum_{j=1}^{3} c_{1j}x_j + \sum_{j=1}^{3} c_{2j}x_j + \cdots + \sum_{j=1}^{3} c_{7j}x_j \;=\; \sum_{i=1}^{7} \sum_{j=1}^{3} c_{ij}x_j$$

which is the first method of computation. The second method

$$x_1\sum_{i=1}^{7}c_{i1} + x_2\sum_{i=1}^{7}c_{i2} + x_3\sum_{i=1}^{7}c_{i3} = \sum_{j=1}^{3}x_j\sum_{i=1}^{7}c_{ij}$$

is to find the weekly receipt through the column totals. All equation (1) says is that the two methods should yield the same result.

2.14 Sums of Coefficients

Various sums of the coefficients c_{ij} given in table 2.14a can be represented by $\sum c_{ij}$ or $\sum\sum c_{ij}$ by imposing different restrictions on the subscripts i and j. To emphasize the fact that c_{ij} are actually numbers, an arbitrary set of numerical values are assigned to them and listed in table 2.14b. These tables are of the dimensions 4×3; that is, m is equal to 4 and n is equal to 3.

TABLE 2.14a

COEFFICIENTS IN SYMBOLS

i \ j	1	2	3	Total
1	c_{11}	c_{12}	c_{13}	$\sum c_{1j}$
2	c_{21}	c_{22}	c_{23}	$\sum c_{2j}$
3	c_{31}	c_{32}	c_{33}	$\sum c_{3j}$
4	c_{41}	c_{42}	c_{43}	$\sum c_{4j}$
Total	$\sum c_{i1}$	$\sum c_{i2}$	$\sum c_{i3}$	$\sum\sum c_{ij}$

TABLE 2.14b

COEFFICIENTS IN NUMBERS

Row \ Column	1	2	3	Total
1	41	25	59	125
2	71	37	64	172
3	35	24	45	104
4	94	81	56	231
Total	241	167	224	632

The column totals, row totals and the grand total of the given example are shown in table 2.14a in symbols and in table 2.14b in numbers. The three column totals can be written as

$$\sum_{i=1}^{4} c_{ij} \qquad j = 1, 2, 3,$$

and a particular column total can be identified by specifying the value of j, such as the first column total being

$$\sum_{i=1}^{4} c_{i1} = 241.$$

Similarly, the four row totals can be written as

$$\sum_{j=1}^{3} c_{ij} \qquad i = 1, 2, 3, 4,$$

and a particular row total can be identified by specifying the value of i, such as the second row total being

$$\sum_{j=1}^{3} c_{2j} = 172.$$

Of course, the grand total

$$\sum_{i=1}^{4} \sum_{j=1}^{3} c_{ij} = 632$$

is unique.

The grand total can be found in two different ways. One can first obtain the three column totals and add these column totals; or one can first obtain the four row totals and add these row totals. The fact that two methods yield the same result should be obvious to every one. Yet when this simple fact is stated in a symbolic language such as

$$\sum_{j=1}^{3} \sum_{i=1}^{4} c_{ij} = \sum_{i=1}^{4} \sum_{j=1}^{3} c_{ij}$$

one may wonder why the position of the two summation signs can be interchanged. Whenever one is bewildered by such symbols, he is advised to arrange the c's systematically such as in table 2.14a. Consulting that table, one can see that the left-hand side respresents the grand total obtained through the column totals and the right-hand side represents the same quantity obtained through the row totals.

By changing the limits of i and j, the symbol $\sum\sum c_{ij}$ can be used in representing the sum of some of the c's rather than all of them. The quantity

$$\sum_{j=1}^{2}\sum_{i=3}^{4}c_{ij} = \sum_{j=1}^{2}(c_{3j}+c_{4j}) = (c_{31}+c_{41})+(c_{32}+c_{42})$$

$$= (35+94)+(24+81) = 234$$

is the sum of four c's at the lower-left corner of table 2.14a.

The sum of the coefficients which appear diagonally in table 2.14a may be expressed in symbols. The sum

$$c_{11}+c_{22}+c_{33} = 41+37+45 = 123$$

may be written as

$$\sum_{i=1}^{3}c_{ii} = 123$$

which represents the sum of all the coefficients with the characteristic of the two subscripts being equal. The sum of the three coefficients immediately below c_{11}, c_{22} and c_{33} is

$$c_{21}+c_{32}+c_{43} = 71+24+56 = 151$$

which may be written as

$$\sum_{i=2}^{4}c_{i,\,i-1} = c_{21}+c_{32}+c_{43}.$$

The above sum, which represents the sum of all coefficients with the characteristic that the second subscript is one less than the first one, can also be written as

$$\sum_{j=1}^{3}c_{j+1,\,j} = c_{21}+c_{32}+c_{43}$$

which represents the sum of all coefficients with the characteristic that the first subscript is one more than the second one.

As another example, one may consider the sum of the three c's at the upper-right corner or table 2.14a. This sum

$$c_{12}+c_{13}+c_{23} = 25+59+64 = 148$$

may be written as

$$\sum_{i=1}^{4}\sum_{j=1}^{3}c_{ij} \qquad \text{for } i<j$$

which represents the sum of all the c's with the characteristic of the first subscript being less than the second one.

The examples of the condensed notations given above sometimes look very profound. However, once the meaning is deciphered through table 2.14a, the facts stated by the symbols are often very simple.

The rectangular arrangement of the coefficients c_{ij} given in table 2.14a is called a *matrix* in algebra. Each c_{ij} is called an *element* of that matrix. In the example under discussed, the elements happen to be the coefficients of the common factors x_j. However, this may not always be the case. Matrix algebra is presented in the following chapter as a special topic.

EXERCISES

1. (a) The following numbers are lengths in yards:

    732   941   842   739   654   930   745   826

    Find the total length in feet by two methods. First, change each number of yards into a number of feet and then add the numbers of feet. Second, add the numbers of yards as they are and then change the total number of yards into a number of feet. Arrange your computation in a tabular form such as table 2.10a.

   (b) Compare your table of part (a) with table 2.10a, and give the numerical values of the following symbols:

    (i) m (ii) x (iii) i (iv) a_2 (v) a_3x

    (vi) $\sum\limits_{i=1}^{m} a_i$ (vii) $\sum\limits_{i=1}^{m} a_i x$ (viii) $x\sum\limits_{i=1}^{m} a_i$

2. (a) Four persons worked on a job. The amount of time spent by them are as follows:

    (i)   4 hours 15 minutes
    (ii) 5 hours 30 minutes
    (iii) 7 hours 12 minutes
    (iv) 3 hours 45 minutes

    Find the total number of hours spent on the job by the four persons in two ways. First, change the amount of time spent by each person into a number of hours and then add the four numbers of hours. Second, add the numbers of hours and the numbers of minutes as they are, but in separate columns, and then change the two totals into one number of hours. Arrange your computation in a tabular form such as table 2.2.

(b) Compare your table of part (a) with table 2.10b, and give the numerical values of the following symbols:

(i) m (ii) a_1 (iii) b_2 (iv) x (v) y

(vi) $\sum\limits_{i=1}^{m} a_i$ (vii) $\sum\limits_{i=1}^{m} b_i$ (viii) $\sum\limits_{i=1}^{m} (a_i x + b_i y)$

(c) Compare your table of part (a) with table 2.12, and give the numerical values of the following symbols:

(i) x_1 (ii) x_2 (iii) m (iv) n (v) c_{12} (vi) c_{21}

(vii) $\sum\limits_{i=1}^{m} c_{i1}$ (viii) $\sum\limits_{i=1}^{m} c_{i2}$ (ix) $\sum\limits_{j=1}^{n} x_j \sum\limits_{i=1}^{m} c_{ij}$

3. Find the values of $(x^2 + 189x + 213)$ for $x = 72$, 80, 88 and 96. Arrange your computation in a tabular form showing the following four columns:

$$x \qquad x + 189 \qquad (x + 189)x \qquad x^2 + 189x + 213$$

4. Express the following sums in terms of the subscript i and the summation sign Σ:

(a) $\dfrac{a_1}{b_1} + \dfrac{a_2}{b_2} + \dfrac{a_3}{b_3}$

(b) $\dfrac{a_1}{a_2} + \dfrac{a_2}{a_3} + \dfrac{a_3}{a_4} + \dfrac{a_4}{a_5}$

(c) $a_1 b_1 + a_2 b_2 + a_3 b_3 + a_4 b_4$

(d) $x_1 x_2 + x_2 x_3 + x_3 x_4$

(e) $x_1^2 + x_2^2 + x_3^2 + x_4^2 + x_5^2$

(f) $x_1 y_1 + x_2 y_2 + x_3 y_3$

5. (a) Collect terms of the following expression:

$$(9w - 3x + 4y + z) + (5w + 4x) + (2w - 7y)$$
$$+ (8x - 3z) + (x + y)$$

(b)   Replace the symbols

$$w \qquad x \qquad y \qquad z$$

of part (a) by

$$x_1 \qquad x_2 \qquad x_3 \qquad x_4$$

and make a table similar to table 2.12.

6. Express the following sums of c's of table 2.14a in terms of i, j and Σ:

(a) $c_{12} + c_{13} + c_{22} + c_{23}$

(b) $c_{12} + c_{23}$

(c) $c_{31} + c_{42}$

(d) $c_{12} + c_{21}$

(e) $c_{13} + c_{22} + c_{31}$

7. Many restrictions can be imposed on the sum $\Sigma\Sigma c_{ij}$ of table 2.14a. Write out the sum in longhand for each of the following restrictions:

(a) $i + j = 4$

(b) $i + j = 5$

(c) $i > j$

(d) $i = 2$

(e) $j = 3$

The numerical values of the sums can be obtained from table 2.14b.

CHAPTER 3

MATRIX

The basic concepts and techniques of matrix algebra are given in this chapter. The subject matter is presented entirely from the utilitarian point of view for the benefit of people who use matrix as a working tool. However, the omission of this chapter does not interrupt the continuity of the text.

3.1 Solution of Linear Equations

In high-school algebra one learns how to solve a system of linear equations involving three unknown quantities such as:

$$5x - 2y + z = 3 \tag{1}$$

$$2x + y - 5z = -6 \tag{2}$$

$$4x - 2y + z = 1 \tag{3}$$

The procedure of solving the system of equations is roughly as follows: Multiplying equation (1) by 4, (2) by 10, and (3) by 5, one obtains the following equations:

$$20x - 8y + 4z = 12 \tag{4}$$

$$20x + 10y - 50z = -60 \tag{5}$$

$$20x - 10y + 5z = 5 \tag{6}$$

Subtracting equation (4) from equations (5) and (6), one has

$$18y - 54z = -72 \tag{7}$$

and

$$- 2y + z = - 7. \tag{8}$$

Adding equation (7) to nine times equation (8), one has

$$- 45z = -135$$

or

$$z = 3.$$

Substituting 3 for z in equation (8), one has

$$y = 5.$$

Substituting 3 for z and 5 for y in equation (1), one has

$$x = 2.$$

Thus the solutions of the system of linear equations are obtained.

The procedure shown above is quite tedious. It involves repeated writing of x, y, z, plus signs and equality signs. A great deal of writing can be saved by omitting these symbols and only using the coefficients of the three unknown quantities. Equations (1), (2) and (3) can be abbreviated as:

$$
\begin{array}{cccc}
5 & -2 & 1 & 3 \\
2 & 1 & -5 & -6 \\
4 & -2 & 1 & 1 \\
\end{array}
\tag{9}
$$

All the other equations can be similarly abbreviated. Of course, the solution thus obtained remains $x = 2$, $y = 5$, and $z = 3$.

Another simplification of the procedure is to use division to equalize the coefficients of the same unknown quantity of different equations. The coefficients of x in equations (1), (2) and (3) are originally 5, 2 and 4 respectively. Those of equations (4), (5) and (6) are made equal to 20 by multiplying the equations with appropriate numbers. However, the same effect can be achieved by dividing equations (1), (2) and (3) by 5, 2 and 4 respectively. As long as one has adequate computing tools, he does not have to use various devices to avoid division as he used to do in high school. The procedure of solving equations (1), (2) and (3) may be carried out step by step as shown in table 3.1 which gives the same solutions as previously obtained. The procedure given in table 3.1 differs from the conventional method taught in high school in the following three respects:

(a) Elimination of repeated writing of x, y, z, plus signs and equality signs. The advantage of doing so is obvious.

(b) Replacement of multiplications by divisions in equalizing the coefficients of the same unknown quantity in different equations. This is an advantage only if adequate computing tools are available.

(c) Consistency in subtracting the first equation from remaining equations. This facilitates checking the result of computation and eliminates the time spent in looking for short cuts which exist only in textbook problems but seldom, if ever, exist in real ones.

TABLE 3.1

SOLUTION OF LINEAR EQUATIONS

Line No.	x	y	z	Right Hand	Operation
1	5	−2	1	3	
2	2	1	−5	−6	
3	4	−2	1	1	
4	1	−0.40	0.20	0.60	(1) ÷ 5
5	1	0.50	−2.50	−3.00	(2) ÷ 2
6	1	−0.50	0.25	0.25	(3) ÷ 4
7	0	0.90	−2.70	−3.60	(5) − (4)
8	0	−0.10	0.05	−0.35	(6) − (4)
9		1	−3.00	−4.00	(7) ÷ 0.9
10		1	−0.50	3.50	(8) ÷ (−0.1)
11		0	2.50	7.50	(10) − (9)
12			1	3.00	(11) ÷ 2.5
13		1		5.00	sub. in (10)
14	1			2.00	sub. in (6)

3.2 Matrix

An array of numbers such as

$$\begin{bmatrix} a_{11} & a_{12} & a_{13} \\ a_{21} & a_{22} & a_{23} \\ a_{31} & a_{32} & a_{33} \end{bmatrix} \tag{1}$$

is called a *matrix*. The array of coefficients of equations (1), (2) and (3) of section 3.1 is an example. The nine coefficients which may be arranged as

$$\begin{bmatrix} 5 & -2 & 1 \\ 2 & 1 & -5 \\ 4 & -2 & 1 \end{bmatrix} \tag{2}$$

constitute a matrix. The numbers on the right-hand side of the same
equations arranged as

$$\begin{bmatrix} 3 \\ -6 \\ 1 \end{bmatrix} \tag{3}$$

constitute another matrix.

The size of a matrix is measured by its number of rows and its
number of columns. An $m \times n$ matrix is one which has m rows and
n columns. For example, matrix (2) is a 3×3 matrix; while matrix
(3) is a 3×1 (not 1×3) matrix. If $m = n$, the matrix is said to be
square. Matrix (2) is a square matrix, and matrix (3) is not.

Each number of a matrix is called an *element* of that matrix.
Matrix (1) has 9 elements. So does matrix (2). But matrix (3) has
3 elements. In general, an $m \times n$ matrix has mn elements. Each
element may consist of any number of digits, even though the
examples given here show only one-digit elements. The plus or
minus sign is an integral part of an element.

Two matrices are said to be *equal*, if their corresponding elements
are equal. For example, the equality of matrices (1) and (2) implies
the following nine equations:

$$a_{11} = 5 \qquad a_{12} = -2 \qquad a_{13} = 1$$

$$a_{21} = 2 \qquad a_{22} = 1 \qquad a_{23} = -5$$

$$a_{31} = 4 \qquad a_{32} = -2 \qquad a_{33} = 1$$

The pair of subscripts of an element specifies the position of that
element in a matrix. The first subscript is the row number and the
second one the column number. The element a_{23} occupies the position
of the second row and the third column. In general, the element a_{ij}
occupies the position of the ith row and the jth column.

Frequently a matrix is represented by one letter only. Matrix
(1) may be written as

$$A = [a_{ij}] \qquad i = 1, 2, 3; \qquad j = 1, 2, 3;$$

where a_{ij} is the element which occupies the ith row and the jth
column of matrix A. An $m \times n$ matrix may be represented by

$$A = [a_{ij}] \qquad i = 1, 2, \cdots, m ; \qquad j = 1, 2, \cdots, n.$$

These abbreviations do not change the meaning of a matrix.

The *transpose* of a matrix is the matrix formed by interchanging the rows and columns of the original matrix. The transpose of the matrix

$$A = \begin{bmatrix} a_{11} & a_{12} & a_{13} \\ a_{21} & a_{22} & a_{23} \\ a_{31} & a_{32} & a_{33} \end{bmatrix} \tag{4}$$

is

$$A' = \begin{bmatrix} a_{11} & a_{21} & a_{31} \\ a_{12} & a_{22} & a_{32} \\ a_{13} & a_{23} & a_{33} \end{bmatrix}. \tag{5}$$

The transpose of matrix (2) is

$$\begin{bmatrix} 5 & 2 & 4 \\ -2 & 1 & -2 \\ 1 & -5 & 1 \end{bmatrix}. \tag{6}$$

The transpose of an $m \times n$ matrix is an $n \times m$ matrix. The matrix

$$B = \begin{bmatrix} 4 & 2 & 1 \\ 5 & -3 & 2 \end{bmatrix} \tag{7}$$

is a 2×3 matrix, but its transpose

$$B' = \begin{bmatrix} 4 & 5 \\ 2 & -3 \\ 1 & 2 \end{bmatrix} \tag{8}$$

is a 3×2 matrix.

A matrix is said to be *symmetric*, if its transpose is identical to itself. An example of a symmetric matrix is

$$\begin{bmatrix} 95 & -42 & 73 \\ -42 & 50 & 82 \\ 73 & 82 & 17 \end{bmatrix}. \tag{9}$$

In symbolic form, a matrix A is said to be symmetric if

$$[a_{ij}] = [a_{ji}] \tag{10}$$

or

$$A = A' \tag{11}$$

where A' is the transpose of A.

A *diagonal* matrix is a square matrix in which all elements are equal to zero except those in the diagonal such as

$$\begin{bmatrix} a_{11} & 0 & 0 \\ 0 & a_{22} & 0 \\ 0 & 0 & a_{33} \end{bmatrix}. \tag{12}$$

Of course, a diagonal matrix is always symmetric.

A diagonal matrix is called a *scalar* matrix, if all its diagonal elements are equal such as

$$\begin{bmatrix} 12 & 0 & 0 \\ 0 & 12 & 0 \\ 0 & 0 & 12 \end{bmatrix}. \tag{13}$$

A scalar matrix is called an *identity* matrix, if all the diagonal elements are equal to 1 such as

$$\begin{bmatrix} 1 & 0 & 0 \\ 0 & 1 & 0 \\ 0 & 0 & 1 \end{bmatrix}. \tag{14}$$

An identity matrix is scalar, diagonal and symmetric.

3.3 Multiplication of Matrices

The product of two matrices

$$A = \begin{bmatrix} a_{11} & a_{12} \\ a_{21} & a_{22} \\ a_{31} & a_{32} \end{bmatrix} \quad \text{and} \quad B = \begin{bmatrix} b_{11} & b_{12} \\ b_{21} & b_{22} \end{bmatrix} \tag{1}$$

is defined as

$$AB = \begin{bmatrix} a_{11}b_{11}+a_{12}b_{21} & a_{11}b_{12}+a_{12}b_{22} \\ a_{21}b_{11}+a_{22}b_{21} & a_{21}b_{12}+a_{22}b_{22} \\ a_{31}b_{11}+a_{32}b_{21} & a_{31}b_{12}+a_{32}b_{22} \end{bmatrix}. \tag{2}$$

The element in the ith row and the jth column of the product matrix AB is the sum of the products of the corresponding elements in the ith row of matrix A and those in the jth column of matrix B. This procedure is called the *row × column* method of multiplication which may be illustrated by the product

$$AB = C$$

or

$$\begin{bmatrix} 1 & 2 & 3 \\ 4 & 5 & 6 \\ 7 & 8 & 9 \end{bmatrix} \begin{bmatrix} 1 & 2 \\ 3 & 4 \\ 5 & 6 \end{bmatrix} = \begin{bmatrix} 22 & 28 \\ 49 & 64 \\ 76 & 100 \end{bmatrix}. \tag{3}$$

The elements of the third row of matrix A are 7, 8 and 9, and those of the second column of matrix B are 2, 4 and 6. The sum of products of these three pairs of elements is

$$7 \times 2 + 8 \times 4 + 9 \times 6 = 100$$

which is the element in the third row and second column of matrix C which is the product of A and B.

Matrices may be used in representing a system of linear equations. For example, equations (1), (2) and (3) of section 3.1 may be expressed in matrix form as

$$\begin{bmatrix} 5 & -2 & 1 \\ 2 & 1 & -5 \\ 4 & -2 & 1 \end{bmatrix} \begin{bmatrix} x \\ y \\ z \end{bmatrix} = \begin{bmatrix} 3 \\ -6 \\ 1 \end{bmatrix}. \tag{4}$$

After the multiplication is carried out, the resulting product is the original system of equations.

The procedure of solving linear equations as shown in table 3.1 may also be expressed as the multiplication of matrices. In table 3.1, lines 1 to 3 constitute a 3×3 matrix; so do lines 4 to 6. The relation between the two matrices may be expressed as

$$\begin{bmatrix} 1/5 & 0 & 0 \\ 0 & 1/2 & 0 \\ 0 & 0 & 1/4 \end{bmatrix} \begin{bmatrix} 5 & -2 & 1 \\ 2 & 1 & -5 \\ 4 & -2 & 1 \end{bmatrix} = \begin{bmatrix} 1 & -0.40 & 0.20 \\ 1 & 0.50 & -2.50 \\ 1 & -0.50 & 0.25 \end{bmatrix}. \tag{5}$$

The 2×3 matrix of lines 7 to 8 of table 3.1 may be obtained by another multiplication such as

$$\begin{bmatrix} -1 & 1 & 0 \\ -1 & 0 & 1 \end{bmatrix} \begin{bmatrix} 1 & -0.40 & 0.20 \\ 1 & 0.50 & -2.50 \\ 1 & -0.50 & 0.25 \end{bmatrix} = \begin{bmatrix} 0 & 0.90 & -2.70 \\ 0 & -0.10 & 0.05 \end{bmatrix} \quad (6)$$

These are some of the examples showing that solving a system of linear equations may be regarded as the manipulation of a matrix; and manipulating a matrix, in turn, may be regarded as multiplying that matrix by other matrices.

3.4   Rules of Multiplication

The commutative law of multiplication generally does not hold for matrices; that is,

$$AB \neq BA \quad (1)$$

where A and B are two matrices. For example,

$$\begin{bmatrix} 1 & 2 \\ 3 & 4 \end{bmatrix} \begin{bmatrix} 5 & 6 \\ 7 & 8 \end{bmatrix} = \begin{bmatrix} 19 & 22 \\ 43 & 50 \end{bmatrix}. \quad (2)$$

When the order of the two matrices are interchanged, the product is

$$\begin{bmatrix} 5 & 6 \\ 7 & 8 \end{bmatrix} \begin{bmatrix} 1 & 2 \\ 3 & 4 \end{bmatrix} = \begin{bmatrix} 23 & 34 \\ 31 & 46 \end{bmatrix} \quad (3)$$

which is different from the product of equation (2). This example illustrates the importance of the order of two matrices in performing a multiplication. The commutative law of multiplication, however, does hold for square matrices if one or both matrices are scalar. For example, the products

$$\begin{bmatrix} a_{11} & a_{12} \\ a_{21} & a_{22} \end{bmatrix} \begin{bmatrix} b & 0 \\ 0 & b \end{bmatrix} = \begin{bmatrix} a_{11}b & a_{12}b \\ a_{21}b & a_{22}b \end{bmatrix} \quad (4)$$

and

$$\begin{bmatrix} b & 0 \\ 0 & b \end{bmatrix} \begin{bmatrix} a_{11} & a_{12} \\ a_{21} & a_{22} \end{bmatrix} = \begin{bmatrix} a_{11}b & a_{12}b \\ a_{21}b & a_{22}b \end{bmatrix} \quad (5)$$

are equal even though the order of the two matrices is interchanged.

Multiplying a matrix $[a_{ij}]$ by a scalar matrix is equivalent to multiplying each element of that matrix by the scalar as shown in equations (4) and (5). For this reason the scalar is frequently represented by a letter rather than by a matrix. For example, equation (5) may be written as

$$b[a_{ij}] = [ba_{ij}] = \begin{bmatrix} ba_{11} & ba_{12} \\ ba_{21} & ba_{22} \end{bmatrix}. \qquad (6)$$

The scalar may be regarded as the common factor of the elements of a matrix. The matrix

$$[a_{ij}] = \begin{bmatrix} 10 & 20 \\ 30 & 40 \end{bmatrix} \qquad (7)$$

may be expressed as

$$10\left[\frac{a_{ij}}{10}\right] = 10\begin{bmatrix} 1 & 2 \\ 3 & 4 \end{bmatrix}, \qquad (8)$$

and the matrix

$$[a_{ij}] = \begin{bmatrix} 1/3 & 2/3 \\ 3/3 & 4/3 \end{bmatrix} \qquad (9)$$

may be expressed as

$$\frac{1}{3}[3a_{ij}] = \frac{1}{3}\begin{bmatrix} 1 & 2 \\ 3 & 4 \end{bmatrix}. \qquad (10)$$

Multiplication of two matrices cannot be performed, unless the number of columns in the left matrix is equal to the number of rows in the right matrix; that is, an $m \times n$ matrix cannot be multiplied by a $p \times q$ matrix unless n is equal to p. If this is the case, the product is an $m \times q$ matrix. For example, when a 2×3 matrix is multiplied by a 3×2 matrix the product is a 2×2 matrix such as

$$\begin{bmatrix} 1 & 2 & 3 \\ 4 & 5 & 6 \end{bmatrix}\begin{bmatrix} 7 & 8 \\ 9 & 10 \\ 11 & 12 \end{bmatrix} = \begin{bmatrix} 58 & 64 \\ 139 & 154 \end{bmatrix}. \qquad (11)$$

But when a 3×2 matrix is multiplied by a 2×3 matrix, the product is a 3×3 matrix such as

$$\begin{bmatrix} 7 & 8 \\ 9 & 10 \\ 11 & 12 \end{bmatrix}\begin{bmatrix} 1 & 2 & 3 \\ 4 & 5 & 6 \end{bmatrix} = \begin{bmatrix} 39 & 54 & 69 \\ 49 & 68 & 87 \\ 59 & 82 & 105 \end{bmatrix}. \qquad (12)$$

Equations (11) and (12) illustrate how the dimensions of the product matrix are determined by the dimensions of the two original matrices. They further illustrate the fact that AB is not necessarily equal to BA, when A and B are two matrices. These two equations show that the two product matrices are not even of the same dimensions.

The associative law of multiplication does hold for matrices; that is,

$$ABC = (AB)C = A(BC) \tag{13}$$

where A, B and C are three matrices. This theorem can be demonstrated by three 2×2 matrices as follows:

$$ABC = \begin{bmatrix} a_{11} & a_{12} \\ a_{21} & a_{22} \end{bmatrix} \begin{bmatrix} b_{11} & b_{12} \\ b_{21} & b_{22} \end{bmatrix} \begin{bmatrix} c_{11} & c_{12} \\ c_{21} & c_{22} \end{bmatrix} \tag{14}$$

$$(AB)C = \begin{bmatrix} a_{11}b_{11}+a_{12}b_{21} & a_{11}b_{12}+a_{12}b_{22} \\ a_{21}b_{11}+a_{22}b_{21} & a_{21}b_{12}+a_{22}b_{22} \end{bmatrix} \begin{bmatrix} c_{11} & c_{12} \\ c_{21} & c_{22} \end{bmatrix} \tag{15}$$

$$A(BC) = \begin{bmatrix} a_{11} & a_{12} \\ a_{21} & a_{22} \end{bmatrix} \begin{bmatrix} b_{11}c_{11}+b_{12}c_{21} & b_{11}c_{12}+b_{12}c_{22} \\ b_{21}c_{11}+b_{22}c_{21} & b_{21}c_{12}+b_{22}c_{22} \end{bmatrix} \tag{16}$$

When the multiplications in equations (15) and (16) are carried out, the resulting 2×2 matrices are identical (exercise 4).

The associative law can also be illustrated by the numerical example given in equations (5) and (6) of section 3.3. The product of the three matrices is

$$ABC = \begin{bmatrix} -1 & 1 & 0 \\ -1 & 0 & 1 \end{bmatrix} \begin{bmatrix} 1/5 & 0 & 0 \\ 0 & 1/2 & 0 \\ 0 & 0 & 1/4 \end{bmatrix} \begin{bmatrix} 5 & -2 & 1 \\ 2 & 1 & -5 \\ 4 & -2 & 1 \end{bmatrix}. \tag{17}$$

One way of obtaining this product is

$$(AB)C = \begin{bmatrix} -0.20 & 0.50 & 0.00 \\ -0.20 & 0.00 & 0.25 \end{bmatrix} \begin{bmatrix} 5 & -2 & 1 \\ 2 & 1 & -5 \\ 4 & -2 & 1 \end{bmatrix} = \begin{bmatrix} 0 & 0.90 & -2.70 \\ 0 & -0.10 & 0.05 \end{bmatrix}. \tag{18}$$

Another way of obtaining the same product is

$$A(BC) = \begin{bmatrix} -1 & 1 & 0 \\ -1 & 0 & 1 \end{bmatrix} \begin{bmatrix} 1 & -0.40 & 0.20 \\ 1 & 0.50 & -2.50 \\ 1 & -0.50 & 0.25 \end{bmatrix} = \begin{bmatrix} 0 & 0.90 & -2.70 \\ 0 & -0.10 & 0.05 \end{bmatrix} \tag{19}$$

which is the same matrix obtained in equation (18).

The transpose of a product of two matrices is the product of their transposes with the order interchanged; that is,

$$(AB)' = B'A'. \tag{20}$$

The product of the two matrices

$$A = \begin{bmatrix} a_{11} & a_{12} \\ a_{21} & a_{22} \\ a_{31} & a_{32} \end{bmatrix} \quad \text{and} \quad B = \begin{bmatrix} b_{11} & b_{12} & b_{13} \\ b_{21} & b_{22} & b_{23} \end{bmatrix} \tag{21}$$

is a 3×3 matrix. The product of the two transposes

$$A' = \begin{bmatrix} a_{11} & a_{21} & a_{31} \\ a_{12} & a_{22} & a_{32} \end{bmatrix} \quad \text{and} \quad B' = \begin{bmatrix} b_{11} & b_{21} \\ b_{12} & b_{22} \\ b_{13} & b_{23} \end{bmatrix} \tag{22}$$

with the order interchanged is $B'A'$ which is also a 3×3 matrix. After the multiplication is carried out, one will see that equation (20) does hold (exercise 6).

Equation (20) may be extended to the product of three matrices as

$$(ABC)' = C'B'A'. \tag{23}$$

Since the product of three matrices is equal to

$$ABC = (AB)C,$$

the transpose of the product must be equal to

$$(ABC)' = C'(AB)'.$$

But $(AB)'$ is equal to $B'A'$. Then the transpose of the product ABC must be equal to $C'B'A'$.

3.5 Inversion of Matrix

The square matrix A^{-1} is called the *inverse* of a square matrix A, if

$$A^{-1}A = AA^{-1} = I$$

where I is an identity matrix. The inverse of

$$A = \begin{bmatrix} 1 & 2 \\ 3 & 4 \end{bmatrix} \tag{1}$$

is

$$A^{-1} = \begin{bmatrix} -2.0 & 1.0 \\ 1.5 & -0.5 \end{bmatrix} \tag{2}$$

because the product of the two matrices is an identity matrix or

$$A^{-1}A = AA^{-1} = \begin{bmatrix} 1 & 0 \\ 0 & 1 \end{bmatrix}.$$

A matrix can be inverted by utilizing the rules of multiplication. First the matrix A and an identity matrix I of the same dimensions are written side by side such as

$$A = \begin{bmatrix} 1 & 2 \\ 3 & 4 \end{bmatrix} \qquad I = \begin{bmatrix} 1 & 0 \\ 0 & 1 \end{bmatrix}.$$

Then the matrix A is multiplied by a series of matrices from the left so that the final product becomes an identity matrix. At the same time the identity matrix I is multiplied by the same series of matrices. By the time matrix A is converted into I, matrix I is converted into A^{-1}. The reason for this is not hard to see. If the series of matrices used in multiplication are B, C and D so that the product is an identity matrix or

$$DCBA = I,$$

the product of D, C and B must be the inverse matrix or

$$(DCB) = A^{-1}$$

because of the relation

$$A^{-1}A = I.$$

Consequently the original identity matrix, after the same multiplications, becomes the inverse matrix or

$$(DCB)I = A^{-1}I = A^{-1}.$$

The inversion of the matrix A given in equation (1) may be used as an illustration. The product of B and A is

$$BA = \begin{bmatrix} 1 & 0 \\ 1 & -1/3 \end{bmatrix}\begin{bmatrix} 1 & 2 \\ 3 & 4 \end{bmatrix} = \begin{bmatrix} 1 & 2 \\ 0 & 2/3 \end{bmatrix}; \tag{3}$$

that of C and BA is

$$C(BA) = \begin{bmatrix} 1 & 0 \\ 0 & 3/2 \end{bmatrix} \begin{bmatrix} 1 & 2 \\ 0 & 2/3 \end{bmatrix} = \begin{bmatrix} 1 & 2 \\ 0 & 1 \end{bmatrix}; \qquad (4)$$

and that of D and CBA is

$$D(CBA) = \begin{bmatrix} 1 & -2 \\ 0 & 1 \end{bmatrix} \begin{bmatrix} 1 & 2 \\ 0 & 1 \end{bmatrix} = \begin{bmatrix} 1 & 0 \\ 0 & 1 \end{bmatrix}. \qquad (5)$$

Now it can be seen that the product DCB is the inverse of A or

$$DCB = \begin{bmatrix} 1 & -2 \\ 0 & 1 \end{bmatrix} \begin{bmatrix} 1 & 0 \\ 0 & 3/2 \end{bmatrix} \begin{bmatrix} 1 & 0 \\ 1 & -1/3 \end{bmatrix} \qquad (6)$$

$$= (DC)B = \begin{bmatrix} 1 & -3 \\ 0 & 3/2 \end{bmatrix} \begin{bmatrix} 1 & 0 \\ 1 & -1/3 \end{bmatrix} \qquad (7)$$

$$= (DCB) = \begin{bmatrix} -2 & 1 \\ 3/2 & -1/2 \end{bmatrix} = \begin{bmatrix} -2.0 & 1.0 \\ 1.5 & -0.5 \end{bmatrix} \qquad (8)$$

which is shown in equation (2).

The procedure of inverting a matrix as described above is not unlike that used in solving a system of linear equations. The connections between the two procedures may be observed by expressing a system of linear equations in matrix form. Equations (1), (2) and (3) of section 3.1 may be expressed in the matrix form as

$$\begin{bmatrix} 5 & -2 & 1 \\ 2 & 1 & -5 \\ 4 & -2 & 1 \end{bmatrix} \begin{bmatrix} x \\ y \\ z \end{bmatrix} = \begin{bmatrix} 3 \\ -6 \\ 1 \end{bmatrix} \qquad (9)$$

and the solutions of these equations expressed as

$$\begin{bmatrix} 1 & 0 & 0 \\ 0 & 1 & 0 \\ 0 & 0 & 1 \end{bmatrix} \begin{bmatrix} x \\ y \\ z \end{bmatrix} = \begin{bmatrix} x \\ y \\ z \end{bmatrix} = \begin{bmatrix} 2 \\ 5 \\ 3 \end{bmatrix}. \qquad (10)$$

By comparing equations (9) and (10), one will realize that, if both sides of equation (9) are multiplied by the inverse of the matrix of the coefficients of the system of linear equations from the left, the resulting equation is (10). The similarity between these two procedures can be revealed by comparing table 3.1 which shows an example of solving a system of equations and table 3.5 which shows an example of inverting a matrix. The inverse matrix obtained in table 3.5 is

$$[c_{ij}] = \begin{bmatrix} 1 & 0 & -1 \\ 22/9 & -1/9 & -3 \\ 8/9 & -2/9 & -1 \end{bmatrix}. \tag{11}$$

When both sides of equation (9) are multiplied by this matrix from the left, the resulting equation is equation (10) which gives the solutions of equations (1), (2) and (3) of section 3.1.

TABLE 3.5

INVERSION OF MATRIX

Matrix A			Matrix I			Procedure	Sequence
5	−2	1	1	0	0	Copy	(1)
2	1	−5	0	1	0	Copy	(2)
4	−2	1	0	0	1	Copy	(3)
1	−0.40	0.20	0.20	0	0	(1) ÷ 5	(4)
1	0.50	−2.50	0	0.50	0	(2) ÷ 2	(5)
1	−0.50	0.25	0	0	0.25	(3) ÷ 4	(6)
1	−0.40	0.20	0.20	0	0	(4)	(7)
0	0.90	−2.70	−0.20	0.50	0	(5) − (4)	(8)
0	−0.10	0.05	−0.20	0	0.25	(6) − (4)	(9)
1	0	−1	1/9	2/9	0	(7) + 0.4(10)	(11)
0	1	−3	−2/9	5/9	0	(8) ÷ 0.9	(10)
0	0	−0.25	−2/9	0.5/9	0.25	(9) + 0.1(10)	(12)
1	0	0	1	0	−1	(11) + (13)	(14)
0	1	0	22/9	−1/9	−3	(10) + 3(13)	(15)
0	0	1	8/9	−2/9	−1	(12) ÷ (−0.25)	(13)

The inversion of an $m \times m$ matrix is exactly equivalent to the solution of m systems of linear equations, each of which consists of m unknown quantities. If the original matrix is

$$[a_{ij}] = \begin{bmatrix} a_{11} & a_{12} \\ a_{21} & a_{22} \end{bmatrix} \tag{12}$$

and its inverse is

$$[c_{ij}] = \begin{bmatrix} c_{11} & c_{12} \\ c_{21} & c_{22} \end{bmatrix}, \tag{13}$$

the product of the two matrices must be an identity matrix or

$$\begin{bmatrix} a_{11} & a_{12} \\ a_{21} & a_{22} \end{bmatrix} \begin{bmatrix} c_{11} \\ c_{21} \end{bmatrix} = \begin{bmatrix} 1 \\ 0 \end{bmatrix} \tag{14}$$

and

$$\begin{bmatrix} a_{11} & a_{12} \\ a_{21} & a_{22} \end{bmatrix} \begin{bmatrix} c_{12} \\ c_{22} \end{bmatrix} = \begin{bmatrix} 0 \\ 1 \end{bmatrix}. \tag{15}$$

This is to say that to invert the matrix $[a_{ij}]$ is equivalent to the solution of the two systems of linear equations given above, with the elements c_{ij} being the unknown quantities. The inversion of the matrix

$$A = \begin{bmatrix} 5 & -2 & 1 \\ 2 & 1 & -5 \\ 4 & -2 & 1 \end{bmatrix} \tag{16}$$

shown in table 3.5 is equivalent to the solution of the following three systems of linear equations:

$$\begin{aligned} 5\,c_{11} - 2\,c_{21} + 1\,c_{31} &= 1 \\ 2\,c_{11} + 1\,c_{21} - 5\,c_{31} &= 0 \\ 4\,c_{11} - 2\,c_{21} + 1\,c_{31} &= 0 \end{aligned} \tag{17}$$

$$\begin{aligned} 5\,c_{12} - 2\,c_{22} + 1\,c_{32} &= 0 \\ 2\,c_{12} + 1\,c_{22} - 5\,c_{32} &= 1 \\ 4\,c_{12} - 2\,c_{22} + 1\,c_{32} &= 0 \end{aligned} \tag{18}$$

$$\begin{aligned} 5\,c_{13} - 2\,c_{23} + 1\,c_{33} &= 0 \\ 2\,c_{13} + 1\,c_{23} - 5\,c_{33} &= 0 \\ 4\,c_{13} - 2\,c_{23} + 1\,c_{33} &= 1 \end{aligned} \tag{19}$$

The procedure of inverting a matrix given in table 3.5 is good only for illustrating the principles involved. It is too tedious to be of practical use. In its place, several short-cut methods may be used. However, one need not learn any of them if he is only interested in the results rather than the short cuts of matrix inversion. Right now almost every computing machine has a ready-made program for matrix inversion. When one has a matrix to invert, all he has to do is to utilize one of these programs and have his matrix inverted for him.

The inverse of the product of two matrices P and A is equal to the product of the inverses P^{-1} and A^{-1} of the two original matrices with the order interchanged or

$$(PA)^{-1} = (A^{-1})(P^{-1}) \tag{20}$$

because of the relation

$$(PA)(A^{-1}P^{-1}) = P(AA^{-1})P^{-1} = PP^{-1} = I \tag{21}$$

where I is an identity matrix. For example, the two original matrices are

$$P = \begin{bmatrix} 5 & 6 \\ 7 & 8 \end{bmatrix} \qquad A = \begin{bmatrix} 1 & 2 \\ 3 & 4 \end{bmatrix} \tag{22}$$

and their inverses are

$$P^{-1} = \begin{bmatrix} -4.0 & 3.0 \\ 3.5 & -2.5 \end{bmatrix} \qquad A^{-1} = \begin{bmatrix} -2.0 & 1.0 \\ 1.5 & -0.5 \end{bmatrix}. \tag{23}$$

The product of the two original matrices is

$$(PA) = \begin{bmatrix} 23 & 34 \\ 31 & 46 \end{bmatrix} \tag{24}$$

whose inverse is

$$(PA)^{-1} = \begin{bmatrix} 11.50 & -8.50 \\ -7.75 & 5.75 \end{bmatrix} \tag{25}$$

which is equal to

$$(A^{-1})(P^{-1}) = \begin{bmatrix} 11.50 & -8.50 \\ -7.75 & 5.75 \end{bmatrix}. \tag{26}$$

It follows from the above theorem that the inverse of the product of three matrices P, A and Q is

$$(PAQ)^{-1} = Q^{-1}(PA)^{-1} = Q^{-1}A^{-1}P^{-1} \tag{27}$$

which is to say that the inverse of the product of three matrices is equal to the product of their inverses with the order reversed.

3.6 Inversion of Matrix with Zero Elements

The inversion of a matrix with smaller square matrices along the diagonal and zeroes elsewhere such as

$$A = \begin{bmatrix} a_{11} & a_{12} & a_{13} & 0 & 0 & 0 \\ a_{21} & a_{22} & a_{23} & 0 & 0 & 0 \\ a_{31} & a_{32} & a_{33} & 0 & 0 & 0 \\ 0 & 0 & 0 & a_{44} & a_{45} & 0 \\ 0 & 0 & 0 & a_{54} & a_{55} & 0 \\ 0 & 0 & 0 & 0 & 0 & a_{66} \end{bmatrix} \tag{1}$$

can be achieved by inverting each of the smaller matrices separately. If the inverse of the smaller matrix

$$A_1 = \begin{bmatrix} a_{11} & a_{12} & a_{13} \\ a_{21} & a_{22} & a_{23} \\ a_{31} & a_{32} & a_{33} \end{bmatrix} \tag{2}$$

is

$$A_1^{-1} = \begin{bmatrix} c_{11} & c_{12} & c_{13} \\ c_{21} & c_{22} & c_{23} \\ c_{31} & c_{32} & c_{33} \end{bmatrix} \tag{3}$$

and that of the matrix

$$A_2 = \begin{bmatrix} a_{44} & a_{45} \\ a_{54} & a_{55} \end{bmatrix} \tag{4}$$

is

$$A_2^{-1} = \begin{bmatrix} c_{44} & c_{45} \\ c_{54} & c_{55} \end{bmatrix} \tag{5}$$

and that of the matrix

$$A_3 = [a_{66}] \tag{6}$$

is

$$A_3^{-1} = [c_{66}], \tag{7}$$

the inverse of A is

$$A^{-1} = \begin{bmatrix} c_{11} & c_{12} & c_{13} & 0 & 0 & 0 \\ c_{21} & c_{22} & c_{23} & 0 & 0 & 0 \\ c_{31} & c_{32} & c_{33} & 0 & 0 & 0 \\ 0 & 0 & 0 & c_{44} & c_{45} & 0 \\ 0 & 0 & 0 & c_{54} & c_{55} & 0 \\ 0 & 0 & 0 & 0 & 0 & c_{66} \end{bmatrix}. \tag{8}$$

To prove this theorem is very simple. All one has to do is multiply the matrix A by A^{-1}. The product AA^{-1} is an identity matrix because of the relations

$$A_1 A_1^{-1} = I$$

$$A_2 A_2^{-1} = I$$

and

$$A_3 A_3^{-1} = I.$$

The matrix

$$A = \begin{bmatrix} 1 & 2 & 0 \\ 3 & 4 & 0 \\ 0 & 0 & 5 \end{bmatrix} \tag{9}$$

may be used as an illustration of the theorem. The two smaller matrices along the diagonal of the above matrix are

$$A_1 = \begin{bmatrix} 1 & 2 \\ 3 & 4 \end{bmatrix} \tag{10}$$

and

$$A_2 = [5] \tag{11}$$

whose inverses are

$$A_1^{-1} = \begin{bmatrix} -2.0 & 1.0 \\ 1.5 & -0.5 \end{bmatrix} \tag{12}$$

and

$$A_2^{-1} = [0.2]. \tag{13}$$

By the theorem under consideration, the inverse of the matrix given in equation (9) is

$$A^{-1} = \begin{bmatrix} -2.0 & 1.0 & 0.0 \\ 1.5 & -0.5 & 0.0 \\ 0.0 & 0.0 & 0.2 \end{bmatrix}. \tag{14}$$

It can be readily verified that the product of the matrices A and A^{-1} given in equations (9) and (14) is a three-row identity matrix.

3.7 Singular Matrix

A system of linear equations does not necessarily have unique solutions. For example, the solutions

$$[x_1 \quad x_2 \quad x_3] = [1 \quad 2 \quad 3] \tag{1}$$

satisfy the equations

$$\begin{bmatrix} 5 & -2 & 1 \\ 2 & 1 & -5 \\ 4 & -2 & 2 \end{bmatrix} \begin{bmatrix} x_1 \\ x_2 \\ x_3 \end{bmatrix} = \begin{bmatrix} 4 \\ -11 \\ 6 \end{bmatrix}. \tag{2}$$

So do the solutions

$$[x_1 \quad x_2 \quad x_3] = [0 \quad -1 \quad 2]. \tag{3}$$

For such a system of equations, the matrix of the coefficients of the unknown quantities x_1, x_2 and x_3 does not have an inverse. A square matrix whose inverse does not exist is called a *singular* matrix. When one attempts to invert such a matrix, he encounters division by zero during the process. As an example, the inversion of the 3×3 matrix of equation (2) is attempted in table 3.7. When only zeros appear in the last row, the process has to stop.

TABLE 3.7

INVERSION OF A SINGULAR MATRIX

Matrix A			Matrix I		
5	−2	1	1	0	0
2	1	−5	0	1	0
4	−2	2	0	0	1
1	−0.40	0.20	0.20	0	0
1	0.50	−2.50	0	0.50	0
1	−0.50	0.50	0	0	0.25
1	−0.40	0.20	0.20	0	0
0	0.90	−2.70	−0.20	0.50	0
0	−0.10	0.30	−0.20	0	0.25
1	0	−1	1/9	2/9	0
0	1	−3	−2/9	5/9	0
0	0	0	−2/9	0.5/9	0.25

The discussion of singularity presented in this section is quite brief. The definition of singularity given here is hazy. The formal procedure of determining singularity of a matrix is not even mentioned. However, clarification of this topic will not be attempted in this book because singular matrices are seldom encountered in practical applications. On occasions when singular matrices do occur, they usually come from two main sources. One is that such matrices are deliberately chosen in solving certain problems. People who choose such matrices are the ones who know how to cope with them. The other source of singular matrices originates from the misunderstanding of the subject-matter field in which the matrix is applied.

3.8 Orthogonal Matrix

A square matrix A is called an *orthogonal* matrix, if its transpose is equal to its inverse or

$$A' = A^{-1}$$

or

$$AA' = AA^{-1} = I$$

where A' is the transpose of matrix A and I an identity matrix. The matrix

$$A = \begin{bmatrix} 0.6 & 0.8 \\ 0.8 & -0.6 \end{bmatrix} \tag{1}$$

is an example of an orthogonal matrix. Its transpose is

$$A' = \begin{bmatrix} 0.6 & 0.8 \\ 0.8 & -0.6 \end{bmatrix} \tag{2}$$

and the product AA' is a 2×2 identity matrix.

The orthogonal matrix is used in transforming the m quantities

$$u_1 \quad u_2 \quad \cdots \quad u_m$$

into another m quantities

$$v_1 \quad v_2 \quad \cdots \quad v_m$$

by the equations

$$V = AU \tag{3}$$

or

$$\begin{bmatrix} v_1 \\ v_2 \\ \cdots \\ v_m \end{bmatrix} \begin{bmatrix} a_{11} & a_{12} & \cdots & a_{1m} \\ a_{21} & a_{22} & \cdots & a_{2m} \\ \cdots & \cdots & \cdots & \cdots & \cdots \\ a_{m1} & a_{m2} & \cdots & a_{mm} \end{bmatrix} \begin{bmatrix} u_1 \\ u_2 \\ \cdots \\ u_m \end{bmatrix} \tag{4}$$

so that the sum of squares of the v's is equal to that of the u's or

$$\sum_{i=1}^{m} v_i^2 = \sum_{i=1}^{m} u_i^2. \tag{5}$$

Such a transformation is called an *orthogonal transformation* and the matrix A of equation (3) is an orthogonal matrix.

The orthogonal transformation may be illustrated by the 2×2 matrix given in equation (1). Two quantities u_1 and u_2 are transformed into another two quantities v_1 and v_2 in the following manner:

$$v_1 = 0.6\,u_1 + 0.8\,u_2$$

$$v_2 = 0.8\,u_1 - 0.6\,u_2$$

The squares of the v's are

$$v_1^2 = 0.36\,u_1^2 + 2(0.6)(0.8)u_1u_2 + 0.64\,u_2^2$$

and

$$v_2^2 = 0.64\,u_1^2 - 2(0.8)(0.6)u_1u_2 + 0.36\,u_2^2$$

whose sum is

$$v_1^2 + v_2^2 = (0.36+0.64)u_1^2 + (0.64 + 0.36)u_2^2 = u_1^2 + u_2^2.$$

The above property shows that the transformation is orthogonal.

The given transformation may be expressed in matrix notation. The equations of transformation are

$$V = AU$$

or

$$\begin{bmatrix} v_1 \\ v_2 \end{bmatrix} = \begin{bmatrix} 0.6 & 0.8 \\ 0.8 & -0.6 \end{bmatrix} \begin{bmatrix} u_1 \\ u_2 \end{bmatrix}.$$

The sum of squares of the v's is the product of the matrix V and its transpose V' or

$$V'V = [v_1 \;\; v_2] \begin{bmatrix} v_1 \\ v_2 \end{bmatrix} = v_1^2 + v_2^2.$$

In terms of the u's, this same sum of squares can be expressed as

$$U'A'AU = [u_1 \quad u_2] \begin{bmatrix} 0.6 & 0.8 \\ 0.8 & -0.6 \end{bmatrix} \begin{bmatrix} 0.6 & 0.8 \\ 0.8 & -0.6 \end{bmatrix} \begin{bmatrix} u_1 \\ u_2 \end{bmatrix}$$

$$= [u_1 \quad u_2] \begin{bmatrix} 1 & 0 \\ 0 & 1 \end{bmatrix} \begin{bmatrix} u_1 \\ u_2 \end{bmatrix}$$

$$= u_1^2 + u_2^2$$

because of the relations (equation 3)

$$V = AU$$

and (equation 20, section 3.4)

$$V' = U'A'.$$

From equations (3) and (4), one can see why the matrix

$$A = [a_{ij}] \qquad i, j = 1, 2, \cdots, m$$

of an orthogonal transformation must have the property that its transpose A' is equal to its inverse A^{-1}. In this kind of transformation, the sum of squares

$$V'V = [v_1 \quad v_2 \quad \cdots \quad v_m] \begin{bmatrix} v_1 \\ v_2 \\ \cdots \\ v_m \end{bmatrix} = \sum_{i=1}^{m} v_i^2 \qquad (6)$$

must be equal to

$$U'U = [u_1 \quad u_2 \quad \cdots \quad u_m] \begin{bmatrix} u_1 \\ u_2 \\ \cdots \\ u_m \end{bmatrix} = \sum_{i=1}^{m} u_i^2. \qquad (7)$$

But V is equal to AU and its transpose V' must be equal to $U'A'$. In order to make the sum of squares of the v's

$$V'V = (U'A')(AU)$$

equal to the sum of squares of the u's

$$U'U = U'A'AU,$$

the product $A'A$ must be an identity matrix. When this is true, the transpose A' by definition becomes the inverse A^{-1} of the matrix A.

The equations of an orthogonal transformation given in equations (3) and (4) are a system of linear equations. However, the problem here is different from the solution of simultaneous equations. In solving equations, the values of v_i and a_{ij} are known and the problem is to express u_i in terms of these known quantities. On the other hand, in an orthogonal transformation, the problem is to determine the values of a_{ij} so that the equation

$$\sum_{i=1}^{m} v_i^2 = \sum_{i=1}^{m} u_i^2$$

holds while the values of u_i and v_i may or may not be known.

The definition of the orthogonal matrix furnishes the rules of constructing such a matrix. The three-row square matrix

$$A = \begin{bmatrix} a_{11} & a_{12} & a_{13} \\ a_{21} & a_{22} & a_{23} \\ a_{31} & a_{32} & a_{33} \end{bmatrix} \tag{8}$$

may be used as an example. To make A an orthogonal matrix, the product AA^I or A^IA must be made equal to an identity matrix or

$$\begin{bmatrix} a_{11} & a_{12} & a_{13} \\ a_{21} & a_{22} & a_{23} \\ a_{31} & a_{32} & a_{33} \end{bmatrix} \begin{bmatrix} a_{11} & a_{21} & a_{31} \\ a_{12} & a_{22} & a_{32} \\ a_{13} & a_{23} & a_{33} \end{bmatrix} = \begin{bmatrix} 1 & 0 & 0 \\ 0 & 1 & 0 \\ 0 & 0 & 1 \end{bmatrix} \tag{9}$$

which implies the following nine equations:

$$a_{11}a_{11} + a_{12}a_{12} + a_{13}a_{13} = 1 \tag{10}$$

$$a_{11}a_{21} + a_{12}a_{22} + a_{13}a_{23} = 0 \tag{11}$$

$$a_{11}a_{31} + a_{12}a_{32} + a_{13}a_{33} = 0 \tag{12}$$

$$a_{21}a_{11} + a_{22}a_{12} + a_{23}a_{13} = 0 \tag{13}$$

$$a_{21}a_{21} + a_{22}a_{22} + a_{23}a_{23} = 1 \tag{14}$$

$$a_{21}a_{31} + a_{22}a_{32} + a_{23}a_{33} = 0 \tag{15}$$

$$a_{31}a_{11} + a_{32}a_{12} + a_{33}a_{13} = 0 \tag{16}$$

$$a_{31}a_{21} + a_{32}a_{22} + a_{33}a_{23} = 0 \tag{17}$$

$$a_{31}a_{31} + a_{32}a_{32} + a_{33}a_{33} = 1 \tag{18}$$

From the above equations, one can see that the sum of squares of the elements of each row of matrix A is equal to 1 or

$$a_{i1}^2 + a_{i2}^2 + a_{i3}^2 = 1 \qquad i = 1, 2, 3 \tag{19}$$

and the sum of products of the corresponding elements of any two rows of matrix A is equal to zero or

$$a_{i1}a_{j1} + a_{i2}a_{j2} + a_{i3}a_{j3} = 0 \qquad i \neq j. \tag{20}$$

When the values 1, 2 and 3 are assigned in turn to the subscript i of equation (19), the results are equations (10), (14) and (18). When the values 1 and 2 are assigned to the subscripts i and j of equation (20), the results are equations (11) and (13). When the values 1 and 3 are assigned to the subscripts i and j, the results are equations (12) and (16). When 2 and 3 are assigned to i and j, the results are equations (15) and (17). Thus equations (19) and (20) summarize the restrictions on the elements of an orthogonal matrix.

Any square matrix satisfies the conditions of equations (19) and (20) is an orthogonal matrix. To construct such a matrix, one may start with a preliminary matrix P which satisfies equation (20) only. Then, as a second step, the preliminary matrix is made to satisfy equation (19) so that an orthogonal matrix can be obtained.

The construction of a three-row orthogonal matrix may be used as an illustration of the procedure. For the preliminary matrix P, one may arbitrarily select the elements

$$1 \qquad 1 \qquad 1$$

for the first row. The elements

$$p_{21} \qquad p_{22} \qquad p_{23}$$

of the second row are not arbitrarily chosen, and they must satisfy the relation

$$1p_{21} + 1p_{22} + 1p_{23} = 0.$$

With this in mind, one may choose the elements

$$2 \qquad -1 \qquad -1$$

for the second row because

$$1(2) + 1(-1) + 1(-1) = 0.$$

The elements

$$p_{31} \quad p_{32} \quad p_{33}$$

of the third row are much harder to choose, because they must satisfy the two restrictions

$$1p_{31} + 1p_{32} + 1p_{33} = 0$$

and

$$2p_{31} - 1p_{32} - 1p_{33} = 0.$$

But the sum of the above two equations

$$3p_{31} = 0$$

indicates that

$$p_{31} = 0$$

which implies

$$p_{32} + p_{33} = 0$$

or

$$p_{32} = -p_{33}.$$

This analysis leads to the elements

$$0 \quad 1 \quad -1$$

for the third row. So far the matrix obtained is the preliminary matrix

$$P = \begin{bmatrix} 1 & 1 & 1 \\ 2 & -1 & -1 \\ 0 & 1 & -1 \end{bmatrix} \tag{21}$$

which satisfies the restriction of equation (20). To further satisfy that of equation (19), every element of each row of the matrix P has to be divided by the square root of the sum of squares of the elements of that row. For the first row the divisor is

$$\sqrt{(1)^2 + (1)^2 + (1)^2} \quad = \sqrt{3},$$

the second row

$$\sqrt{(2)^2 + (-1)^2 + (-1)^2} \quad = \sqrt{6}$$

and the third row

$$\sqrt{(0)^2 + (1)^2 + (-1)^2} \quad = \sqrt{2}.$$

After the divisions, the preliminary matrix P becomes

$$A = \begin{bmatrix} \dfrac{1}{\sqrt{3}} & \dfrac{1}{\sqrt{3}} & \dfrac{1}{\sqrt{3}} \\[2mm] \dfrac{2}{\sqrt{6}} & \dfrac{-1}{\sqrt{6}} & \dfrac{-1}{\sqrt{6}} \\[2mm] 0 & \dfrac{1}{\sqrt{2}} & \dfrac{-1}{\sqrt{2}} \end{bmatrix} \tag{22}$$

which is an orthogonal matrix. The orthogonality can be tested by multiplying the matrix A with its transpose A'. The product AA' is an identity matrix if the matrix A is orthogonal.

The elements of each row of the preliminary matrix P may be multiplied by a constant number without changing the corresponding elements of the orthogonal matrix A. For example, the elements

$$1 \qquad 1 \qquad 1$$

of the first row of P may be replaced by the elements

$$2 \qquad 2 \qquad 2$$

without changing the corresponding elements

$$\frac{1}{\sqrt{3}} \qquad \frac{1}{\sqrt{3}} \qquad \frac{1}{\sqrt{3}}$$

of matrix A because

$$\frac{1}{\sqrt{1^2 + 1^2 + 1^2}} = \frac{2}{\sqrt{2^2 + 2^2 + 2^2}} = \frac{1}{\sqrt{3}}.$$

In general, it can be said that the elements

$$p_{i1} \qquad p_{i2} \qquad p_{i3}$$

of the ith row of the matrix P may be multiplied by the constant C_i without changing the values of a_{ij}. This is due to the fact that the elements of the ith row of A obtained from $C_i p_{ij}$ are equal to

$$\frac{C_i p_{i1}}{\sqrt{C_i^2 p_{i1}^2 + C_i^2 p_{i2}^2 + C_i^2 p_{i3}^2}} \quad \frac{C_i p_{i2}}{\sqrt{C_i^2 p_{i1}^2 + C_i^2 p_{i2}^2 + C_i^2 p_{i3}^2}} \quad \frac{C_i p_{i3}}{\sqrt{C_i^2 p_{i1}^2 + C_i^2 p_{i2}^2 + C_i^2 p_{i3}^2}}$$

which, after both numerators and denominators are divided by the constant C_i, becomes

$$\frac{p_{i1}}{\sqrt{p_{i1}^2 + p_{i2}^2 + p_{i3}^2}} \qquad \frac{p_{i2}}{\sqrt{p_{i1}^2 + p_{i2}^2 + p_{i3}^2}} \qquad \frac{p_{i3}}{\sqrt{p_{i1}^2 + p_{i2}^2 + p_{i3}^2}}$$

the elements obtained from p_{ij}. As a result, only integers are selected for the elements of the preliminary matrix P. Elements such as

$$-\frac{1}{2} \qquad -\frac{1}{3} \qquad -\frac{1}{6}$$

may very well be multiplied by their common denominator -6 and replaced by

$$3 \qquad\qquad 2 \qquad\qquad 1$$

which are simpler to work with. Both sets of elements reduce to

$$\frac{3}{\sqrt{14}} \qquad \frac{2}{\sqrt{14}} \qquad \frac{1}{\sqrt{14}}$$

for the orthogonal matrix A.

In constructing an orthogonal matrix A of a given dimension, many sets of values can be found for the elements of a_{ij} of that matrix. For example, the matrix

$$A = \begin{bmatrix} \dfrac{1}{\sqrt{14}} & \dfrac{2}{\sqrt{14}} & \dfrac{3}{\sqrt{14}} \\[2ex] \dfrac{13}{\sqrt{182}} & \dfrac{-2}{\sqrt{182}} & \dfrac{-3}{\sqrt{182}} \\[2ex] 0 & \dfrac{3}{\sqrt{13}} & \dfrac{-2}{\sqrt{13}} \end{bmatrix} \tag{23}$$

is another three-row orthogonal matrix. In an application, however, only a particular matrix is used and the elements are not arbitrarily chosen.

Trial-and-error is not a recommended way of constructing an orthogonal matrix especially when the matrix is large. This method can keep one occupied for hours or even days. The feeling that the result is within his reach urges him to go on. Yet the fact that the prize persistently eludes his grasp keeps him working—frequently in vain.

The usual purpose of constructing an orthogonal matrix is to satisfy the need in a field of application. The physical meaning of the problem furnishes the best guide for the determination of the values of a_{ij}. It is not at all unusual for an experienced person who is familiar with the subject matter of the field of application to construct a 10×10 or even larger orthogonal matrix in a few minutes.

Here the values of a_{ij} are not arbitrarily chosen. Instead, they are purposefully selected for the problem at hand.

3.9 Sum as Product of Matrices

Many algebraic expressions in chapter 2 can be expressed as products of matrices. The $m \times 1$ matrix $[a_i x]$ of table 2.10a may be expressed as the product of the m-row scalar matrix

$$[x] = \begin{bmatrix} x & 0 & \cdots & 0 \\ 0 & x & \cdots & 0 \\ \cdots & \cdots & \cdots & \cdots \\ 0 & 0 & \cdots & x \end{bmatrix} \tag{1}$$

and the $m \times 1$ matrix

$$[a_i] = \begin{bmatrix} a_1 \\ a_2 \\ \cdots \\ a_m \end{bmatrix}. \tag{2}$$

After multiplication, the product is the $m \times 1$ matrix

$$[x][a_i] = \begin{bmatrix} xa_1 \\ xa_2 \\ \cdots \\ xa_m \end{bmatrix} \tag{3}$$

given in table 2.10a.

The sum $\sum xa_i$ of the m elements of the above matrix can also be expressed as the product of two matrices. When the scalar matrix $[x]$ of equation (3) is replaced by the $1 \times m$ matrix

$$X = [x \quad x \quad \cdots \quad x], \tag{4}$$

the product $X[a_i]$ is

$$[x \quad x \quad \cdots \quad x] \begin{bmatrix} a_1 \\ a_2 \\ \cdots \\ a_m \end{bmatrix} = xa_1 + xa_2 + \cdots + xa_m = x\sum_{i=1}^{m} a_i \tag{5}$$

which is the total given in table 2.10a.

The $m \times n$ matrix of table 2.12 can be expressed as the product of the $m \times n$ matrix

$$[c_{ij}] = \begin{bmatrix} c_{11} & c_{12} & \cdots & c_{1n} \\ c_{21} & c_{22} & \cdots & c_{2n} \\ \cdots & \cdots & \cdots & \cdots \\ c_{m1} & c_{m2} & \cdots & c_{mn} \end{bmatrix} \tag{6}$$

and the n-row diagonal matrix

$$[x_j] = \begin{bmatrix} x_1 & 0 & \cdots & 0 \\ 0 & x_2 & \cdots & 0 \\ \cdots & \cdots & \cdots & \cdots \\ 0 & 0 & \cdots & x_n \end{bmatrix} . \tag{7}$$

After multiplication, the product is the $m \times n$ matrix

$$[c_{ij}][x_j] = [c_{ij}x_j] \tag{8}$$

given in table 2.12.

The grand total $\sum\sum c_{ij}x_j$ of the mn elements of table 2.12 can also be expressed as the product of matrices. If the $1 \times m$ matrix

$$B = [1 \quad 1 \quad \cdots \quad 1] \tag{9}$$

is multiplied by the $m \times n$ matrix $[c_{ij}]$, the product is the $1 \times n$ matrix

$$B\,[c_{ij}] = \left[\sum_{i=1}^{m} c_{i1} \quad \sum_{i=1}^{m} c_{i2} \quad \cdots \quad \sum_{i=1}^{m} c_{in} \right] . \tag{10}$$

When the above $1 \times n$ matrix is multiplied by the $n \times 1$ matrix

$$X = \begin{bmatrix} x_1 \\ x_2 \\ \cdots \\ x_n \end{bmatrix} , \tag{11}$$

the resulting product is the 1×1 matrix

$$B\,[c_{ij}]\,X = x_1 \sum_{i=1}^{m} c_{i1} + x_2 \sum_{i=1}^{m} c_{i2} + \cdots + x_n \sum_{i=1}^{m} c_{in}$$

$$= \sum_{j=1}^{n} x_j \sum_{i=1}^{m} c_{ij} = \sum_{i=1}^{m} \sum_{j=1}^{n} c_{ij} x_j \tag{12}$$

which is the grand total of the mn elements of table 2.12.

Table 3.9
Matrix of $y_i a_{ij} x_j$

i \\ j	1	2	$\cdots$	n
1	$y_1 a_{11} x_1$	$y_1 a_{12} x_2$	$\cdots$	$y_1 a_{1n} x_n$
2	$y_2 a_{21} x_1$	$y_2 a_{22} x_2$	$\cdots$	$y_2 a_{2n} x_n$
$\cdots$	$\cdots$	$\cdots$	$\cdots$	$\cdots$
m	$y_m a_{m1} x_1$	$y_m a_{m2} x_2$	$\cdots$	$y_m a_{mn} x_n$

The $m \times n$ matrix $[y_i a_{ij} x_j]$ of table 3.9 may be expressed as the product of three matrices—the m-row diagonal matrix

$$[y_i] = \begin{bmatrix} y_1 & 0 & \cdots & 0 \\ 0 & y_2 & \cdots & 0 \\ \cdots & \cdots & \cdots & \cdots \\ 0 & 0 & \cdots & y_m \end{bmatrix}, \tag{13}$$

the $m \times n$ matrix

$$[a_{ij}] = \begin{bmatrix} a_{11} & a_{12} & \cdots & a_{1n} \\ a_{21} & a_{22} & \cdots & a_{2n} \\ \cdots & \cdots & \cdots & \cdots \\ a_{m1} & a_{m2} & \cdots & a_{mn} \end{bmatrix} \tag{14}$$

and the n-row diagonal matrix

$$[x_j] = \begin{bmatrix} x_1 & 0 & \cdots & 0 \\ 0 & x_2 & \cdots & 0 \\ \cdots & \cdots & \cdots & \cdots \\ 0 & 0 & \cdots & x_n \end{bmatrix}. \tag{15}$$

After multiplication, the product

$$[y_i][a_{ij}][x_j] = [y_i a_{ij} x_j] \tag{16}$$

is the $m \times n$ matrix given in table 3.9.

The grand total of the mn elements of table 3.9 can be expressed as the product of three matrices. If the matrix $[y_i]$ in equation (16) is replaced by the $1 \times m$ matrix

$$Y = [y_1 \quad y_2 \quad \cdots \quad y_m] \tag{17}$$

and the matrix $[x_j]$ by the $n \times 1$ matrix

$$X = \begin{bmatrix} x_1 \\ x_2 \\ \cdots \\ x_n \end{bmatrix}, \tag{18}$$

the resulting product is the grand total

$$Y[a_{ij}]X = \sum_{i=1}^{m}\sum_{j=1}^{n} y_i\, a_{ij}\, x_j \tag{19}$$

of the *mn* elements of the matrix $[y_i a_{ij} x_j]$ given in table 3.9.

EXERCISES

1. Solve the following systems of linear equations by the method given in table 3.1:

(a) $20u + 10v + w = 32$ (b) $20x_1 + 4x_2 - 15x_3 = -85$

  $5u + 2v + 4w = 51$ $16x_1 + 3x_2 - 10x_3 = -53$

  $2u - v + w = 6$ $4x_1 + 2x_2 - 8x_3 = -58$

(c) $5b_1 + 6b_2 - 3b_3 = 5$

  $2b_1 - 5b_2 + 2b_3 = -17$

  $4b_1 + 2b_2 - 5b_3 = -7$

2. Find the products of the following pairs of matrices:

(a) $\begin{bmatrix} 3 & 1 \\ -2 & 3 \end{bmatrix}\begin{bmatrix} 4 & 2 \\ -7 & 1 \end{bmatrix}$ (b) $\begin{bmatrix} 4 & 3 \\ 2 & 1 \end{bmatrix}\begin{bmatrix} 5 & 6 & 7 \\ 1 & 2 & 3 \end{bmatrix}$

(c) $\begin{bmatrix} 1 & 2 & 3 \end{bmatrix}\begin{bmatrix} 10 \\ 11 \\ 12 \end{bmatrix}$ (d) $\begin{bmatrix} 1 & 2 & 3 \\ 7 & -8 & 9 \end{bmatrix}\begin{bmatrix} 4 \\ 5 \\ 6 \end{bmatrix}$

(e) $\begin{bmatrix} x_1 & x_2 & x_3 \end{bmatrix}\begin{bmatrix} x_1 \\ x_2 \\ x_3 \end{bmatrix}$ (f) $\begin{bmatrix} b_1 & b_2 \end{bmatrix}\begin{bmatrix} x_1 \\ x_2 \end{bmatrix}$

(g) $\begin{bmatrix} a_{11} & a_{12} & a_{13} & a_{14} \\ a_{21} & a_{22} & a_{23} & a_{24} \\ a_{31} & a_{32} & a_{33} & a_{34} \end{bmatrix}\begin{bmatrix} b_{11} & b_{12} \\ b_{21} & b_{22} \\ b_{31} & b_{32} \\ b_{41} & b_{42} \end{bmatrix}$

3. Express each of the systems of linear equations of exercise 1 in a matrix form.

4. Show that the two matrices obtained from equations (15) and (16) of section 3.4 are identical.

5. Each of the systems of linear equations of exercise 1 may be expressed as $AX = B$. For each system, find the inverse of A, show that $AA^{-1} = I$, and show that $A^{-1}B = C$, where C is the 3×1 matrix of the solutions of the linear equations.

6. For the matrices A and B given in equation (21) of section 3.4, show that $(AB)' = B'A'$.

7. Given:

$$\begin{bmatrix} a_1 \\ a_2 \\ a_3 \end{bmatrix} = \begin{bmatrix} b_{11} & b_{12} & b_{13} \\ b_{21} & b_{22} & b_{23} \\ b_{31} & b_{32} & b_{33} \end{bmatrix} \begin{bmatrix} c_1 \\ c_2 \\ c_3 \end{bmatrix}$$

Express the matrix $[a_1 \quad a_2 \quad a_3]$ as the product of two matrices.

8. In exercise 5, three 3×3 matrices are inverted. For each inversion, express all the operations in terms of a series of multiplications of matrices.

9. Find the inverse of the 2×2 matrix

$$A = \begin{bmatrix} a & b \\ c & d \end{bmatrix}.$$

All the elements of the inverse matrix should be expressed in terms of a, b, c and d.

10. Multiply the elements of the first row of the matrix P given in equation (21) of section 3.8 by 5, the second row by $-1/2$, and the third row by $1/4$. Then find the orthogonal matrix from this new preliminary matrix, and see if the result obtained is the matrix A given in equation (22) of section 3.8.

11. Test the orthogonality of the matrix A given in equation (23) of section 3.8 by finding the product of A and its transpose A'.

12. Let $m = 2$ and $n = 3$ for the matrices given in equations (13), (14) and (15) of section 3.9. Then demonstrate that equation (16) is true by actually performing the multiplications.

CHAPTER 4

FUNCTIONAL RELATION

Methods of presenting the functional relations between two variables are discussed in this chapter. The three methods—table, equation and curve—may be attributed to three branches of mathematics. In terms of arithmetic, the presentation is a table. In terms of algebra, the presentation is an equation. In terms of geometry, the presentation is a curve. The interfusion of these methods are explored in this chapter.

4.1 Variable

A *variable* is a quantity which can have many numerical values. In contrast, a *constant* can have only one value. In the equation

$$A = \pi r^2$$

which expresses the relation between the area A of a circle and its radius r, both A and r are called variables and the quantity

$$\pi = 3.14159\cdots$$

is called a constant. This is due to the fact that both the area and radius can have many values and π is a fixed quantity.

A quantity can be a variable in one place and a constant in another. For circles in general, both the area A and the radius r are variables. But, for a particular circle, they are constants.

Other examples can be cited to illustrate the point. To a growing child, his height is a variable which changes with time. But to a fully grown man, his height becomes a constant. The temperature of a room is a variable, but it may become a constant when the room is properly air-conditioned.

Variables can be classified as *dependent* and *independent*. In the equation

$$A = \pi r^2$$

the area A is called a dependent variable and the radius r an independent variable, because the area of a circle depends on its radius.

However, this distinction—dependent and independent—is not absolute. It is drawn for the convenience of the user of the equation. For example, the relation

$$A = \pi r^2$$

can be expressed as

$$r = \sqrt{A/\pi}$$

which uses the radius r as the dependent variable and the area A as the independent variable. Even though there is no law against the latter equation, one prefers the former one. This is due to the fact that the radius r can be easily measured and the area A can be computed from the known radius. One would not measure the area first and then compute the radius, because the area of a circle is hard to measure.

In an equation, the dependent variable is usually the quantity to be predicted and the independent one is the quantity already known. The equation

$$A = \pi r^2$$

is used to predict the area A of a circle from its known radius r.

The most commonly used symbol for the dependent variable is y and that for the independent variable is x. The relation between the area of a circle and its radius may be expressed as

$$y = \pi x^2$$

where y is the area and x the radius of a circle.

The dependent variable y is called a *function* of the independent variable x. This is to say that the value of y depends on the value of x. The fact that the height of a child depends on his age can be said that the height of a child is a function of his age.

One can think of many examples where the term function can be used in his daily life. The population of the world is a function of time. The amount of money earned by a plumber is a function of the amount of time he worked. The price of an airline ticket is a function of the distance travelled.

The commonly used symbols for the function of x are $F(x)$, $f(x)$, $g(x)$, $h(x)$ and so forth, with the different letters indicating different functions. For the circle with radius x, its area may be expressed as

$$F(x) = \pi x^2 \tag{1}$$

and its circumference as

$$f(x) = 2\pi x. \tag{2}$$

When the radius is 3 inches, the area is

$$F(3) = \pi 3^2 = 28.27$$

square inches and the circumference is

$$f(3) = 2\pi 3 = 18.85$$

inches as shown in table 4.1. The symbols $F(3)$ and $f(3)$ represent the values of $F(x)$ and $f(x)$ at the point where x is equal to 3.

TABLE 4.1

AREA AND CIRCUMFERENCE OF CIRCLE

(1) Radius x	(2) Area $F(x)$	(3) Circumference $f(x)$
0	0.00000	0.00000
1	3.14159	6.28318
2	12.56636	12.56636
3	28.27431	18.84954
4	50.26544	25.13272
5	78.53975	31.41590

The independent variable x usually has limits within which the functional relation holds. For the relation

$$y = \pi x^2$$

between the area y and the radius x of a circle, the limit of the independent variable x is that it cannot assume a negative value.

In addition to equations, tables are also used in presenting the relations between x and y. Table 4.1 is an example of functional relations presented in tabular form. The tables in the appendix of this book are other examples. In these days of computers, tables become more and more commonly used as a means of presenting functional relations.

Tables do not necessarily come from equations. In fact, it is frequently the other way around. The results of scientific experiments are tables of numbers. The scientific laws which are expressed as equations frequently come from these tables of experimental data.

4.2 Rectangular Coordinates

The functional relations between x and y given in equations or tables can be translated into curves through a device called *rectangular coordinates*. The system is illustrated in figure 4.2a which shows two intersecting straight lines perpendicular to each other. The horizontal line is called the x axis, and the vertical one the y axis. The point of intersection of these axes is called the *origin*.

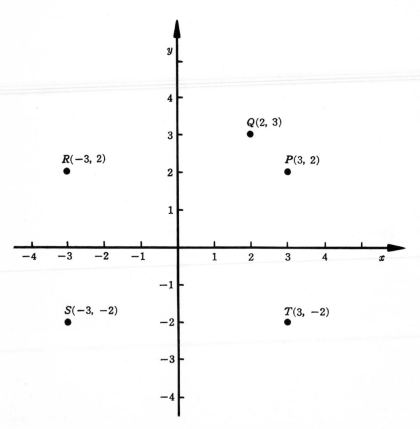

Fig. 4.2a. Rectangular coordinates.

The axes are graduated as shown in figure 4.2a. Both axes are measured from the origin which is the zero point. Along the x axis the points 1, 2, 3 and so forth increase towards the right, and -1, -2, -3 and so forth decrease towards the left. Along the y axis, the positive values increase upwards and the negative ones decrease downwards.

There is no profound reason behind the convention that x increases towards the right and y increases upwards. This arrangement is a lot like traffic rules. In some countries the traffic keeps to the left, and in others to the right. While driving, one should not argue about which way being correct. The important thing is to follow the rules consistently. In the rectangular coordinates, the rules are set and are being universally followed. One should not attempt to change them by himself. For otherwise, the graphs he makes will confuse his readers.

The location of a point can be determined by a pair of values (x, y) through the coordinate system. The point P of figure 4.2a can be pinpointed by the values $(3, 2)$, Q by $(2, 3)$, R by $(-3, 2)$, S by $(-3, -2)$, and T by $(3, -2)$.

The pair of values (x, y) which identifies the location of a point are called the *coordinates* of that point. The first value is called the *x-coordinate* or *abscissa*, and the second value is called the *y-coordinate* or *ordinate* of that point.

The coordinate system described above is called the *rectangular coordinates*. This is not the only system being used, but it is by far the most commonly used one.

A plane is divided into four parts by the axes. The upper right-hand part is called the first *quadrant;* and the others consecutively counterclockwise are called the second, third and fourth quadrants as shown in figure 4.2b. The x values are positive in the first (I) and fourth (IV) quadrants, and negative in the other two quadrants. The y values are positive in the first (I) and second (II) quadrants, and negative in the other two.

The rectangular coordinates are commonly used in street addresses in American cities. It is doubtful that any city is completely covered by one system, but almost every city uses it partially. By this

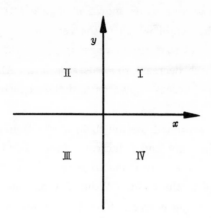

Fɪɢ. 4.2b. Four quadrants of rectangular coordinates.

system, two intersecting throughfares are designated as the axes. These axis streets invariably bear names rather than numbers to avoid being called the Zeroth Street or the Zeroth Avenue.

The directions in the city refer to these axes. The first and fourth quadrants (figure 4.2b) are called the east, the second and third quadrants the west, the first and second quadrants the north, and the third and fourth quadrants the south. By this arrangement, an address like 1845 South Twenty-first Street could have the coordinates $(21, -18.45)$ depending on the layout of the city. Such an address may not sound poetic, but it surely helps a stranger to locate the house he is looking for.

The coordinate system is the link between algebra and geometry. Through a table of values of (x, y) and the coordinate system, an equation can be translated into a curve. The function

$$y = F(x) = \pi x^2$$

given in equation (1) of section 4.1 may be used as an illustration of this translation. For different x values, the corresponding y values are computed as shown in the first two columns of table 4.1. Then each pair of values of x and y is plotted as a point on a sheet of graph paper as shown in figure 4.2c. When the points are linked together, the result is a curve which is the geometric representation of the equation $y = \pi x^2$.

The coordinate system is truly remarkable. Through such a simple device, an equation or a table of values of (x, y) can be translated into a curve. Thus a third method of presenting the functional relation between x and y is generated, in addition to the methods of equation and table which are given in the preceding section.

In plotting graphs, the coordinate system described in this section is frequently modified. First, the scales of the axes may not be the same. In figure 4.2c, one unit of x is of the same length as ten units of y. Of course, the units are not the same either. If x is measured in inches, y is measured in square inches. Second, any two lines parallel to the x and y axes may be used as the axes. Consequently the axes of a graph may intersect at any point and not necessarily at the origin.

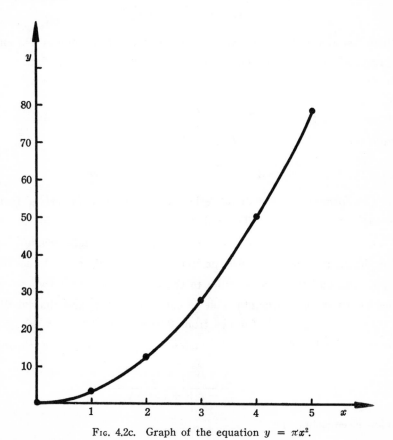

Fɪɢ. 4.2c. Graph of the equation $y = \pi x^2$.

A good graph should be easy to read and not necessarily easy to make. Lengthy instructions can be written on how to make a good graph, but all the instructions can be boiled down to two words— be considerate. A graph maker should think of the convenience of his readers and not that of himself.

In analytic geometry, a branch of mathematics where algebra is applied to geometry, the scales of x and y axes are always the same. There the system should be called *square coordinates*, a special case of rectangular coordinates.

4.3 Distance and Slope

By the rectangular coordinates, the distance between two points P_1 and P_2 is equal to

$$D = \sqrt{(x_2 - x_1)^2 + (y_2 - y_1)^2} \tag{1}$$

where (x_1, y_1) and (x_2, y_2) are the coordinates of the points P_1 and P_2 respectively. For the points $P_1(2, 1)$ and $P_2(4, 5)$ of figure 4.3, the distance between them is

$$\sqrt{(4 - 2)^2 + (5 - 1)^2} = \sqrt{20} = 4.47 \, ;$$

while for $P_3(-4, 3)$ and $P_4(3, -2)$ the distance is

$$\sqrt{[3 - (-4)]^2 + [-2 - 3]^2} = \sqrt{74} = 8.60 \, .$$

The formula for the distance between two points is derived from Pythagorean Theorem. To find the distance between the points $P_1(x_1, y_1)$ and $P_2(x_2, y_2)$, one can complete a right-angle triangle as that shown in figure 4.3 with the line connecting P_1 and P_2 as the hypotenuse and the lines parallel to the axes as the other two sides. The length of the horizontal side is equal to $x_2 - x_1$ and that of the vertical side $y_2 - y_1$. It follows from Pythagorean Theorem that the length of the hypotenuse, or the distance between the points P_1 and P_2, is

$$D = \sqrt{(x_2 - x_1)^2 + (y_2 - y_1)^2}$$

which is equation (1).

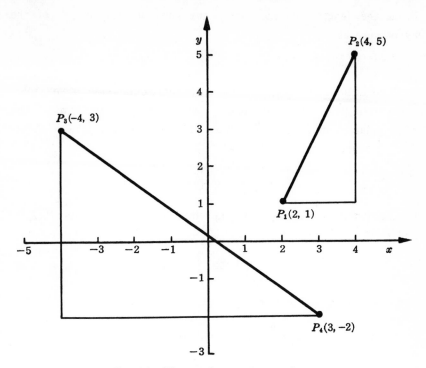

Fɪɢ. 4.3.   Distance between two points.

The distance formula becomes obvious when one looks at the two triangles of figure 4.3. For the triangle which involves the points $P_1(2, 1)$ and $P_2(4, 5)$, the length of the horizontal side is

$$x_2 - x_1 = 4 - 2 = 2$$

and that of the vertical side is

$$y_2 - y_1 = 5 - 1 = 4.$$

Then the length of the hypotenuse is

$$\sqrt{2^2 + 4^2} = \sqrt{4 + 16} = \sqrt{20} = 2.47.$$

For the triangle which involves the points $P_3(-4, 3)$ and $P_4(3, -2)$, the length of the horizontal side is

$$x_4 - x_3 = 3 - (-4) = 7$$

and that of the vertical side is

$$y_4 - y_3 = -2 - 3 = -5.$$

From the lengths of the sides, one can find the length of the hypotenuse as

$$\sqrt{7^2 + (-5)^2} \ = \ \sqrt{49 + 25} \ = \ \sqrt{74} \ = 8.60 \,.$$

The ratio of the vertical side to the horizontal side of a right-angle triangle is called the *slope* of the hypotenuse. In terms of the rectangular coordinates, the slope of the line joining the points $P_1(x_1, y_1)$ and $P_2(x_2, y_2)$ is

$$\frac{y_2 - y_1}{x_2 - x_1} \ = \ \frac{y_1 - y_2}{x_1 - x_2} \,. \tag{2}$$

By this definition, the slope of the line joining the points $P_1(2, 1)$ and $P_2(4, 5)$ of figure 4.3 is

$$\frac{5 - 1}{4 - 2} \ = \ \frac{4}{2} \ = 2 \,,$$

and that for $P_3(-4, 3)$ and $P_4(3, -2)$ is

$$\frac{-2 - 3}{3 - (-4)} \ = \ \frac{-5}{7} \ = \ - \, 0.714286 \,.$$

The sign of the slope indicates whether the value of y increases or decreases as the value of x increases. A positive slope indicates that y increases with x, and a negative one indicates that y decreases with x. The line joining $P_1(2, 1)$ and $P_2(4, 5)$ of figure 4.3 has a positive slope, because the y value increases by

$$5 - 1 = 4$$

units as the x value increases by

$$4 - 2 = 2$$

units. For the same reason one can see that the line joining $P_3(-4, 3)$ and $P_4(3, -2)$ has a negative slope. As x increases from -4 to 3, the value of y decreases from 3 to -2.

The numerical value of a slope measures the steepness of the line. The line P_1P_2 of figure 4.3 with the slope of 2 has a steeper grade than the line P_3P_4 whose slope is -0.714286.

The slope of a line measures the rate of change of the value of y with respect to x. For example, a boy was 30 inches tall at the age of one and 38 inches tall at the age of three. The boy has grown eight inches in two years or he was growing at the rate of four inches per year during the period when he was one to three years old. Now this rate of growth can be represented by the slope of a line. The data of the boy's age and height can be represented by the points $P_1(1, 30)$ and $P_2(3, 38)$ with x being the age and y the height. The slope of the line joining P_1 and P_2 is

$$\frac{y_2 - y_1}{x_2 - x_1} = \frac{38 - 30}{3 - 1} = \frac{8}{2} = 4$$

which is the boy's growth rate or the rate of change of height with respect to age.

The unit of a slope is the number of y units per x unit. For the example of growth rate, the change in height is

$$38 - 30 = 8$$

inches and that in age is

$$3 - 1 = 2$$

years. Thus the slope is

$$8/2 = 4$$

inches per year.

The value of a slope is influenced by the units used. Four inches per year is equivalent to one-third inch per month. Both values 4 and 1/3 are the slope of the same line depending on the unit of time being used.

The unit of a slope is an integral part of that slope and cannot be ignored. One should not jump into the conclusion that the slope of 0.5 represents a lower rate of change than that of 4. In fact, the conclusion is the other way around if the former slope is 0.5 inch per month and the latter is 4 inches per year.

4.4 Linear Function

There are many kinds of functions. The simplest one is the *linear function*. The characteristic of this function is that *the value of y changes at a constant rate with respect to x*. Two examples of linear function are given in table 4.4. In example 1, the value of y changes at the constant rate of 3. In example 2, the rate is -2.

TABLE 4.4

EXAMPLES OF LINEAR FUNCTION

Example 1			Example 2	
$y = 2 + 3x$			$y = 15 - 2x$	
x	y		x	y
0	2		0	15
1	5		1	13
2	8		2	11
3	11		3	9
4	14		4	7
5	17		5	5

In terms of geometry, the characteristic of the linear function is that the slope found from any two points of the function is a constant. For example 1 of table 4.4, the slope for the points (1, 5) and (3, 11) is equal to

$$\frac{11 - 5}{3 - 1} = \frac{6}{2} = 3$$

and that for (2, 8) and (5, 17) is also equal to

$$\frac{17 - 8}{5 - 2} = \frac{9}{3} = 3$$

which is the rate of change of y with respect to x. Similarly, one can find that the slope for any two points of example 2 is always equal to -2.

The graph of a function with a constant rate of change is a straight line, and thus the name linear function. The two functions of table 4.4 are plotted in figure 4.4a. The points of each function are located on a straight line.

In terms of algebra, the linear function can be represented by the equation

$$y = b_0 + b_1 x \tag{1}$$

where b_0 is the *intercept* or the value of y at $x = 0$, and b_1 is the slope of the straight line or the constant rate of change of the function with respect to x. In example 1 of table 4.4, the value of y at $x = 0$ is

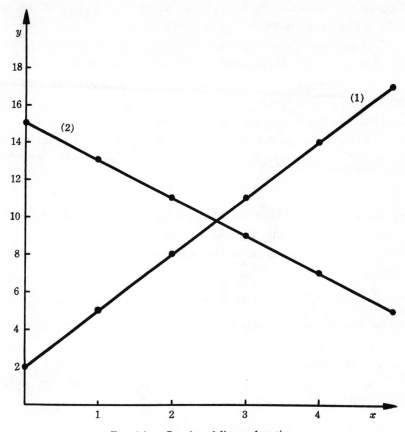

FIG. 4.4a. Graphs of linear functions.

$$b_0 = 2$$

and the constant rate of change of y is

$$b_1 = 3.$$

Thus the equation representing the given function is

$$y = 2 + 3x. \tag{2}$$

Similarly, the equation of example 2 is

$$y = 15 - 2x. \tag{3}$$

The intercept b_0 is the ordinate of the point $(0, b_0)$ where the straight line intersects the y axis. This can be seen from figure 4.4a. The straight line of example 1 with b_0 equal to 2 meets the y axis at the point $(0, 2)$, and that of example 2 with b_0 equal to 15 at the point $(0, 15)$.

The quantity b_1 needs no further explanation. It is the slope of the straight line or the constant rate of change of y with respect to x. From figure 4.4a one can see that line 1 with b_1 equal to 3 is an increasing function while line 2 with b_1 equal to -2 is a decreasing function. Furthermore, line 1 is steeper than line 2.

A straight line passes through the origin $(0, 0)$ if the intercept b_0 is equal to zero. The equation

$$y = f(x) = 2\pi x$$

(equation 2, section 4.1) is an example of this kind of lines. From columns 1 and 3 of table 4.1, one can tell that the intercept b_0 is equal to zero and the slope, or the constant rate of change of y, is equal to

$$2\pi = 6.28318.$$

In this special case of linear function where the intercept is equal to zero, the variable y is said to be *proportional* to x and the slope is called the *constant of proportionality*.

The straight line assumes a horizontal position when the slope b_1 is equal to zero. The equation

$$y = b_0 \tag{4}$$

implies that the value of y is always equal to b_0 regardless of the value of x. In this case, the variable y is said to be *independent* of x or not a function of x.

In this kind of lines, the value b_0 indicates the position of a horizontal line. The line with the equation

$$y = 5$$

is a line parallel to but 5 units above the x axis. The one with the equation

$$y = -3$$

is also a line parallel to the x axis but 3 units below it.

The equation of a straight line can be found from the slope and any given point not necessarily the intercept. The slope of example 1 of table 4.4 is known to be 3. An arbitrary point $(2, 8)$ is chosen from that table to determine the equation. With the slope known, the required equation must be

$$y = b_0 + 3x.$$

When the values $(2, 8)$ are substituted for (x, y) in the above equation, the result is

$$8 = b_0 + 3(2)$$

or

$$b_0 = 8 - 6 = 2.$$

Consequently the required equation is

$$y = 2 + 3x$$

which is the same one given in equation (2).

The equation of a straight line can also be determined by any two points of a linear function. The points $(1, 5)$ and $(3, 11)$ of example 1 of table 4.4 are used for the demonstration of this method. The slope of the line is

$$\frac{y_2 - y_1}{x_2 - x_1} = \frac{11 - 5}{3 - 1} = \frac{6}{2} = 3.$$

With the slope known, the required equation is known to be

$$y = b_0 + 3x.$$

When the values $(1, 5)$ are substituted for (x, y) in the above equation, the result is

$$5 = b_0 + 3(1)$$

or

$$b_0 = 2.$$

Thus the equation obtained is still the one given in equation (2).

With two points (x_1, y_1) and (x_2, y_2) given, the equation of a straight line can also be obtained through the knowledge that the slope found from any two points of a linear function is a constant. The coordinates of a point on the line may be represented by (x, y). Then it follows that

$$\frac{y - y_1}{x - x_1} = \frac{y_2 - y_1}{x_2 - x_1} . \tag{5}$$

For the same given points (1, 5) and (3, 11), the equation is

$$\frac{y - 5}{x - 1} = \frac{11 - 5}{3 - 1}$$

which, after simplification, becomes

$$y = 2 + 3x$$

which is the same one given in equation (2).

With two given points such as (1, 5) and (3, 11), the equation of the straight line can also be obtained by solving simultaneous equations. The general equation of a straight line is known to be

$$y = b_0 + b_1 x .$$

Now it is a matter of determining the values of b_0 and b_1 from the given points to specify the particular line. When the values (1, 5) and (3, 11) are substituted for (x, y) in the above equation, the result is the system of simultaneous equations

$$5 = b_0 + 1b_1$$

$$11 = b_0 + 3b_1$$

whose solutions are

$$b_0 = 2$$

$$b_1 = 3 .$$

Consequently the required equation is

$$y = 2 + 3x$$

which is the same one given in equation (2).

For the general case where the two given points may be represented by (x_1, y_1) and (x_2, y_2), the system of simultaneous equations is

$$y_1 = b_0 + b_1 x_1$$

$$y_2 = b_0 + b_1 x_2$$

which, in matrix notation, is

$$\begin{bmatrix} y_1 \\ y_2 \end{bmatrix} = \begin{bmatrix} 1 & x_1 \\ 1 & x_2 \end{bmatrix} \begin{bmatrix} b_0 \\ b_1 \end{bmatrix} \tag{6}$$

or

$$Y = X[b_i] \qquad i = 0,1.$$

To obtain the solutions $[b_i]$ of the simultaneous equations, one can find the inverse

$$X^{-1} = \frac{1}{x_2 - x_1} \begin{bmatrix} x_2 & -x_1 \\ -1 & 1 \end{bmatrix} \tag{7}$$

of the matrix X. When equation (6) is multiplied by X^{-1} from the left, the resulting equation is

$$X^{-1}Y = X^{-1}X[b_i]$$

or

$$[b_i] = X^{-1}Y \tag{8}$$

which, in longhand, is

$$\begin{bmatrix} b_0 \\ b_1 \end{bmatrix} = \frac{1}{x_2 - x_1} \begin{bmatrix} x_2 & -x_1 \\ -1 & 1 \end{bmatrix} \begin{bmatrix} y_1 \\ y_2 \end{bmatrix}$$

or

$$b_0 = \frac{x_2 y_1 - x_1 y_2}{x_2 - x_1} \tag{9}$$

$$b_1 = \frac{y_2 - y_1}{x_2 - x_1}. \tag{10}$$

For the given points (1, 5) and (3, 11), the solutions of the simultaneous equations are

$$b_0 = \frac{(3)(5) - (1)(11)}{3 - 1} = \frac{4}{2} = 2$$

$$b_1 = \frac{11 - 5}{3 - 1} = \frac{6}{2} = 3$$

and the resulting equation is

$$y = 2 + 3x$$

which is the same one given in equation (2).

In practical problems, the limits of x should be attached to the equation representing the functional relation between x and y. In other words, a straight line used in a practical problem is only a segment of a line and not a whole line. In tables and graphs, the limits are automatically imposed. Table 4.4 shows that the value of x ranges from 0 to 5 and figure 4.4a also has such limits. For the corresponding equations, the same limits may be indicated as

$$y = 2 + 3x \qquad 0 \leqq x \leqq 5$$

and

$$y = 15 - 2x \qquad 0 \leqq x \leqq 5$$

where the sign $<$ is the shorthand for "is less than" and the sign $\leqq$ is for "is equal to or less than". The purpose of attaching the limits of x to an equation is to indicate that the functional relation given by the equation may not hold outside the given limits.

The slopes of two lines cannot be compared through their graphs unless the scales of the graphs are the same. In analytic geometry where the system of square coordinates is used, one takes for granted that the line with a steeper grade has a greater value of slope than the one with a flatter grade. However, this is true only if the two lines are plotted on graphs of the same scale. For graphs of different scales, this may not be true at all. The visual grade of a line can be changed by the choice of scale even if the numerical slope remains the same. For illustration, the straight line

$$y = x$$

is plotted in figure 4.4b in different scales. In the left graph, the lengths of x and y units are the same; and in the right graph, the y unit is twice as long as that of the x unit. As a result, the line in the right graph looks much steeper even though the slope of the line is equal to 1 in both graphs. Furthermore, the line on the left bisects the angle between the axes and the one on the right does not. The line

$$y = x$$

bisects the angle between the axes only if the square coordinates are used and does not otherwise.

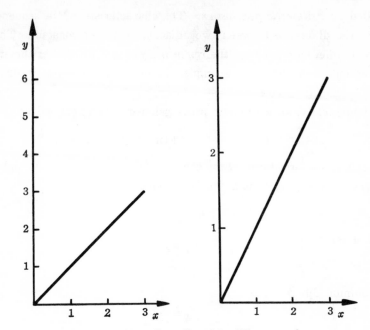

Fig. 4.4b. Same line plotted in different scales.

The slope, or the rate of change of y with respect to x, is an important characteristic of the functional relation between x and y. The whole field of *differential calculus* is devoted to this subject.

The linear equation

$$y = f(x) = b_0 + b_1 x$$

is commonly used in representing the functional relation between x and y. It is done mainly because the function is simple and not necessarily because the linear function occurs abundantly in nature. However, such a simple function is frequently adequate. In practical problems, a short segment of a curve can be replaced by a straight line without much harm. The situation is very much like ignoring the curvature of the earth in building a house. Even though one knows that the surface of the earth is curved, in building a house he can safely consider the surface flat because the lot is such a tiny fraction of the surface of the earth.

4.5 Arithmetic Progression

A sequence of numbers such as

$$3 \quad 5 \quad 7 \quad 9 \quad 11$$

is called an *arithmetic progression*. The characteristic of the sequence is that the difference between two adjacent terms is a constant. This constant difference is called the *common difference* of the arithmetic progression. For the given example, the common difference is equal to 2.

Symbolically, an arithmetic progression can be expressed as

$$A \quad A+D \quad A+2D \quad \cdots \quad A+(n-2)D \quad A+(n-1)D$$

where A is the first term, D the common difference, and n the number of terms of the progression. For the sequence

$$3 \quad 5 \quad 7 \quad 9 \quad 11,$$

the first terms is

$$A = 3$$

the common difference is

$$D = 2$$

and the number of terms is

$$n = 5.$$

In general, the ith term of an arithmetic progression is

$$A_i = A + (i-1)D \qquad i = 1, 2, \cdots, n. \tag{1}$$

For the above example, the fourth term is equal to

$$A_4 = 3 + (4-1)2 = 9.$$

The common difference may be either positive or negative. In the sequence

$$64 \quad 60 \quad 56 \quad 52 \quad 48 \quad 44$$

whose first term is $A = 64$ and whose number of terms is $n = 6$, the common difference is

$$D = -4.$$

When the common difference is equal to zero, all terms of an arithmetic progression are equal to the first term. In this case, the sequence becomes

$$A \quad A \quad \cdots \quad A.$$

The sum of the n terms of an arithmetic progression is equal to

$$\sum_{i=1}^{n} A_i = \frac{n(A_1 + A_n)}{2}. \tag{2}$$

For the sequence

$$3 \quad 5 \quad 7 \quad 9 \quad 11,$$

the sum is equal to

$$\sum_{i=1}^{5} A_i = \frac{5(3 + 11)}{2} = 35$$

which is exactly equal to

$$3 + 5 + 7 + 9 + 11 = 35.$$

The formula for the sum of the n terms of an arithmetic progression, which is given in equation (2), can be readily seen by writing out the n terms of the progression

$$A \qquad A + D \qquad \cdots \qquad A + (n-2)D \quad A + (n-1)D$$

and also the same progression in the reverse order

$$A + (n-1)D \quad A + (n-2)D \qquad \cdots \qquad A + D \qquad A.$$

The sum of any pair of corresponding terms of the above two progressions is equal to

$$A + A + (n - 1)D = A_1 + A_n.$$

Then the sum of all the terms of the two progressions must be equal to n times that amount or

$$n(A_1 + A_n).$$

But this is the sum of all the terms of two progressions with the same sum. Consequently the sum of the n terms of one arithmetic progression is only one half of that amount which is equation (2).

The first n positive integers

$$1 \quad 2 \quad 3 \quad \cdots \quad n$$

is an arithmetic progression with both the first term and the common difference equal to 1. Then the sum of the n integers from 1 to n

must be equal to

$$\sum_{i=1}^{n} A_i = \sum_{i=1}^{n} i = \frac{n(1+n)}{2}.$$

For example, the sum of 1, 2, 3 and 4 is

$$\sum_{i=1}^{4} i = \frac{4(1+4)}{2} = 10$$

which is exactly equal to

$$1 + 2 + 3 + 4 = 10$$

as one would expect.

The arithmetic progression is a linear function of the integers 0, 1, 2, $\cdots$, $n-1$. The linear equation

$$y = A + Dx \tag{3}$$

yields the terms of an arithmetic progression if the x values are 0, 1, 2, $\cdots$, $(n-1)$, such as:

x	0	1	2	$\cdots$	$n-1$
y	A	$A+D$	$A+2D$	$\cdots$	$A+(n-1)D$

All the n terms of the arithmetic progression lie on the straight line whose intercept is A and whose slope is D. For example, the progression

$$3 \quad 5 \quad 7 \quad 9 \quad 11$$

can be represented by the equation

$$y = 3 + 2x$$

with x being equal to 0, 1, 2, 3, 4. The progression

$$64 \quad 60 \quad 56 \quad 52 \quad 48 \quad 44$$

can be represented by the equation

$$y = 64 - 4x$$

with x being equal to 0, 1, $\cdots$, 5. From these equations, one can see that an arithmetic progression represents the linear functions of the integers 0, 1, 2, $\cdots$, $n-1$.

An amount of money which draws a simple interest constitutes an arithmetic progression at the end of a sequence of years. If one starts with a principal of $100 drawing 6% simple interest per year, the amount grows at the rate of $6 a year. The money accumulated at the end of 0, 1, 2, 3 and 4 years constitutes the arithmetic progression

$$\$100 \quad \$106 \quad \$112 \quad \$118 \quad \$124$$

with the principal as the amount accumulated at the end of the zeroth year.

The worth of a piece of equipment which depreciates at a constant rate constitutes an arithmetic progression. The equipment, which is purchased at $10,000 but depreciates at the rate of $1,000 a year, is worth

$$\$10,000 \quad \$9,000 \quad \$8,000 \quad \$7,000$$

at the end of the zeroth, first, second and third year. In this arithmetic progression, the common difference is $-\$1,000$, which is the depreciating rate of $1,000 a year.

4.6 Polynomial Function

The most commonly used general-purpose function is the *polynomial* in x

$$y = f(x) = b_0 + b_1x + b_2x^2 + \cdots + b_mx^m \tag{1}$$

where the b's are constants and the exponents of x are positive integers. In abbreviated symbols, the equation may be expressed as

$$y = \sum b_ix^i \qquad i = 0, 1, 2, \cdots, m \tag{2}$$

because x^0 is equal to 1 and x^1 is equal to x. The letter m is called the *degree* of the polynomial, if b_m is different from zero. When m is equal to 1, the polynomial

$$y = b_0 + b_1x$$

is the first-degree or linear equation. When m is equal to 2, the polynomial

$$y = b_0 + b_1x + b_2x^2$$

is the second-degree or *quadratic* equation. If $m = 3$, the equation is said to be *cubic;* and $m = 4$, *quartic.*

The degree of a polynomial influences the shape of its graph. A zeroth-degree equation such as

$$y = b_0 \tag{3}$$

is a horizontal line. A first-degree equation

$$y = b_0 + b_1 x \tag{4}$$

is a straight line but not horizontal. A second-degree equation

$$y = b_0 + b_1 x + b_2 x^2 \tag{5}$$

can bend once, either upwards or downwards. Figure 4.6a shows the graph of the equation

$$y = 2 + 6x - x^2. \tag{6}$$

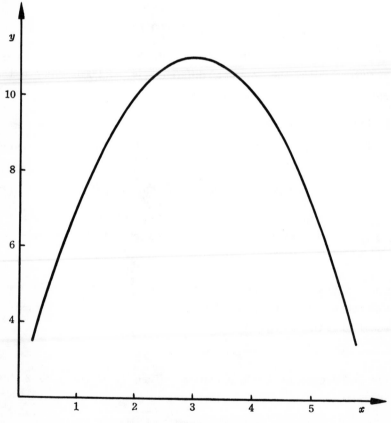

Fig. 4.6a. Graph of $y = 2 + 6x - x^2$.

A third-degree equation

$$y = b_0 + b_1x + b_2x^2 + b_3x^3$$

can bend twice, upwards and downwards. Figure 4.6b shows the graph of the equation

$$y = 100 + 63x - 30x^2 + 4x^3. \tag{7}$$

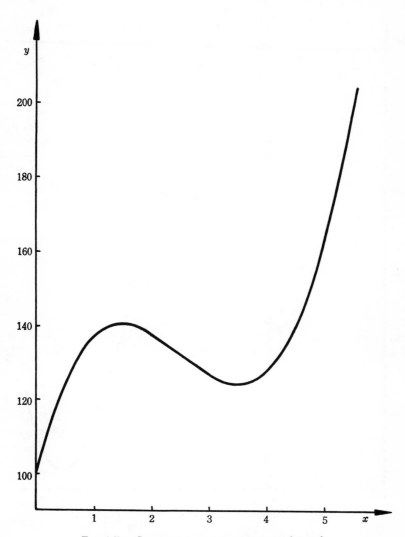

Fig. 4.6b. Graph of $y = 100 + 63x - 30x^2 + 4x^3$.

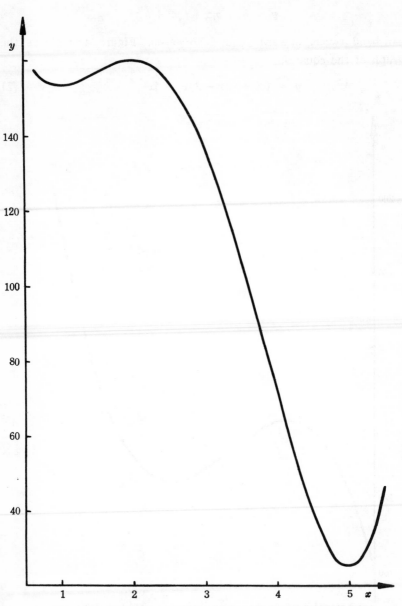

F<small>IG.</small> 4.6c. Graph of $y = 200 - 120x + 102x^2 - 32x^3 + 3x^4$.

A fourth-degree equation

$$y = b_0 + b_1x + b_2x^2 + b_3x^3 + b_4x^4 \tag{8}$$

can bend upwards and downwards for three times. Figure 4.6c shows the graph of the equation of

$$y = 200 - 120x + 102x^2 - 32x^3 + 3x^4. \tag{9}$$

In general, the graph of an mth-degree equation can bend a maximum of $m-1$ times.

The number $m-1$ is the maximum number that the curve of an mth-degree polynomial can bend and not necessarily the exact number. The curve of the fourth-degree equation

$$y = x^4 \tag{10}$$

bends only once as shown in figure 4.6d. Furthermore, for practical

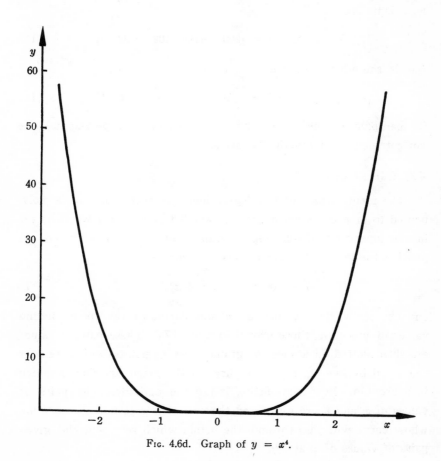

Fig. 4.6d. Graph of $y = x^4$.

problems only a segment of a curve is used. Regardless of the degree of an equation, a segment of its curve may not make a complete bend at all. In fact, if a segment is small enough, it can be represented by a straight line.

The degree of a polynomial determines the flexibility of its graph. The straight line of the first-degree equation is as rigid as a straight-edge ruler. As the degree increases, the graph increases the number of its bends and thus becomes more flexible. If the first-degree equation is regarded a straight-edge ruler, the higher-degree equations are the various pieces of French curves.

The coefficients b_0, b_1, $\cdots$, b_m of a polynomial also influence the shape of its graph. Both equations (9) and (10) are of the fourth degree; yet their graphs look quite different. In one equation, the coefficients are

$$[b_0 \quad b_1 \quad b_2 \quad b_3 \quad b_4] = [200 \quad -120 \quad 102 \quad -32 \quad 3] \tag{11}$$

and, in the other, they are

$$[b_0 \quad b_1 \quad b_2 \quad b_3 \quad b_4] = [\; 0 \quad\quad 0 \quad 0 \quad\quad 0 \quad 1]. \tag{12}$$

By manipulating the degree and the coefficients of a polynomial, one can get a curve of practically any shape.

4.7 Curve-Fitting

The manipulation of the degree and the coefficients of a polynomial to fit a given set of points is called *curve-fitting* which is the inverse operation of plotting a graph from a given equation. In plotting the graph of a given equation such as

$$y = 100 + 5x - 2x^2 + x^3 , \tag{1}$$

one chooses various values of x and computes the corresponding values of y such as those shown in table 4.7a. These pairs of values are then plotted on a sheet of graph paper as points, which are later connected by lines to form the curve of the given equation as shown in figure 4.7a. Now curve-fitting is just the opposite. The pairs of values of x and y are given and the objective is to find the equation whose curve will pass through the points which represent the given pairs of values of x and y.

TABLE 4.7a

FOUR GIVEN PAIRS OF VALUES OF x AND y

x	2	4	6	8
y	110	152	274	524

The four pairs of values of x and y of table 4.7a may be used as an illustration of curve-fitting. A third-degree polynomial

$$y = b_0 + b_1 x + b_2 x^2 + b_3 x^3$$

with four undetermined coefficients can be made to pass through the four given points by assigning appropriate values to the coefficients. At this stage, the coefficients are unknown but the four given pairs of values of x and y are known to satisfy the third-degree polynomial. When the four pairs of values of x and y are substituted in turn into the equation

$$y = b_0 + b_1 x + b_2 x^2 + b_3 x^3 \,,$$

the resulting equations are

$$
\begin{aligned}
110 &= b_0 + 2b_1 + \ \ 4b_2 + \ \ \ \ 8b_3 \\
152 &= b_0 + 4b_1 + 16b_2 + \ \ 64b_3 \\
274 &= b_0 + 6b_1 + 36b_2 + 216b_3 \\
524 &= b_0 + 8b_1 + 64b_2 + 512b_3
\end{aligned}
\tag{2}
$$

or, in matrix notation,

$$
\begin{bmatrix}
1 & 2 & 4 & 8 \\
1 & 4 & 16 & 64 \\
1 & 6 & 36 & 216 \\
1 & 8 & 64 & 512
\end{bmatrix}
\begin{bmatrix}
b_0 \\
b_1 \\
b_2 \\
b_3
\end{bmatrix}
=
\begin{bmatrix}
110 \\
152 \\
274 \\
524
\end{bmatrix}
\tag{3}
$$

which constitute a system of simultaneous linear equations with the b's being the unknown quantities. The solutions

$$[b_0 \ \ \ b_1 \ \ \ b_2 \ \ \ b_3] = [100 \ \ \ 5 \ \ \ -2 \ \ \ 1] \tag{4}$$

yield the desired equation

$$y = 100 + 5x - 2x^2 + x^3$$

which is exactly the one given in equation (1), from which the four pairs of values of x and y of table 4.7a are originally obtained.

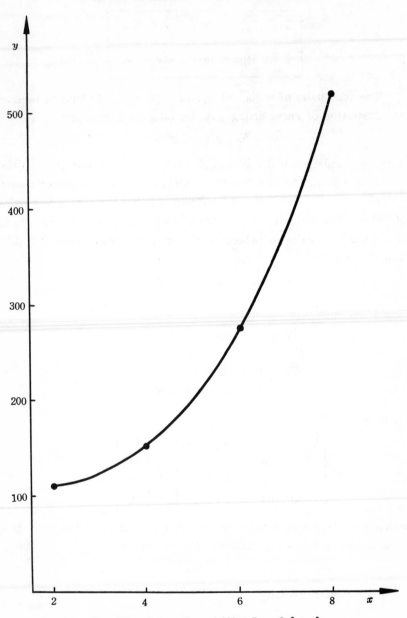

F<small>IG</small>. 4.7a. Curve of $y = 100 + 5x - 2x^2 + x^3$.

This happy event can only happen when the functional relation between the variables x and y is truly a polynomial. Otherwise, the polynomial produced by curve-fitting is an approximation of the true function. The reason why one would accept such an approximation is that the true function is unknown and the polynomial is a whole lot better than nothing.

The fact that a polynomial $P(x)$ can be used as an approximation of the unknown function $F(x)$ may be illustrated by the function

$$y = F(x) = \frac{30{,}000}{x} \tag{5}$$

which is not a polynomial in x. For the sake of illustration, one can pretend that only four points

$$(5, 6000) \quad (10, 3000) \quad (15, 2000) \quad (20, 1500)$$

which are obtained from equation (5) are known and the true function $F(x)$ is not. Now one may proceed to fit a polynomial to the data. The simultaneous equations for this operation are

$$\begin{bmatrix} 1 & 5 & 25 & 125 \\ 1 & 10 & 100 & 1{,}000 \\ 1 & 15 & 225 & 3{,}375 \\ 1 & 20 & 400 & 8{,}000 \end{bmatrix} \begin{bmatrix} b_0 \\ b_1 \\ b_2 \\ b_3 \end{bmatrix} = \begin{bmatrix} 6{,}000 \\ 3{,}000 \\ 2{,}000 \\ 1{,}500 \end{bmatrix} \tag{6}$$

whose solutions lead to the polynomial

$$y = P(x) = 12{,}500 - 1{,}750x + 100x^2 - 2x^3 . \tag{7}$$

At a glance one can tell that the polynomial function $P(x)$ of equation (7) has no resemblance to the true function $F(x)$ of equation (5). Yet the four given points

$$(5, 6000) \quad (10, 3000) \quad (15, 2000) \quad (20, 1500)$$

satisfy both equations. Furthermore, for the other values of x between 5 and 20, the values of the polynomial function $P(x)$ and those of the true function $F(x)$ are fairly close to each other as shown in table 4.7b and figure 4.7b. For example, at $x = 7$ the value of $P(x)$ is

TABLE 4.7b

COMPARISON OF POLYNOMIAL AND TRUE FUNCTION

Given Points		Polynomial	30,000/x	Discrepancy	Percentage
x	y	$P(x)$	$F(x)$	$P(x)-F(x)$	$\dfrac{P(x)-F(x)}{F(x)}$
5	6,000	6,000	6,000	0	0.00
6		5.168	5,000	168	3.36
7		4,464	4,286	178	4.15
8		3,876	3,750	126	3.36
9		3,392	3,333	59	1.77
10	3,000	3,000	3,000	0	0.00
11		2,688	2,727	−39	−1.43
12		2,444	2,500	−56	−2.24
13		2,256	2,308	−52	−2.25
14		2,112	2,143	−31	−1.45
15	2,000	2,000	2,000	0	0.00
16		1,908	1,875	33	1.76
17		1,824	1,765	59	3.34
18		1,736	1,667	69	4.14
19		1,632	1,579	53	3.36
20	1,500	1,500	1,500	0	0.00

$$P(7) = 12,500 - 1,750(7) + 100(7)^2 - 2(7)^3 = 4,464$$

and that of the true function $F(x)$ is

$$F(7) = \frac{30,000}{7} = 4,286.$$

The discrepancy between the two values is

$$P(7) - F(7) = 4,464 - 4,286 = 178$$

which is the largest discrepancy in table 4.7b. When this discrepancy is expressed as a percentage of the true function, the error is

$$\frac{P(7) - F(7)}{F(7)} = \frac{178}{4,286} = 4.15\%$$

which is also the largest in the table. If an error of this magnitude cannot be tolerated, one may use more points and a higher-degree polynomial to reduce it.

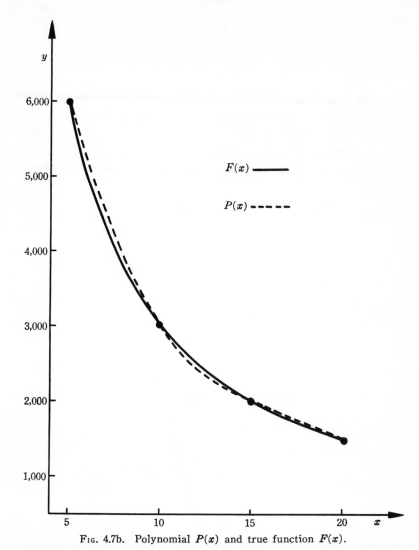

Fig. 4.7b. Polynomial $P(x)$ and true function $F(x)$.

This text gives only the most rudimentary method of obtaining an equation from given points. For other methods, the reader is referred to the author's *Statistical Inference* and W. E. Milne's *Numerical Calculus*. The theoretical justification of approximating a function by polynomial is given in chapter 13 of this text.

4.8 Locus

The *locus* is the path along which a point moves. The equation of the locus can be found when the conditions under which the point moves are given. To find the equation is a process of translating geometry into algebra. Several examples are given in this section to illustrate this process.

The locus of a moving point P which is equidistant from two fixed points is a straight line as shown in figure 4.8a. The two fixed points P_1 and P_2 are given the coordinates $(1, 2)$ and $(4, 1)$, and the moving point P the coordinates (x, y). Then the distance from $P(x, y)$ to $P_1(1, 2)$ is equal to (equation 1, section 4.3)

$$d_1 = \sqrt{(x-1)^2 + (y-2)^2}$$

and that from $P(x, y)$ to $P_2(4, 1)$ is equal to

$$d_2 = \sqrt{(x-4)^2 + (y-1)^2}.$$

But, under the given condition, the two distances are equal, or

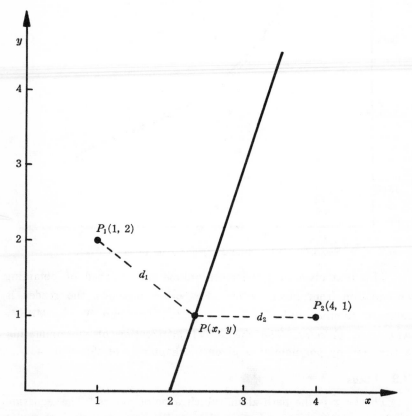

Fig. 4.8a. Locus of point equidistant from two fixed points.

$$d_1 = d_2$$

which implies that

$$d_1^2 = d_2^2$$

or

$$(x-1)^2 + (y-2)^2 = (x-4)^2 + (y-1)^2$$

or

$$(x^2 - 2x + 1) + (y^2 - 4y + 4) = (x^2 - 8x + 16) + (y^2 - 2y + 1).$$

After simplification, the above equation can be reduced to

$$y = 3x - 6$$

which is a linear equation.

The locus of the moving point $P(x, y)$ which is equidistant from a fixed point and a fixed straight line is a *parabola*. To illustrate the procedure of finding the equation of the locus, the fixed point F is placed at $(0, 2)$ and the fixed line at the x axis as shown in figure 4.8b. The distance from (x, y) to $(0, 2)$ is

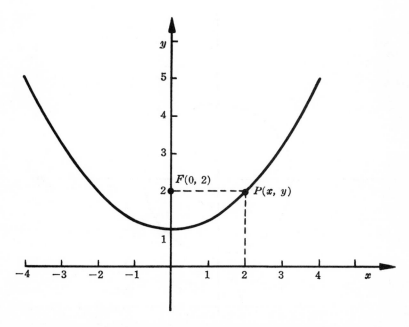

FIG. 4.8b. Parabola with $(0, 2)$ as fixed point and x axis as fixed line.

$$\sqrt{(x-0)^2 + (y-2)^2} = \sqrt{x^2 + y^2 - 4y + 4}$$

and the perpendicular distance from (x, y) to the x axis is simply y. Under the given condition of the locus, the two distances are equal, or

$$y = \sqrt{x^2 + y^2 - 4y + 4}.$$

When both sides of the above equation are squared, the result is

$$y^2 = x^2 + y^2 - 4y + 4.$$

After simplification, the above equation becomes the quadratic equation

$$y = 0.25\, x^2 + 1$$

which represents the locus of the given parabola.

The locus of the moving point $P(x, y)$ which maintains a constant distance from a fixed point is a circle. The constant distance is the radius and the fixed point is the center of the circle. To find the equation of the circle with radius equal to 2 and center at the origin as shown in figure 4.8c, one may use the distance formula

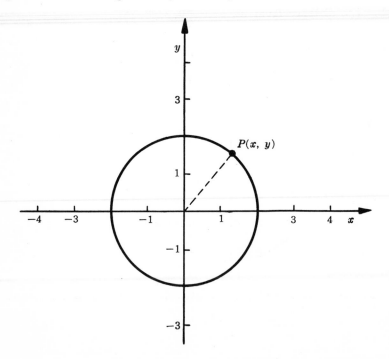

Fɪɢ. 4.8c. Circle with radius equal to 2 and center at the origin.

given in equation (1) of section 4.3. The distance between the points (x, y) and $(0, 0)$ is

$$\sqrt{(x - 0)^2 + (y - 0)^2} = 2.$$

After both sides of the above equation are squared, the result

$$x^2 + y^2 = 4$$

is the equation of the given circle.

The locus of the moving point $P(x, y)$ whose sum of distances from two fixed points P_1 and P_2 is an *ellipse*. To illustrate the process of determining the equation of the locus, the two fixed points are placed at $P_1(-3, 0)$ and $P_2(3, 0)$ and the sum of the two distances PP_1 and PP_2 is made equal to 10 as shown in figure 4.8d.

The equation of the locus can be derived from the given condition that the sum of the distances is equal to 10, or

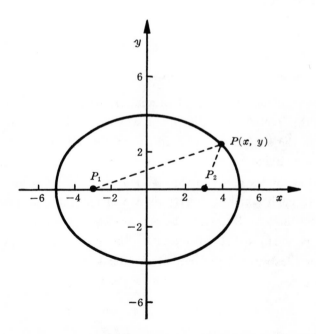

Fig. 4.8d. Ellipse with fixed points at $P_1(-3, 0)$ and $P_2(3, 0)$ and total distance equal to 10.

$$\sqrt{(x+3)^2 + y^2} \;+\; \sqrt{(x-3)^2 + y^2} \;=\; 10.$$

With the second radical being subtracted from both sides, the above equation can be expressed as

$$\sqrt{(x+3)^2 + y^2} \;=\; 10 - \sqrt{(x-3)^2 + y^2}.$$

When both sides are squared, the above equation becomes

$$x^2 + 6x + 9 + y^2 \;=\; 100 - 20\sqrt{(x-3)^2 + y^2} + x^2 - 6x + 9 + y^2$$

which is equivalent to

$$20\sqrt{(x-3)^2 + y^2} \;=\; 100 - 12x.$$

After both sides being squared, the above equation becomes

$$400(x^2 - 6x + 9 + y^2) \;=\; 10{,}000 - 2{,}400x + 144x^2.$$

After simplification, it becomes

$$256\,x^2 + 400\,y^2 \;=\; 6{,}400$$

or

$$\frac{x^2}{25} + \frac{y^2}{16} \;=\; 1$$

which is the equation of the ellipse.

Locus problems are covered in analytic geometry. The examples given in this section are the simplest ones. Readers who are interested in the subject are referred to any text on analytic geometry where the characteristics of the curves are discussed in great detail.

In all examples given in this section, it is understood that the medium through which geometry is translated into algebra is the square coordinates. However, the appearance of the graph of a given equation is not fixed but influenced by the choice of scales of the axes. For illustrations, the unit of x is made twice as long as that of y in figures 4.8e and 4.8f. In this scale, the equation

$$x^2 + y^2 \;=\; 4$$

which represents a circle in figure 4.8c becomes an ellipse in figure 4.8e. Instead, the ellipse

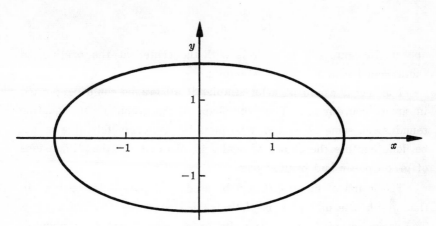

FIG. 4.8e. Graph of $x^2 + y^2 = 4$ with different units for the axes.

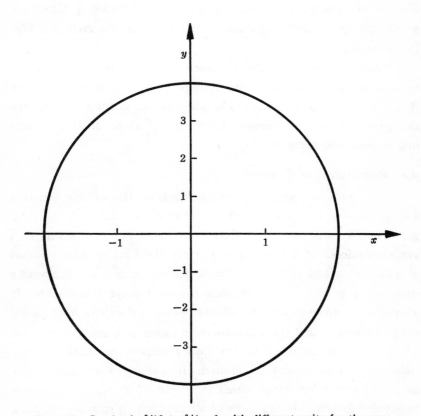

FIG. 4.8f. Graph of $y^2/16 + x^2/4 = 1$ with different units for the axes.

$$\frac{y^2}{16} + \frac{x^2}{4} = 1$$

appears in figure 4.8f as a circle with the center at the origin and radius equal to 2 x-units or 4 y-units.

The world would be a lot simpler if all graphs could be plotted in square coordinates. Then the shape of the graph of an equation remains the same no matter who plots it. Unfortunately, this cannot be done because the choice of scales is dictated by the dimensions of graph paper and printed page.

The graph of figure 4.7b can be used to illustrate the point. In that graph, one unit of x is of the same length as 250 units of y. The space occupied by the 15 units of x from 5 to 20 is about 3 inches wide. By the same scale, that occupied by the 4,500 units of y from 1,500 to 6,000 would be 900 inches or 75 feet long. Now one can see why the scales of x and y are usually different in plotting a graph and also why the appearance of the graph of a given equation is not fixed.

Another example of the influence of choice of scales on the appearance of a graph is given in figure 4.4b. It is shown there that the visual grade of a straight line can be manipulated by the change of scales even though the numerical slope of the straight line remains the same.

4.9 Presentation of Function

Three ways of presenting the functional relations—table, equation and curve—are discussed in the preceding sections. A function given in one form can be translated into the other two forms through various devices. If a function is given in the form of two columns of values of x and y, the data can be translated into an equation by curve-fitting or into a curve through the rectangular coordinates. If a function is given in the form of an equation, values can be assigned to the variable x and the corresponding values of y can be computed. The pairs of values of x and y thus obtained constitute a table, from which a curve can be plotted. If a function is given as a curve, the conditions under which the point (x, y) moves enable one to express the locus in the form of an equation. From the equation, a table of values of x and y can be obtained.

It is not necessary to present the same function in all three ways. By necessity or preference, usually only one way is predominant for a given purpose. When computers are used, a function is usually expressed in the tabular form as two columns of figures. In mathematics textbooks including this one, functions are mostly expressed as equations. The curves seem to be preferred by experimental scientists as means of communication. The experimental data are frequently translated into their geometric equivalent. A casual examination of scientific journals will reveal the abundance of curves.

For the sake of only presenting the functional relation between the variables x and y, one method may be as good as another. But, for the deduction of further consequences from the function, the equation method is by far the most useful one. Only on a function expressed in this form can mathematics be effectively applied. Even when computers are used, one cannot completely escape from equations.

4.10 Zero of Function

The zero of a function of x is the value of x at which the function $f(x)$ is equal to zero. For the function

$$f(x) = 4 - x,$$

the value 4 is the zero of $f(x)$ because $f(4)$ is equal to zero.

To find the zero of the function $f(x)$ is to solve the equation

$$f(x) = 0.$$

The solution of the equation

$$f(x) = 4 - x = 0$$

is

$$x = 4$$

which is called the zero of the function $f(x)$.

In high-school algebra, one only learns how to solve linear and quadratic equations. The methods given there for solving higher-degree equations are not always dependable. For example, factoring is a commonly-mentioned device of solving equations. By this method, a fourth-degree equation such as

$$x^4 - 13x^2 + 36 = 0$$

is expressed as

$$(x^2 - 4)(x^2 - 9) = 0$$

which immediately shows that

$$-2 \qquad 2 \qquad -3 \qquad 3$$

are the roots of the equation. When one encounters such an equation, this is indeed the best method to use. However, one cannot always depend on such luck in every fourth-degree equation. For this reason, a numerical method of solving an equation—any equation and not necessarily a polynomial—is given in this section.

The general-purpose method of solving equations is that of *successive approximation*. By this method, an approximate root of the equation

$$f(x) = 0$$

is first obtained through a rough graph or a shrewd guess. Then different values of x selected from the neighborhood of the approximate root are substituted into the function $f(x)$ until the sign of $f(x)$ changes—positive to negative or vice versa. If $f(x_1)$ and $f(x_2)$ are of different signs, there must be a value x_0 which lies between x_1 and x_2 so that $f(x_0)$ is equal to zero. Now the root x_0 is known to be between x_1 and x_2. Again various values of x, now selected between x_1 and x_2, are substituted into $f(x)$ until $f(x_3)$ and $f(x_4)$ are of different signs. Now the root x_0 is known to be between x_3 and x_4 which is a sub-interval within the interval x_1 to x_2. The two approximations of x_0 carried out so far can be illustrated by the following diagram:

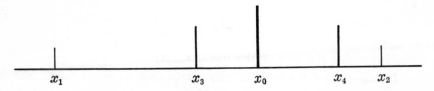

By repeating this process over and over again, the root of any desired degree of accuracy can be obtained.

To find the positive root of the quadratic equation

$$f(x) \;=\; 44 - 2x - 2x^2 \;=\; c + bx + ax^2 \;=\; 0 \qquad (1)$$

is used as an illustration. The roots of the equation are known to be

$$x_0 \;=\; \frac{-b \pm \sqrt{b^2 - 4ac}}{2a} \;=\; \frac{2 \pm \sqrt{356}}{-4}$$

and the positive root is

$$x_0 \;=\; \frac{2 - \sqrt{356}}{-4} \;=\; \frac{-16.867962}{-4} \;=\; 4.216991 \,. \qquad (2)$$

Now one can pretend that the root x_0 is unknown and proceed to find the same value by the method of successive approximation as a demonstration of the procedure. The details of computation are shown in table 4.10. The first approximation indicates that the root x_0 is somewhere between 4 and 5 because $f(4)$ is positive and $f(5)$ is negative. The second approximation is to substitute 4.1, 4.2 and so forth into $f(x)$ until the sign of $f(x)$ changes. This series of substitutions indicates that the root is somewhere between 4.2 and 4.3. The third approximation is to substitute 4.21, 4.22 and so forth

TABLE 4.10

SOLUTION OF EQUATION BY SUCCESSIVE APPROXIMATION

First Approximation			Second Approximation	
x	$f(x)$		x	$f(x)$
3	20		4.1	2.18
4	4		4.2	0.32
5	−16		4.3	−1.58

Third Approximation			Fourth Approximation	
x	$f(x)$		x	$f(x)$
4.21	0.1318		4.215	0.037550
4.22	−0.0568		4.216	0.018688
			4.217	−0.000178

into $f(x)$ until the sign of $f(x)$ changes. By now the root is known to be somewhere between 4.21 and 4.22 because $f(4.21)$ is positive and $f(4.22)$ is negative. This process goes on until the desired degree of accuracy of the root x_0 is obtained. The fourth approximation of table 4.10 indicates that the root lies between 4.216 and 4.217, but it is closer to 4.217 than to 4.216 because $f(4.217)$ being equal to —0.000178 is closer to zero than $f(4.216)$ or 0.018688 is. So the root x_0 is equal to 4.217 if only a three-decimal accuracy is required. This value is in agreement with the root 4.216991 (equation 2) obtained by the formal analytic method.

4.11   Intersection of Functions

The intersection of two functions of x is the value of x at which the two functions are equal. An example of two functions $g(x)$ and $h(x)$ is given in table 4.11. To find the intersection is to go down the two columns of figures labeled $g(x)$ and $h(x)$ to find the place where the figure of one column is equal to that of the other.

TABLE 4.11

INTERSECTION OF FUNCTIONS

x	$g(x)$	$h(x)$	$g(x) - h(x)$
0	0	0	0
1	40	0	40
2	80	48	32
3	120	100	20
4	160	156	4
5	200	216	−16
6	240	280	−40
7	280	348	−68

A more formal way of finding the intersection is to find the differences $g(x) - h(x)$ as shown in table 4.11. The value of x at which the difference is equal to zero is the intersection. The data of table 4.11 show that the intersection is at $x = 0$ and also somewhere between 4 and 5 because the difference

$$g(4) - h(4) = 160 - 156 = 4$$

is positive and the difference

$$g(5) - h(5) = 200 - 216 = -16$$

is negative.

The graphical method may be used if a more accurate value of the second intersection is desired. As an illustration, the data of $g(x)$ and $h(x)$ are plotted into graphs in figure 4.11. From the intersecting point of the two curves, a straight line parallel to the y axis is drawn. This line meets the x axis at the point $x = 4.2$ which is the intersection of the two functions.

From figure 4.11, the coordinates of the point of intersection of the two curves representing $g(x)$ and $h(x)$ can be read. The point

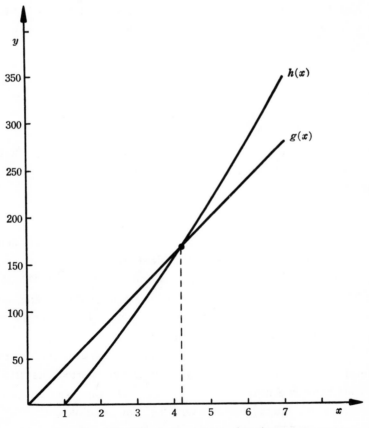

Fɪɢ. 4.11. Intersection of two functions.

is located approximately at (4.2, 168). This is to say that at $x = 4.2$ both functions $g(x)$ and $h(x)$ are equal to 168.

An even more accurate method of finding the intersection of two functions $g(x)$ and $h(x)$ is to fit polynomials to the data (section 4.7). In so doing, the equations obtained for the two functions are

$$g(x) = 40x \qquad\qquad 0 \leq x \leq 7$$

and

$$h(x) = 0 \qquad\qquad 0 \leq x < 1$$
$$h(x) = -44 + 42x + 2x^2 \qquad 1 \leq x \leq 7.$$

The function $g(x)$ is one equation for the entire interval of x from 0 to 7, but the function $h(x)$ is expressed as two equations—one for each of the two intervals 0 to 1 and 1 to 7 because both $h(0)$ and $h(1)$ are equal to zero as shown in table 4.11.

Once the functions are expressed in terms of equations, the problem of finding the intersection of $g(x)$ and $h(x)$ becomes that of solving the equation

$$f(x) = g(x) - h(x) = 0$$

whose root x_0 is the intersection of the two functions. For the given example, the equation is (equation 1, section 4.10)

$$f(x) = g(x) - h(x) = 44 - 2x - 2x^2 = 0 \qquad 1 \leq x \leq 7$$

whose root $x_0 = 4.217$ yields the intersection of the two functions $g(x)$ and $h(x)$. At this point the values of the two functions are equal, or

$$g(x_0) = h(x_0) = 168.680.$$

Then the coordinates of the point of intersection of the two curves representing $g(x)$ and $h(x)$ are (4.217, 168.680).

No physical meaning is attached to the data of table 4.11. However, if one wishes, one may consider x as time, with 0 being noon, 1 being 1:00 pm, 2 being 2:00 pm and so forth. The function $g(x)$ may be considered as the number of miles driven by George and $h(x)$ by Henry. George started his journey at noon and drove at the uniform speed of 40 miles an hour. But Henry started his trip at the same place one hour later at 1:00 pm. He did not drive at a uniform speed. During the first hour he drove 48 miles, the second hour 100−48 or 52 miles, the third hour 156−100 or 56 miles and so forth. Evidently Henry was driving faster and faster to catch up with George. The distance between them is indicated by the values of $g(x) - h(x)$ of table 4.11. At 4:00 pm, George is 4 miles ahead of Henry. At 5:00 pm, he is 16 miles behind Henry. Obviously Henry passed George on the road sometime between 4:00 and 5:00 pm. The problem of finding the intersection of $g(x)$ and $h(x)$ is to determine the time at which Henry caught up with George. This is the time at which the distance between them $g(x) - h(x)$ is equal to zero. The root $x_0 = 4.217$ of the equation

$$f(x) = g(x) - h(x) = 0$$

indicates that the time was 4:13 pm. At this time, both of them have driven 168.68 miles.

The above illustration is a demonstration of translating a situation into mathematics and not an example of application of the subject. There are many things unrealistic about the illustration. In the first place, George could not possibly drive at an uniform speed of 40 miles an hour on the highway for seven hours continuously in an afternoon. It would be even harder for Henry to drive according to the equation

$$h(x) = -44 + 42x + 2x^2 \qquad 1 \leqq x \leqq 7.$$

Furthermore, why should anybody make a mountain out of a molehill. If Henry wanted to know the time at which he caught up with George, all he had to do was look at his watch while he was passing George on the road.

EXERCISES

1. Find the distance between each of the following pairs of points:
   - (a) $(0, 1)$ $(8, 17)$ (b) $(-3, 12)$ $(7, 0)$
   - (c) $(4.1, 7.6)$ $(11.6, 16.9)$

2. Find the slope of the line which joins each of the three pairs of points given in exercise 1.

3. Find the equation of the straight line which passes through each of the three pairs of points given in exercise 1 through the slopes obtained in exercise 2.

4. Find the equation of the straight line which passes through each of the three pairs of points of exercise 1 by equations (9) and (10) of section 4.4.

5. Choose three different pairs of points from example 2 of table 4.4, and find the slope for each pair. See if the slope obtained for every pair is equal to -2.

6. Plot the following straight lines for the interval $-2 \leq x \leq 2$:

      (a) $y = 3x$ (b) $y = 1.5x$

      (c) $y = 3$ (d) $y = -4$

7. For the arithmetic progression 5.00, 5.25, 5.50, $\cdots$, find

    (a)   the 10th term,

    (b)   the sum of the first 50 terms

and

    (c)   the linear equation which represents the progression.

8. For the arithmetic progression 100, 95, 90, $\cdots$, find

    (a)   the 8th term,

    (b)   the sum of the first 15 terms

and

    (c)   the linear equation which represents the progression.

9. Plot the graph of each of the following equations for the interval $0 \leq x \leq 9$:

    (a) $y = 5 + 4x - x^2$ (b) $y = 9 - 6x + x^2$

    (c) $y = 21 - 31x + 11x^2 - x^3$ (d) $y = 125 - 75x + 15x^2 - x^3$

10. Find the equation of the polynomial which passes through each of the following sets of points:

    (a) $(0, 0)$ $(3, 5)$ $(6, 0)$

    (b) $(0, 3)$ $(1, 6)$ $(2, 4)$ $(3, 7)$

11. Find the zero x_0 between 0 and 5 of the function

$$f(x) = 4x^3 - 45x^2 + 68x + 117$$

by successive approximation. Substitute x_0 into $f(x)$, and see if $f(x_0)$ is equal to zero.

12. Find the intersection x_0 of the functions

$$g(x) = 100 + 63x - 30 x^2 + 4x^3$$

and

$$h(x) = 142 + 6 x - x^2$$

between $x = 4$ and $x = 5$. The intersection x_0 should be carried to three decimal places by successive approximation. Then substitute x_0 into $g(x)$ and $h(x)$, and see if $g(x_0)$ is equal to $h(x_0)$.

CHAPTER 5

DIFFERENTIATION—FINITE INTERVAL

Calculus consists of two parts, namely, differentiation and integration. The first part is introduced in this chapter and the following one. The second part is covered in chapters 7 and 8.

Differentiation is the operation of finding the rate of change of a function of x with respect to x. The function discussed in this chapter is limited to the polynomial in x, and the method used is entirely numerical.

5.1 Varying Rate of Change

The rate of change of the linear function

$$y = b_0 + b_1 x$$

is the constant b_1 for every interval of x. But for any other function, it is a variable and changes with x. Such an example is given in table 5.1a. The values of x and those of its function

$$y = F(x)$$

are listed in columns 2 and 3. The 9 given values of x create 8 intervals, each of which is bounded by two adjacent values of x. For each interval of x, the rate of change of y is computed. For example, the rate of change for the interval bounded by points no. 1 and no. 2 is

$$\frac{y_2 - y_1}{x_2 - x_1} = \frac{\Delta y}{\Delta x} = \frac{165 - 160}{0.5 - 0.0} = \frac{5}{0.5} = 10$$

and that for points no. 2 and no. 3 is

$$\frac{y_3 - y_2}{x_3 - x_2} = \frac{\Delta y}{\Delta x} = \frac{176 - 165}{1.0 - 0.5} = \frac{11}{0.5} = 22$$

as given in column 7 of table 5.1a which shows the rates of change for all the 8 intervals of x.

TABLE 5.1a

RATES OF CHANGE OF y WITH RESPECT TO x

(1)	(2)	(3)	(4)	(5)	(6)	(7)
Point No.	x	$y = F(x)$	Δx	Δy	$\bar{x}$	$\dfrac{\Delta y}{\Delta x} = f(\bar{x})$
1	0.0	160				
			0.5	5	0.25	10
2	0.5	165				
			0.5	11	0.75	22
3	1.0	176				
			0.5	11	1.25	22
4	1.5	187				
			0.5	5	1.75	10
5	2.0	192				
			0.5	-7	2.25	-14
6	2.5	185				
			0.5	-25	2.75	-50
7	3.0	160				
			0.5	-49	3.25	-98
8	3.5	111				
			0.5	-79	3.75	-158
9	4.0	32				

Two new symbols Δx and Δy are introduced in this chapter. The quantity Δx, which is called an *increment* of x, is the length of the interval bounded by two adjacent values of x. Symbolically, the increment of x is

$$\Delta x = x_{i+1} - x_i \qquad i = 1, 2, \cdots, 8$$

which, for the given example, happens to be a constant and equal to 0.5 as shown in column 4 of table 5.1a. Here the two-character symbol Δx represents only one quantity and is not the product of two quantities Δ and x. In fact, Δ is not even a quantity. It is an operator and stands for "the difference of". Similarly, the symbol Δy, which is called an increment of y, is defined as

$$\Delta y = y_{i+1} - y_i \qquad i = 1, 2, \cdots, 8$$

which is a function of x as shown in column 5 of table 5.1a. The ratios

$$\frac{\Delta y}{\Delta x} = \frac{y_{i+1} - y_i}{x_{i+1} - x_i} \qquad i = 1, 2, \cdots, 8$$

given in column 7 are the rates of change of y with respect to x for the 8 intervals. Now each value of $\Delta y/\Delta x$ is associated with an interval x_i to x_{i+1} or with the single value which is the mid-point

$$\bar{x}_i = \frac{x_i + x_{i+1}}{2}$$

of that interval. These mid-points are given in column 6 of table 5.1a.

The mid-points and the rates of change of the intervals of x are listed side by side in columns 6 and 7 of table 5.1a. Now a new function of x

$$\frac{\Delta y}{\Delta x} = f(\bar{x})$$

is derived from the original function

$$y = F(x).$$

This new function $f(\bar{x})$, which gives the rates of change of $F(x)$ at different values of $\bar{x}$, is called the *derivative* of $F(x)$. The operation of finding the derivative is called *differentiation*. To *differentiate* the function $F(x)$ is to find the derivative of $F(x)$. The procedure of differentiation for m points is summarized in table 5.1b.

All through this text, the value of $\Delta y/\Delta x$ of an interval is called the rate of change of that interval. A sequence of values of $\Delta y/\Delta x$ collectively is referred to as the derivative of $y = F(x)$. It is the sequence of the mid-points $\bar{x}$ of the intervals and their corresponding values of $\Delta y/\Delta x$ that constitute the new function

$$\frac{\Delta y}{\Delta x} = f(\bar{x})$$

which is called the derivative of $F(x)$.

The process of differentiation is frequently indicated by the symbol $\Delta/\Delta x$. In terms of this new operator, the fact that the derivative

Table 5.1b

Procedure of Differentiation

Point No.	Function		Intermediate Steps		Derivative of Function	
	x	$y = F(x)$	Δx	Δy	$\bar{x}$	$\dfrac{\Delta y}{\Delta x} = f(\bar{x})$
1	x_1	y_1	$x_2 - x_1$	$y_2 - y_1$	$(x_1 + x_2)/2$	$(y_2 - y_1)/(x_2 - x_1)$
2	x_2	y_2	$x_3 - x_2$	$y_3 - y_2$	$(x_2 + x_3)/2$	$(y_3 - y_2)/(x_3 - x_2)$
3	x_3	y_3				
...	...	...				
i	x_i	y_i	$x_{i+1} - x_i$	$y_{i+1} - y_i$	$(x_i + x_{i+1})/2$	$(y_{i+1} - y_i)/(x_{i+1} - x_i)$
$i+1$	x_{i+1}	y_{i+1}				
...	...					
$m-1$	x_{m-1}	y_{m-1}	$x_m - x_{m-1}$	$y_m - y_{m-1}$	$(x_{m-1} + x_m)/2$	$(y_m - y_{m-1})/(x_m - x_{m-1})$
m	x_m	y_m				

of $F(x)$ is equal to $f(\bar{x})$ may be expressed as

$$\frac{\Delta}{\Delta x}F(x) \;=\; f(\bar{x})\,.$$

Here the symbol $\Delta/\Delta x$ may be read as "the derivative of".

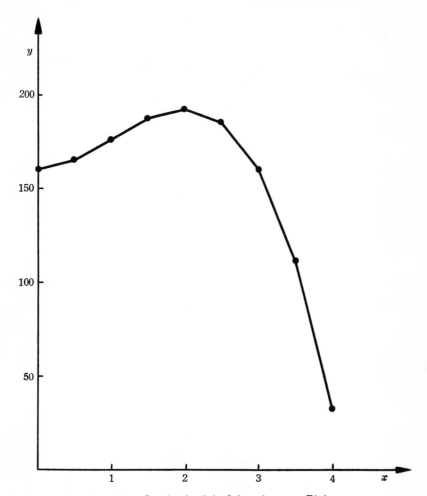

Fɪɢ. 5.1a.   Graph of original function $y = F(x)$.

The geometric interpretation of the derivative is given in figure 5.1a. The 9 pairs of values of (x, y) given in table 5.1a are plotted as points. Straight lines are drawn to connect the adjacent points. The derivative $f(\bar{x})$ of the original function $F(x)$ is the collection of slopes of these connecting lines.

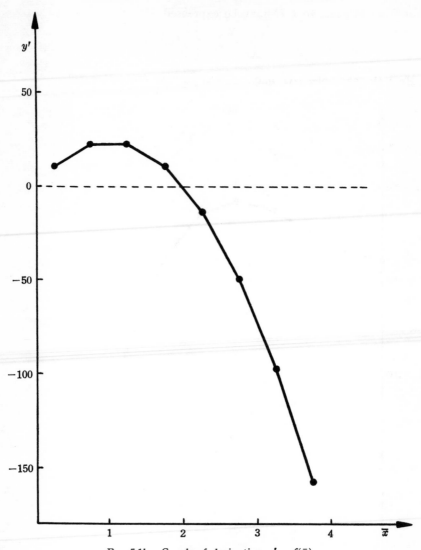

Fɪɢ. 5.1b. Graph of derivative $y' = f(\bar{x})$.

The derivative

$$y' \;=\; \frac{\Delta y}{\Delta x} \;=\; f(\bar{x})$$

itself can also be graphically presented as shown in figure 5.1b.
This is simply the graph plotted from the numbers given in columns
6 and 7 of table 5.1a. Comparison of figures 5.1a and 5.1b reveals
that the way in which the function y changes determines the sign

of the derivative y'. From $x = 0$ to $x = 2$, the function y steadily increases in value and its derivative y' is positive. From $x = 2$ to $x = 4$, the function y decreases in value and its derivative y' is negative. Thus the sign of $f(\bar{x}_0)$ enables one to tell whether the original function $F(x)$ is increasing or decreasing in the interval of which $\bar{x}_0$ is the mid-point.

The differentiation is presented here as a series of arithmetic operations, and no physical meaning is attached to the operation. However, if one wishes, one may impose some physical meaning on the data of table 5.1a. A value of x may be considered the number of hours elapsed from a given time, and y the number of gallons of water in a tank. In the very beginning, the tank contains 160 gallons of water. Half an hour later, it contains 165 gallons. So the original function $F(x)$ keeps the record of the amount of water in the tank at various times. On the other hand, the derivative $f(\bar{x})$ indicates how fast is the water level fluctuating. For the first half hour, the water increases at the rate of 10 gallons an hour. During the second half hour, the water increases at the rate of 22 gallons an hour. This is just about what the derivative means.

This section deals only with the basic concept and the most rudimentary method of differentiation. The purpose is to show that the basic operations of differentiation is the subtraction

$$\Delta y = y_{i+1} - y_i$$

followed by the division

$$\frac{\Delta y}{\Delta x} = y'.$$

When the original function is given in the form of two columns of figures, the method described here is only one among many. For other methods, the reader is referred to W. E. Milne's *Numerical Calculus* under the heading numerical differentiation.

5.2 Some Rules of Differentiation

Many rules of differentiation can be derived directly from the definition of the operation. The first rule is that *the derivative of a constant is equal to zero*, or

$$\frac{\Delta}{\Delta x} C = 0 \tag{1}$$

where C is a constant. When the function is

$$y = C,$$

the increment of y for every interval is

$$\Delta y = y_{i+1} - y_i = C - C = 0$$

and consequently the derivative of C is equal to

$$\frac{\Delta y}{\Delta x} = \frac{0}{\Delta x} = 0.$$

TABLE 5.2a

DERIVATIVE OF CONSTANT

x	y	Δx	Δy	$\dfrac{\Delta y}{\Delta x}$
1	8			
		1	0	0
2	8			
		1	0	0
3	8			
		1	0	0
4	8			
		1	0	0
5	8			

The numerical demonstration of this rule is given in table 5.2a. For every value of x, the function y is equal to 8. It is obvious that the rate of change of y is equal to zero for every interval of x. However, the usefulness of table 5.2a is in showing that the derivative of a constant is a sequence of zeros and not just one zero. The reason why equation (1) gives only one zero is that the equation shows only the rate of change of y for the single interval x_i to x_{i+1}.

The second rule of differentiation is that *the derivative of x with respect to x is equal to* 1, or

$$\frac{\Delta}{\Delta x} x = 1. \tag{2}$$

This seems to be a foregone conclusion. If the function of x is

$$y = x,$$

the increment of y for the interval x_i to x_{i+1} is

$$\Delta y = y_{i+1} - y_i = x_{i+1} - x_i = \Delta x.$$

Then the derivative of y is obviously

$$\frac{\Delta y}{\Delta x} = \frac{\Delta x}{\Delta x} = 1.$$

The numerical demonstration of this rule of differentiation is given in table 5.2b where the corresponding values of x and y are the same. Then it follows that the values of Δx and Δy are equal for every interval of x. Hence the derivative of x is equal to 1.

TABLE 5.2b

DERIVATIVE OF x WITH RESPECT TO x

x	y	Δx	Δy	$\dfrac{\Delta y}{\Delta x}$
0.0	0.0			
		0.1	0.1	1
0.1	0.1			
		0.1	0.1	1
0.2	0.2			
		0.1	0.1	1
0.3	0.3			
		0.1	0.1	1
0.4	0.4			

The derivative of x with respect to x is a sequence of 1's, one for every interval. It is not just a single 1 as suggested by equation (2). The reason why only one 1 is used in that equation is that the derivative expressed in the form of an equation gives only the rate of change for the single interval x_i to x_{i+1}.

The third rule of differentiation is that *the derivative of the product of a constant k and a function of x is equal to k times the derivative of that function*, or

$$\frac{\Delta}{\Delta x} k u(x) = k \frac{\Delta}{\Delta x} u(x) \tag{3}$$

where $u(x)$ is a function of x. This rule can be derived from the definition of the derivative. When the original function is

$$y = ku(x),$$

the increment of y for the interval x_i to x_{i+1} is

$$\Delta y = y_{i+1} - y_i = ku_{i+1} - ku_i = k(u_{i+1} - u_i)$$

where u_i is the value of $u(x)$ at $x = x_i$. Then, by definition, the derivative of y is

$$\frac{\Delta y}{\Delta x} = \frac{k(u_{i+1} - u_i)}{\Delta x} = \frac{k\Delta u}{\Delta x}$$

which is k times the derivative of the function $u(x)$.

TABLE 5.2c

DERIVATIVE OF PRODUCT OF CONSTANT AND FUNCTION

x	$u(x)$	$y = 3u(x)$	Δx	Δu	Δy	$\dfrac{\Delta u}{\Delta x}$	$\dfrac{\Delta y}{\Delta x}$
0.0	10	30					
			0.5	1	3	2	6
0.5	11	33					
			0.5	3	9	6	18
1.0	14	42					
			0.5	−5	−15	−10	−30
1.5	9	27					
			0.5	−3	−9	−6	−18
2.0	6	18					

The numerical demonstration of the third rule of differentiation is given in table 5.2c. The values of x and $u(x)$ are arbitrarily chosen. The values of

$$y = 3u(x)$$

are computed from those of u. After the differentiation of both u and y with respect to x, the result shows that

$$\frac{\Delta y}{\Delta x} = 3\frac{\Delta u}{\Delta x}$$

for every interval of x. This is the meaning of the third rule of differentiation.

The combination of the rules

$$\frac{\Delta}{\Delta x} x = 1$$

and

$$\frac{\Delta}{\Delta x} ku(x) = k\frac{\Delta}{\Delta x} u(x)$$

enables one to tell that the derivative of

$$y = 5x$$

is equal to 5. In the given function

$$y = ku(x) = 5x,$$

k is equal to 5 and $u(x)$ is equal to x. Thus the derivative of y with respect to x is

$$\frac{\Delta y}{\Delta x} = 5\frac{\Delta x}{\Delta x}.$$

But $\Delta x/\Delta x$ is equal to 1. Then it follows that the derivative of $5x$ is equal to 5.

TABLE 5.2d

DERIVATIVE OF $5x$

x	$y = 5x$	Δx	Δy	$\frac{\Delta y}{\Delta x}$
0.0	0.0			
		0.1	0.5	5
0.1	0.5			
		0.1	0.5	5
0.2	1.0			
		0.1	0.5	5
0.3	1.5			
		0.1	0.5	5
0.4	2.0			

The numerical demonstration of this result is given in table 5.2d. The values of x are arbitrarily chosen, and those of y are obtained by multiplying each value of x by 5. The differentiation is carried out in the usual way, and the result shows that the rate of change of y or $5x$ is equal to 5 for every interval of x. This is the meaning of the equation

$$\frac{\Delta}{\Delta x} 5x = 5$$

or the statement that the derivative of $5x$ is equal to 5.

The fourth rule of differentiation is that *the derivative of the sum of a number of functions is equal to the sum of the derivatives of those functions*, or

$$\frac{\Delta}{\Delta x}[u(x) + v(x) + \cdots] = \frac{\Delta}{\Delta x}u(x) + \frac{\Delta}{\Delta x}v(x) + \cdots. \qquad (4)$$

This rule may be examined for the case of two functions. When the given function is

$$y = u(x) + v(x),$$

the increment of y for the interval x_i to x_{i+1} is

$$\Delta y = y_{i+1} - y_i = (u_{i+1} + v_{i+1}) - (u_i + v_i)$$

where u_i and v_i are the values of $u(x)$ and $v(x)$ at $x = x_i$. After collecting the u's and v's in the above equation, the increment of y can be expressed as

$$\Delta y = (u_{i+1} - u_i) + (v_{i+1} - v_i)$$
$$= \Delta u + \Delta v.$$

Then the derivative of y with respect to x is

$$\frac{\Delta y}{\Delta x} = \frac{\Delta u}{\Delta x} + \frac{\Delta v}{\Delta x}$$

or

$$\frac{\Delta}{\Delta x}[u(x) + v(x)] = \frac{\Delta}{\Delta x}u(x) + \frac{\Delta}{\Delta x}v(x).$$

The numerical demonstration of this rule is given in table 5.2e. The values of x, $u(x)$ and $v(x)$ are given. The values of y are

TABLE 5.2e

DERIVATIVE OF SUM OF FUNCTIONS

Derivative of $u(x)$				
x	$u(x)$	Δx	Δu	$\dfrac{\Delta u}{\Delta x}$
0.0	7			
		0.1	2	20
0.1	9			
		0.1	5	50
0.2	14			
		0.1	-2	-20
0.3	12			
		0.1	-4	-40
0.4	8			

Derivative of $v(x)$				
x	$v(x)$	Δx	Δv	$\dfrac{\Delta v}{\Delta x}$
0.0	-8			
		0.1	5	50
0.1	-3			
		0.1	4	40
0.2	1			
		0.1	3	30
0.3	4			
		0.1	12	120
0.4	16			

Derivative of $y = u(x) + v(x)$				
x	y	Δx	Δy	$\dfrac{\Delta y}{\Delta x}$
0.0	-1			
		0.1	7	70
0.1	6			
		0.1	9	90
0.2	15			
		0.1	1	10
0.3	16			
		0.1	8	80
0.4	24			

obtained by adding the corresponding values of u and v. Then the differentiation of u, v and y are carried out separately. The result in table 5.2e shows that the equation

$$\frac{\Delta y}{\Delta x} = \frac{\Delta u}{\Delta x} + \frac{\Delta v}{\Delta x}$$

holds for every interval of x. This is the meaning of equation (4) which enables one to differentiate a function term by term.

The fourth rule of differentiation offers two alternative ways of carrying out an operation. In differentiating the function

$$y = 3x + 2x,$$

one may combine the two terms and differentiate the function

$$y = 5x$$

and obtains the derivative

$$\frac{\Delta y}{\Delta x} = 5.$$

Or, if one prefers, he may differentiate term by term and obtains

$$\frac{\Delta y}{\Delta x} = 3\frac{\Delta x}{\Delta x} + 2\frac{\Delta x}{\Delta x} = 3 + 2 = 5$$

which is the same result.

The rules of differentiation are time-saving devices. The rules

$$\frac{\Delta}{\Delta x}C = 0$$

and

$$\frac{\Delta}{\Delta x}x = 1$$

enable one to write down the derivative of a constant C and that of x without going through the process of differentiation. The rule

$$\frac{\Delta}{\Delta x}ku(x) = k\frac{\Delta}{\Delta x}u(x)$$

enables one to concentrate on the differentiation of the function $u(x)$ and temporarily ignore the constant multiplier k until the differentiation of $u(x)$ is completed. The rule

$$\frac{\Delta}{\Delta x}[u(x) + v(x)] = \frac{\Delta}{\Delta x}u(x) + \frac{\Delta}{\Delta x}v(x)$$

enables one to differentiate a function term by term. These are the reasons why the rules of differentiation are developed.

The rules of differentiation are useful, but their combinations are even more useful. Through the rules, one can tell that the derivative of the linear function

$$y = a + bx$$

is equal to

$$\frac{\Delta y}{\Delta x} = b$$

without going through the process of differentiation. On account of the fact that the derivative of a sum of functions is equal to the sum of the derivatives, the derivative of y must be

$$\frac{\Delta y}{\Delta x} = \frac{\Delta}{\Delta x}a + \frac{\Delta}{\Delta x}bx.$$

By using the rules

$$\frac{\Delta}{\Delta x}C = 0$$

$$\frac{\Delta}{\Delta x}ku(x) = k\frac{\Delta}{\Delta x}u(x)$$

and

$$\frac{\Delta}{\Delta x}x = 1,$$

the derivative can be simplified into

$$\frac{\Delta y}{\Delta x} = 0 + b\frac{\Delta x}{\Delta x} = b(1) = b.$$

The numerical demonstration of this result is left to the reader as an exercise.

Many other short cuts can be generated by the combination of the rules of differentiation. For example, the rule

$$\frac{\Delta}{\Delta x}(y + C) = \frac{\Delta y}{\Delta x}$$

can be derived from the given rules. From the rule

$$\frac{\Delta}{\Delta x}[u(x) + v(x)] = \frac{\Delta}{\Delta x}u(x) + \frac{\Delta}{\Delta x}v(x)$$

one can obtain

$$\frac{\Delta}{\Delta x}(y + C) = \frac{\Delta}{\Delta x}y + \frac{\Delta}{\Delta x}C.$$

Then from the rule

$$\frac{\Delta}{\Delta x}C = 0,$$

one can further obtain

$$\frac{\Delta}{\Delta x}(y + C) = \frac{\Delta y}{\Delta x}.$$

This newly derived rule can be used in lightening the burden of computation. The y-values such as

$$109.7 \quad 112.8 \quad 114.3 \quad 123.6 \quad 115.7$$

may be changed to

$$9.7 \quad 12.8 \quad 14.3 \quad 23.6 \quad 15.7$$

by subtracting 100 from each of the original values of y. The derivative obtained from the smaller numbers is the same as that obtained from the original ones.

This new rule also enables one to eliminate the negative values of y if one finds them inconvenient to work with. The y-values such as

$$-87 \quad -64 \quad -15 \quad 21 \quad 46$$

may be changed to

$$13 \quad 36 \quad 85 \quad 121 \quad 146$$

by adding 100 to each value of y. The derivative obtained from either set of values remains the same.

The fact

$$\frac{\Delta}{\Delta x}(y + C) = \frac{\Delta y}{\Delta x} \tag{5}$$

creates quite a little trouble in finding the original function

$$y = F(x)$$

from its derivative

$$\frac{\Delta y}{\Delta x} = f(\bar{x}) .$$

For a given function $F(x)$, its derivative $f(\bar{x})$ can be uniquely determined. But from the derivative

$$\frac{\Delta y}{\Delta x} = f(\bar{x})$$

one can only determine the original function as far as

$$y + C = F(x)$$

with the constant C being unknown, because

$$\frac{\Delta}{\Delta x}(y + C) = \frac{\Delta y}{\Delta x} = f(\bar{x})$$

regardless of the value of C. This dilemma is discussed in sections 7.2 and 7.3.

5.3 Differentiation of Product of Functions

The rule for differentiating the sum of two functions is given in the preceding section, and that for differentiating the product of two functions is given in this one. In deriving this rule a slight change of notation is made to simplify the algebraic manipulation involved. The point (x_i, y_i) is simply designated as (x, y) without any subscripts, and the point (x_{i+1}, y_{i+1}) thus becomes $(x + \Delta x, y + \Delta y)$ because

$$\Delta x = x_{i+1} - x_i = x_{i+1} - x$$

and

$$\Delta y = y_{i+1} - y_i = y_{i+1} - y .$$

These new symbols (x, y) and $(x + \Delta x, y + \Delta y)$ are used interchangeably with old ones (x_i, y_i) and (x_{i+1}, y_{i+1}) in later sections.

When y is the product of two functions $u(x)$ and $v(x)$, the derivative of y is equal to

$$\frac{\Delta y}{\Delta x} = \frac{\Delta}{\Delta x}(uv) = u\frac{\Delta v}{\Delta x} + (v + \Delta v)\frac{\Delta u}{\Delta x} \tag{1}$$

or

$$\frac{\Delta y}{\Delta x} = \frac{\Delta}{\Delta x}(uv) = (u + \Delta u)\frac{\Delta v}{\Delta x} + v\frac{\Delta u}{\Delta x} \cdot \qquad (2)$$

If the value of y at the ith point is

$$y_i = y = u_i v_i = uv,$$

the value at the $(i+1)$st point is

$$y_{i+1} = u_{i+i} \, v_{i+1} = (u + \Delta u)(v + \Delta v).$$

When the product of the above equation is multiplied out, the same equation can be expressed as

$$y_{i+1} = uv + v\Delta u + u\Delta v + \Delta u\Delta v.$$

Then from the values of y_i and y_{i+1}, it can be deduced that the increment of y for the interval x_i to x_{i+1} is

$$\Delta y = y_{i+1} - y_i = v\Delta u + u\Delta v + \Delta u\Delta v.$$

When the first and the third term are combined, the result is

$$\Delta y = u\Delta v + (v + \Delta v)\Delta u$$

and consequently the derivative of y with respect to x is

$$\frac{\Delta y}{\Delta x} = u\frac{\Delta v}{\Delta x} + (v + \Delta v)\frac{\Delta u}{\Delta x}$$

which is equation (1). However, if the second and the third term of Δy are combined, the increment of y becomes

$$\Delta y = (u + \Delta u)\Delta v + v\Delta u$$

and the derivative of y thus becomes

$$\frac{\Delta y}{\Delta x} = (u + \Delta u)\frac{\Delta v}{\Delta x} + v\frac{\Delta u}{\Delta x}$$

which is equation (2).

The numerical demonstration of equations (1) and (2) is given in table 5.3a. The values of x, $u(x)$ and $v(x)$ are the same ones given in table 5.2e, and the values of y are obtained by multiplying the corresponding values of u and v. Then the differentiation of y with respect to x is carried out in the usual way, and the derivative is given in the last column of table 5.3a.

TABLE 5.3a

DERIVATIVE OF PRODUCT OF FUNCTIONS

x	$u(x)$	$v(x)$	$y = uv$	Δx	Δy	$\dfrac{\Delta y}{\Delta x}$
0.0	7	− 8	− 56			
				0.1	29	290
0.1	9	− 3	− 27			
				0.1	41	410
0.2	14	1	14			
				0.1	34	340
0.3	12	4	48			
				0.1	80	800
0.4	8	16	128			

The relation among the derivatives of $u(x)$ and $v(x)$ and that of their product uv are shown in table 5.3b. The first four columns of that table are reproduced from table 5.2e. Columns 5 and 7 are both obtained by multiplying the derivative of v by the corresponding value of u, but the difference is in using u_i or u_{i+1} as the multiplier. The values in column 5 are obtained by using u_i or 7, 9, 14 and 12 as the multipliers; while in column 7, u_{i+1} or 9, 14, 12 and 8 are used as multipliers. This is also true for columns 6 and 8 where the products of v and the derivative of u are shown. Now what equation (1) says is that the derivative of y with respect to x is the sums of the corresponding values of columns 5 and 6 or

$$350 - 60 = 290$$

$$360 + 50 = 410$$

$$420 - 80 = 340$$

$$1{,}440 - 640 = 800$$

which are the values given in the last column of table 5.3a. Equation (2) says that the same derivative can be obtained by adding the corresponding numbers of columns 7 and 8 or

$$450 - 160 = 290$$

$$560 - 150 = 410$$

$$360 - 20 = 340$$

$$960 - 160 = 800$$

which are also the values given in the last column of table 5.3a.

TABLE 5.3b

VERIFICATION OF DERIVATIVE OF PRODUCT

(1)	(2)	(3)	(4)	(5)	(6)	(7)	(8)
$u(x)$	$v(x)$	$\dfrac{\Delta u}{\Delta x}$	$\dfrac{\Delta v}{\Delta x}$	$u\dfrac{\Delta v}{\Delta x}$	$(v + \Delta v)\dfrac{\Delta u}{\Delta x}$	$(u + \Delta u)\dfrac{\Delta v}{\Delta x}$	$v\dfrac{\Delta u}{\Delta x}$
7	−8						
		20	50	350	− 60	450	−160
9	−3						
		50	40	360	50	560	−150
14	1						
		−20	30	420	− 80	360	− 20
12	4						
		−40	120	1,440	−640	960	−160
8	16						

From the rule

$$\frac{\Delta}{\Delta x}(uv) = u\frac{\Delta v}{\Delta x} + (v + \Delta v)\frac{\Delta u}{\Delta x},$$

one can derive the rule

$$\frac{\Delta}{\Delta x}x^2 = 2x + \Delta x = x_i + x_{i+1} = 2\bar{x} \tag{3}$$

where $\bar{x}$ is the mid-point of the interval x_i to x_{i+1}. When both functions $u(x)$ and $v(x)$ are equal to x, the product of the two functions becomes

$$y = uv = xx = x^2$$

and the derivative of the product x^2 becomes

$$\frac{\Delta}{\Delta x}x^2 = x\frac{\Delta x}{\Delta x} + (x + \Delta x)\frac{\Delta x}{\Delta x} \cdot$$

But $\Delta x/\Delta x$ is equal to 1. Then the derivative of x^2 can be simplified into

$$\frac{\Delta}{\Delta x}x^2 = x + (x + \Delta x) = 2x + \Delta x$$

which is equation (3).

TABLE 5.3c

DERIVATIVE OF x^2

x	$y = x^2$	Δx	Δy	$\bar{x}$	$\dfrac{\Delta y}{\Delta x}$
2	4				
		2	12	3	6
4	16				
		2	20	5	10
6	36				
		2	28	7	14
8	64				
		2	36	9	18
10	100				

The numerical demonstration of the derivative of x^2 is given in table 5.3c. The values of x are arbitrarily chosen, and those of y are obtained by squaring the values of x. The differentiation is carried out in the usual way, and the derivative is given in the last column of that table. What equation (3) says is that the derivative of

$$y = x^2$$

is equal to

$$\frac{\Delta y}{\Delta x} = 2x_i + \Delta x$$

or

$$6 = 2(2) + 2$$

$$10 = 2(4) + 2$$

$$14 = 2(6) + 2$$

$$18 = 2(8) + 2$$

which is obviously true. Note that the x in equation (3) is x_i. This is why only the x-values 2, 4, 6 and 8 are used in the above equations and the last value 10 is ignored.

Equation (3) suggests that the derivative of x^2 is

$$2x + \Delta x = x + (x + \Delta x) = x_i + x_{i+1}$$

which is the sum of the two values defining an interval of x. From table 5.3c, it can be seen that the derivative of $y = x^2$ can be obtained by simply adding two adjacent values of x such as:

$$2 + 4 = 6$$

$$4 + 6 = 10$$

$$6 + 8 = 14$$

$$8 + 10 = 18$$

Equation (3) further suggests that the derivative of x^2 is equal to

$$\frac{\Delta}{\Delta x} x^2 = 2\bar{x} \tag{4}$$

where $\bar{x}$ is the mid-point of an interval of x. This is a foregone conclusion, because the mid-point of an interval is

$$\bar{x}_i = \frac{x_i + x_{i+1}}{2}$$

and twice that amount must be equal to

$$2\bar{x} = x_i + x_{i+1} = x + (x + \Delta x) = 2x + \Delta x$$

which is the derivative of x^2 given in equation (3).

The derivative of x^2 given in equation (3) can be derived in a more straight-forward manner. If the function is

$$y = x^2,$$

the increment of y for the interval x_i to x_{i+1} is

$$\Delta y \;=\; y_{i+1} - y_i \;=\; x_{i+1}^2 - x_i^2 \;=\; (x_{i+1} - x_i)(x_{i+1} + x_i).$$

But the increment of x is equal to

$$\Delta x \;=\; x_{i+1} - x_i.$$

Then the derivative of x^2 must be

$$\frac{\Delta y}{\Delta x} \;=\; x_{i+1} + x_i \;=\; (x + \Delta x) + x \;=\; 2x + \Delta x$$

which is the result given in equation (3).

The same result can be obtained by using the symbols (x, y) and $(x + \Delta x, y + \Delta y)$ for the points (x_i, y_i) and (x_{i+1}, y_{i+1}). At the point (x, y) the relation between x and y is

$$y \;=\; x^2,$$

and at the point $(x + \Delta x, y + \Delta y)$ the relation is

$$y + \Delta y \;=\; (x + \Delta x)^2 \;=\; x^2 + 2x\Delta x + (\Delta x)^2.$$

The difference between the two equations gives the increment of y as

$$\Delta y \;=\; 2x\Delta x + (\Delta x)^2.$$

Then the derivative of y or x^2 is

$$\frac{\Delta y}{\Delta x} \;=\; 2x + \Delta x$$

which is the result given in equation (3).

Through the rules of differentiation, now it is possible to find the derivative of the second-degree polynomial without going through the numerical process of differentiation. For the function

$$y \;=\; 4x^2 - 3x + 6,$$

one can differentiate term by term and obtain

$$\frac{\Delta y}{\Delta x} \;=\; 4\frac{\Delta}{\Delta x}x^2 - 3\frac{\Delta}{\Delta x}x + \frac{\Delta}{\Delta x}6.$$

But it is known that

$$\frac{\Delta}{\Delta x}x^2 \;=\; 2x + \Delta x \;=\; 2\bar{x}$$

$$\frac{\Delta}{\Delta x} x = 1$$

and

$$\frac{\Delta}{\Delta x} 6 = 0 .$$

Then the derivative of y must be equal to

$$\frac{\Delta y}{\Delta x} = 4(2\bar{x}) - 3 = 8\bar{x} - 3 .$$

This result is obtained purely by deduction from the rules of differentiation.

TABLE 5.3d

DERIVATIVE OF $y = 4x^2 - 3x + 6$

x	y	Δx	Δy	$\bar{x}$	$\dfrac{\Delta y}{\Delta x}$
0.0	6.00				
		0.5	−0.5	0.25	− 1
0.5	5.50				
		0.5	1.5	0.75	3
1.0	7.00				
		0.5	3.5	1.25	7
1.5	10.50				
		0.5	5.5	1.75	11
2.0	16.00				

The numerical demonstration of this result is given in table 5.3d. The x-values are arbitrarily chosen, and the y-values are computed from the equation

$$y = 4x^2 - 3x + 6 .$$

The differentiation is carried out in the usual way, and the derivative of y with respect to x is given in the last column of that table. The purpose of this differentiation is to demonstrate that the derivative of y is equal to

$$\frac{\Delta y}{\Delta x} = 8\bar{x} - 3$$

where $\bar{x}$ is the mid-point of the interval x_i to x_{i+1}. From the last two columns of table 5.3d, one can see that this is obviously true. For the four intervals, the values of $(8\bar{x}-3)$ are

$$8(0.25) - 3 = 2 - 3 = -1$$

$$8(0.75) - 3 = 6 - 3 = 3$$

$$8(1.25) - 3 = 10 - 3 = 7$$

$$8(1.75) - 3 = 14 - 3 = 11$$

which constitute the derivative of y as shown in the last column of table 5.3d. Now one can see that the rules of differentiation are indeed short cuts. By means of these rules, the derivative of y can be directly obtained from the x-values and the computation of the values of y and Δy are completely bypassed.

An interesting special case of the derivative of the product of two functions is that one of the functions is a constant. If the function is ku with k being a constant and u a function of x, its derivative, according to equation (1), is

$$\frac{\Delta}{\Delta x}ku = k\frac{\Delta u}{\Delta x} + (u + \Delta u)\frac{\Delta k}{\Delta x}.$$

But $\Delta k/\Delta x$ is equal to zero, and the derivative of the product becomes

$$\frac{\Delta}{\Delta x}ku = k\frac{\Delta u}{\Delta x}$$

which is the result given in equation (3) of section 5.2.

5.4 Differentiation of Power of x

In this section the rule of differentiating x^n is discussed, where n is a positive integer such as 1, 2, 3 and so forth. The special case where $n = 1$ is covered in section 5.2, and the derivative of x is given as

$$\frac{\Delta}{\Delta x}x = 1 \tag{1}$$

in equation (2) of that section. Furthermore, the case where $n = 2$ is covered in section 5.3, and the derivative of x^2 is given as

$$\frac{\Delta}{\Delta x}x^2 = 2x + \Delta x = 2\bar{x} \tag{2}$$

in equation (3) of that section. Now, in this section, the general case of differentiating x^n is discussed. Unfortunately the derivative of x^n cannot be represented by a single neat formula for all values of n.

The derivative of x^3 is equal to

$$\frac{\Delta}{\Delta x}x^3 = 3x(x + \Delta x) + (\Delta x)^2 \tag{3}$$

or

$$\frac{\Delta}{\Delta x}x^3 = 3(\bar{x})^2 + \frac{1}{4}(\Delta x)^2 \tag{4}$$

where $\bar{x}$ is the mid-point of the interval x to $x + \Delta x$. The derivative of x^3 can be derived by looking upon the function as the product of

$$u(x) = x^2$$

and

$$v(x) = x.$$

From equation (1) of section 5.3, one can see that the derivative of x^3 should be

$$\frac{\Delta}{\Delta x}x^3 = \frac{\Delta}{\Delta x}x^2 x = x^2\frac{\Delta x}{\Delta x} + (x + \Delta x)\frac{\Delta}{\Delta x}x^2.$$

But it is known that

$$\frac{\Delta x}{\Delta x} = 1$$

and

$$\frac{\Delta}{\Delta x}x^2 = 2x + \Delta x.$$

Then the derivative of x^3 can be expressed as

$$\frac{\Delta}{\Delta x}x^3 = x^2 + (x + \Delta x)(2x + \Delta x)$$

$$= x^2 + 2x^2 + 2x\Delta x + x\Delta x + (\Delta x)^2$$

$$= 3x^2 + 3x\Delta x + (\Delta x)^2$$

$$= 3x(x + \Delta x) + (\Delta x)^2$$

which is equation (3).

This result can also be obtained in a more direct manner. At the point (x, y) the relation between x and y is

$$y = x^3,$$

and at the next point $(x + \Delta x, y + \Delta y)$ the relation must be

$$y + \Delta y = (x + \Delta x)^3 = x^3 + 3x^2\Delta x + 3x(\Delta x)^2 + (\Delta x)^3.$$

The difference between the above equations is

$$\Delta y = 3x^2\Delta x + 3x(\Delta x)^2 + (\Delta x)^3.$$

Then the derivative of y or x^3 is

$$\frac{\Delta y}{\Delta x} = 3x^2 + 3x\Delta x + (\Delta x)^2$$

$$= 3x(x + \Delta x) + (\Delta x)^2$$

which is equation (3).

TABLE 5.4a

DERIVATIVE OF $y = x^3$

x	y	Δx	Δy	$\bar{x}$	$\dfrac{\Delta y}{\Delta x}$
0.0	0.000				
		0.5	0.125	0.25	0.25
0.5	0.125				
		0.5	0.875	0.75	1.75
1.0	1.000				
		0.5	2.375	1.25	4.75
1.5	3.375				
		0.5	4.625	1.75	9.25
2.0	8.000				

The numerical demonstration of equation (3) is given in table 5.4a. The x-values are arbitrarily chosen, and the y-values are obtained by cubing the values of x. Then the differentiation is carried out in the usual way, and the derivative of y or x^3 is given in the last column of that table. Equation (3) says that the computation of y and Δy can be bypassed and the same derivative can be obtained by computing the quantities

$$\frac{\Delta y}{\Delta x} = 3x(x + \Delta x) + (\Delta x)^2.$$

For the example of table 5.4a, the values of x are 0.0, 0.5, 1.0 and 1.5 and those of $x + \Delta x$ are 0.5, 1.0, 1.5 and 2.0. Of course, the value of Δx is 0.5. From these values the derivative computed is

$$3(0.0)(0.5) + (0.5)^2 = 0.25$$
$$3(0.5)(1.0) + (0.5)^2 = 1.75$$
$$3(1.0)(1.5) + (0.5)^2 = 4.75$$
$$3(1.5)(2.0) + (0.5)^2 = 9.25$$

which are the same values given in the last column of table 5.4a.

Another way of computing the derivative of x^3 is to find the mid-point $\bar{x}$ for each interval and then find the quantity

$$\frac{\Delta}{\Delta x} x^3 = 3(\bar{x})^2 + \frac{1}{4}(\Delta x)^2.$$

The mid-point of each interval is

$$\bar{x} = \frac{1}{2}(x_i + x_{i+1}) = \frac{1}{2}[x + (x + \Delta x)] = \frac{1}{2}(2x + \Delta x)$$

and its square must be

$$(\bar{x})^2 = \frac{1}{4}[4x^2 + 4x\Delta x + (\Delta x)^2]$$

$$= x^2 + x\Delta x + \frac{1}{4}(\Delta x)^2$$

$$= x(x + \Delta x) + \frac{1}{4}(\Delta x)^2.$$

Then the derivative of x^3 being (equation 3)

$$\frac{\Delta}{\Delta x} x^3 = 3x(x + \Delta x) + (\Delta x)^2$$

must be equal to

$$\frac{\Delta}{\Delta x} x^3 = 3x(x + \Delta x) + \frac{3}{4}(\Delta x)^2 + \frac{1}{4}(\Delta x)^2$$

$$= 3[x(x + \Delta x) + \frac{1}{4}(\Delta x)^2] + \frac{1}{4}(\Delta x)^2$$

$$= 3(\bar{x})^2 + \frac{1}{4}(\Delta x)^2$$

which is equation (4).

The numerical demonstration of equation (4) is given in table 5.4a. The mid-point $\bar{x}$ of each interval is given in that table, and the length of each interval is $\Delta x = 0.5$. Then by equation (4) the derivative of y or x^3 is

$$3(0.25)^2 + \frac{1}{4}(0.5)^2 \ = \ 0.25$$

$$3(0.75)^2 + \frac{1}{4}(0.5)^2 \ = \ 1.75$$

$$3(1.25)^2 + \frac{1}{4}(0.5)^2 \ = \ 4.75$$

$$3(1.75)^2 + \frac{1}{4}(0.5)^2 \ = \ 9.25$$

which are the same values given in the last column of table 5.4a. This is what equation (4) says.

The derivative of x^4 is equal to

$$\frac{\Delta}{\Delta x}x^4 \ = \ 4(\bar{x})^3 + \bar{x}(\Delta x)^2 \tag{5}$$

where $\bar{x}$ is the mid-point of the interval x to $x + \Delta x$. In deriving this rule one may look upon x^4 as the product of $u(x)$ and $v(x)$, where

$$u(x) \ = \ v(x) \ = \ x^2 .$$

From equation (1) of section 5.3, one can see that the derivative of x^4 is equal to

$$\frac{\Delta}{\Delta x}x^4 \ = \ \frac{\Delta}{\Delta x}x^2 x^2 \ = \ x^2\frac{\Delta}{\Delta x}\,x^2 + (x + \Delta x)^2\frac{\Delta}{\Delta x}x^2 .$$

But it is known that

$$\frac{\Delta}{\Delta x}x^2 \ = \ 2\bar{x}$$

and

$$(x + \Delta x)^2 \ = \ x^2 + 2x\Delta x + (\Delta x)^2 .$$

Then the derivative of x^4 can be expressed as

$$\frac{\Delta}{\Delta x}x^4 \ = \ 2\bar{x}\,[2x^2 + 2x\Delta x + (\Delta x)^2] .$$

To change the expression in the bracket of the above equation into a function of $\bar{x}$, one may utilize the identities

$$\bar{x} = \frac{1}{2}(x_i + x_{i+1}) = \frac{1}{2}(x + x + \Delta x) = x + \frac{1}{2}\Delta x$$

$$(\bar{x})^2 = x^2 + x\Delta x + \frac{1}{4}(\Delta x)^2$$

and

$$2(\bar{x})^2 = 2x^2 + 2x\Delta x + \frac{1}{2}(\Delta x)^2.$$

With the aid of the above equations, the derivative of x^4 can be expressed as

$$\frac{\Delta}{\Delta x}x^4 = 2\bar{x}\left[2(\bar{x})^2 + \frac{1}{2}(\Delta x)^2\right]$$

$$= 4(\bar{x})^3 + \bar{x}(\Delta x)^2$$

which is the expression given in equation (5).

TABLE 5.4b

DERIVATIVE OF $y = x^4$

x	y	Δx	Δy	$\bar{x}$	$\dfrac{\Delta y}{\Delta x}$
−2	16				
		1	−15	−1.5	−15
−1	1				
		1	− 1	−0.5	− 1
0	0				
		1	1	0.5	1
1	1				
		1	15	1.5	15
2	16				

The numerical demonstration of equation (5) is given in table 5.4b. To avoid complicated computation the simple numbers −2, −1, 0, 1 and 2 are used as the x-values. The values of y or x^4 are computed from these chosen values. Then the differentiation of y

with respect to x is carried out in the usual way, and the derivative is given in the last column of that table. Equation (5) says that the computation of the values of y and Δy can be bypassed and the derivative can be directly obtained from that equation. The mid-points $\bar{x}$ are given in table 5.4b, and the value of Δx is equal to 1. From these values, the derivative computed from equation (5) should be

$$4(-1.5)^3 - 1.5(1)^2 = -15$$

$$4(-0.5)^3 - 0.5(1)^2 = -1$$

$$4(+0.5)^3 + 0.5(1)^2 = 1$$

$$4(+1.5)^3 + 1.5(1)^2 = 15$$

which are exactly the same values given in the last column of table 5.4b. This is what equation (5) says.

In general the derivative of x^n can be expressed as

$$\frac{\Delta}{\Delta x} x^n = n(\bar{x})^{n-1} + g(x)(\Delta x)^2 \tag{6}$$

where $g(x)$ is some function of x. For $n = 1$, the derivative of x is

$$\frac{\Delta}{\Delta x} x = (1)(\bar{x})^{1-1} = 1x^0 = 1 \tag{7}$$

because x^0 is equal to 1. In this case, the function $g(x)$ is equal to 0. For $n = 2$, the derivative of x^2 is

$$\frac{\Delta}{\Delta x} x^2 = 2(\bar{x})^{2-1} = 2\bar{x} \tag{8}$$

as shown in equation (2). In this case the function $g(x)$ is also equal to 0. For $n = 3$, the derivative of x^3 is

$$\frac{\Delta}{\Delta x} x^3 = 3(\bar{x})^2 + \frac{1}{4}(\Delta x)^2 \tag{9}$$

as shown in equation (4). In this case the function $g(x)$ is equal to 1/4. For $n = 4$, the derivative of x^4 is

$$\frac{\Delta}{\Delta x} x^4 = 4(\bar{x})^3 + \bar{x}(\Delta x)^2 \tag{10}$$

as shown in equation (5). In this case the function $g(x)$ is

$$\bar{x} = \frac{1}{2}(x_i + x_{i+1}) = \frac{1}{2}(x + x + \Delta x) = x + \frac{1}{2}\Delta x. \tag{11}$$

Thus equation (6) can generalize the derivative of x^n for $n = 1, 2, 3$ and 4. However, it can be proven that the equation can represent the derivative of x^n for all values of n with the function $g(x)$ changes with the value of n.

With the aid of the rules derived so far, now it is possible to differentiate a fourth-degree polynomial such as

$$y = x^4 - 4x^3 + 2x^2 - 3x + 5 \tag{12}$$

without finding the values of y and Δy. Differentiating term by term, one obtains

$$\frac{\Delta y}{\Delta x} = [4(\bar{x})^3 + \bar{x}(\Delta x)^2] - 4\left[3(\bar{x})^2 + \frac{1}{4}(\Delta x)^2\right] + 2[2\bar{x}] - 3[1] + 0$$

which can be expressed as

$$\frac{\Delta y}{\Delta x} = 4(\bar{x})^3 - 12(\bar{x})^2 + 4\bar{x} - 3 + (\bar{x} - 1)(\Delta x)^2. \tag{13}$$

TABLE 5.4c

DERIVATIVE OF $y = x^4 - 4x^3 + 2x^2 - 3x + 5$

x	y	Δx	Δy	$\bar{x}$	$\dfrac{\Delta y}{\Delta x}$
−2	67				
		1	−52	−1.5	−52
−1	15				
		1	−10	−0.5	−10
0	5				
		1	− 4	0.5	− 4
1	1				
		1	−10	1.5	−10
2	− 9				

The numerical demonstration of the differentiation of the fourth-degree polynomial is given in table 5.4c. Five simple values are assigned to the independent variable x, and the corresponding values of y are computed from these chosen values according to equation (12) such as

$$y_1 = (-2)^4 - 4(-2)^3 + 2(-2)^2 - 3(-2) + 5 = 67.$$

Then the differentiation of y with respect to x is carried out in the usual way, and the derivative is shown in the last column of that table.

Equation (13) says that the same derivative can be computed directly from that equation without the aid of the values of y and Δy. The mid-points $\bar{x}$ are listed in table 5.4c and the value of Δx is equal to 1 for all intervals of x. The derivative computed from these values is

$$4(-1.5)^3 - 12(-1.5)^2 + 4(-1.5) - 3 + (-1.5 - 1)(1)^2 = -52$$
$$4(-0.5)^3 - 12(-0.5)^2 + 4(-0.5) - 3 + (-0.5 - 1)(1)^2 = -10$$
$$4(+0.5)^3 - 12(+0.5)^2 + 4(+0.5) - 3 + (+0.5 - 1)(1)^2 = -4$$
$$4(+1.5)^3 - 12(+1.5)^2 + 4(+1.5) - 3 + (+1.5 - 1)(1)^2 = -10$$

which are exactly the same values given in the last column of table 5.4c. This example demonstrates that differentiation by rule offers alternative ways of carrying out the operation and enables one to choose the simplest one among different methods.

5.5 Differentiation of Quotient of Functions

The derivative of the quotient of two functions $u(x)$ and $v(x)$ is

$$\frac{\Delta}{\Delta x}\left(\frac{u}{v}\right) = \frac{v\dfrac{\Delta u}{\Delta x} - u\dfrac{\Delta v}{\Delta x}}{v(v + \Delta v)} \qquad v \neq 0. \tag{1}$$

The value of the function

$$y = \frac{u(x)}{v(x)}$$

at the ith point is

$$y_i = \frac{u_i}{v_i} = \frac{u}{v},$$

and that at the $(i+1)$st point is

$$y_{i+1} = \frac{u_{i+1}}{v_{i+1}} = \frac{u + \Delta u}{v + \Delta v}.$$

Then the increment of y for the interval x_i to x_{i+1}, or x to $x+\Delta x$, is

$$\Delta y = y_{i+1} - y_i = \frac{u + \Delta u}{v + \Delta v} - \frac{u}{v}.$$

Adding the two fractions, one obtains

$$\Delta y = \frac{uv + v\Delta u - uv - u\Delta v}{v(v + \Delta v)} = \frac{v\Delta u - u\Delta v}{v(v + \Delta v)}.$$

Dividing the above equation by Δx, one obtains the derivative

$$\frac{\Delta y}{\Delta x} = \frac{v\dfrac{\Delta u}{\Delta x} - u\dfrac{\Delta v}{\Delta x}}{v(v + \Delta v)}$$

which is equation (1).

The numerical demonstration of the above result is given in table 5.5a. The values of x, $u(x)$ and $v(x)$ are reproduced from table 5.2e, and the values of y are computed by dividing u by v. Now it should be clear that none of the v-values can be equal to zero as indicated in equation (1), for otherwise the corresponding y-value cannot be obtained. After the y-values are computed the differentiation can be carried out, and the derivative is shown in the last column of table 5.5a.

TABLE 5.5a

DERIVATIVE OF $y = u(x)/v(x)$

x	$u(x)$	$v(x)$	$y = \dfrac{u}{v}$	Δx	Δy	$\dfrac{\Delta y}{\Delta x}$
0.0	7	− 8	− 0.875			
				0.1	− 2.125	− 21.25
0.1	9	− 3	− 3.000			
				0.1	17.000	170.00
0.2	14	1	14.000			
				0.1	− 11.000	− 110.00
0.3	12	4	3.000			
				0.1	− 2.500	− 25.00
0.4	8	16	0.500			

TABLE 5.5b

VERIFICATION OF DERIVATIVE OF QUOTIENT

(1)	(2)	(3)	(4)	(5)	(6)	(7)	(8)	(9)
$u(x)$	$v(x)$	$\dfrac{\Delta u}{\Delta x}$	$\dfrac{\Delta v}{\Delta x}$	$v\dfrac{\Delta u}{\Delta x}$	$u\dfrac{\Delta v}{\Delta x}$	$v\dfrac{\Delta u}{\Delta x} - u\dfrac{\Delta v}{\Delta x}$	$v(v+\Delta v)$	$\dfrac{\Delta y}{\Delta x}$
7	-8							
		20	50	-160	350	-510	24	-21.25
9	-3							
		50	40	-150	360	-510	-3	170.00
14	1							
		-20	30	-20	420	-440	4	-110.00
12	4							
		-40	120	-160	1,440	$-1,600$	64	-25.00
8	16							

The verification of equation (1) is given in table 5.5b. The first four columns of that table give the values of $u(x)$, $v(x)$ and their derivatives, all of which are reproduced from table 5.2e. Column 5 gives the products of v-values and the rates of change of u. Here a value of v is that of v_i and not that of v_{i+1}. Only the four v-values -8, -3, 1 and 4 are used as the multipliers, and the last value 16 is ignored. This is also true for column 6 where the products of u-values and the rates of change of v are given. Column 7 gives the differences of the corresponding numbers of columns 5 and 6. Column 8 gives the products

$$v(v + \Delta v) \ = \ v_i(v_{i+1}).$$

For the five v-values

$$-8 \quad -3 \quad 1 \quad 4 \quad 16,$$

the four products are

$$(-8)(-3) \ = \ 24$$
$$(-3)\ (1) \ = \ -3$$
$$(1)\ (4) \ = \ 4$$
$$(4)\ (16) \ = \ 64$$

which are given in column 8. Finally, the derivative of the quotient u/v given in column 9 is the collection of quotients obtained by dividing each value in column 7 by its corresponding value in column 8. The derivative thus obtained is the same as that given in table 5.5a where the derivative is obtained through the computation of the values of y and Δy. This is what equation (1) says.

The rule of differentiating the quotient of two functions enables one to differentiate the numerator and the denominator of the function

$$y = \frac{u(x)}{v(x)}$$

separately. To find the derivative of

$$y = \frac{u}{v} = \frac{x}{x^2 + 1}, \tag{2}$$

one may first find the derivatives

$$\frac{\Delta u}{\Delta x} = \frac{\Delta x}{\Delta x} = 1$$

and

$$\frac{\Delta v}{\Delta x} = \frac{\Delta}{\Delta x}(x^2 + 1) = 2\bar{x} = 2x + \Delta x.$$

Then the derivative of y with respect to x can be expressed as (equation 1)

$$\frac{\Delta y}{\Delta x} = \frac{(x^2 + 1)(1) - x(2x + \Delta x)}{(x^2 + 1)[(x + \Delta x)^2 + 1]}.$$

In terms of (x_i, y_i) and (x_{i+1}, y_{i+1}), the derivative is simply

$$\frac{\Delta y}{\Delta x} = \frac{(x_i^2 + 1) - x_i(x_i + x_{i+1})}{(x_i^2 + 1)(x_{i+1}^2 + 1)} = \frac{1 - x_i x_{i+1}}{(x_i^2 + 1)(x_{i+1}^2 + 1)}. \tag{3}$$

Now the derivative of y can be found by two different ways. One is to compute y from equation (2) and differentiate the function through the definition of the derivative. The other way is to compute the derivative directly from equation (3) and thus bypass the values of y and Δy. The first method is shown in table 5.5c and the second one in table 5.5d. The results obtained in the two different ways are identical as they should be.

TABLE 5.5c

DIFFERENTIATION OF $y = x/(x^2 + 1)$ BY DEFINITION

x	x^2+1	$y = \dfrac{x}{x^2+1}$	Δx	Δy	$\dfrac{\Delta y}{\Delta x}$
−2	5	−0.4			
			1	−0.1	−0.1
−1	2	−0.5			
			1	0.5	0.5
0	1	0.0			
			1	0.5	0.5
1	2	0.5			
			1	−0.1	−0.1
2	5	0.4			

TABLE 5.5d

DIFFERENTIATION OF $y = x/(x^2 + 1)$ BY RULE

x_i	$x_i^2 + 1$	$x_i x_{i+1}$	$1 - x_i x_{i+1}$	$(x_i^2 + 1)(x_{i+1}^2 + 1)$	$\dfrac{\Delta y}{\Delta x}$
−2	5				
		2	−1	10	−0.1
−1	2				
		0	1	2	0.5
0	1				
		0	1	2	0.5
1	2				
		2	−1	10	−0.1
2	5				

5.6 Differentiation of Function of Function

A differentiation may be carried out in successive stages. If y is a function of u which in turn is a function of x, the differentiation of y with respect to x can be carried out by differentiating y with respect to u and then differentiating u with respect to x. The derivative of y with respect to x is equal to

$$\frac{\Delta y}{\Delta x} = \frac{\Delta y}{\Delta u} \cdot \frac{\Delta u}{\Delta x} \tag{1}$$

which is the product of the other two derivatives.

This obvious conclusion may be demonstrated by the function

$$y = (x^2 + 1)^2 \tag{2}$$

which implies that

$$y = u^2$$

and

$$u = x^2 + 1.$$

The derivative of y with respect to u is equal to

$$\frac{\Delta y}{\Delta u} = 2u + \Delta u = u_i + u_{i+1}$$

and that of u with respect to x is equal to

$$\frac{\Delta u}{\Delta x} = 2x + \Delta x = x_i + x_{i+1}.$$

Then, by equation (1), the derivative of y with respect to x is

$$\frac{\Delta y}{\Delta x} = (u_i + u_{i+1})(x_i + x_{i+1}). \tag{3}$$

TABLE 5.6a

DIFFERENTIATION OF $y = (x^2 + 1)^2$ BY DEFINITION

x	$x^2 + 1$	$y = (x^2 + 1)^2$	Δx	Δy	$\frac{\Delta y}{\Delta x}$
-2	5	25			
			1	-21	-21
-1	2	4			
			1	-3	-3
0	1	1			
			1	3	3
1	2	4			
			1	21	21
2	5	25			

TABLE 5.6b

DIFFERENTIATION OF $y = (x^2 + 1)^2$ AS FUNCTION OF FUNCTION

x_i	$u_i = x_i^2 + 1$	$x_i + x_{i+1}$	$u_i + u_{i+1}$	$\dfrac{\Delta y}{\Delta x}$
-2	5			
		-3	7	-21
-1	2			
		-1	3	-3
0	1			
		1	3	3
1	2			
		3	7	21
2	5			

The numerical demonstration of this result is given in tables 5.6a and 5.6b. In the former table, the values of y are computed from equation (2) and the differentiation is carried out according to the definition of the operation. In the later table, the derivative is computed from equation (3) and the values of y and Δy are bypassed. The final results shown in these two tables are the same as they should be.

The same function

$$y = (x^2 + 1)^2$$

may also be differentiated as the product of two functions $u(x)$ and $v(x)$, where

$$u(x) = v(x) = x^2 + 1.$$

From equation (1) of section 5.3, it can be determined that the derivative of y with respect to x is

$$\frac{\Delta y}{\Delta x} = u\frac{\Delta v}{\Delta x} + (v + \Delta v)\frac{\Delta u}{\Delta x}.$$

But u in the above equation is u_i, and $v + \Delta v$ is v_{i+1} which is also u_{i+1} because $u(x)$ is equal to $v(x)$. Furthermore, the derivative of $u(x)$ or $v(x)$ is

$$\frac{\Delta u}{\Delta x} = \frac{\Delta v}{\Delta x} = 2x + \Delta x = x_i + x_{i+1}.$$

Thus the derivative of y with respect to x can be expressed as

$$\frac{\Delta y}{\Delta x} = (u_i + u_{i+1})\frac{\Delta u}{\Delta x}$$

$$= (u_i + u_{i+1})(x_i + x_{i+1})$$

which is the same expression given in equation (3).

The same function

$$y = (x^2 + 1)^2 = x^4 + 2x^2 + 1 \tag{4}$$

may also be differentiated as a fourth-degree polynomial. Differentiating term by term, one obtains

$$\frac{\Delta y}{\Delta x} = \frac{\Delta}{\Delta x}x^4 + 2\frac{\Delta}{\Delta x}x^2 + 0.$$

But the derivative of x^4 is equal to (equation 5, section 5.4)

$$\frac{\Delta}{\Delta x}x^4 = 4(\bar{x})^3 + \bar{x}(\Delta x)^2$$

and that of x^2 is equal to (equation 2, section 5.4)

$$\frac{\Delta}{\Delta x}x^2 = 2\bar{x}.$$

Then the derivative of y must be equal to

$$\frac{\Delta y}{\Delta x} = 4(\bar{x})^3 + \bar{x}(\Delta x)^2 + 4\bar{x}$$

$$= 4(\bar{x})^3 + \bar{x}[(\Delta x)^2 + 4] \tag{5}$$

which yields a method of computing the derivative through the midpoints $\bar{x}$ of the intervals. The numerical demonstration of this method is given in table 5.6c, and result obtained is the same as that given in table 5.6a or 5.6b.

The given example demonstrates that the differentiation of a function can be done in many different ways. In carrying out the operation one can choose any one he wishes. As long as the rules are used correctly, the result is always the same.

TABLE 5.6c

DIFFERENTIATION OF $y = (x^2 + 1)^2$ AS POLYNOMIAL

x	$\bar{x}$	Δx	$4(\bar{x})^3$	$(\Delta x)^2 + 4$	$\bar{x}\,[(\Delta x)^2 + 4]$	$\dfrac{\Delta y}{\Delta x}$
-2						
	-1.5	1	-13.5	5	-7.5	-21.0
-1						
	-0.5	1	-0.5	5	-2.5	-3.0
0						
	0.5	1	0.5	5	2.5	3.0
1						
	1.5	1	13.5	5	7.5	21.0
2						

5.7 Summary of Rules of Differentiation

The derivative of the function

$$y = F(x)$$

for the interval x_i to x_{i+1} is defined as

$$\frac{\Delta y}{\Delta x} = \frac{y_{i+1} - y_i}{x_{i+1} - x_i} \qquad x_{i+1} > x_i$$

where y_i and y_{i+1} are the values of $F(x)$ at the points x_i and x_{i+1} respectively. When the interval is expressed as x to $x+\Delta x$, the derivative of the function $F(x)$ can also be expressed as

$$\frac{\Delta}{\Delta x} F(x) = \frac{F(x + \Delta x) - F(x)}{\Delta x}$$

where Δx is always positive. The derivative

$$\frac{\Delta y}{\Delta x} = \frac{\Delta}{\Delta x} F(x) = f(\bar{x})$$

is a function of $\bar{x}$ and Δx, where

$$\bar{x} = \frac{1}{2}(x_i + x_{i+1}) = \frac{1}{2}(2x + \Delta x) = x + \frac{1}{2}\Delta x$$

is the mid-point of the given interval of x. It is also a function of x and Δx, because $\bar{x}$ is a function of x and Δx.

The rules of differentiation given in this chapter are listed as follows:

(1) $\quad \dfrac{\Delta}{\Delta x} C = 0$

(2) $\quad \dfrac{\Delta}{\Delta x} x = 1$

(3) $\quad \dfrac{\Delta}{\Delta x} x^2 = 2\bar{x}$

(4) $\quad \dfrac{\Delta}{\Delta x} x^3 = 3(\bar{x})^2 + \dfrac{1}{4}(\Delta x)^2$

(5) $\quad \dfrac{\Delta}{\Delta x} x^4 = 4(\bar{x})^3 + \bar{x}(\Delta x)^2$

(6) $\quad \dfrac{\Delta}{\Delta x} ku = k\dfrac{\Delta}{\Delta x} u$

(7) $\quad \dfrac{\Delta}{\Delta x}[u + v + \cdots] = \dfrac{\Delta u}{\Delta x} + \dfrac{\Delta v}{\Delta x} + \cdots$

(8) $\quad \dfrac{\Delta}{\Delta x}(uv) = u\dfrac{\Delta v}{\Delta x} + (v + \Delta v)\dfrac{\Delta u}{\Delta x}$

(9) $\quad \dfrac{\Delta}{\Delta x}(uv) = (u + \Delta u)\dfrac{\Delta v}{\Delta x} + v\dfrac{\Delta u}{\Delta x}$

(10) $\quad \dfrac{\Delta}{\Delta x}\left(\dfrac{u}{v}\right) = \dfrac{v\dfrac{\Delta u}{\Delta x} - u\dfrac{\Delta v}{\Delta x}}{v(v + \Delta v)} \qquad v \neq 0$

(11) $\quad \dfrac{\Delta y}{\Delta x} = \dfrac{\Delta y}{\Delta u} \cdot \dfrac{\Delta u}{\Delta x}$

Each of the above equations enables one to find the rate of change of y for an interval of x without finding y and Δy. The differentiation of the function y with respect to x can be accomplished by repeatedly using the equations for a sequence of intervals.

The only restriction on Δx is that it is always positive. It does not have to be a small quantity such as 1.0, 0.5 and 0.1 which are frequently used in the examples. Furthermore, Δx does not have to be the same for the whole range of x, even though all examples in this chapter use constant Δx.

All these rules are short cuts of differentiation in some sense or the other. Equations (1) and (2) enable one to write out the derivatives without computation. Equations (3) to (5) enable one to compute the derivatives directly from the x-values and bypass the values of y and Δy. Equations (6) to (10) enable one to find the derivatives of functions through their components $u(x)$ and $v(x)$. Equation (11) enables one to differentiate a given function in two stages. However, the most important reason for deriving these rules in this chapter is to find the limits of these derivatives as Δx approaches zero. This is discussed in the following chapter.

EXERCISES

1. Follow the procedure outlined in table 5.1b and differentiate the function $y = 5$ for $x = 2, 4, 6, 8, 10$ and 12. This is to demonstrate that the derivative of a constant is equal to zero.

2. Follow the procedure outlined in table 5.1b and differentiate the function $y = x$ for $x = 0.0, 0.2, 0.4, 0.6$ and 0.8. This is to demonstrate that the derivative of x with respect to x is equal to 1.

3. Follow the procedure outlined in table 5.1b and differentiate the function $y = 2x^3 - x$ for $x = 0.0, 0.2, 0.4, 0.6, 0.8, 1.0$ and 1.2. Then compute the derivative directly from the x-values through the rules and see if the result obtained remains the same.

4. Demonstrate that the derivative of $y = a + bx$ is equal to the slope b through the procedure outlined in table 5.1b. The values 0, 1, 2, 3, 4 and 5 may be assigned to x.

5. Differentiate the following function:

x	2	4	6	8	10
y	109.7	112.8	114.3	123.6	115.7

Then subtract 100 from each value of y and differentiate again. The derivatives obtained for the two sets of y-values should be identical. The purpose of this exercise is to show that adding a constant to the dependent variable y does not change the derivative of y with respect to x or

$$\frac{\Delta}{\Delta x}(y + C) = \frac{\Delta y}{\Delta x}.$$

The constant C in this exercise is -100

6. Differentiate each of the functions

$$u = 2x$$
$$v = x^2 + 4$$

and

$$y = u + v = x^2 + 2x + 4$$

separately. Use 2, 4, 6 as the x-values and follow the procedure outlined in table 5.1b in the differentiation. Then demonstrate that equation (7) of section 5.7 is correct.

7. Find the values of $y = uv$ where u and v are given in exercise 6. Then differentiate y with respect to x through the procedure outlined in table 5.1b. Then demonstrate that equations (8) and (9) of section 5.7 are correct.

8. Find the values of $y = u/v$ where u and v are given in exercise 6. Then differentiate y with respect to x through the procedure outlined in table 5.1b. Then demonstrate that equation (10) of section 5.7 is correct.

9. The function

$$y = (2x + 1)^3 = 8x^3 + 12x^2 + 6x + 1$$

may be regarded as $y = u^3$ where $u = 2x + 1$. For $x = 0, 2, 4, 6, 8$ and 10, find the values of both u and y. Then find the derivative of y with respect to x, that of y with respect to u, and that of u with respect to x. By means of the three derivatives, demonstrate that equation (11) of section 5.7 is correct.

10. Differentiate the following functions:

    (a) $y = 3x^2 - 2x + 10$ (b) $y = x^4 + x^2$

In each case assign $-4, -2, 0, 2$ and 4 to the independent variable x and follow the procedure outlined in table 5.1b. Then compute the derivatives from the rules given in section 5.7 and bypass the values of y and Δy, and see if the results obtained are the same.

CHAPTER 6

DIFFERENTIATION—INFINITESIMAL INTERVAL

This chapter is a continuation of the preceding one. The topic is still differential calculus, but the emphasis is on the limiting value of the derivative as Δx approaches zero. In addition, some applications of differentiation are discussed.

6.1 Limiting Value of Derivative

With the rules of differentiation out of the way, it is about time to impose some physical meaning on the derivative. An x-value in table 6.1a represents the number of hours of driving, and the corresponding y-value represents the number of miles travelled. The table says that the car was driven 44 miles in one hour and 92 miles in two hours. The derivative given in that table indicates that the car travelled at an *average speed* of 44 miles an hour during the first hour and 48 miles an hour during the second hour. However, this table does not give a complete picture of the trip. Despite the fact that the average speed is 44 or 48 miles an hour, the driver might have stopped for coffee and thus reduced the speed to zero mile an hour. On the other hand, he might also have driven at 100 miles an hour for a few minutes. All these are possibilities which might have been overlooked by the record of table 6.1a.

TABLE 6.1a

DERIVATIVE OF y WITH Δx EQUAL TO 1

x hours	y miles	Δx hour	Δy miles	$\dfrac{\Delta y}{\Delta x}$ miles/hour
0	0			
		1	44	44
1	44			
		1	48	48
2	92			

163

TABLE 6.1b

DERIVATIVE OF y WITH Δx EQUAL TO 0.5

x hours	y miles	Δx hour	Δy miles	$\dfrac{\Delta y}{\Delta x}$ miles/hour
0.0	0.0			
		0.5	21.5	43
0.5	21.5			
		0.5	22.5	45
1.0	44.0			
		0.5	23.5	47
1.5	67.5			
		0.5	24.5	49
2.0	92.0			

To get a clearer picture of the trip, a more detailed record may be kept. In table 6.1b the distance travelled is recorded at half-hour intervals. The derivative in that table shows the *average speeds* of four half-hour intervals for the two hours of driving. If this is not enough, one may keep the record at intervals of one tenth of an hour or six minutes as shown in table 6.1c. Smaller is the interval Δx, more complete is the record. If one really wants to go to the extreme and let Δx be an infinitesimal, the speed would be the instantaneous one which is shown by the speedometer. Even if a car is driven at an average speed of 44 miles an hour for a whole hour, the indicator of the speedometer usually fluctuates and does not necessarily show that one particular speed during the whole period. The speed being indicated at any moment is the instantaneous speed of the car at that moment. That speed, in terms of differential calculus, is the rate of change of y with respect to x for Δx being equal to an infinitesimal.

To find the derivative of

$$y = F(x)$$

with Δx equal to zero is an impossible job. For the function

$$y = x^3,$$

TABLE 6.1c

DERIVATIVE OF y WITH Δx EQUAL TO 0.1

x hours	y miles	Δx hour	Δy miles	$\dfrac{\Delta y}{\Delta x}$ miles/hour
0.0	0.00			
		0.1	4.22	42.2
0.1	4.22			
		0.1	4.26	42.6
0.2	8.48			
		0.1	4.30	43.0
0.3	12.78			
		0.1	4.34	43.4
0.4	17.12			
		0.1	4.38	43.8
0.5	21.50			
		0.1	4.42	44.2
0.6	25.92			
		0.1	4.46	44.6
0.7	30.38			
		0.1	4.50	45.0
0.8	34.88			
		0.1	4.54	45.4
0.9	39.42			
		0.1	4.58	45.8
1.0	44.00			
		0.1	4.62	46.2
1.1	48.62			
		0.1	4.66	46.6
1.2	53.28			
		0.1	4.70	47.0
1.3	57.98			
		0.1	4.74	47.4
1.4	62.72			
		0.1	4.78	47.8
1.5	67.50			
		0.1	4.82	48.2
1.6	72.32			
		0.1	4.86	48.6
1.7	77.18			
		0.1	4.90	49.0
1.8	82.08			
		0.1	4.94	49.4
1.9	87.02			
		0.1	4.98	49.8
2.0	92.00			

the rate of change of y for the interval $x = 1$ to $x = 2$ is

$$\frac{\Delta y}{\Delta x} = \frac{2^3 - 1^3}{2 - 1} = 7 .$$

When the interval Δx is reduced from 1 to 0.1, the rate of change of y for the interval $x = 1$ to $x = 1.1$ is

$$\frac{\Delta y}{\Delta x} = \frac{(1.1)^3 - 1^3}{1.1 - 1} = \frac{1.331 - 1}{0.1} = 3.31 .$$

If the interval Δx is further reduced to 0.01, the rate of change of y for the interval $x = 1$ to $x = 1.01$ is

$$\frac{\Delta y}{\Delta x} = \frac{(1.01)^3 - 1^3}{1.01 - 1} = \frac{1.030301 - 1}{0.01} = 3.0301 .$$

As Δx is getting closer to zero, the average rate of change of y is getting closer to the instantaneous rate of change at the point $x = 1$. But the fact remains that the rate of change of y cannot be found when Δx is equal to zero. The trouble is that, when Δx is equal to zero, the two points defining the interval are both located at $x = 1$ and the rate of change of y at that point is

$$\frac{\Delta y}{\Delta x} = \frac{1^3 - 1^3}{1 - 1} = \frac{0}{0}$$

which can be any value. To overcome this difficulty, the instantaneous rate of change of y at a given point x is defined as the limiting value of $\Delta y/\Delta x$ for the interval x to $x + \Delta x$ as Δx approaches zero. The limiting value is the value towards which the rate $\Delta y/\Delta x$ is moving as Δx moves towards zero. This limiting value is represented by the new symbol

$$\frac{dy}{dx} = \lim_{\Delta x \to 0} \frac{\Delta y}{\Delta x} .$$

The idea of the limit is demonstrated in table 6.1d which shows the rates of change of the function x^3 for the interval $x = 1$ to $x = 1 + \Delta x$. In that table, the values of $\Delta y/\Delta x$ are computed for a sequence of decreasing values of Δx. This is to show that the rate of change of y for the interval $x = 1$ to $x = 1 + \Delta x$ is not a constant but a function of Δx. From the sequence of values of $\Delta y/\Delta x$ for the decreasing values of Δx, one can surmise that the value of $\Delta y/\Delta x$ is heading towards 3 as Δx approaches zero. Symbolically, this fact is expressed as

$$\frac{d}{dx} x^3 = 3 \tag{1}$$

at the point $x = 1$. The interval $x = 1$ to $x = 1 + \Delta x$ shrinks to that point when Δx approaches zero.

TABLE 6.1d

RATES OF CHANGE OF x^3 FOR INTERVAL 1 TO $1 + \Delta x$

x	$y = x^3$	Δx	Δy	$\dfrac{\Delta y}{\Delta x}$
1	1			
		1	7	7
2	8			
1.0	1.000			
		0.1	0.331	3.31
1.1	1.331			
1.00	1.000000			
		0.01	0.030301	3.0301
1.01	1.030301			
1.000	1.000000000			
		0.001	0.003003001	3.003001
1.001	1.003003001			
1.0000	1.000000000000			
		0.0001	0.000300030001	3.00030001
1.0001	1.000300030001			
1.00000	1.000000000000000			
		0.00001	0.000030000300001	3.0000300001
1.00001	1.000030000300001			

The limit of $\Delta y / \Delta x$ can be readily obtained from the rules of differentiation. For example, the rate of change of x^3 for the interval x to $x + \Delta x$ is (equation 3, section 5.4)

$$\frac{\Delta}{\Delta x} x^3 = 3x(x + \Delta x) + (\Delta x)^2 \qquad (2)$$

which is clearly a function of x as well as Δx. When Δx is equal to zero, the interval shrinks to the single point x and the instantaneous rate of change at that point becomes

$$\frac{dy}{dx} = 3x^2 . \tag{3}$$

At the point $x = 1$, the rate is

$$\frac{dy}{dx} = 3(1)^2 = 3$$

which is the same value given in equation (1). This example demonstrates that, even though the rate of change of y cannot be directly evaluated when Δx is equal to zero because the ratio becomes

$$\frac{\Delta y}{\Delta x} = \frac{0}{0} ,$$

its limit can be readily obtained in a roundabout way.

The rates of change of x^3 given in table 6.1d can be directly computed from equation (2). For example, when $x = 1$ and $\Delta x = 0.00001$, the rate is

$$\frac{\Delta}{\Delta x} x^3 = 3(1)(1.00001) + (0.00001)^2$$

$$= 3.00003 + 0.0000000001$$

$$= 3.0000300001$$

which is the last value given in table 6.1d. For a smaller interval of x such as

$$\Delta x = 0.0000000001 ,$$

the rate of change of x^3 for the interval $x = 1$ to $x = 1 + \Delta x$ is

$$\frac{\Delta}{\Delta x} x^3 = 3.00000000030000000001 .$$

For a even smaller interval of x such as

$$\Delta x = 0.00000000000000000001$$

the rate becomes

$$\frac{\Delta}{\Delta x} x^3 = 3.00000000000000000003000000000000000000001$$

which clearly demonstrates that the limit of the rate at $x = 1$ is

$$\frac{d}{dx}x^3 = 3$$

as Δx approaches zero.

As Δx approaches zero, the mid-point $\bar{x}_i$ and the two end-points x_i and x_{i+1} of the ith interval merge into one point which may be called x. The ith interval of x is bounded by

$$x_i = x$$

and

$$x_{i+1} = x + \Delta x.$$

As Δx approaches zero, both points becomes the single point x. At the same time, the mid-point

$$\bar{x}_i = \frac{1}{2}(x_i + x_{i+1}) = \frac{1}{2}(x + x + \Delta x) = x + \frac{1}{2}\Delta x$$

of that interval also becomes x.

The consequence of the degeneration of each interval of x into a point is that the derivative

$$\frac{\Delta y}{\Delta x} = f(\bar{x})$$

of the function

$$y = F(x)$$

becomes

$$\frac{dy}{dx} = f(x)$$

with the bar over the x removed. The derivative $f(\bar{x})$ is associated with intervals of x; while $f(x)$ is associated with points because intervals shrink into points when Δx approaches zero.

6.2 Differentiation by Formula

Ordinarily, the differentiation of a function

$$y = F(x)$$

which is expressed in the form of an equation is to find the derivative

$$\frac{dy}{dx} = \lim_{\Delta x \to 0} \frac{\Delta y}{\Delta x} = f(x)$$

which is also expressed in the form of an equation. When one is interested in the numerical value of the instantaneous rate of change of y at a particular point x_0, he simply finds the value of $f(x_0)$. The only computation involved is the evaluation of $f(x)$ at $x = x_0$.

For each rule of differentiation which yields $\Delta y/\Delta x$, there is a corresponding one for obtaining the instantaneous rate of change

$$\frac{dy}{dx} = \lim_{\Delta x \to 0} \frac{\Delta y}{\Delta x}.$$

By finding the limits of the expressions for $\Delta y/\Delta x$, one can find a parallel set of rules.

The rule (equation 1, section 5.2)

$$\frac{\Delta}{\Delta x} C = 0$$

leads to the parallel rule

$$\frac{d}{dx} C = 0. \tag{1}$$

The reason for this can be seen from table 5.2a. The function of x is always equal to 8 in that table regardless of the value of x. Then the increment of y for every interval of x is always

$$\Delta y = 8 - 8 = 0$$

no matter how small is the interval Δx. Therefore the limit of the derivative is equal to

$$\lim_{\Delta x \to 0} \frac{\Delta}{\Delta x} C = \frac{d}{dx} C = 0.$$

The rule (equation 2, section 5.2)

$$\frac{\Delta}{\Delta x} x = 1$$

leads to the parallel rule

$$\frac{d}{dx} x = 1. \tag{2}$$

The reason for this can be seen from table 5.2b. Since the values of x and y are equal, the values of Δx and Δy are also equal. Then the ratio $\Delta y/\Delta x$ is always equal to 1 for every interval as long as Δx is not equal to 0. But as Δx approaches 0, the derivative remains equal to 1. Thus the limiting value of this derivative is equal to

$$\lim_{\Delta x \to 0} \frac{\Delta}{\Delta x} x = \frac{d}{dx} x = 1.$$

The rule (equation 3, section 5.2)

$$\frac{\Delta}{\Delta x} ku(x) = k \frac{\Delta}{\Delta x} u(x)$$

leads to the parallel rule

$$\frac{d}{dx} ku(x) = k \frac{d}{dx} u(x). \tag{3}$$

The reason for this can be seen from table 5.2c. It is demonstrated in that table that

$$\frac{\Delta}{\Delta x} ku(x) = k \frac{\Delta}{\Delta x} u(x).$$

As Δx approaches zero, Δu also approaches zero; but the limit of their ratio becomes

$$\lim_{\Delta x \to 0} \frac{\Delta u}{\Delta x} = \frac{du}{dx}.$$

Then the parallel rule becomes that given in equation (3).

The rule (equation 4, section 5.2)

$$\frac{\Delta}{\Delta x}[u(x) + v(x)] = \frac{\Delta}{\Delta x} u(x) + \frac{\Delta}{\Delta x} v(x)$$

leads to the parallel rule

$$\frac{d}{dx}[u(x) + v(x)] = \frac{d}{dx} u(x) + \frac{d}{dx} v(x). \tag{4}$$

As Δx approaches zero, both Δu and Δv approach zero and their rates of change become

$$\lim_{\Delta x \to 0} \frac{\Delta}{\Delta x} u(x) = \frac{d}{dx} u(x)$$

and

$$\lim_{\Delta x \to 0} \frac{\Delta}{\Delta x} v(x) = \frac{d}{dx} v(x).$$

Then the parallel rule becomes that given in equation (4).

The rule (equation 1, section 5.3)

$$\frac{\Delta}{\Delta x}(uv) = u\frac{\Delta v}{\Delta x} + (v + \Delta v)\frac{\Delta u}{\Delta x}$$

leads to the parallel rule

$$\frac{d}{dx}(uv) = u\frac{dv}{dx} + v\frac{du}{dx}. \tag{5}$$

As Δx approaches zero, Δv also approaches zero and the rates of change become

$$\underset{\Delta x \to 0}{\text{limit}} \ \frac{\Delta u}{\Delta x} = \frac{du}{dx}$$

and

$$\underset{\Delta x \to 0}{\text{limit}} \ \frac{\Delta v}{\Delta x} = \frac{dv}{dx}.$$

Thus the parallel rule is obtained.

The rule (equation 6, section 5.4)

$$\frac{\Delta}{\Delta x}x^n = n(\bar{x})^{n-1} + g(x)(\Delta x)^2$$

leads to the parallel rule

$$\frac{d}{dx}x^n = nx^{n-1}. \tag{6}$$

The reason for this can be seen from the fact that the mid-point of the ith interval is

$$\bar{x} = \frac{x_i + x_{i+1}}{2} = \frac{x + (x + \Delta x)}{2} = x + \frac{1}{2}\Delta x$$

whose limit is x, as Δx approaches zero. Furthermore, the quantity $g(x)(\Delta x)^2$ can be made as small as one wishes by using a small enough Δx. Thus its limit is zero, as Δx approaches zero. Combining the limits

$$\underset{\Delta x \to 0}{\text{limit}} \ \bar{x} = x$$

and

$$\underset{\Delta x \to 0}{\text{limit}} \ g(x)(\Delta x)^2 = 0,$$

one obtains the result given in equation (6).

Equation (6) can be generalized into

$$\frac{d}{dv}v^n = nv^{n-1}.$$

(7)

This is done by replacing the variable x with v which is a function of x.

The rule (equation 1, section 5.5)

$$\frac{\Delta}{\Delta x}\left(\frac{u}{v}\right) = \frac{v\dfrac{\Delta u}{\Delta x} - u\dfrac{\Delta v}{\Delta x}}{v(v + \Delta v)} \qquad v \neq 0$$

leads to the parallel rule

$$\frac{d}{dx}\left(\frac{u}{v}\right) = \frac{v\dfrac{du}{dx} - u\dfrac{dv}{dx}}{v^2} \qquad v \neq 0.$$

(8)

As Δx approaches zero, Δv also approaches zero and the rates of change become

$$\lim_{\Delta x \to 0} \frac{\Delta u}{\Delta x} = \frac{du}{dx}$$

and

$$\lim_{\Delta x \to 0} \frac{\Delta v}{\Delta x} = \frac{dv}{dx}.$$

Thus the parallel rule is obtained.

The rule (equation 1, section 5.6)

$$\frac{\Delta y}{\Delta x} = \frac{\Delta y}{\Delta u} \cdot \frac{\Delta u}{\Delta x},$$

leads to the parallel rule

$$\frac{dy}{dx} = \frac{dy}{du} \cdot \frac{du}{dx}.$$

(9)

This result comes from the fact that, as Δx approaches zero, both Δu and Δy approach zero and the limits of their ratios become

$$\lim_{\Delta x \to 0} \frac{\Delta y}{\Delta x} = \frac{dy}{dx}$$

$$\underset{\Delta x \to 0}{\text{limit}} \frac{\Delta y}{\Delta u} = \underset{\Delta u \to 0}{\text{limit}} \frac{\Delta y}{\Delta u} = \frac{dy}{du}$$

and

$$\underset{\Delta x \to 0}{\text{limit}} \frac{\Delta u}{\Delta x} = \frac{du}{dx}.$$

Thus the parallel rule is obtained.

The results given in the nine numbered-equations in this section summarize the rules of differentiation developed so far. They are used in differentiating the functions expressed in equations.

TABLE 6.2a

CONTRAST BETWEEN $\dfrac{\Delta y}{\Delta x}$ AND $\dfrac{dy}{dx}$ FOR $y = 3x^2 - 6x + 10$

x	y	Δx	Δy	$\bar{x}$	$\dfrac{\Delta y}{\Delta x}$	$\dfrac{dy}{dx}$
0.0	10.00					
		0.2	−1.08	0.1	−5.4	−5.4
0.2	8.92					
		0.2	−0.84	0.3	−4.2	−4.2
0.4	8.08					
		0.2	−0.60	0.5	−3.0	−3.0
0.6	7.48					
		0.2	−0.36	0.7	−1.8	−1.8
0.8	7.12					
		0.2	−0.12	0.9	−0.6	−0.6
1.0	7.00					
		0.2	0.12	1.1	0.6	0.6
1.2	7.12					
		0.2	0.36	1.3	1.8	1.8
1.4	7.48					
		0.2	0.60	1.5	3.0	3.0
1.6	8.08					
		0.2	0.84	1.7	4.2	4.2
1.8	8.92					
		0.2	1.08	1.9	5.4	5.4
2.0	10.00					

The fact that Δx approaches zero does not change the meaning of the derivative. In fact one can consider dy/dx as a special case of $\Delta y/\Delta x$. For some functions, the two versions of derivative are identical. In others, they are quite close when Δx is small. The kinship between dy/dx and $\Delta y/\Delta x$ is demonstrated numerically in tables 6.2a and 6.2b.

The second-degree polynomial

$$y = F(x) = 3x^2 - 6x + 10 \tag{10}$$

is used in table 6.2a to demonstrate that $\Delta y/\Delta x$ and dy/dx are identical regardless of the magnitude of Δx. The x-values in that table are arbitrarily chosen and the corresponding y-values are computed from the given function $F(x)$ such as

$$F(0.0) = 3(0.0)^2 - 6(0.0) + 10 = 10.00$$

and

$$F(0.2) = 3(0.2)^2 - 6(0.2) + 10 = 8.92 \,.$$

Then the derivative $\Delta y/\Delta x$ is obtained through the usual numerical process. Now, by the parallel rules, the limit of the derivative as Δx approaches zero is found to be

$$\frac{dy}{dx} = f(x) = 3(2)x^{2-1} - 6(1) + 0 = 6x - 6 \,.$$

Then this derivative is evaluated at the mid-points $\bar{x}$ such as

$$f(0.1) = 6(0.1) - 6 = -5.4$$

and

$$f(0.3) = 6(0.3) - 6 = -4.2$$

which are given in table 6.2a. These are the same values as $\Delta y/\Delta x$ which are obtained by the numerical process. However, the advantage of obtaining

$$\frac{dy}{dx} = f(x)$$

is that the derivative can be evaluated at any point and not necessarily at the mid-points of the intervals of x. In fact, all intervals of x disappeared because the interval x to $x + \Delta x$ becomes the point x when Δx approaches zero.

It is no coincidence that $\Delta y/\Delta x$ and dy/dx are identical for the function

$$y = 3x^2 - 6x + 10.$$

In fact, this is true for all the first-degree or the second-degree polynomials. From equation (1), one can see that the derivative of 10 is

$$\frac{\Delta}{\Delta x}10 = \frac{d}{dx}10 = 0.$$

From equations (2) and (3), one can see that the derivative of $-6x$ is

$$\frac{\Delta}{\Delta x}(-6x) = \frac{d}{dx}(-6x) = -6(1) = -6.$$

From equation (4) of section 5.3, one can see that the derivative of $3x^2$ is

$$\frac{\Delta}{\Delta x}3x^2 = 3(2\bar{x}) = 6\bar{x}.$$

But the limit of the derivative of the same function is (equation 6)

$$\frac{d}{dx}3x^2 = 3(2)x^{2-1} = 6x = 6\bar{x}$$

when the derivative is evaluated at the mid-points of the intervals of x. This is why the values of $\Delta y/\Delta x$ and those of dy/dx are identical at the mid-points as shown in the last two columns of table 6.2a.

The fact that $\Delta y/\Delta x$ is equal to dy/dx is true only for polynomials of the first or second degree. For any other kind of function, they are not equal but can be made as close as one wishes by choosing a small enough Δx. The function

$$y = F(x) = x^3 + 3x^2 - 6x + 10 \tag{11}$$

can be used as an illustration. The numerical differentiation of this function is given in table 6.2b. The x-values are arbitrarily chosen, and their corresponding y-values are computed from the given function $F(x)$ such as

TABLE 6.2b

CONTRAST BETWEEN $\dfrac{\Delta y}{\Delta x}$ AND $\dfrac{dy}{dx}$ FOR $y = x^3 + 3x^2 - 6x + 10$

x	y	Δx	Δy	$\bar{x}$	$\dfrac{\Delta y}{\Delta x}$	$\dfrac{dy}{dx}$
0.0	10.000					
		0.2	−1.072	0.1	−5.36	−5.37
0.2	8.928					
		0.2	−0.784	0.3	−3.92	−3.93
0.4	8.144					
		0.2	−0.448	0.5	−2.24	−2.25
0.6	7.696					
		0.2	−0.064	0.7	−0.32	−0.33
0.8	7.632					
		0.2	0.368	0.9	1.84	1.83
1.0	8.000					
		0.2	0.848	1.1	4.24	4.23
1.2	8.848					
		0.2	1.376	1.3	6.88	6.87
1.4	10.224					
		0.2	1.952	1.5	9.76	9.75
1.6	12.176					
		0.2	2.576	1.7	12.88	12.87
1.8	14.752					
		0.2	3.248	1.9	16.24	16.23
2.0	18.000					

$$F(0.0) = (0.0)^3 + 3(0.0)^2 - 6(0.0) + 10 = 10.000$$

and

$$F(0.2) = (0.2)^3 + 3(0.2)^2 - 6(0.2) + 10 = 8.928.$$

Then the differentiation is carried out by the numerical process, and the derivative thus obtained is labelled $\Delta y/\Delta x$ in table 6.2b. At the same time the given function $F(x)$ is differentiated through the parallel rules, and the derivative thus obtained is

$$\frac{dy}{dx} = f(x) = 3x^2 + 6x - 6.$$

Then this derivative is evaluated at the mid-point $\bar{x}$ of each interval of x such as

$$f(0.1) = 3(0.1)^2 + 6(0.1) - 6 = -5.37$$

and

$$f(0.3) = 3(0.3)^2 + 6(0.3) - 6 = -3.93.$$

These values of $f(x)$ are listed in the last column of table 6.2b and are labelled dy/dx. Comparison of the last two columns of that table reveals that the difference between the corresponding values of the two columns is

$$\frac{\Delta y}{\Delta x} - \frac{dy}{dx} = 0.01$$

for every interval of x.

The discrepancy between $\Delta y/\Delta x$ and dy/dx comes from the difference between (equation 4, section 5.4)

$$\frac{\Delta}{\Delta x}x^3 = 3(\bar{x})^2 + \frac{1}{4}(\Delta x)^2$$

and (equation 6)

$$\frac{d}{dx}x^3 = 3x^2.$$

When evaluated at the mid-points $\bar{x}$ of the intervals of x, the discrepancy is

$$\frac{\Delta y}{\Delta x} - \frac{dy}{dx} = \frac{1}{4}(\Delta x)^2 = \frac{1}{4}(0.2)^2 = 0.01$$

for the given example. The remaining three terms of the function

$$y = x^3 + 3x^2 - 6x + 10$$

contributed no discrepancy as shown in table 6.2a which lists the values of $\Delta y/\Delta x$ and dy/dx for the function

$$y = 3x^2 - 6x + 10.$$

The discrepancy between $\Delta y/\Delta x$ and dy/dx can be made as small as one wishes by using a small enough interval of x. For the given example, the discrepancy

$$\frac{\Delta y}{\Delta x} - \frac{dy}{dx} = \frac{1}{4}(\Delta x)^2$$

can be made equal to 0.0001 by using 0.02 as Δx, or equal to 0.000001 by using 0.002 as the length of the interval.

The formulas of differentiation developed in this section are listed below:

(1) $\quad \dfrac{d}{dx} C = 0$

(2) $\quad \dfrac{d}{dx} x = 1$

(3) $\quad \dfrac{d}{dx} ku = k\dfrac{d}{dx} u$

(4) $\quad \dfrac{d}{dx}(u + v) = \dfrac{d}{dx}u + \dfrac{d}{dx}v$

(5) $\quad \dfrac{d}{dx}(uv) = u\dfrac{dv}{dx} + v\dfrac{du}{dx}$

(6) $\quad \dfrac{d}{dx}x^n = nx^{n-1}$

(7) $\quad \dfrac{d}{dv}v^n = nv^{n-1}$

(8) $\quad \dfrac{d}{dx}\left(\dfrac{u}{v}\right) = \dfrac{v\dfrac{du}{dx} - u\dfrac{dv}{dx}}{v^2} \qquad v \neq 0$

(9) $\quad \dfrac{dy}{dx} = \dfrac{dy}{du} \cdot \dfrac{du}{dx}$

6.3 Successive Differentiation

A function of x may be repeatedly differentiated with respect to x. For example, the original function of x is

$$y = x^3 + 3x^2 - 6x + 10. \tag{1}$$

Differentiating y with respect to x, one obtains the derivative

$$y' = \frac{dy}{dx} = 3x^2 + 6x - 6. \tag{2}$$

Differentiating the above derivative with respect to x, one obtains

$$y'' = \frac{d}{dx}\left(\frac{dy}{dx}\right) = \frac{d^2y}{dx^2} = \frac{d}{dy}(3x^2 + 6x - 6) = 6x + 6. \quad (3)$$

This derivative of the derivative of y is called the *second derivative* of y. In contrast, the derivative of y given in equation (2) is called the *first derivative* of y.

A function can be differentiated beyond the second derivative. The derivative

$$y''' = \frac{d^3y}{dx^3} = \frac{d}{dx}(6x + 6) = 6 \quad (4)$$

of the second derivative is called the *third derivative* of y. The derivative

$$y^{(iv)} = \frac{d^4y}{dx^4} = \frac{d}{dx}6 = 0 \quad (5)$$

of the third derivative is called the *fourth derivative* of y. The above equation shows that all the derivatives of y of orders higher than 3 are equal to zero. The numerical demonstration of the successive differentiation is given in the tables of this section.

The first derivative of the function

$$y = x^3 + 3x^2 - 6x + 10$$

is given in table 6.2b. After this differentiation, the derivative, which consists of the two columns of figures labelled $\bar{x}$ and $\Delta y/\Delta x$, is reproduced in table 6.3a and the process of differentiation is carried out again. Since the function to be differentiated now is $\Delta y/\Delta x$, the increment of this function becomes

$$\Delta\left[\frac{\Delta y}{\Delta x}\right] = \frac{\Delta^2 y}{\Delta x} \quad (6)$$

and the derivative of this function becomes

$$\frac{\Delta}{\Delta x}\left[\frac{\Delta y}{\Delta x}\right] = \frac{\Delta^2 y}{(\Delta x)^2}. \quad (7)$$

The second derivative thus obtained is the same as that given in equation (3) as shown in the last two columns of table 6.3a. This is due to the fact that the first derivative

TABLE 6.3a

SECOND DERIVATIVE OF $y = x^3 + 3x^2 - 6x + 10$

x	$\dfrac{\Delta y}{\Delta x}$	Δx	$\Delta\left[\dfrac{\Delta y}{\Delta x}\right]$	$\bar{x}$	$\dfrac{\Delta}{\Delta x}\left[\dfrac{\Delta y}{\Delta x}\right]$	$\dfrac{d^2 y}{d x^2}$
0.1	− 5.36					
		0.2	1.44	0.2	7.2	7.2
0.3	− 3.92					
		0.2	1.68	0.4	8.4	8.4
0.5	− 2.24					
		0.2	1.92	0.6	9.6	9.6
0.7	− 0.32					
		0.2	2.16	0.8	10.8	10.8
0.9	1.84					
		0.2	2.40	1.0	12.0	12.0
1.1	4.24					
		0.2	2.64	1.2	13.2	13.2
1.3	6.88					
		0.2	2.88	1.4	14.4	14.4
1.5	9.76					
		0.2	3.12	1.6	15.6	15.6
1.7	12.88					
		0.2	3.36	1.8	16.8	16.8
1.9	16.24					

$$\frac{dy}{dx} = 3x^2 + 6x - 6$$

is a second-degree polynomial (section 6.2). Ordinarily, there is a discrepancy between the derivative obtained from the numerical process where Δx is a positive quantity and that obtained by formulas which give the limit of the derivative as Δx approaches zero.

Equation (7) introduces new symbols. The square which appears in the numerator has a different meaning than that appears in the denominator. The symbol $\Delta^2 y$ means that the operator Δ operates twice on y. To operate once, the symbol Δy means the difference between two values of y. To operate twice, the symbol $\Delta^2 y$ means the difference between two differences of y. However, the symbol $(\Delta x)^2$ in the denominator is simply the square of the quantity Δx. For this reason the symbol dx^2 in equation (3) should be $(dx)^2$, but traditionally the parentheses are omitted.

TABLE 6.3b

THIRD DERIVATIVE OF $y = x^3 + 3x^2 - 6x + 10$

x	$\dfrac{\Delta^2 y}{(\Delta x)^2}$	Δx	$\Delta\left[\dfrac{\Delta^2 y}{(\Delta x)^2}\right]$	$\bar{x}$	$\dfrac{\Delta}{\Delta x}\left[\dfrac{\Delta^2 y}{(\Delta x)^2}\right]$	$\dfrac{d^3 y}{dx^3}$
0.2	7.2					
		0.2	1.2	0.3	6	6
0.4	8.4					
		0.2	1.2	0.5	6	6
0.6	9.6					
		0.2	1.2	0.7	6	6
0.8	10.8					
		0.2	1.2	0.9	6	6
1.0	12.0					
		0.2	1.2	1.1	6	6
1.2	13.2					
		0.2	1.2	1.3	6	6
1.4	14.4					
		0.2	1.2	1.5	6	6
1.6	15.6					
		0.2	1.2	1.7	6	6
1.8	16.8					

The third derivative of the function

$$y = x^3 + 3x^2 - 6x + 10$$

is given in table 6.3b. The first two columns of that table are reproduced from the second derivative shown in table 6.3a. Then the differentiation is carried out in the usual way. However, the function to be differentiated now is the second derivative of y. The increment of this function is

$$\Delta\left[\frac{\Delta^2 y}{(\Delta x)^2}\right] = \frac{\Delta^3 y}{(\Delta x)^2} \tag{8}$$

and the derivative of this function becomes

$$\frac{\Delta}{\Delta x}\left[\frac{\Delta^2 y}{(\Delta x)^2}\right] = \frac{\Delta^3 y}{(\Delta x)^3}. \tag{9}$$

The third derivative thus obtained is the same as that given in equation (4) as shown in the last two columns of table 6.3b.

Equations (7) and (9) suggest that the successive differentiation can be carried out by finding the successive differences of y. The increment

$$\Delta y_i = y_{i+1} - y_i \tag{10}$$

is called the *first difference* of y. The increment

$$\Delta^2 y_i = \Delta y_{i+1} - \Delta y_i \tag{11}$$

which is an increment of Δy is called the *second difference* in y. Similarly, the increment

$$\Delta^3 y_i = \Delta^2 y_{i+1} - \Delta^2 y_i \tag{12}$$

which is an increment of $\Delta^2 y$ is called the *third difference* of y. Here, like differentiation, the process of finding the differences is repeated. The kth derivative of y is simply the sequence of the kth differences each divided by the kth power of Δx, provided that Δx is a constant through the whole range of x. This method has the advantage of shrinking k divisions by Δx into one division by $(\Delta x)^k$.

The numerical demonstration of successive differentiation through the successive differences is given in table 6.3c. The values of x and y are reproduced from table 6.2b. The first, second and third differences are given in columns 3, 4 and 5. The fourth differences which are omitted are obviously all zeros, because the third differences in column 5 are equal to the constant 0.048.

The derivatives can be obtained from these differences. The second derivative given in column 6 is obtained by dividing each number in column 4 by

$$(\Delta x)^2 = (0.2)^2 = 0.04,$$

and the third derivative given in column 7 is obtained by dividing each number in column 5 by

$$(\Delta x)^3 = (0.2)^3 = 0.008.$$

The second and third derivatives thus obtained are the same as those given in tables 6.3a and 6.3b.

TABLE 6.3c

SUCCESSIVE DIFFERENTIATION THROUGH DIFFERENCES

(1)	(2)	(3)	(4)	(5)	(6)	(7)
x	y	Δy	$\Delta^2 y$	$\Delta^3 y$	$\dfrac{\Delta^2 y}{(\Delta x)^2}$	$\dfrac{\Delta^3 y}{(\Delta x)^3}$
0.0	10.000					
0.1		−1.072				
0.2	8.928		0.288		7.2	
0.3		−0.784		0.048		6
0.4	8.144		0.336		8.4	
0.5		−0.448		0.048		6
0.6	7.696		0.384		9.6	
0.7		−0.064		0.048		6
0.8	7.632		0.432		10.8	
0.9		0.368		0.048		6
1.0	8.000		0.480		12.0	
1.1		0.848		0.048		6
1.2	8.848		0.528		13.2	
1.3		1.376		0.048		6
1.4	10.224		0.576		14.4	
1.5		1.952		0.048		6
1.6	12.176		0.624		15.6	
1.7		2.576		0.048		6
1.8	14.752		0.672		16.8	
1.9		3.248				
2.0	18.000					

Equations (10) and (11) suggest that the second derivative of y can be obtained directly from y, and the first derivative can be bypassed completely. For the interval x_i to x_{i+1}, the first difference of y is

$$\Delta y_i = y_{i+1} - y_i.$$

For the next interval which is bounded by x_{i+1} and x_{i+2}, the first difference is

$$\Delta y_{i+1} = y_{i+2} - y_{i+1}.$$

Then it follows that the second difference of y for these two intervals is

$$\begin{aligned}
\Delta^2 y_i &= \Delta y_{i+1} - \Delta y_i \\
&= (y_{i+2} - y_{i+1}) - (y_{i+1} - y_i) \\
&= y_i - 2y_{i+1} + y_{i+2}.
\end{aligned} \tag{13}$$

From the second differences thus computed, the second derivative can be found by dividing each of the differences by $(\Delta x)^2$.

TABLE 6.3d

SECOND DERIVATIVE DIRECTLY FROM y

(1)	(2)	(3)	(4)	(5)
i	x_i	y_i	$\Delta^2 y =$ $y_i - 2y_{i+1} + y_{i+2}$	$\dfrac{\Delta^2 y}{(\Delta x)^2}$
1	0.0	10.000		
2	0.2	8.928	0.288	7.2
3	0.4	8.144	0.336	8.4
4	0.6	7.696	0.384	9.6
5	0.8	7.632	0.432	10.8
6	1.0	8.000	0.480	12.0
7	1.2	8.848	0.528	13.2
8	1.4	10.224	0.576	14.4
9	1.6	12.176	0.624	15.6
10	1.8	14.752	0.672	16.8
11	2.0	18.000		

The numerical demonstration of this method of finding the second derivative is given in table 6.3d. The values of x and y are reproduced from table 6.2b. The second differences are computed from equation (13). For $i = 1$, the second difference is

$$\Delta^2 y_1 = y_1 - 2y_2 + y_3$$
$$= 10.000 - 2(8.928) + 8.144$$
$$= 0.288$$

which is listed against $x = 0.2$ which is the mid-point of the double interval 0.0 to 0.4. For $i = 2$, the second difference is

$$\Delta^2 y_2 = y_2 - 2y_3 + y_4$$
$$= 8.928 - 2(8.144) + 7.696$$
$$= 0.336$$

which is listed against $x = 0.4$ which is the mid-point of the double interval 0.2 to 0.6. This computation goes on until $i+2$ reaches m, the number of points. For the given example, m is equal to 11 and the number of second differences is 9 as shown in table 6.3d. Then each of these second differences is divided by

$$(\Delta x)^2 = (0.2)^2 = 0.04$$

to obtain the second derivative given in column 5 of that table. The result thus obtained is the same as that given in table 6.3a.

Equations (12) and (13) suggest that the third derivative of y can also be obtained directly from y. If the ith second-difference is

$$\Delta^2 y_i = y_i - 2y_{i+1} + y_{i+2},$$

the $(i+1)$st one must be

$$\Delta^2 y_{i+1} = y_{i+1} - 2y_{i+2} + y_{i+3}.$$

Then the corresponding third difference, being the difference between the two, is

$$\Delta^3 y_i = \Delta^2 y_{i+1} - \Delta^2 y_i$$
$$= (y_{i+1} - 2y_{i+2} + y_{i+3}) - (y_i - 2y_{i+1} + y_{i+2})$$
$$= -y_i + 3y_{i+1} - 3y_{i+2} + y_{i+3}. \tag{14}$$

From the third differences thus computed, the third derivative can be found by dividing each of the differences by $(\Delta x)^3$.

TABLE 6.3e

THIRD DERIVATIVE DIRECTLY FROM y

(1)	(2)	(3)	(4)	(5)	(6)
i	x_i	y_i	$3y_i$	$\Delta^3 y = -y_i + 3y_{i+1} - 3y_{i+2} + y_{i+3}$	$\dfrac{\Delta^3 y}{(\Delta x)^3}$
1	0.0	10.000	30.000		
	0.1				
2	0.2	8.928	26.784		
	0.3			0.048	6
3	0.4	8.144	24.432		
	0.5			0.048	6
4	0.6	7.696	23.088		
	0.7			0.048	6
5	0.8	7.632	22.896		
	0.9			0.048	6
6	1.0	8.000	24.000		
	1.1			0.048	6
7	1.2	8.848	26.544		
	1.3			0.048	6
8	1.4	10.224	30.672		
	1.5			0.048	6
9	1.6	12.176	36.528		
	1.7			0.048	6
10	1.8	14.752	44.256		
	1.9				
11	2.0	18.000	54.000		

The numerical demonstration of this method of finding the third derivative is given in table 6.3e. The values of x and y are reproduced from table 6.2b. The third differences are computed from equation (14). For $i = 1$, the third difference is

$$\begin{aligned}
\Delta^3 y_1 &= -y_1 + 3y_2 - 3y_3 + y_4 \\
&= -10.000 + 3(8.928) - 3(8.144) + 7.696 \\
&= 0.048
\end{aligned}$$

which is listed against $x = 0.3$ which is the mid-point of the triple interval from $x = 0.0$ to $x = 0.6$. For $i = 2$, the third difference is

$$\Delta^3 y_2 = -y_2 + 3y_3 - 3y_4 + y_5$$
$$= -8.928 + 3(8.144) - 3(7.696) + 7.632$$
$$= 0.048$$

which is listed against $x = 0.5$ which is the mid-point of the triple interval from $x = 0.2$ to $x = 0.8$. This computation goes on until $i+3$ reaches 11, the number of points given in the example. Then each of these third differences is divided by

$$(\Delta x)^3 = (0.2)^3 = 0.008$$

to obtain the third derivative given in column 6 of table 6.3e. The result thus obtained is the same as that given in table 6.3b.

6.4 Meaning of Derivatives

The first and second derivatives can be illustrated by the data of table 6.4. The x and y values are arbitrarily chosen, and the first and second derivatives are obtained by numerical differentiation. On this set of data, one can impose any physical meaning he wishes. For example, the independent variable x may be considered the number of hours of driving, and the dependent variable y the number of miles travelled. Columns 1 and 2 show the record of the trip such as the car was driven 22 miles in half of an hour, 46 miles in an hour, 66 miles in an hour and a half, and 81 miles in two hours. Column 3 shows that the record of mileage is kept at half-hour intervals. Column 4 shows the numbers of miles travelled during the four half-hour periods. Column 5 shows the average speeds at which the car was driven during the four periods. Column 6 shows the change in the average speed from period to period. The number 4 in that column indicates that the speed is increased from 44 miles an hour during the first period to 48 miles an hour in the second period. The number −8 in the same column indicates that the speed is dropped from 48 miles an hour to 40 miles an hour. The number −10 indicates that the speed is dropped by another 10 miles an hour from 40 to 30 miles an hour. All these changes in speed occurred in half-hour intervals. Column 7 converts these numbers, 4, −8 and −10, into hourly basis, and the resulting quantities

8, -16 and -20 miles per hour per hour constitute the second derivative. In this example, y is the distance in miles; the first derivative is the speed in miles per hour; and the second derivative is the acceleration in miles per hour per hour. The positive values of the first derivative given in column 5 show that the speed of the car is positive or, in plain language, the car is moving ahead. A zero value indicates that the car has stopped, and a negative value indicates that the car is moving in the opposite direction. However, the values for the second derivative given in column 7 have entirely different meaning. Here a positive value indicates that the car is picking up speed. A negative value indicates that the car is losing speed or slowing down. A zero value indicates that the car is being driven at a constant speed. Whether the second derivative is positive, negative or zero, the car may be moving ahead all the time.

TABLE 6.4

FIRST AND SECOND DERIVATIVES

(1)	(2)	(3)	(4)	(5)	(6)	(7)
x	y	Δx	Δy	$\dfrac{\Delta y}{\Delta x}$	$\Delta\left[\dfrac{\Delta y}{\Delta x}\right]$	$\dfrac{\Delta^2 y}{(\Delta x)^2}$
0.0	0					
		0.5	22	44		
0.5	22				4	8
		0.5	24	48		
1.0	46				-8	-16
		0.5	20	40		
1.5	66				-10	-20
		0.5	15	30		
2.0	81					

Another physical meaning may be imposed on the data of table 6.4. The independent variable x may be considered the number of years, and the dependent variable y the number of dollars saved. The data show that a man started from nothing in his savings account, but saved \$ 22 in half a year, \$ 46 in a year, \$ 66 in one and a half year, and $ 81 in two years. The quantity Δy is the amount saved in a six-month period. The first derivative is the annual rate of saving. If $ 22 is saved in six months, the rate is $ 44 per year. The second derivative indicates the change in the rate of saving. In this example, y is the amount saved in dollars; the first derivative is the rate of saving in dollars per year; and the second derivative is the rate of change of the rate of saving in dollars per year per year. The positive values of the first derivative indicate that the man is saving his money during the two-year period though not at a uniform rate. A positive value of the second derivative indicates that he is saving more money than the previous period, and a negative value indicates that he is saving less. But, fast or slow, he is accumulating his wealth.

All these examples are illustrations rather than applications of the derivatives. It is doubtful that anybody ever resorts to calculus to keep track of his savings account.

It is a common occurrence that the first derivative is positive and the second derivative is negative. If a teen-ager is still growing but does not grow so fast any more, it can be said that the first derivative of his height with respect to time is still positive but the second derivative is negative now. If the population of a country is still growing but becoming stabilized, it can be said that the first derivative of the number of people with respect to time is positive but the second derivative is negative.

6.5 Maximum and Minimum

To determine the maximum and minimum values of a function is one of the most important applications of differentiation. The whole process is illustrated by the data given in table 6.5a. The x-values in that table range from -0.25 to 3.25 with Δx equal to 0.25, and the corresponding y-values are computed from the equation

$$y = F(x) = 16x^3 - 72x^2 + 81x + 30 \tag{1}$$

whose graph is given in figure 6.5a.

TABLE 6.5a

MAXIMUM AND MINIMUM OF FUNCTION

Point No.	x	y	Δy	$\dfrac{\Delta y}{\Delta x}$	$\dfrac{\Delta^2 y}{\Delta x}$	$\dfrac{\Delta^2 y}{(\Delta x)^2}$
1	−0.25	5.0				
			25.0	100		
2	0.00	30.0			−36	−144
			16.0	64		
3	0.25	46.0			−30	−120
			8.5	34		
4	0.50	54.5			−24	− 96
			2.5	10		
5	0.75	57.0 (max.)			−18	− 72
			− 2.0	− 8		
6	1.00	55.0			−12	− 48
			− 5.0	− 20		
7	1.25	50.0			− 6	− 24
			− 6.5	− 26		
8	1.50	43.5			0	0
			− 6.5	− 26		
9	1.75	37.0			6	24
			− 5.0	− 20		
10	2.00	32.0			12	48
			− 2.0	− 8		
11	2.25	30.0 (min.)			18	72
			2.5	10		
12	2.50	32.5			24	96
			8.5	34		
13	2.75	41.0			30	120
			16.0	64		
14	3.00	57.0			36	144
			25.0	100		
15	3.25	82.0				

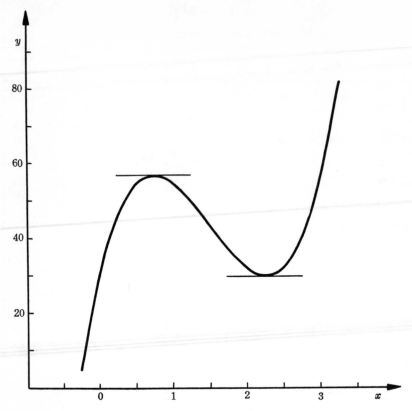

Fɪɢ. 6.5a.   Graph of $y = 16x^3 - 72x^2 + 81x + 30$.

Examination of table 6.5a shows that the smallest value of y is 5.0 of point no. 1 and the largest is 82.0 of point no. 15.   However, the value 5.0 is not called the minimum value of y and neither is 82.0 the maximum.   Instead, the value 57.0 of point no. 5 is called a maximum value of y, and 30.0 of point no. 11 is called a minimum.

A *maximum* is a value of y which is the greatest in its immediate neighborhood.   It is a sort of big fish in a small pond.   The value 57.0 of point no. 5 is greater than both of its neighboring values 54.5 of point no. 4 and 55.0 of point no. 6.   Then the y-value 57.0 located at $x = 0.75$ is called a maximum value of the function of x, even though there are larger y-values elsewhere.   Furthermore, the same value 57.0 of point no. 14 is not considered a maximum of y because it is less than its neighboring value 82.0 of point no. 15. By this definition, it is entirely possible that a function of x may have several maximum values even though only one exists in the given example. Symbolically, a maximum of

$$y = F(x)$$

is defined as the value $F(x_0)$ if

$$F(x_0 - \Delta x) < F(x_0) > F(x_0 + \Delta x)$$

with Δx being an infinitesimal quantity.

The presence of a maximum in y is indicated by the change of sign in the derivative of y. This can be observed from table 6.5a and figure 6.5a. Before the function reaches its maximum, the value of y increases with x and the derivative of y is positive. After the function passes the maximum, the value of y decreases with x and the derivative of y is negative. While the derivative of y changes its sign from positive to negative, it must be momentarily equal to zero when y arrives at its maximum. For this reason, one can differentiate the given function (equation 1)

$$y = F(x) = 16x^3 - 72x^2 + 81x + 30$$

and obtain the derivative

$$\frac{dy}{dx} = f(x) = 48x^2 - 144x + 81 \qquad (2)$$

and determine the value of x that can make this derivative equal to zero and at the same time make y a maximum. To do so, one can set the derivative equal to 0 and solve the equation

$$f(x) = 48x^2 - 144x + 81 = 0.$$

The roots 0.75 and 2.25, which are called *critical values*, are the possible sites where a maximum in y may occur. Upon investigating the neighborhood of $x = 0.75$, one finds that

$$F(0.75) = 16(0.75)^3 - 72(0.75)^2 + 81(0.75) + 30 = 57.000000$$

is greater than its neighboring values

$$F(0.74) = 16(0.74)^3 - 72(0.74)^2 + 81(0.74) + 30 = 56.996384$$

and

$$F(0.76) = 16(0.76)^3 - 72(0.76)^2 + 81(0.76) + 30 = 56.996416.$$

This establishes $y = 57.0$, located at $x = 0.75$, as a maximum value of $F(x)$. The other critical value $x = 2.25$, which yields a minimum in y, is to be investigated later.

A maximum in y can also be established by the second derivative being negative at the critical value of x. At point no. 5 of table 6.5a where a maximum in y occurs, the derivative which changes from positive to negative is decreasing with x. So the second derivative must be negative at that point. For the given example, the second derivative of y with respect to x is

$$\frac{d^2y}{dx^2} = s(x) = 96x - 144 \tag{3}$$

which is obtained by differentiating the first derivative given in equation (2). At the critical value $x = 0.75$, the second derivative is

$$s(0.75) = 96(0.75) - 144 = -72$$

which is the same value given in table 6.5a. This negative value of the second derivative at the critical value $x = 0.75$ establishes

$$F(0.75) = 57.0$$

as a maximum in y or $F(x)$.

All the characteristics of a maximum in y are shown in table 6.5a. The y-value 57.0 located at $x = 0.75$ is greater than its neighboring values on both sides. The first derivative of y changes sign from positive to negative at the same location. Furthermore, the second derivative is negative at the critical value $x = 0.75$.

A minimum in y is established in a similar fashion. A minimum is the least value of y in its immediate neighborhood. By this definition, the y-value 30.0 located at $x = 2.25$ of point no. 11 in table 6.5a is a minimum because it is smaller than both of its neighboring values 32.0 and 32.5.

The characteristics of a minimum in y are also shown in table 6.5a. The y-value 30.0 located at $x = 2.25$ is less than its neighboring values on both sides. The first derivative of y changes sign from negative to positive at the critical value $x = 2.25$. In addition, the second derivative

$$s(2.25) = 96(2.25) - 144 = 72$$

is positive at the same location.

The zeros of the first derivative are only the possible sites of maxima and minima. There is no assurance that a maximum or minimum will occur at any one of the critical values unless further investigations are made. A negative second derivative at a critical value establishes that a maximum in y occurs there, and a positive second derivative establishes a minimum. If the second derivative is zero, which is neither negative nor positive, no maximum or minimum occurs at the critical value of x.

TABLE 6.5b

FIRST AND SECOND DERIVATIVES OF $y = x^3$

x	y	Δy	$\dfrac{\Delta y}{\Delta x}$	$\Delta\left[\dfrac{\Delta y}{\Delta x}\right]$	$\dfrac{\Delta^2 y}{(\Delta x)^2}$
−2.0	−8.000				
		4.625	9.25		
−1.5	−3.375			−4.5	−18
		2.375	4.75		
−1.0	−1.000			−3.0	−12
		0.875	1.75		
−0.5	−0.125			−1.5	− 6
		0.125	0.25		
0.0	0.000			0.0	0
		0.125	0.25		
0.5	0.125			1.5	6
		0.875	1.75		
1.0	1.000			3.0	12
		2.375	4.75		
1.5	3.375			4.5	18
		4.625	9.25		
2.0	8.000				

The function

$$y = F(x) = x^3$$

is used to illustrate this point. To find the critical values, one differentiates the function and sets the derivative

$$\frac{dy}{dx} = f(x) = 3x^2$$

equal to zero. The root of the equation

$$f(x) = 3x^2 = 0$$

is

$$x = 0$$

which is the only critical value. At this point, the second derivative

$$\frac{d^2y}{dx^2} = s(x) = 6x$$

is also equal to zero. So at the critical value $x = 0$, the first derivative is equal to zero but no maximum or minimum occurs.

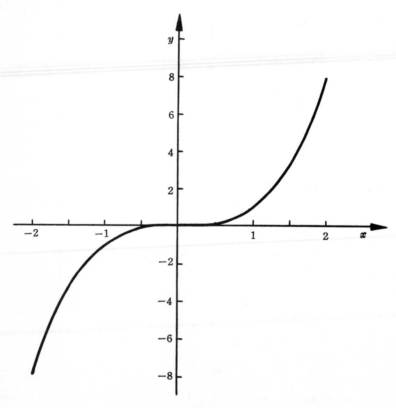

Fig. 6.5b. Graph of $y = x^3$.

This situation is demonstrated in table 6.5b. The y-values in that table steadily increase with x. There is neither a maximum or a minimum. This is demonstrated by the positive values of the first derivative. The rate of change decreases with x at first, but it picks up again after it dips to zero at the critical value $x = 0$. Furthermore, the second derivative is neither negative nor positive but equal to zero at the same point. The conditions for a maximum or a minimum in y are simply not there. The same situation can also be observed in figure 6.5b which shows the graph of $y = x^3$.

Now the procedure of determining the maximum and minimum values in the function

$$y = F(x)$$

can be summarized as follows: Differentiate the function $F(x)$ and set the first derivative

$$\frac{dy}{dx} = f(x)$$

equal to zero. The real roots of the equation

$$f(x) = 0$$

are the critical values. Then differentiate the first derivative $f(x)$ to obtain the second derivative

$$\frac{d^2y}{dx^2} = s(x).$$

A negative value of the second derivative at a critical value indicates that y has a maximum at that point, and a positive value indicates a minimum. In other words, the conditions for $F(x_0)$ to be a maximum are

$$f(x_0) = 0$$

and

$$s(x_0) < 0,$$

and those for $F(x_0)$ to be a minimum are

$$f(x_0) = 0$$

and

$$s(x_0) > 0.$$

However, for most practical problems, the second derivative of y and the comparison of $F(x_0)$ with its surrounding values of $F(x)$ are usually not necessary. This is due to the fact that in such cases one knows in advance what he is seeking. It is simply a matter of determining the critical values.

The procedure of determining the maximum and minimum values of a function summarized above is applicable only when the function is given in the form of an equation. If it is given in the from of two columns of figures, the procedure is quite simple. All one has to do is examine the data and locate the maximum and minimum values. If the volume of data is huge and the job is done on a computer, one only need find Δy for each interval and see where the sign of Δy changes. A change in sign of Δy from positive to negative indicates the presence of a maximum, and a change from negative to positive indicates a minimum. This can be observed in table 6.5a.

6.6 Examples of Maximum and Minimum

An example of the determination of the maximum value of a function is used here to illustrate the process of translating a practical situation into mathematical language. Suppose the perimeter of a rectangle is fixed at 10 feet. The problem is to determine the maximum area that can be enclosed by such a rectangle. In analyzing the problem one may construct a few rectangles with various

TABLE 6.6a

AREA OF RECTANGLE WITH FIXED PERIMETER

Length x	Width w	Perimeter p	Area a	$\dfrac{\Delta a}{\Delta x}$	$\dfrac{\Delta^2 a}{(\Delta x)^2}$
1	4	10	4		
				2	
2	3	10	6		-2
				0	
3	2	10	6		-2
				-2	
4	1	10	4		

dimensions but with a fixed perimeter of 10 feet. Four of these attempts are given in table 6.6a. The length of the rectangle is x feet, and the width is w feet. For each rectangle the perimeter is

$$p = 2x + 2w = 10 \tag{1}$$

feet, and the area is

$$a = xw \tag{2}$$

square feet. Judging from the pattern of the values of the area a, one can surmise that the maximum area occurs at $x = 2.5$. At this point, the rectangle becomes a square and its area is

$$a = xw = (2.5)(2.5) = 6.25.$$

To confirm the notion that 6.25 is the maximum area, one can investigate the area a in the neighborhood of $x = 2.5$. At $x = 2.49$, the area is

$$a = xw = (2.49)(2.51) = 6.2499;$$

and at $x = 2.51$, the area is

$$a = xw = (2.51)(2.49) = 6.2499.$$

Both of these values are less than 6.25. This establishes the fact that 6.25 square feet is the maximum area that can be enclosed by a rectangle with a perimeter of 10 feet.

The same problem can be readily solved through the formulas of differentiation. From equation (1), it can be seen that

$$x + w = 5$$

or

$$w = 5 - x.$$

Then it follows from equation (2) that the area of the rectangle is

$$a = xw = x(5 - x) = 5x - x^2.$$

Differentiating a with respect to x, one obtains the first derivative

$$\frac{da}{dx} = 5 - 2x.$$

Setting the derivative equal to zero and solving the equation

$$5 - 2x = 0,$$

one obtains the critical value

$$x = 2.5.$$

At this point or anywhere else, the second derivative

$$\frac{d^2a}{da^2} = -2$$

is negative. This establishes the fact that the maximum in a occurs at $x = 2.5$. At this point, the area is

$$a = 5x - x^2 = 5(2.5) - (2.5)^2 = 6.25.$$

The answer thus obtained is still the same. The maximum area that can be enclosed in a rectangle with a perimeter of 10 feet is 6.25 square feet.

When the above example is turned around, a problem of determination of the minimum value of a function results. The problem now is to determine the shortest possible perimeter of a rectangle to enclose an area of 6.25 square feet. In this problem, the area

$$a = xw = 6.25 \tag{3}$$

is a constant, and the perimeter

$$p = 2x + 2w \tag{4}$$

becomes a function of x. Now the problem is to determine the value of x which can make p a minimum.

The numerical attempt to solve this problem is given in table 6.6b. The numbers 1, 2, 3 and 4 are assigned to the length x, and the corresponding value of the width w is computed from the equation

$$w = \frac{6.25}{x} \tag{5}$$

so that the area xw is equal to the constant 6.25. The pattern of the values of p and its first and second derivatives in the upper half of table 6.6b suggests that a minimum in p occurs somewhere between $x = 2$ and $x = 3$. To further investigate the problem, the effort is concentrated in this interval and the Δx is reduced from 1.0 to 0.2 as shown in the lower half of table 6.6b. The result suggests that the minimum in p occurs somewhere between $x = 2.4$ to $x = 2.6$. Of course, this narrower interval can be further investigated with a reduced Δx until the minimum in p is obtained. However, the numerical process is stopped here and the formulas of differentiation are given a chance to solve the problem.

TABLE 6.6b

PERIMETER OF RECTANGLE WITH FIXED AREA

Length x	Width w	Area a	Perimeter p	$\dfrac{\Delta p}{\Delta x}$	$\dfrac{\Delta^2 p}{(\Delta x)^2}$
1	6.2500	6.25	14.5000		
				−4.2500	
2	3.1250	6.25	10.2500		4.1667
				−0.0833	
3	2.0833	6.25	10.1667		1.0416
				0.9583	
4	1.5625	6.25	11.1250		
2.2	2.8409	6.25	10.0818		
				−0.3670	
2.4	2.6042	6.25	10.0084		1.8150
				−0.0040	
2.6	2.4038	6.25	10.0076		1.4350
				0.2830	
2.8	2.2321	6.25	10.0642		

To use the formulas, the perimeter p has to be expressed as a function of the length x. However, this is easily done. From equations (4) and (5) it can be determined that the function is

$$p = 2x + \frac{12.5}{x}. \tag{6}$$

To determine the critical values, the above function has to be differentiated. The first derivative of the first term is simply 2, and the second term may be differentiated as the quotient

$$\frac{12.5}{x} = \frac{u}{v}$$

whose derivative is (equation 8, section 6.2)

$$\frac{d}{dx}\left[\frac{12.5}{x}\right] = \frac{x(0) - 12.5(1)}{x^2} = \frac{-12.5}{x^2}.$$

Then the first derivative of p with respect to x is

$$\frac{dp}{dx} = 2 - \frac{12.5}{x^2}. \tag{7}$$

Setting the derivative equal to zero and solving the equation

$$2x^2 - 12.5 = 0$$

or

$$x^2 = 6.25,$$

one obtains the critical values $x = -2.5$ and $x = 2.5$. But the value -2.5 is useless, because the length x of a rectangle cannot be negative. The only critical value worth investigating is $x = 2.5$.

To determine whether a minimum occurs at $x = 2.5$, the first derivative given in equation (7) has to be differentiated. The derivative of the first term is zero, and the second term may be differentiated as the quotient

$$\frac{-12.5}{x^2} = \frac{u}{v}$$

whose derivative is

$$\frac{d}{dx}\left[\frac{-12.5}{x^2}\right] = \frac{x^2(0) - (-12.5)(2x)}{x^4} = \frac{25}{x^3}.$$

Then the second derivative of p with respect to x is

$$\frac{d^2p}{dx^2} = \frac{25}{x^3}$$

which, at the critical value $x = 2.5$, is equal to the positive value 1.6. This establishes the fact that the perimeter is a minimum when the length is 2.5 feet and the width is also

$$w = \frac{6.25}{2.5} = 2.5$$

feet. At this length and width, the minimum perimeter is

$$p = 2x + 2w = 2(2.5) + 2(2.5) = 10$$

feet. So the answer to the original question is that the shortest possible perimeter of a rectangle which encloses 6.25 square feet is 10 feet.

A problem of *least squares* may be used to illustrate the fact that the second derivative is not always necessary in determining a maximum or a minimum of a function. Three values 1, 2 and 9 are given. The problem is to determine the value of m so that the function

$$u(m) = (1 - m)^2 + (2 - m)^2 + (9 - m)^2$$

is a minimum. The name *least squares* for this type of problem comes from the fact the function $u(m)$, which is a sum of squares, is to be minimized.

In solving this problem, one has to find the critical value. Differentiating u with respect to m, one obtains

$$\frac{du}{dm} = 2(1 - m)(-1) + 2(2 - m)(-1) + 2(9 - m)(-1).$$

Setting the derivative equal to 0 and solving the equation

$$(-1)(2)[(1 - m) + (2 - m) + (9 - m)] = 0$$

or

$$1 + 2 + 9 - 3m = 0,$$

one obtains the critical value

$$m = 4.$$

The answer is that $u(m)$ is a minimum when m is equal to 4.

From the nature of the problem, one can tell that $u(m)$ cannot have a maximum. The value of the function can be made as large as one wishes by placing m far enough away from the given values 1, 2 and 9. At the same time, $u(m)$ must have a minimum because either a small m such as $-1,000$ or a large m such as 1,000 can make $u(m)$ large. Only a value close to the three given values can make $u(m)$ small. The problem is to determine that value of m which is close to the given values 1, 2 and 9. Thus the determination of the critical value is sufficient for this type of problem. A subsequent test of the critical value, such as the second derivative, is not necessary.

However, one may still find the second derivative. The operation will not hurt anything. On the contrary, it will confirm that $m = 4$ will minimize the function $u(m)$. Differentiating the first derivative of u with respect to m, one obtains the second derivative

$$\frac{d^2u}{dm^2} = 2(-1)(-1) + 2(-1)(-1) + 2(-1)(-1) = 6.$$

The positive value 6 shows that $u(m)$ has a minimum at $m = 4$.

One may also compare $u(4)$ with its surrounding values of $u(m)$ to establish that $u(4)$ is a minimum, even though this operation is not necessary. The values

$$u(3.9) = (1-3.9)^2 + (2-3.9)^2 + (9-3.9)^2 = 38.03$$

$$u(4.0) = (1-4.0)^2 + (2-4.0)^2 + (9-4.0)^2 = 38.00$$

$$u(4.1) = (1-4.1)^2 + (2-4.1)^2 + (9-4.1)^2 = 38.03$$

do show that $u(m)$ has a minimum at $m = 4$.

To generalize the problem of least squares, the given values may be designated by

$$x_1 \quad x_2 \quad \cdots \quad x_n$$

which are constants and not variables. Then the function to be minimized becomes

$$u(m) = \sum_{i=1}^{n}(x_i - m)^2 = (x_1 - m)^2 + (x_2 - m)^2 + \cdots + (x_n - m)^2$$

which is a function of m and not of x. Differentiating u with respect to m, one obtains

$$\frac{du}{dm} = 2(x_1 - m)(-1) + 2(x_2 - m)(-1) + \cdots + 2(x_n - m)(-1)$$

$$= -2 \sum_{i=1}^{n}(x_i - m).$$

Setting the derivative equal to 0 and solving the equation

$$\sum_{i=1}^{n}(x_i - m) = (x_1 - m) + (x_2 - m) + \cdots + (x_n - m) = 0$$

or

$$x_1 + x_2 + \cdots + x_n - nm = 0,$$

one obtains the critical value

$$m = \frac{x_1 + x_2 + \cdots + x_n}{n} = \frac{1}{n}\sum_{i=1}^{n} x_i$$

which minimizes the function $u(m)$. In plain language, the solution says that the sum of the squares of the deviations of the n given values from m is a minimum when m is equal to the average of the n given values. When the given values are 1, 2 and 9, the value of m which minimizes $u(m)$ must be their average 4.

6.7 Related Rates

Another example of application of differentiation is the *related rates*. In this type of problem, y is a function of x. At the same time both variables x and y are functions of a third variable t which represents time. From the known rate of change of x with respect to t, that of y with respect to t can be determined from the relation

$$\frac{dy}{dt} = \frac{dy}{dx} \cdot \frac{dx}{dt} \tag{1}$$

which is equation (9) of section 6.2 with x in that equation replaced by t, and u by x.

As an illustration, one may consider a square whose area is represented by y and whose side by x. If the side x is expanding at 0.2 inch an hour when it is 100 inches long, what is the rate of expansion of the area y of the square at that time? The numerical solution of this problem is given in table 6.7a. Two arbitrary values

TABLE 6.7a

RATE OF EXPANSION OF AREA OF SQUARE

Time	Side	Area	Mid-point	Rate of Side	Rate of Area
t	x	$y = x^2$	$\bar{x}$	$\dfrac{\Delta x}{\Delta t}$	$\dfrac{\Delta y}{\Delta t}$
Hour	inches	sq. in.	inches	in./hr.	sq. in./hr.
0	99.9	9,980.01			
			100	0.2	40
1	100.1	10,020.01			

0 and 1 are assigned to the time t. The advantage of using these two values is that Δt is equal to 1 which simplifies future divisions by Δt. After the values of t are fixed, the values of x are automatically determined by the given conditions. The value of Δx is determined by the condition

$$\frac{\Delta x}{\Delta t} = \frac{\Delta x}{1} = 0.2 .$$

To satisfy the additional condition that the side is 100 inches long, the x-values have to be

$$100 - \frac{1}{2}\Delta x = 99.9$$

and

$$100 + \frac{1}{2}\Delta x = 100.1$$

so that the mid-point of the interval is 100 as specified. Then, from these values of x, the corresponding areas y can be computed. The difference between these two values of y is the rate of change of the area of the square with respect to time, because Δt is equal to 1. The result of table 6.7a says that, when the side of a square is 100 inches long and expanding at the rate of 0.2 inch an hour, the area of that square is expanding at 40 square inches an hour.

Now the formulas of differentiation are used in solving the same problem. The area of the square is

$$y = x^2 \tag{2}$$

where x is the length of the side. Differentiating y with respect to x, one obtains the derivative

$$\frac{dy}{dx} = 2x . \tag{3}$$

Then, from equation (1), it can be established that

$$\frac{dy}{dt} = 2x\frac{dx}{dt} \tag{4}$$

which is the relation between the two rates of change. With the aid of the given conditions

$$\frac{dx}{dt} = 0.2$$

and

$$x = 100,$$

the rate of change of the area of the square with respect to time can be determined as

$$\frac{dy}{dt} = 2(100)(0.2) = 40$$

square inches an hour. This is the same answer given in table 6.7a.

Ordinarily, there is a discrepancy between the result obtained from the numerical process and that obtained through the formulas which yield the limit of the derivative as Δx approaches zero. But in this example where the function involved is

$$y = x^2,$$

the results obtained are always the same no matter how large is Δx. The reason for this is given in section 6.2.

To demonstrate the discrepancy between the two methods, the example may be changed from the area of a square to the volume of a cube. Now the problem is to determine the rate of expansion of the volume V of a cube when its side x is 100 feet long and expanding at the rate of 0.2 inch an hour. The numerical solution is given in table 6.7b which is similar to table 6.7a except that the area

$$y = x^2$$

is changed to the volume

$$V = x^3.$$

The difference between the two values of V is the required rate, because Δt is equal to 1. So the answer is that the volume of a cube is expanding at the rate of 6,000.002 cubic inches an hour when its side is 100 inches long and expanding at 0.2 inch an hour as shown in table 6.7b.

TABLE 6.7b

RATE OF EXPANSION OF VOLUME OF CUBE WITH HOURLY INTERVAL

Time	Side	Volume	Mid-point	Rate of Side	Rate of Vol.
t	x	$V = x^3$	$\bar{x}$	$\dfrac{\Delta x}{\Delta t}$	$\dfrac{\Delta V}{\Delta t}$
hour	inches	cubic inches	inches	in./hr.	cu. in./hr.
0	99.9	997,002.999			
			100	0.2	6,000.002
1	100.1	1,003,003.001			

Through the formulas of differentiation, the required rate can be expressed as

$$\frac{dV}{dt} = \frac{dV}{dx} \cdot \frac{dx}{dt} = 3x^2 \frac{dx}{dt}$$

which is equal to

$$\frac{dV}{dt} = 3(100)^2(0.2) = 6,000$$

under the given conditions. So the answer by this method is that the volume of a cube is expanding at the rate of 6,000 cubic inches an hour when its side is 100 inches long and expanding at 0.2 inch an hour.

The discrepancy of

$$6,000.002 - 6,000 = 0.002$$

between the two results can be predicted from the equation (equation 4, section 5.4)

$$\frac{\Delta}{\Delta x} x^3 = 3(\bar{x})^2 + \frac{1}{4}(\Delta x)^2.$$

The difference

$$\frac{\Delta}{\Delta x} x^3 - \frac{d}{dx} x^3 = \frac{1}{4}(\Delta x)^2$$

at the point $x = \bar{x}$ is the cause of the discrepancy between the results. When this difference is multiplied by the rate of change of x with respect to t, the result is the discrepancy

$$\frac{1}{4}(\Delta x)^2 \frac{\Delta x}{\Delta t} = \frac{1}{4}(0.2)^2(0.2) = 0.002.$$

This example demonstrates the fact that the solutions to a problem obtained through $\Delta y/\Delta x$ and dy/dx are remarkable close if Δx is small. If the discrepancy 0.002 is considered too large, one may use a smaller Δt. Table 6.7c shows that the discrepancy is reduced to 0.00002 when Δt is reduced to 0.1. Therefore, for all practical purposes dy/dx may be regarded as $\Delta y/\Delta x$ with Δx being a small but positive quantity.

TABLE 6.7c

RATE OF EXPANSION OF VOLUME OF CUBE WITH 0.1-HOUR INTERVAL

Time	Side	Volume	Mid-point	Rate of Side	Rate of Vol.
t	x	$V = x^3$	$\bar{x}$	$\dfrac{\Delta x}{\Delta t}$	$\dfrac{\Delta V}{\Delta t}$
hour	inches	cubic inches	inches	in./hr.	cu. in./hr.
0.0	99.99	999,700.029999			
			100	0.2	6,000.00002
0.1	100.01	1,000,300.030001			

6.8 Remarks

This section consists of nothing but the author's opinion and speculation. The reader may skip it completely, if he is not interested in such things.

It is demonstrated in the preceding section and elsewhere that the solutions to a problem obtained through $\Delta y/\Delta x$ and dy/dx are usually different. The natural question to ask is: which one is right and which one is wrong. The discrepancy between the solutions is frequently referred to as the error. If it is an error, on whose part is it? This is indeed a philosophical question.

The discrepancy or error stems from the difference between the real world and the mathematicians' dream world—dream is used here in the very best sense of the word. In a geometry class, a student is taught that a line has no width. Of course, such a line is invisible. However, when a student takes his teacher seriously and turns in his homework with an invisible graph or a blank sheet of paper, his teacher undoubtedly will not accept it. By this time, the teacher has come back to the real world where a line does have a width however narrow. This illustrates the difference between

$\Delta y/\Delta x$ and dy/dx. In the real world, the derivative is $\Delta y/\Delta x$; and in the dream world, it is dy/dx. People in the real world may consider dy/dx as an oversimplification of a real situation. On the other hand, people in the dream world are likely to consider $\Delta y/\Delta x$ as a crude approximation of the ideal—an ideal which exists only in one's mind.

The author's intention of presenting $\Delta y/\Delta x$ and dy/dx side by side is to constantly remind the reader of the physical meaning of the derivative. In this fashion, the new operation of differentiation is explained in terms of the four familiar operations of arithmetic. With the understanding of the meaning of differentiation, perhaps the reader can make use of the formulas which yield dy/dx. The handling of Δx has become a special branch of mathematics which is called numerical calculus.

Even though $\Delta y/\Delta x$ is used as a teaching device in this text, the method has become fashionable and practical since the invention of digital computers. When such a tool is used in carrying out a differentiation, the job is done in a numerical process and the derivative obtained is $\Delta y/\Delta x$ and not dy/dx. A computer does not take a sheet of paper marked with x^2 and return it with an additional marking of $2x$. The only machine that can do this is the kind which walks on two legs.

In a way, a student who takes a course in calculus is being made a coding machine. In order to be proficient with differentiation, one must not only remember formulas but he also needs a lot of drill so that the operation can eventually be carried out by reflex. Unfortunately, by the time a college freshman or sophomore has acquired such proficiency, it is more often than not that the meaning of the derivative has long been forgotten. When this happens, his ability of applying differentiation becomes limited only to the textbook problems. This is indeed a dilemma. How calculus should be taught is a problem that has not been extensively investigated. There are many speculations but very little experimental evidence to back them up.

EXERCISES

1. Demonstrate numerically (table 6.1d) that the instantaneous rate

of change of $4x^2$ is equal to 80 at the point $x = 10$. Let Δx be 0.1, 0.01, 0.001 and 0.0001 in the numerical demonstration.

2. Differentiate the function

$$y = (x + 3)^2$$

numerically for the interval $x = 1$ to $x = 2$ with Δx equal to 0.2. Then differentiate the same function by formula and find the instantaneous rates of change of y at the six mid-points. Check if the results obtained by the two methods are the same.

3. Repeat exercise 2 with the function

$$y = (x + 3)^3,$$

and see if the results obtained by the two methods are the same. If not, what is the discrepancy?

4. (a) Find numerically the first and second derivatives of the function

$$y = 4x^2 + 6$$

for the interval $x = 10$ to $x = 20$ with Δx equal to 2. Tabulate your computation as shown in tables 6.2b and 6.3a.

(b) Find the second derivative directly from the values of y as shown in table 6.3d.

(c) Find the first and second derivatives by formula and evaluate them at the mid-points. Check and see if the results obtained by all these methods are the same.

5. Find the maximum or minimum value of the function

$$y = x^2.$$

Then demonstrate the characteristics of the maximum or minimum numerically (table 6.5a) for the interval $x = -2$ to $x = 2$ with Δx equal to 0.5.

6. Repeat exercise 5 with the function $y = x^4$.

7. Repeat exercise 5 with the function $y = 4 - x^2$.

8. Find the maximum and minimum values of the function

$$y = 4x^3 - 18x^2 + 15x + 100.$$

Then demonstrate the characteristics of the maximum and minimum numerically (table 6.5a) for the interval $x = 0$ to $x = 3$ with Δx equal to 0.2.

9. Differentiate the following functions by formula, and find the instantaneous rates of change at the point $x = 10$:

$$(\,a\,)\quad y = 3$$

$$(\,b\,)\quad y = 5x$$

$$(\,c\,)\quad y = 7x^2$$

$$(\,d\,)\quad y = 9x^3$$

$$(\,e\,)\quad y = 2x^4 + 4x^2 + 6x + 8$$

$$(\,f\,)\quad y = (x^2 + 1)(x^3 + 5)$$

$$(\,g\,)\quad y = \frac{1}{x^3}$$

$$(\,h\,)\quad y = \frac{x^2}{x^3 + 1}$$

$$(\,i\,)\quad y = \frac{x}{x^2 + 6}$$

$$(\,j\,)\quad y = \frac{x^3}{5x^4 + 8}$$

10. Find the minimum value of the function

$$y = 100\left(\frac{1}{a} + \frac{1}{b}\right)$$

with the sum of a and b being equal to the constant 10. Solve the problem by formula, and then demonstrate the solution numerically.

11. Three hundred square inches of sheet metal is used in making a box which has an open top and a square base. What are the dimensions of the box so that its holding capacity is a maximum? What is the maximum capacity?

12. What is the rate of expansion of the total surface of a cube if its side is expanding at the rate of 0.01 inch per minute while it is 50 inches long? Solve the problem numerically, and then repeat the solution by formula. See if the results obtained are the same.

CHAPTER 7

INTEGRATION—FINITE INTERVAL

The new operation to be introduced in this chapter is *integration*, which is the inverse operation of differentiation. The subtractions and divisions of differentiation are counteracted by multiplications and additions of integration.

7.1 Inverse Operation

Mathematical operations often occur in pairs with one counteracting the other. When this happens, one operation is called the *inverse operation* of the other. One example of such a pair of operations is addition and subtraction. If 5 is added to 100, the sum is

$$100 + 5 = 105.$$

To neutralize this action one may subtract 5 from the sum and return to the original number

$$(100 + 5) - 5 = 100.$$

Then subtraction is the inverse operation of addition or vice versa.

Another example of such a pair of operations is multiplication and division. When 100 is multiplied by 5, the product is

$$100 \times 5 = 500.$$

To counteract this operation, one may divide the product 500 by 5 and return to the original number

$$(100 \times 5) \div 5 = 100.$$

Thus multiplication is the inverse operation of division or vice versa.

Another example of such a pair of operations is squaring and the extraction of square root. The square of 100 is

$$100^2 = 10,000.$$

The extraction of the square root of the square of 100 yields

$$\sqrt{100^2} = 100$$

which is the original number. Thus squaring is the inverse operation of the extraction of square root or vice versa.

These are the familiar examples of the inverse operation. In the following section, a new operation is presented as the inverse operation of differentiation.

7.2 Integration

Integration is the inverse operation of differentiation. In differentiating the function

$$y = F(x),$$

the difference Δy is found for each interval of x. Then each of these differences is divided by Δx. The sequence of the mid-points $\bar{x}$ of the intervals of x and the corresponding values of the ratio

$$\frac{\Delta y}{\Delta x} = f(\bar{x})$$

constitute the derivative of the function $F(x)$.

In integration, the whole process is reversed. In integrating the function $f(\bar{x})$, the first step is to multiply $f(\bar{x})$ by Δx for each interval of x to obtain the product

$$f(\bar{x})\Delta x = \Delta y$$

which is the inverse operation of the division of Δy by Δx. The second step is to add these products together to obtain the sum

$$\sum f(\bar{x})\Delta x = \sum \left(\frac{\Delta y}{\Delta x}\right)\Delta x = \sum(\Delta y) = y = F(x)$$

which is the inverse operation of finding the differences Δy. This is the essence of integration. Briefly, differentiation consists of subtractions followed by divisions, and integration involves multiplications followed by additions.

The numerical demonstration of an integration is given in table 7.2a which shows the inverse operations of table 5.1a. Columns 2 and 3 of table 7.2a are reproduced from columns 6 and 7 of table 5.1a. The function to be integrated in table 7.2a is $f(\bar{x})$. The finished product of this operation is the function $F(x)$ given in column 6 of that table. Here the function $F(x)$ is called the *integral* of $f(\bar{x})$. In table 5.1a where differentiation is carried out, $f(\bar{x})$ is called the derivative of $F(x)$.

TABLE 7.2a

INTEGRATION AS INVERSE OPERATION OF DIFFERENTIATION

(1)	(2)	(3)	(4)	(5)	(6)	(7)
Interval No.	Mid-point $\bar{x}$	$f(\bar{x})$	$\Delta y = f(\bar{x})\Delta x$	End-point x	$y = F(x)$	$F(x)$ $(C = 160)$
				0.0	C	160
1	0.25	10	5			
				0.5	$C +\ \ 5$	165
2	0.75	22	11			
				1.0	$C +\ 16$	176
3	1.25	22	11			
				1.5	$C +\ 27$	187
4	1.75	10	5			
				2.0	$C +\ 32$	192
5	2.25	$-\ 14$	$-\ 7$			
				2.5	$C +\ 25$	185
6	2.75	$-\ 50$	-25			
				3.0	$C +\ \ 0$	160
7	3.25	$-\ 98$	-49			
				3.5	$C -\ 49$	111
8	3.75	-158	-79			
				4.0	$C - 128$	32

Tables 5.1a and 7.2a have different numbers of points. The former table has 9 points and the latter has only 8. The reason for this difference is that the points in the former table are the end-points x of the intervals and those in the latter are the mid-points $\bar{x}$. It takes 9 points on the x axis to create the 8 intervals, each of which has a mid-point (section 1.3).

The first step of integration is to find the product of $f(\bar{x})$ and Δx for each interval of x. In table 7.2a, Δx is equal to 0.5 which is the difference between two adjacent mid-points such as

$$0.75 - 0.25 = 0.50$$

and

$$1.25 - 0.75 = 0.50.$$

The values of the product $f(\bar{x})\Delta x$ are given in column 4 of table 7.2a. These are also the values of Δy given in column 5 of table 5.1a. This is due to the fact that the product is nothing but

$$f(\bar{x})\Delta x = \frac{\Delta y}{\Delta x}\Delta x = \Delta y.$$

The second step of integration is to obtain the values of y from the values of Δy. Here one runs into difficulty right away. The difference in y for the first interval is

$$\Delta y = y_2 - y_1$$

whose value is known to be

$$\Delta y = f(\bar{x})\Delta x = 10(0.5) = 5$$

as shown in column 4 of table 7.2a. But the knowledge of this difference alone is not sufficient to determine the values of y_1 and y_2. The difference of 5 could come from $6 - 1$, $15 - 10$, $5.1 - 0.1$, or many other pairs of values of y; and, of course, it could also come from $165 - 160$ which is the source of the difference $\Delta y = 5$ as shown in table 5.1a. In order to proceed with the integration, the value of y_1 is temporarily designated by the letter C which stands for an unknown constant.

After y_1 is designated by C, the other values of y can be obtained by successive additions. The fact (table 7.2a)

$$f(\bar{x}_1)\Delta x = \Delta y_1 = y_2 - y_1 = y_2 - C = 5$$

implies

$$y_2 = C + 5.$$

The fact

$$f(\bar{x}_2)\Delta x = \Delta y_2 = y_3 - y_2 = 11$$

implies

$$y_3 = y_2 + 11 = (C + 5) + 11 = C + 16.$$

The other values of y can be similarly determined. They are

$$y_4 = y_3 + 11 = (C + 16) + 11 = C + 27$$

$$y_5 = y_4 + 5 = (C + 27) + 5 = C + 32$$

$$y_6 = y_5 - 7 = (C + 32) - 7 = C + 25$$

$$y_7 = y_6 - 25 = (C + 25) - 25 = C + 0$$

$$y_8 = y_7 - 49 = (C + 0) - 49 = C - 49$$

$$y_9 = y_8 - 79 = (C - 49) - 79 = C - 128$$

which are listed in column 6 of table 7.2a.

In general, the values of the integral y or $F(x)$ are obtained in this way: The unknown constant C is assigned to y_1, and each of the remaining values of y is obtained by adding $f(\bar{x})\Delta x$ to the preceding value of y. Thus the values of y are:

$$y_1 = C$$

$$y_2 = y_1 + f(\bar{x}_1)\Delta x$$

$$y_3 = y_2 + f(\bar{x}_2)\Delta x$$

$$\cdots$$

$$y_i = y_{i-1} + f(\bar{x}_{i-1})\Delta x$$

$$\cdots$$

$$y_m = y_{m-1} + f(\bar{x}_{m-1})\Delta x$$

This pattern can be observed in columns 4 and 6 of table 7.2a. This also explains why 8 values of $f(\bar{x})$ can generate 9 values of $F(x)$. When the subscript i of $\bar{x}_i$ runs its course from 1 to $m-1$ for the $m-1$ given mid-points, m values of y or $F(x)$ are generated.

The values of y or $F(x)$ are associated with the end-points of the intervals of x. These end-points x, which are listed in column 5 of table 7.2a, are obtained from the mid-points $\bar{x}$. The end-points of the ith interval whose mid-point is $\bar{x}_i$ are

$$x_i = \bar{x}_i - \frac{1}{2}\Delta x$$

and

$$x_{i+1} = \bar{x}_i + \frac{1}{2}\Delta x .$$

For example, the mid-point of the second interval is 0.75 and Δx is 0.5 as shown in column 2 of table 7.2a. The end-points of that interval are

$$x_2 = 0.75 - \frac{1}{2}(0.5) = 0.50$$

and

$$x_3 = 0.75 + \frac{1}{2}(0.5) = 1.00$$

as shown in column 5 of the same table. For this reason, the 8 mid-points of the given intervals generate 9 end-points. In general, $m-1$ mid-points $\bar{x}$ create m end-points x, each of which is associated with a value of the integral $F(x)$.

The finished product of this integration, which is the integral of the function $f(x)$, is given in columns 5 and 6 of table 7.2a. It is the sequence of the values of the end-points of the intervals of x given in column 5 and their corresponding values of $F(x)$ given in column 6 that constitute the integral, or more specifically the *indefinite integral*, of the function $f(\bar{x})$.

The unknown constant C of an indefinite integral is called the *constant of integration*. It can be determined by the knowledge of one value of y. For example, the knowledge of

$$y_2 = 165 ,$$

which is given in column 3 of table 5.1a, is sufficient to determine the value of C in column 6 of table 7.2a. The value

$$y_2 = C + 5$$

given in that column implies

$$165 = C + 5$$

or

$$C = 165 - 5 = 160 .$$

When every C in column 6 of table 7.2a is replaced by 160, the result is the function $F(x)$ given in column 7 of the same table.

The listed values of that column are the same ones given in column 3 of table 5.1a.

Tables 5.1a and 7.2a jointly demonstrate that the function

$$\frac{\Delta y}{\Delta x} = f(\bar{x})$$

is the derivative of the function

$$y = F(x)$$

and the function $F(x)$ is the integral of $f(\bar{x})$. The purpose of this demonstration is to show that integration is the inverse operation of differentiation or vice versa. Furthermore, the demonstration also shows that there is a hitch in the reversibility of the two operations. In differentiating the function $F(x)$, the derivative $f(\bar{x})$ is uniquely determined. But, in integrating $f(\bar{x})$, the integral $F(x)$ contains an unknown constant C which cannot be determined unless at least one value of $F(x)$ is known. The reason for this ambiguity is

$$\frac{\Delta}{\Delta x}(y + C) = \frac{\Delta y}{\Delta x}$$

which is equation (5) of section 5.2.

There are many ways of carrying out an integration. Only one of them is described in this section. To distinguish this particular one from the rest of them, it is named the *standard method* of integration for the convenience of reference. This is not a commonly used term, but it is used all through this text.

The procedure of the standard method of integration is summarized in table 7.2b. That table is simply table 7.2a with all numbers changed into symbols. The function $f(\bar{x})$ to be integrated is given in the form of $m-1$ points in columns 2 and 3. The given values of x are considered mid-points $\bar{x}$ around which $m-1$ intervals are created. The finished product of the integration is listed in columns 5 and 6. The m values of x given in column 5, being the end-points of the $m-1$ intervals, are obtained from the mid-points $\bar{x}$; and the corresponding values of $F(x)$ are obtained by adding the product $f(\bar{x})\Delta x$ to the preceding value of $F(x)$ with the initial value of $F(x)$ being an unknown constant C. The raw material $f(\bar{x})$ for this operation is called the *integrand*, and the finished product $F(x)$

TABLE 7.2b

STANDARD METHOD OF INTEGRATION

(1) Interval No.	(2) Mid-point $\bar{x}$	(3) $f(\bar{x})$	(4) $f(\bar{x})\Delta x$	(5) End-point x	(6) $F(x)$
1	$\bar{x}_1$	$f(\bar{x}_1)$	$f(\bar{x}_1)\Delta x$	$x_1 = \bar{x}_1 - \dfrac{1}{2}\Delta x$	C
2	$\bar{x}_2$	$f(\bar{x}_2)$	$f(\bar{x}_2)\Delta x$	$x_2 = \bar{x}_2 - \dfrac{1}{2}\Delta x$	$C + f(\bar{x}_1)\Delta x$
		$\cdots$	$\cdots$	$x_3 = \bar{x}_3 - \dfrac{1}{2}\Delta x$	$F(x_2) + f(\bar{x}_2)\Delta x$
i	$\bar{x}_i$	$f(\bar{x}_i)$	$f(\bar{x}_i)\Delta x$	$x_i = \bar{x}_i - \dfrac{1}{2}\Delta x$	$F(x_{i-1}) + f(\bar{x}_{i-1})\Delta x$
				$x_{i+1} = \bar{x}_{i+1} - \dfrac{1}{2}\Delta x$	$F(x_i) + f(\bar{x}_i)\Delta x$
		$\cdots$	$\cdots$		$\cdots$
$m-1$	$\bar{x}_{m-1}$	$f(\bar{x}_{m-1})$	$f(\bar{x}_{m-1})\Delta x$	$x_{m-1} = \bar{x}_{m-1} - \dfrac{1}{2}\Delta x$	$F(x_{m-2}) + f(\bar{x}_{m-2})\Delta x$
				$x_m = \bar{x}_{m-1} + \dfrac{1}{2}\Delta x$	$F(x_{m-1}) + f(\bar{x}_{m-1})\Delta x$

is called the *integral*. To *integrate* is to carry out such an operation, and the operation itself is called *integration*. The steps of integration are multiplications followed by additions. The integral $F(x)$ thus obtained is a function x. It is more specifically called the *indefinite* integral of $f(x)$ in contrast to the *definite* integral to be discussed in the following section.

The characteristic of the standard method of integration is that the values of the integrand $f(\bar{x})$ are given at the mid-points $\bar{x}$ of the $m-1$ intervals and the values of the integral $F(x)$ thus obtained are located at the m end-points x of the $m-1$ intervals.

The integral $F(x)$ given in column 6 of table 7.2b includes an unknown constant C; that is,

$$F(x) \;=\; C + \textstyle\sum f(\bar{x})\Delta x. \tag{1}$$

By this definition of $F(x)$, the value of $F(x)$ at the initial point x_1 is

$$F(x_1) \;=\; C \tag{2}$$

as shown in column 6 of table 7.2b. A numerical example of this version of $F(x)$ is given in column 6 of table 7.2a. However, this is by no means the universal way of expressing an indefinite integral. The symbol $F(x)$ is more frequently used in representing the accumulated sum of $f(\bar{x})\Delta x$; that is,

$$F(x) \;=\; \textstyle\sum f(\bar{x})\Delta x. \tag{3}$$

By this definition of $F(x)$, the value of $F(x)$ at the initial point x_1 is

$$F(x_1) \;=\; 0 \tag{4}$$

and the integral of $f(\bar{x})$ is expressed as $F(x) + C$. A numerical example of the second version of $F(x)$ is given in column 6 of table 7.2a. For this example, the value of $F(x)$ are

$$0 \quad 5 \quad 16 \quad \cdots \quad -128.$$

The difference between these two versions of $F(x)$ is the constant C. If the values

$$0 \quad 5 \quad 16 \quad \cdots \quad -128$$

given in column 6 of table 7.2a are represented by $F(x)$, the values of column 7 of that table have to be represented by $F(x) + 160$. In fact, the values

$$10 \quad 15 \quad 26 \quad \cdots \quad -118$$

can also be represented by $F(x)$. If so, the values of column 7 must be represented by $F(x) + 150$. In the following chapters, the symbol $F(x)$ is used in this flexible sense. The difference in the definitions of $F(x)$ is taken care of by the unknown constant C.

7.3 Definite Integral

The sum of the products $f(\bar{x})\Delta x$ of a number of consecutive intervals of x is called a *definite integral* of the function $f(\bar{x})$. For example, the sum of products

$$f(\bar{x}_2)\Delta x + f(\bar{x}_3)\Delta x + f(\bar{x}_4)\Delta x \;=\; 11 + 11 + 5 \;=\; 27 \tag{1}$$

obtained from column 4 of table 7.2a is a definite integral of $f(\bar{x})$.

A definite integral are bounded by two values of x which are called the *limits* of the integral. The definite integral of equation (1) extends over intervals no. 2, 3 and 4 of table 7.2a. In terms of the end-points given in column 6 of that table, the limits of this triple interval are $x = 0.5$ and $x = 2.0$, For this reason, the given integral is usually expressed as

$$\sum_{0.5}^{2.0} f(\bar{x})\Delta x \;=\; 11 + 11 + 5 \;=\; 27 \tag{2}$$

where 2.0 and 0.5 are the upper and lower limits of the integral. This is merely a convenient way of expressing a definite integral which may consist of a large number of terms. The new expression, however, does not change the definition or meaning of the definite integral.

A definite integral is equal to the difference between the values of the indefinite integral corresponding to the limits of the definite integral. For the given example, the limits are $x = 0.5$ and $x = 2.0$. The corresponding values of the indefinite integral $F(x)$, which are given in column 6 of table 7.2a, are

$$F(2.0) \;=\; C + 32$$

and

$$F(0.5) \; = \; C + 5.$$

The difference between them is

$$F(2.0) - F(0.5) \; = \; (C + 32) - (C + 5) \; = \; 32 - 5 \; = \; 27 \qquad (3)$$

which is the same value given in equations (1) and (2).

This result should be obvious to anyone who knows how to obtain the numbers in column 6 of table 7.2a. The value

$$F(2.0) \; = \; C + 32$$

is originally obtained by adding

$$f(\bar{x}_2)\Delta x + f(\bar{x}_3)\Delta x + f(\bar{x}_4)\Delta x \; = \; 11 + 11 + 5 \; = \; 27$$

to the value

$$F(0.5) \; = \; C + 5.$$

Then the difference between them cannot be anything but

$$F(2.0) - F(0.5) \; = \; f(\bar{x}_2)\Delta x + f(\bar{x}_3)\Delta x + f(\bar{x}_4)\Delta x \qquad (4)$$

which is a definite integral by definition.

The above example demonstrates that, in evaluating a definite integral, the unknown constant C of the indefinite integral can be ignored. Column 6 of table 7.2a shows that every value of the indefinite integral contains the unknown constant C. Then the difference between any two of these values is independent of C, because

$$C - C \; = \; 0$$

regardless of the value of C.

Equations (2) and (4) can be combined and generalized into the single equation

$$\sum_{a}^{b} f(\bar{x})\Delta x \; = \; F(b) - F(a) \qquad (5)$$

where a and b are two values of x, and $F(x)$ is the indefinite integral of $f(\bar{x})$. The above equation provides alternative ways of evaluating a definite integral. It may either be obtained by computing the sum of the products of $f(\bar{x})$ and Δx as shown on the left-hand side of equation (5) or by obtaining the difference between $F(b)$ and $F(a)$

as shown on the right-hand side. The latter method appears to be much simpler. But the catch is that the indefinite integral $F(x)$ has to be known, or at least can be readily obtained, for otherwise $F(a)$ and $F(b)$ cannot be evaluated.

A definite integral is sometimes expressed as

$$\sum_a^b f(\bar{x})\Delta x = \left[F(x) \right]_a^b \qquad (6)$$

if $F(x)$ is the indefinite integral of $f(\bar{x})$. This is merely a new symbol, and the new symbol does not add any new meaning to the definite integral. It is just another way of writing $F(b) - F(a)$. As a practice of using this new symbol, one may consider the following examples:

$$\left[F(x) \right]_a^b = F(b) - F(a)$$

$$\left[F(x) \right]_1^5 = F(5) - F(1)$$

$$\left[2x + C \right]_a^b = (2b + C) - (2a + C) = 2(b - a)$$

$$\left[x^2 + 5 \right]_1^3 = (3^2 + 5) - (1^2 + 5) = 3^2 - 1^2 = 8$$

$$\left[x^2 - x \right]_2^4 = (4^2 - 4) - (2^2 - 2) = 10$$

A definite integral is equal to zero if its limits are equal. This can be seen from the integral given in equation (5). If the lower limit a is equal to the upper limit b, that integral becomes

$$\sum_a^a f(\bar{x})\Delta x = \left[F(x) \right]_a^a = F(a) - F(a) = 0. \qquad (7)$$

This fact can also be observed in table 7.2a. When both a and b are the same value $x = 0.5$, there leaves no interval of x between the limits. Consequently, no value of $f(\bar{x})\Delta x$ is accumulated. As a result, the definite integral is equal to zero.

The definite integral being equal to zero does not necessarily imply that its limits are equal. This can be observed in table 7.2a. The definite integral of $f(\bar{x})$ from $x = 0$ to $x = 3$ given in that table is

$$\sum_{0}^{3} f(\bar{x}) \Delta x = 5 + 11 + 11 + 5 - 7 - 25 = 0$$

or

$$\Big[F(x) \Big]_{0}^{3} = F(3) - F(0) = C - C = 0,$$

but the limits 0 and 3 are not equal. This shows that a zero definite integral may come from the fact that the sum of the positive $f(\bar{x}) \Delta x$ is balanced by that of the negative ones. In this example, the zero integral comes from

$$5 + 11 + 11 + 5 = 7 + 25.$$

Indeed a definite integral can be a negative value. If the sum of the numerical values of the negative $f(\bar{x}) \Delta x$ is greater than that of the positive ones, the definite integral has a negative value. The integral

$$\sum_{1}^{3} f(\bar{x}) \Delta x = 11 + 5 - 7 - 25 = -16$$

or

$$\Big[F(x) \Big]_{1}^{3} = C - (C + 16) = -16$$

given in table 7.2a is an example of a definite integral with a negative value.

The interchange of the limits of a definite integral results in a change in sign in the integral. When the lower and upper limits of the integral given in equation (5) are interchanged, the integral becomes

$$\sum_{b}^{a} f(\bar{x}) \Delta x = F(a) - F(b) = -[F(b) - F(a)]$$

which is the original integral with the sign changed. This discussion can be summarized by the equation

$$\sum_{b}^{a} f(\bar{x}) \Delta x = - \sum_{a}^{b} f(\bar{x}) \Delta x \qquad (8)$$

where a and b are values of x.

The above change in sign in the integral comes from the change in sign in Δx and not in $f(\bar{x})$. This can be seen from column 5 of table 7.2a. If the integration proceeds in the ascending order of x, the length of an interval is defined as

$$\Delta x = 0.5 - 0.0 = 1.0 - 0.5 = \cdots = 4.0 - 3.5 = 0.5.$$

However, if the operation proceeds in the descending order, the value of Δx becomes

$$3.5 - 4.0 = 3.0 - 3.5 = \cdots = 0.0 - 0.5 = -0.5$$

which is the original Δx with its sign changed.

A definite integral can be expressed as the sum of a number of definite integrals. For example, the integral

$$\sum_{0.5}^{2.5} f(\bar{x})\Delta x = 11 + 11 + 5 - 7 = 20$$

of table 7.2a may be expressed as the sum

$$\sum_{0.5}^{1.5} f(\bar{x})\Delta x + \sum_{1.5}^{2.5} f(\bar{x})\Delta x = (11 + 11) + (5 - 7) = 20.$$

Indeed, if so desired, the given integral may also be expressed as the sum of the four integrals

$$\sum_{0.5}^{1.0} f(\bar{x})\Delta x = 11$$

$$\sum_{1.0}^{1.5} f(\bar{x})\Delta x = 11$$

$$\sum_{1.5}^{2.0} f(\bar{x})\Delta x = 5$$

$$\sum_{2.0}^{2.5} f(\bar{x})\Delta x = -7$$

each of which covers only one interval of x. The above discussion can be summarized by the equation

$$\sum_{a}^{c} f(\bar{x})\Delta x = \sum_{a}^{b} f(\bar{x})\Delta x + \sum_{b}^{c} f(\bar{x})\Delta x \qquad (9)$$

where a, b and c are values of the independent variable x.

A definite integral is a function of its limits. When the limits are changed, the value of the definite integral changes with them. This can be seen from table 7.2a that the definite integrals

$$\sum_{0.0}^{1.0} f(\bar{x})\Delta x \; = \; 5 + 11 \; = \; F(1.0) - F(0.0) \; = \; 176 - 160 \; = \; 16$$

$$\sum_{1.5}^{2.5} f(\bar{x})\Delta x \; = \; 5 - 7 \; = \; F(2.5) - F(1.5) \; = \; 185 - 187 \; = \; -2$$

$$\sum_{0.5}^{1.0} f(\bar{x})\Delta x \; = \; 11 \; = \; F(1.0) - F(0.5) \; = \; 176 - 165 \; = \; 11$$

do have different values when their limits are different. This is to say that the value of a definite integral depends on its limits, or the value of a definite integral is a function of its limits.

An indefinite integral can be expressed as a definite integral with the variable x as the upper limit. This can be deduced from the integral given in equation (5). When the upper limit b is replaced by the variable x, that integral becomes

$$\sum_{a}^{x} f(\bar{x})\Delta x \; = \; \Big[F(x) \Big]_{a}^{x} \; = \; F(x) - F(a) \, . \tag{10}$$

Since a is a constant, it follows that $F(a)$ is a constant. Then the integral can be expressed as

$$\sum_{a}^{x} f(\bar{x})\Delta x \; = \; F(x) + C \tag{11}$$

which has the appearance of a definite integral but in reality an indefinite integral.

Now both definite and indefinite integrals can be expressed as definite integrals. However, one should realize that this is only a matter of notation. The real difference between the two kinds of integrals is still there. This manipulation of symbols only shifts the emphasis to the upper limit of an integral. If the upper limit is the independent variable x and the lower limit a constant, the integral is a function of x. On the other hand, if both limits are constants, the integral is a constant. However, in the common usage of the terms, a definite integral is one with constant limits, and an indefinite integral is one with the upper limit being the variable x and the lower limit alone being a constant.

So far the integrand is expressed as $m-1$ points $[\bar{x}, f(\bar{x})]$ and the indefinite integral as m points $[x, F(x)]$ to emphasize the fact that $f(\bar{x})$ is a function of the mid-point $\bar{x}$ and $F(x)$ a function of the end-points x. This system of notation is the relics from the days of differentiation. If one starts freshly with integration, the integrand can very well be expressed as p points $[x, f(x)]$ with the bar over x omitted. However, in so doing, the end-points of an interval becomes $x \pm \frac{1}{2}\Delta x$ and the number of points of the indefinite integral becomes $p+1$.

In terms of the new system of notation, the standard method of evaluating a definite integral can be summarized as this: The integrand $f(x)$ is given as a set of p points

$$[x_1, f(x_1)], \quad [x_2, f(x_2)], \quad \cdots, \quad [x_p, f(x_p)]$$

where the x's are equally spaced with x_1 being the smallest and x_p the largest value of x. The definite integral of $f(x)$ is

$$\sum_a^b f(x)\Delta x = f(x_1)\Delta x + f(x_2)\Delta x + \cdots + f(x_p)\Delta x$$

$$= \Delta x\,[f(x_1) + f(x_2) + \cdots + f(x_p)] \tag{12}$$

with the limits being

$$a = x_1 - \frac{1}{2}\Delta x \tag{13}$$

$$b = x_p + \frac{1}{2}\Delta x \tag{14}$$

and the distance between the limits being

$$b - a = p\Delta x \tag{15}$$

and not $(p-1)\Delta x$. The fact that the limits extend beyond the range x_1 to x_p of the given integrand is a characteristic of the standard method not shared by the methods given in sections 8.6 and 8.7.

7.4 Interpretation of Integral

So far integration is presented only as a sequence of arithmetic operations. Attempts are made in this section to attach some physical meaning to the operations.

The example used for illustration is the data of table 6.1b where the driving record (x, y) is given and the speed of the car is found by differentiation. Now the process is reversed. The derivative of table 6.1b is reproduced in table 7.4 as the integrand $f(\bar{x})$. The integration is carried out by the standard method, and the integral obtained is the sequence of values listed in column 6 of table 7.4. These are the values of y given in table 6.1b if 0 is assigned to the constant C.

TABLE 7.4

INTEGRATION OF SPEED

(1)	(2)	(3)	(4)	(5)	(6)
Interval No.	$\bar{x}$ hours	$f(\bar{x})$ miles/hour	$f(\bar{x})\Delta x$ miles	x hours	$F(x) + C$ miles
				0.0	C
1	0.25	43	21.5		
				0.5	$C + 21.5$
2	0.75	45	22.5		
				1.0	$C + 44.0$
3	1.25	47	23.5		
				1.5	$C + 67.5$
4	1.75	49	24.5		
				2.0	$C + 92.0$

For this example, the original data are given in columns 2 and 3 of table 7.4. The values of $\bar{x}$ given in column 2 are the mid-points of the four periods of time, and those of $f(\bar{x})$ given in column 3 are the rates of speed in miles per hour for the four periods. The length of a period is

$$\Delta x = 0.75 - 0.25 = 1.25 - 0.75 = 1.75 - 1.25 = 0.50$$

hour, which is obtained from the given values of $\bar{x}$.

The first step of integration shown in table 7.4 is to find the values of $f(\bar{x})\Delta x$ for each of the four periods. For each period, the speed of the car is $f(\bar{x})$ miles per hour and the time travelled is $\Delta x = 0.5$ hour. Then the distance covered in that period is $f(\bar{x})\Delta x$ miles. For example, the speed for the first period is 43 miles an hour. In half an hour, the distance travelled is $\frac{1}{2}(43)$ or 21.5 miles.

This is the first value of $f(\bar{x})\Delta x$ listed in column 4. The remaining values of that column are obtained in a similar manner.

The second step of integration is to find the accumulated distance at a particular time. At the zero hour or the time at which the trip starts, the distance travelled is C miles as given in columns 5 and 6. This C is the mileage reading on the speedometer immediately before the trip starts. It is the distance for which the car has been driven so far. It is called an unknown constant because it cannot be determined from the given data and not because it cannot be known. The mystery can be solved by a peek at the speedometer.

The mileage reading at the end of each period is obtained by adding the distance travelled during that period to the reading at the beginning of that period. This is surely as obvious as can be. But, this is exactly how the values in column 6 are obtained. At 0.0 hour, the mileage reading is C. Half an hour later, at 0.5 hour, the reading is $C+21.5$ because the car travelled 21.5 miles during that period. In another half an hour, at 1.0 hour, the reading becomes

$$(C + 21.5) + 22.5 \;=\; C + 44.0$$

because the car travelled another 22.5 miles during the second half-hour period.

A definite integral in this example is the distance travelled within certain limits of time. The definite integral from $x = 0.5$ to $x = 1.5$ is

$$\sum_{0.5}^{1.5} f(\bar{x})\Delta x \;=\; 22.5 + 23.5 \;=\; 46.0 \,. \tag{1}$$

This is to say that the total distance travelled during the second and third periods is 46.0 miles. To obtain this number, one would, of course, add the distances travelled during those two periods.

The same definite integral can be evaluated by finding the difference between the values of $F(x)$ at the limits $x = 0.5$ and $x = 1.5$; that is,

$$\sum_{0.5}^{1.5} f(\bar{x})\Delta x \;=\; F(1.5) - F(0.5)$$

$$= (C + 67.5) - (C + 21.5)$$

$$= 46.0 \,. \tag{2}$$

This is to say that one can find the distance travelled during a period by subtracting the mileage reading at the beginning of a period from that at the end of the period. Here again is a common practice whether one knows calculus or not.

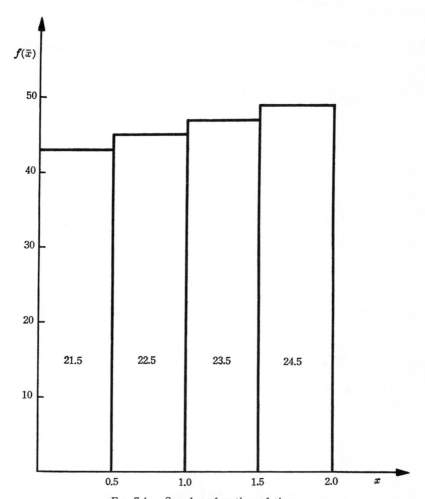

Fɪɢ. 7.4a. Speed as function of time.

An integral can be interpreted geometrically. The data of table 7.4 are presented graphically in figure 7.4a as an illustration. In that figure, a rectangle is constructed for each interval of x with Δx as the width and $f(\bar{x})$ as the height so that the area of the rectangle is $f(\bar{x})\Delta x$. The integral being

$$F(x) = \sum_0^x f(\bar{x})\Delta x$$

becomes the total area of a number of these rectangles.   At $x = 0.5$, the area is (figure 7.4a)

$$F(0.5) = 21.5.$$

At $x = 1.0$, the area is

$$F(1.0) = 21.5 + 22.5 = 44.0.$$

At $x = 1.5$, the area is

$$F(1.5) = 21.5 + 22.5 + 23.5 = 67.5.$$

At $x = 2.0$, the area is

$$F(2.0) = 21.5 + 22.5 + 23.5 + 24.5 = 92.0.$$

These are the same values of $F(x)$ given in column 6 of table 7.4.

Geometrically, a definite integral is the sum of the areas of a number of rectangles. For example, the definite integral

$$\sum_{0.5}^{1.5} f(\bar{x})\Delta x = 22.5 + 23.5 = 46.0$$

is the total area of the two rectangles bounded by $x = 0.5$ and $x = 1.5$ as shown in figure 7.4a.

By this geometric interpretation, a negative $f(\bar{x})$ creates a negative area $f(\bar{x})\Delta x$. This negative area is represented by a rectangle below the x axis because the point representing a negative $f(\bar{x})$ is plotted below that axis. As an illustration, the definite integral

$$\sum_0^3 f(\bar{x})\Delta x = 5 + 11 + 11 + 5 - 7 - 25 = 0$$

of table 7.2a is plotted in figure 7.4b. The definite integral being equal to zero is shown in the graph by the equality of the two total areas above and below the x axis.

When one evaluates the total area of the rectangles, he may not be interested in the geometric figure as such. His interest may be in anything that can be geometrically interpreted as the total area of a number of rectangles. For the given example, the objective is to find the distance $F(x)$ from the given speed $f(\bar{x})$. Yet, if one wishes, he may translate the problem into a geometric one and solve the geometric problem. In figure 7.4a, the abscissa is the time x and the ordinate is the speed $f(\bar{x})$. Because of this designation of axes, the total area of the rectangles becomes necessarily the distance travelled.

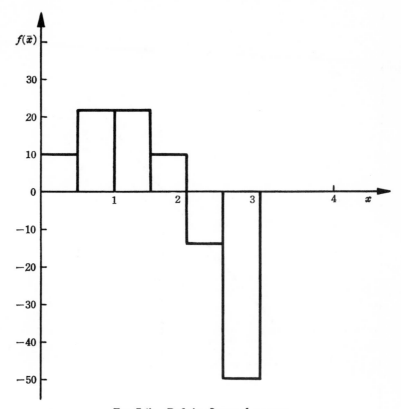

Fɪɢ. 7.4b.   Definite Integral as area.

The independent variable x, the integrand $f(\bar{x})$ and the integral $F(x)$ each has its own unit of measurement. For the given example where x is a number of hours and $f(\bar{x})$ a number of miles per hour, the unit of

$$F(x) = \sum f(\bar{x}) \Delta x$$

becomes necessarily

$$\frac{\text{mile}}{\text{hour}} (\text{hour}) = \text{mile}.$$

For a problem where x is a number of years and $f(\bar{x})$ a number of students per year, the integral $F(x)$ is a number of students. When both x and $f(\bar{x})$ are numbers of inches, the integral $F(x)$ is a number of square inches.

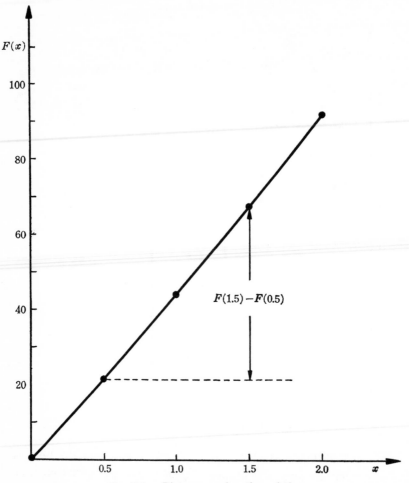

Fɪɢ. 7.4c. Distance as function of time.

The same problem can also be interpreted geometrically in a different way. In figure 7.4c the abscissa is still the time x, but the ordinate is changed to the distance $F(x)$. The curve is plotted from the values of columns 5 and 6 of table 7.4 with the constant C being equal to zero. Now the distance travelled is the ordinate of the curve rather than the total area of rectangles. Then the definite integral given in equation (1) becomes the difference of the ordinates located at $x = 0.5$ and $x = 1.5$. So an integral may or may not be the total area of a number of rectangles. It all depends on what the ordinate represents. Only if the ordinate represents the integrand, does the area represent the integral.

7.5 Some Rules of Integration

Like differentiation, integration has many rules. Three of them are given in this section. In all these rules, the integrands such as $f(\bar{x})$, $u(\bar{x})$ and $v(\bar{x})$ are functions of the mid-points $\bar{x}$ and their corresponding integrals $F(x)$, $U(x)$ and $V(x)$ are functions of the end-points x.

The first rule of integration is that the integral of a constant k is equal to

$$\sum_{a}^{x} k\Delta x = kx + C. \tag{1}$$

This result can be derived from the fact that the derivative of the integral is

$$\frac{\Delta}{\Delta x}(kx + C) = k\frac{\Delta x}{\Delta x} + 0 = k.$$

The integration of the derivative of a function should yield that function itself, because integration is the inverse operation of differentiation.

TABLE 7.5a

INTEGRAL OF $f(x) = 5$

$\bar{x}$	$f(\bar{x})$	$f(\bar{x})\Delta x$	x	$F(x) + C$
			0	C
1	5	10		
			2	$C + 10$
3	5	10		
			4	$C + 20$
5	5	10		
			6	$C + 30$

The numerical demonstration of equation (1) is given in table 7.5a. For every value of $\bar{x}$ given in that table, the corresponding value of the integrand is equal to the constant 5. After the integration is carried out, the integral is equal to

$$F(x) + C = 5x + C$$

for all values of x.

Equation (1) is a short cut. When the integrand is a constant, one can immediately write out its integral without computation. For example, one can tell from the rule that the indefinite integral of

$$f(\bar{x}) = 4$$

is

$$F(x) + C = 4x + C$$

and the definite integral of $f(\bar{x})$ from $x = 2$ to $x = 8$ is

$$\left[F(x)\right]_2^8 = \left[4x\right]_2^8 = F(8) - F(2) = 32 - 8 = 24.$$

When the constant k is equal to 1, equation (1) becomes

$$\sum_a^x \Delta x = x + C \tag{2}$$

which shows that the operators Σ and Δ neutralize each other. This is to be expected, because Σ stands for "the sum of" and Δ "the difference of" and additions are inverse operations of subtractions.

This neutralizing effect of Σ and Δ also shows in the rule

$$\sum_a^x \Delta U(x) = U(x) + C. \tag{3}$$

If $U(x) + C$ is a function of x, its derivative is

$$\frac{\Delta}{\Delta x}(U + C) = \frac{\Delta U}{\Delta x}.$$

Then the integral of this derivative

$$\sum_a^x \left(\frac{\Delta U}{\Delta x}\right)\Delta x = \sum_a^x \Delta U$$

becomes necessarily the original function $U(x) + C$ because integration is the inverse operation of differentiation.

The second rule of integration is that the integral of $ku(\bar{x})$, where k is a constant multiplier and $u(\bar{x})$ a function of $\bar{x}$, is equal to k times that of $u(\bar{x})$; that is,

$$\sum_a^x ku(\bar{x})\Delta x \;=\; k\sum_a^x u(\bar{x})\Delta x . \tag{4}$$

This rule is more or less obvious. The integration consists of multiplications and additions. During these operations, the constant k is just a common factor. Then it can be treated as such.

TABLE 7.5b

INTEGRATION OF $f(x) \;=\; ku(x)$

$\bar{x}$	$u(\bar{x})$	$u(\bar{x})\Delta x$	x	$U(x) + C_1$
			0	C_1
1	5	10		
			2	$C_1 + 10$
3	10	20		
			4	$C_1 + 30$
5	20	40		
			6	$C_1 + 70$

$\bar{x}$	$f(\bar{x}) = ku(\bar{x})$	$f(\bar{x})\Delta x$	x	$F(x) + C$
			0	$C = kC_1$
1	$5\,k$	$10\,k$		
			2	$C + 10\,k$
3	$10\,k$	$20\,k$		
			4	$C + 30\,k$
5	$20\,k$	$40\,k$		
			6	$C + 70\,k$

The numerical demonstration of equation (4) is given in table 7.5b. The upper half of the table shows the integration of an arbitrary function $u(\bar{x})$. The integral is designated by

$$\sum_a^x u(\bar{x})\Delta x = U(x) + C_1$$

where C_1 is the constant of integration. Then in the lower half of the table, the integrand is

$$f(\bar{x}) = ku(\bar{x})$$

and the resulting integral is

$$\sum_a^x f(\bar{x})\Delta x = \sum_a^x ku(\bar{x})\Delta x = F(x) + C$$

with the constant of integration being made equal to

$$C = kC_1.$$

Comparing the values of $U(x)$ and $F(x)$ of table 7.5b, one will note that the equation

$$F(x) = kU(x)$$

holds for every value of x. This is what equation (4) says.

Table 7.5b is only a numerical demonstration of equation (4). If one is interested in an algebraic proof of the rule, all he has to do is replace the numbers in that table by symbols such as $\bar{x}_i$ and $\bar{u}_i$. After the integrations are carried out, the result is the proof of equation (4).

The rule given in equation (4) enables one to concentrate on the integration of $u(\bar{x})$ even though his objective is to integrate $ku(\bar{x})$. After the integral $U(x)$ of $u(\bar{x})$ is obtained, that of $ku(\bar{x})$ can be obtained by multiplying $U(x)$ by k. The basic idea is that of the common factor.

The third rule of integration is that the integral of the sum of two functions is equal to the sum of the integrals of those two functions; that is,

$$\sum_a^x [u(\bar{x}) + v(\bar{x})]\Delta x = \sum_a^x u(\bar{x})\Delta x + \sum_a^x v(\bar{x})\Delta x \qquad (5)$$

where $u(\bar{x})$ and $v(\bar{x})$ are functions of $\bar{x}$. The numerical demonstration of this rule is given in tables 7.5c and 7.5d. In the former table, an arbitrary function $v(\bar{x})$ is integrated and the resulting integral is $V(x) + C_2$. In the latter table, the integrand is

TABLE 7.5c

INTEGRATION OF $v(x)$

$\bar{x}$	$v(\bar{x})$	$v(\bar{x})\Delta x$	x	$V(x) + C_2$
			0	C_2
1	2	4		
			2	$C_2 + 4$
3	0	0		
			4	$C_2 + 4$
5	4	8		
			6	$C_2 + 12$

TABLE 7.5d

INTEGRATION OF $f(x) = u(x) + v(x)$

$\bar{x}$	$f(\bar{x})$	$f(\bar{x})\Delta x$	x	$F(x) + C$	$U(x) + V(x) + C_1 + C_2$
			0	C	$C_1 + C_2$
1	7	14			
			2	$C + 14$	$C_1 + C_2 + 10 + 4$
3	10	20			
			4	$C + 34$	$C_1 + C_2 + 30 + 4$
5	24	48			
			6	$C + 82$	$C_1 + C_2 + 70 + 12$

$$f(\bar{x}) = u(\bar{x}) + v(\bar{x})$$

with $u(\bar{x})$ being given in the upper half of table 7.5b and $v(\bar{x})$ in table 7.5c. After the integration is carried out, the resulting integral is $F(x) + C$ with the constant of integration being designated by

$$C = C_1 + C_2 .$$

Comparing the integral

$$\sum_{a}^{x} u(\bar{x})\Delta x = U(x) + C_1$$

of table 7.5b, the integral

$$\sum_a^x v(\bar{x})\Delta x \;=\; V(x) + C_2$$

of table 7.5c, and the integral

$$\sum_a^x [u(\bar{x}) + v(\bar{x})]\Delta x \;=\; F(x) + C$$

of table 7.5d, one will note that the equation

$$F(x) \;=\; U(x) + V(x)$$

holds for every value of x as shown in table 7.5d. This is what equation (5) says.

The algebraic proof of equation (5) can be readily obtained. For this purpose, the numbers in the tables may be replaced by symbols such as $\bar{x}_i$, $\bar{u}_i$ and $\bar{v}_i$. When the integrations are carried out as indicated in the tables, the result will show that the rule holds true.

Equation (5) can be extended to any number of functions. The integral of $u + v$ is known to be equal to the sum of the integrals $U + V$. Then it follows that the integral of

$$(u + v) + w \;=\; u + v + w$$

is equal to

$$(U + V) + W \;=\; U + V + W$$

which is the sum of the integrals of the three functions $u(\bar{x})$, $v(\bar{x})$ and $w(\bar{x})$. By this argument, the rule can be extended to the sum of any number of functions of $\bar{x}$. The importance of this rule lies in the fact that it enables one to integrate a function term by term if the function consists of more than one term.

7.6 Integration of Power of x

Rules of integrating the powers of x, such as x, x^2 and x^3, are discussed in this section. All the rules are derived from those of differentiation, or more specifically, from the derivatives

$$\frac{\Delta}{\Delta x}x^2 \;=\; 2\bar{x} \tag{1}$$

$$\frac{\Delta}{\Delta x}x^3 = 3(\bar{x})^2 + \frac{1}{4}(\Delta x)^2 \tag{2}$$

$$\frac{\Delta}{\Delta x}x^4 = 4(\bar{x})^3 + \bar{x}(\Delta x)^2 \tag{3}$$

which are given in equations (3) to (5) of section 5.7.

The basic principle used in deriving the rules of integration is that the integration is the inverse operation of differentiation. If the derivative of x^n is

$$\frac{\Delta}{\Delta x}x^n = f(\bar{x}),$$

the integral of the derivative $f(\bar{x})$ is

$$\sum_{a}^{x} f(\bar{x})\Delta x = x^n + C.$$

An alternative way of expressing the above equation is

$$\sum_{a}^{x}\left(\frac{\Delta}{\Delta x}x^n\right)\Delta x = \sum_{a}^{x}(\Delta x^n) = x^n + C \tag{4}$$

where the operators $\sum$ and Δ neutralize each other. The above equation is a special case of equation (3) of section 7.5 with $U(x)$ being x^n.

The integral of $\bar{x}$ is equal to

$$\sum_{a}^{x}\bar{x}\Delta x = \frac{1}{2}x^2 + C. \tag{5}$$

This rule is derived from equation (1). From that equation, one can obtain

$$\bar{x} = \frac{1}{2}\cdot\frac{\Delta}{\Delta x}x^2.$$

Integrating both sides of the above equation, one obtains

$$\sum_{a}^{x}\bar{x}\Delta x = \frac{1}{2}\sum_{a}^{x}\left(\frac{\Delta}{\Delta x}x^2\right)\Delta x = \frac{1}{2}(x^2 + C_1) = \frac{1}{2}x^2 + C$$

where C is equal to $C_1/2$.

The numerical demonstration of this rule is given in table 7.6a. The integrand in that table is

$$f(\bar{x}) = \bar{x}$$

which is a function of the mid-point $\bar{x}$, and the integral obtained is

$$F(x) + C = \frac{1}{2}x^2 + C$$

which is a function of the end-point x.

TABLE 7.6a

INTEGRATION OF $f(x) = x$

$\bar{x}$	$f(\bar{x}) = \bar{x}$	$f(\bar{x})\Delta x$	x	$F(x) + C$
			0	C
1	1	2		
			2	$C + 2$
3	3	6		
			4	$C + 8$
5	5	10		
			6	$C + 18$

The integral of $(\bar{x})^2$ is equal to

$$\sum_{a}^{x}(\bar{x})^2\Delta x = \frac{1}{3}x^3 - \frac{x}{12}(\Delta x)^2 + C. \tag{6}$$

This rule is derived from equation (2). From that equation, one can obtain

$$(\bar{x})^2 = \frac{1}{3}\cdot\frac{\Delta}{\Delta x}x^3 - \frac{1}{12}(\Delta x)^2.$$

Integrating the above equation term by term, one obtains

$$\sum_{a}^{x}(\bar{x})^2\Delta x = \frac{1}{3}\sum_{a}^{x}\left(\frac{\Delta}{\Delta x}x^3\right)\Delta x - \frac{1}{12}(\Delta x)^2\sum_{a}^{x}\Delta x$$

$$= \frac{1}{3}(x^3 + C_1) - \frac{1}{12}(\Delta x)^2(x + C_2)$$

$$= \frac{1}{3}x^3 - \frac{x}{12}(\Delta x)^2 + C$$

where the constant of integration is

$$C = \frac{1}{3}C_1 - \frac{1}{12}(\Delta x)^2C_2$$

because C_1, C_2 and Δx are all constants and can be consolidated into one constant C.

TABLE 7.6b

INTEGRATION OF $f(x) = x^2$

$\bar{x}$	$f(\bar{x}) = (\bar{x})^2$	$f(\bar{x})\Delta x$	x	$F(x) + C$
			0	C
1	1	2		
			2	$C + 2$
3	9	18		
			4	$C + 20$
5	25	50		
			6	$C + 70$

The numerical demonstration of this rule is given in table 7.6b. The integrand in that table is

$$f(\bar{x}) = (\bar{x})^2$$

which is a function of the mid-point $\bar{x}$, and the integral is

$$\sum_{a}^{x}(\bar{x})^2\Delta x = F(x) + C$$

which is a function of the end-point x. The purpose of this demonstration is to show that the integral is equal to (equation 6)

$$F(x) + C = \frac{1}{3}x^3 - \frac{x}{12}(\Delta x)^2 + C.$$

Taking advantage of the fact that the length of the interval is

$$\Delta x = 5 - 3 = 3 - 1 = 2,$$

one can simplify the integral to

$$F(x) + C = \frac{1}{3}(x^3 - x) + C.$$

At the given end-points of x, the values of $F(x)$ are

$$F(0) = 0$$

$$F(2) = 2$$

$$F(4) = 20$$

$$F(6) = 70$$

which are the same values given in table 7.6b.

The integral of $(\bar{x})^3$ is equal to

$$\sum_a^x (\bar{x})^3 \Delta x = \frac{1}{4}x^4 - \frac{1}{8}x^2(\Delta x)^2 + C. \tag{7}$$

This rule is derived from equation (3). From that equation, one can obtain

$$(\bar{x})^3 = \frac{1}{4} \cdot \frac{\Delta}{\Delta x}x^4 - \frac{1}{4}\bar{x}(\Delta x)^2.$$

Integrating the above equation term by term, one obtains

$$\sum_a^x (\bar{x})^3 \Delta x = \frac{1}{4}\sum_a^x \left(\frac{\Delta}{\Delta x}x^4\right)\Delta x - \frac{1}{4}(\Delta x)^2\sum_a^x \bar{x}\Delta x$$

$$= \frac{1}{4}(x^4 + C_1) - \frac{1}{4}(\Delta x)^2\left(\frac{1}{2}x^2 + C_2\right)$$

$$= \frac{1}{4}x^4 - \frac{1}{8}x^2(\Delta x)^2 + C$$

where the constant of integration is

$$C = \frac{1}{4}C_1 - \frac{1}{4}(\Delta x)^2 C_2$$

which consolidates the three constants C_1, C_2 and Δx.

The numerical demonstration of this rule is given in table 7.6c. The integrand in that table is

$$f(\bar{x}) = (\bar{x})^3$$

which is a function of the mid-point $\bar{x}$, and the integral is

$$\sum_a^x (\bar{x})^3 \Delta x = F(x) + C$$

which is a function of the end-point x. The purpose of this demonstration is to show that the integral is equal to (equation 7)

$$F(x) + C = \frac{1}{4}x^4 - \frac{1}{8}x^2(\Delta x)^2 + C$$

or

$$F(x) = \frac{1}{4}(x^4 - 2x^2)$$

because the chosen Δx is equal to 2. For the given values of the end-points x, the values of $F(x)$ are

$$F(0) = 0$$

$$F(2) = 2$$

$$F(4) = 56$$

$$F(6) = 306$$

which are the same values given in table 7.6c.

TABLE 7.6c

INTEGRATION OF $f(x) = x^3$

$\bar{x}$	$f(\bar{x}) = (\bar{x})^3$	$f(\bar{x})\Delta x$	x	$F(x) + C$
			0	C
1	1	2		
			2	$C + 2$
3	27	54		
			4	$C + 56$
5	125	250		
			6	$C + 306$

The rules for integrating $(\bar{x})^n$ go only as far as n being equal to 3 in this section. The reason for this is that those for differentiating x^n have gone only as far as n being equal to 4 in chapter 5. However, the rules for integrating higher powers of $\bar{x}$ can be developed. For example, in developing the rule for integrating $(\bar{x})^4$ the first step is to differentiate x^5 and obtain (equation 6, section 5.4)

$$\frac{\Delta}{\Delta x}x^5 = 5(\bar{x})^4 + g(x)(\Delta x)^2$$

where $g(x)$ has to be determined. The second step is to solve the above equation for $(\bar{x})^4$ and obtain

$$(\bar{x}) = \frac{1}{5}\left[\frac{\Delta}{\Delta x}x^5 - g(x)(\Delta x)^2\right].$$

The third step is to integrate the above equation term by term and obtain the integral of $(\bar{x})^4$. By this method, the rule for integrating any integral power of $\bar{x}$ can be developed.

7.7 Summary of Rules of Integration

The integrand $f(\bar{x})$ is a function of the mid-point $\bar{x}$, and the indefinite integral

$$\sum_a^x f(\bar{x})\Delta x = F(x) + C$$

is a function of the end-point x. The mid-point of the ith interval is $\bar{x}_i$, and the end-points of the same interval are

$$x_i = \bar{x}_i - \frac{1}{2}\Delta x$$

and

$$x_{i+1} = \bar{x}_i + \frac{1}{2}\Delta x.$$

As a result, $m-1$ values of $f(\bar{x})$ generate m values of $F(x)$.

The rules of integration developed in the preceding sections are listed as follows:

(1) $\displaystyle\sum_a^x \Delta x = x + C$

(2) $\displaystyle\sum_a^x \Delta U(x) = U(x) + C$

(3) $\displaystyle\sum_a^x k\Delta x = kx + C$

(4) $\displaystyle\sum_a^x ku(\bar{x})\Delta x = k\sum_a^x u(\bar{x})\Delta x$

(5) $\displaystyle\sum_a^x [u(\bar{x}) + v(\bar{x})]\Delta x = \sum_a^x u(\bar{x})\Delta x + \sum_a^x v(\bar{x})\Delta x$

(6) $\quad \sum\limits_{a}^{x} \bar{x}\,\Delta x \quad = \quad \dfrac{1}{2}x^2 + C$

(7) $\quad \sum\limits_{a}^{x} (\bar{x})^2 \Delta x \quad = \quad \dfrac{1}{3}x^3 - \dfrac{x}{12}(\Delta x)^2 + C$

(8) $\quad \sum\limits_{a}^{x} (\bar{x})^3 \Delta x \quad = \quad \dfrac{1}{4}x^4 - \dfrac{1}{8}x^2(\Delta x)^2 + C$

The first five rules of the above list may be used on an integrand whether it is given in the form of two columns of figures or in the form of an equation. But the last three can only be used when the integrand is given as an equation.

Each of the rules is a short cut, and each may be used individually. However, to take full advantage of the rules, one has to use them in concert. This is demonstrated in the following two sections.

7.8 Integration of Polynomial

With the aid of the rules listed in the preceding section, a polynomial of the third degree

$$f(x) \;=\; b_0 + b_1 x + b_2 x^2 + b_3 x^3$$

can be integrated. By rule 5 of section 7.7, the function $f(x)$ can be integrated term by term. By rule 3, the integral of b_0 is known to be $b_0 x + C$. By rule 4, the integral of $b_n x^n$ is known to be b_n times that of x^n. Finally, by rules 6, 7 and 8, the function x^n can be integrated for $n = 1$, 2 and 3. Thus by a combination of the known rules, a polynomial of the third degree can be integrated. However, during the process of integration, an interval has to be created around each value of x with the given value of x as the mid-point $\bar{x}$.

The integration by rules is illustrated by the integration of the function

$$f(x) \;=\; 4x^3 - 3x^2 + 2x - 1 \tag{1}$$

which is a polynomial of the third degree. By means of the rules of integration, one can find that the integral of $f(\bar{x})$ is

$$F(x) + C = 4\left(\frac{1}{4}x^4 - \frac{1}{8}x^2(\Delta x)^2 + C_4\right)$$

$$- 3\left(\frac{1}{3}x^3 - \frac{x}{12}(\Delta x)^2 + C_3\right)$$

$$+ 2\left(\frac{1}{2}x^2 + C_2\right)$$

$$- (x + C_1).$$

After simplification, the integral can be expressed as

$$F(x) + C = x^4 - x^3 + x^2 - x - \frac{1}{4}(\Delta x)^2(2x^2 - x) + C \qquad (2)$$

with the constants of integration being consolidated into

$$C = 4C_4 - 3C_3 + 2C_2 - C_1.$$

This integral is obtained purely by deduction without any computation.

TABLE 7.8

INTEGRATION OF $f(x) = 4x^3 - 3x^2 + 2x - 1$

$\bar{x}$	$f(\bar{x})$	$f(\bar{x})\Delta x$	x	$F(x) + C$
			0	C
1	2	4		
			2	$C + \quad 4$
3	86	172		
			4	$C + \quad 176$
5	434	868		
			6	$C + 1,044$

The numerical integration of the same function $f(x)$ is given in table 7.8. The x-values used are 1, 3 and 5, and the corresponding values of $f(x)$ are computed from equation (1). These pairs of values are designated by $\bar{x}$ and $f(\bar{x})$ during the process of integration, because each of the given values of x is considered the mid-point of an interval. After the integration is carried out, the integral obtained is the sequence of values labelled $F(x) + C$ where $F(x)$ is a function of the end-point x.

Now one can investigate whether the results obtained by the two methods are the same. In table 7.8, the Δx used is 2. As a result, the integral given in equation (2) can be simplified to

$$F(x) + C = x^4 - x^3 - x^2 + C. \tag{3}$$

For the given values of x, the values of $F(x)$ are

$$F(0) = \quad\ \ 0$$

$$F(2) = \quad\ \ 4$$

$$F(4) = \quad 176$$

$$F(6) = 1{,}044$$

which are exactly the values of $F(x)$ given in table 7.8.

The algebraic derivation and the numerical demonstration of the rules of integration given in this chapter serve several purposes. However, the direct application of these results to practical problems is not one of them, even though examples of applications are given in the following section.

The first purpose is to show that integration is the inverse operation of differentiation. As a result, the rules of integration can be obtained from those of differentiation. This is the procedure used in deriving the formulas of integration in the following chapter.

The second purpose is to show that the meaning of integration remains the same, whether the operation is carried out by rules or by a numerical process. When integration by formula is introduced in the following chapter, one should not get the impression that integration is mere manipulation of equations. Behind every equation, there are a lot of numbers. For example, the rule

$$\sum_{a}^{x} k\Delta x = kx + C$$

does not contain a single number but it states the relation among many numbers as demonstrated in table 7.5a.

The third purpose is to show that the integral of x^n is a function of x as well as that of Δx when n is greater than 1. This is indicated in equations (5), (6) and (7) of section 7.6. As a result, two people integrating the same function $f(x)$ do not obtain the same integral $F(x)$, unless both of them choose the same value for Δx. Furthermore, these three equations are very useful in finding the limit of the integral of x^n as Δx approaches zero. This is discussed in the following chapter.

The last and perhaps the most important purpose of the demonstrations is to show that the rules of integration are short cuts. The evaluation of a definite integral of the function $f(x)$ given in table 7.8 may be used as an illustration. By the standard method of integration, the definite integral from $x = 0$ to $x = 6$ is

$$\sum_0^6 f(\bar{x})\Delta x = \Delta x\,[f(\bar{x}_1) + f(\bar{x}_2) + f(\bar{x}_3)]$$

$$= 2\,[2 + 86 + 434]$$

$$= 1{,}044 \tag{4}$$

whose evaluation requires three substitutions in $f(x)$, two additions and one multiplication. But this example is only a textbook illustration. In a real problem where an integral covers one million intervals, the number of substitutions becomes 1,000,000 and that of additions 999,999. Furthermore, each substitution requires several arithmetic operations. Altogether, an integration like this amounts to a tremendous amount of computation.

Now the same job can be done through the rules of integration. Utilizing the integral $F(x)$ given in equation (3), which is obtained through the rules, one can obtain the definite integral

$$F(6) - F(0) = 1{,}044 - 0 = 1{,}044 \tag{5}$$

whose evaluation requires only two substitutions in $F(x)$ followed by one subtraction regardless of the number of intervals involved.

These rules are marvelous short cuts. As a general practice, the rules are used as much as possible in integration. The numerical integration is only used as a last resort. Unfortunately, outside of the textbook problems, this last resort is so frequently used that it almost becomes the standard practice of integration.

7.9 Applications of Integration

To add a touch of reality to the integrals of x^n, the rules are used here in evaluating the sum of the nth powers of the first m positive integers. For such a problem, the sum

$$\sum_{i=1}^{m} i^n = 1^n + 2^n + 3^n + \cdots + m^n \tag{1}$$

is first equated to the definite integral

$$\sum_{a}^{b} f(\bar{x})\Delta x = \Delta x \left[f(\bar{x}_1) + f(\bar{x}_2) + f(\bar{x}_3) + \cdots + f(\bar{x}_m) \right].$$

Then the sum is obtained by the rules of integration.

The conditions for the integral to be equal to the sum are: that the Δx is equal to 1, that the mid-points $\bar{x}$ are

$$1 \quad 2 \quad 3 \quad \cdots \quad m,$$

and that the integrand is

$$f(\bar{x}) = (\bar{x})^n.$$

When these conditions are met, the integral becomes

$$\sum_{a}^{b} (\bar{x})^n \Delta x = 1(1^n + 2^n + 3^n + \cdots + m^n)$$

which is the sum given in equation (1). The limits of this integral are (equations 13 and 14, section 7.3)

$$a = 1 - \frac{1}{2}\Delta x = 1 - 0.5 = 0.5$$

and

$$b = m + \frac{1}{2}\Delta x = m + 0.5.$$

For the case $n = 1$, the sum of the first m positive integers

$$\sum_{i=1}^{m} i = 1 + 2 + 3 + \cdots + m$$

is the definite integral (rule 6, section 7.7)

$$\sum_{0.5}^{m+0.5} \bar{x}\,\Delta x = \left[\frac{1}{2}x^2 \right]_{0.5}^{m+0.5}$$

$$= \frac{1}{2}[(m+0.5)^2 - (0.5)^2]$$

$$= \frac{1}{2}(m^2 + m)$$

$$= \frac{1}{2}m(m+1).$$

Then the conclusion is

$$1 + 2 + 3 + \cdots + m = \frac{1}{2}m(m+1). \tag{2}$$

For $m = 5$, the above equation says

$$1 + 2 + 3 + 4 + 5 = \frac{1}{2}(5)(6) = 15$$

which is obviously true.

For the case $n = 2$, the sum of the squares of the first m positive integers

$$\sum_{i=1}^{m} i^2 = 1^2 + 2^2 + 3^2 + \cdots + m^2$$

is the definite integral (rule 7, section 7.7)

$$\sum_{0.5}^{m+0.5} (\bar{x})^2 \, \Delta x = \left[\frac{1}{3} x^3 - \frac{x}{12} \right]_{0.5}^{m+0.5}$$

because Δx is equal to 1. After substitutions, the integral can be expressed as

$$\frac{1}{3}(m + 0.5)^3 - \frac{m + 0.5}{12} - \frac{1}{3}(0.5)^3 + \frac{0.5}{12}$$

$$= \frac{1}{3}[m^3 + 3m^2(0.5) + 3m(0.5)^2] - \frac{m}{12}$$

$$= \frac{1}{12}(4m^3 + 6m^2 + 2m)$$

$$= \frac{1}{6}m(m + 1)(2m + 1).$$

Then the conclusion is

$$1^2 + 2^2 + 3^2 + \cdots + m^2 = \frac{1}{6}m(m+1)(2m+1). \tag{3}$$

When m is equal to 3, the above equation says

$$1^2 + 2^2 + 3^2 = \frac{1}{6}(3)(4)(7) = 14$$

which is obviously true.

For the case $n = 3$, the sum of the cubes of the first m positive integers

$$\sum_{i=1}^{m} i^3 = 1^3 + 2^3 + 3^3 + \cdots + m^3$$

is the definite integral (rule 8, section 7.7)

$$\sum_{0.5}^{m+0.5} (\bar{x})^3 \, \Delta x = \left[\frac{1}{4}x^4 - \frac{1}{8}x^2\right]_{0.5}^{m+0.5}$$

because Δx is equal to 1. After substitutions, the integral can be expressed as

$$\frac{1}{4}(m + 0.5)^4 - \frac{1}{8}(m + 0.5)^2 - \frac{1}{4}(0.5)^4 + \frac{1}{8}(0.5)^2$$

$$= \frac{1}{4}[m^4 + 4m^3(0.5) + 6m^2(0.5)^2 + 4m(0.5)^3] - \frac{1}{8}(m^2 + m)$$

$$= \frac{1}{8}(2m^4 + 4m^3 + 2m^2)$$

$$= \frac{1}{4}m^2(m + 1)^2.$$

Then the conclusion is

$$1^3 + 2^3 + 3^3 + \cdots + m^3 = \frac{1}{4}m^2(m + 1)^2. \qquad (4)$$

For $m = 4$, the above equation says that the sum

$$1^3 + 2^3 + 3^3 + 4^3 = 1 + 8 + 27 + 64 = 100$$

is equal to

$$\frac{1}{4}(4)^2(5)^2 = 100.$$

An interesting sidelight can be observed in equations (2) and (4). When these two equations are combined, the invariable conclusion is

$$\left(\sum_{i=1}^{m} i\right)^2 = \sum_{i=1}^{m} i^3$$

or

$$(1 + 2 + 3 + \cdots + m)^2 = 1^3 + 2^3 + 3^3 + \cdots + m^3. \qquad (5)$$

For $m = 1$, the above equation says

$$1^2 = 1^3 = 1.$$

For $m = 3$, equation (5) says

$$(1 + 2 + 3)^2 = 1^3 + 2^3 + 3^3 = 36.$$

For $m = 6$, equation (5) says that

$$(1 + 2 + 3 + 4 + 5 + 6)^2 = (21)^2 = 441$$

is equal to

$$1^3 + 2^3 + 3^3 + 4^3 + 5^3 + 6^3 = 1 + 8 + 27 + 64 + 125 + 216 = 441.$$

This result may be used as a computing short-cut if the occasion calls for it.

The integration of the polynomial by rules can find an application in the evaluation of the sum

$$\sum_{i=1}^{m} i(i + 1) = 1 \times 2 + 2 \times 3 + 3 \times 4 + \cdots + m(m + 1). \tag{6}$$

This sum is first equated to the definite integral

$$\sum_{a}^{b} f(\bar{x})\Delta x = \Delta x \left[f(\bar{x}_1) + f(\bar{x}_2) + f(\bar{x}_3) + \cdots + f(\bar{x}_m) \right].$$

Then the sum is obtained by the rules of integration.

The conditions for the integral to be equal to the sum are: that the Δx is equal to 1, that the mid-points $\bar{x}$ are

$$1 \quad 2 \quad 3 \quad \cdots \quad m,$$

and that the integrand is

$$f(\bar{x}) = \bar{x}(\bar{x} + 1).$$

When these conditions are met, the integral becomes

$$\sum_{0.5}^{m+0.5} \bar{x}(\bar{x} + 1)\Delta x = 1 \left[1 \times 2 + 2 \times 3 + 3 \times 4 + \cdots + m(m + 1) \right]$$

which is the sum given in equation (6).

The integral of the function

$$f(\bar{x}) = \bar{x}(\bar{x} + 1) = (\bar{x})^2 + \bar{x}$$

can be obtained by the rules listed in section 7.7. By those rules, the integral should be

$$\sum_{0.5}^{m+0.5} \left[(\bar{x})^2 + \bar{x} \right]\Delta x = \left[\frac{1}{3}x^3 - \frac{x}{12} + \frac{1}{2}x^2 \right]_{0.5}^{m+0.5}$$

because Δx is equal to 1. After substitutions, the integral becomes

$$\frac{1}{3}(m+0.5)^3 - \frac{1}{12}(m+0.5) + \frac{1}{2}(m+0.5)^2$$

$$- \frac{1}{3}(0.5)^3 + \frac{0.5}{12} - \frac{1}{2}(0.5)^2$$

$$= \frac{1}{3}[m^3 + 3m^2(0.5) + 3m(0.5)^2] - \frac{m}{12} + \frac{1}{2}(m^2 + m)$$

$$= \frac{1}{12}(4m^3 + 6m^2 + 3m) - \frac{m}{12} + \frac{1}{12}(6m^2 + 6m)$$

$$= \frac{1}{12}(4m^3 + 12m^2 + 8m)$$

$$= \frac{1}{3}m(m+1)(m+2).$$

The conclusion reached from the integration is

$$1 \times 2 + 2 \times 3 + 3 \times 4 + \cdots + m(m+1) = \frac{1}{3}m(m+1)(m+2). \quad (7)$$

When m is equal to 1, the above equation says

$$1 \times 2 = \frac{1}{3}(1)(2)(3) = 2.$$

When m is equal to 2, equation (7) says

$$1 \times 2 + 2 \times 3 = \frac{1}{3}(2)(3)(4) = 8.$$

When m is equal to 10, equation (7) says that

$$1 \times 2 + 2 \times 3 + 3 \times 4 + 4 \times 5 + 5 \times 6 + 6 \times 7 + 7 \times 8 + 8 \times 9$$

$$+ 9 \times 10 + 10 \times 11$$

$$= 2 + 6 + 12 + 20 + 30 + 42 + 56 + 72 + 90 + 110$$

$$= 440$$

is equal to

$$\frac{1}{3}(10)(11)(12) = 440.$$

The advantage of equation (7) really shows up, when m is large. For example, the sum

$$\sum_{i=1}^{500} i(i+1) \;=\; \frac{1}{3}(500)(501)(502) \;=\; 41{,}917{,}000$$

of 500 terms is obtained by 2 multiplications and 1 division instead of 500 multiplications followed by 499 additions.

The basic idea of integration can be illustrated by the evaluation of the sum

$$\sum_{i=1}^{m} \frac{1}{i(i+1)} \;=\; \frac{1}{1\times2} + \frac{1}{2\times3} + \frac{1}{3\times4} + \cdots + \frac{1}{m(m+1)}. \qquad (8)$$

The comparison of the above sum with the definite integral

$$\sum_{a}^{b} f(\bar{x})\Delta x \;=\; \Delta x \,[f(\bar{x}_1) + f(\bar{x}_2) + f(\bar{x}_3) + \cdots + f(\bar{x}_m)]$$

suggests that the length of the interval is

$$\Delta x \;=\; 1$$

and the integrand is

$$\frac{1}{x(x+1)} \;=\; \frac{1}{x(x+\Delta x)}$$

with the limits a and b temporarily undetermined.

Now the objective is to find the function $F(x)$ so that its derivative is equal to

$$\frac{\Delta F}{\Delta x} \;=\; \frac{F(x+\Delta x)-F(x)}{\Delta x} \;=\; \frac{1}{x(x+1)}$$

or

$$\Delta F \;=\; F(x+1) - F(x) \;=\; \frac{1}{x(x+1)} \;=\; \frac{1}{x} - \frac{1}{x+1}$$

because Δx is equal to 1. The above equation suggests that the integral is

$$F(x) \;=\; -\frac{1}{x}$$

because

$$\Delta F \;=\; F(x+1) - F(x) \;=\; -\frac{1}{x+1} + \frac{1}{x} \;=\; \frac{1}{x(x+1)}.$$

Now what remain to be determined are the limits of the integral.

TABLE 7.9

DIFFERENTIATION OF $F(x) = -\dfrac{1}{x}$

x	$F(x) = -\dfrac{1}{x}$	$\bar{x}$	$\dfrac{\Delta F}{\Delta x}$
1	$-\dfrac{1}{1}$		
		1.5	$\dfrac{1}{2} = \dfrac{1}{1 \times 2}$
2	$-\dfrac{1}{2}$		
		2.5	$\dfrac{1}{6} = \dfrac{1}{2 \times 3}$
3	$-\dfrac{1}{3}$		
...	...	...	...
$m-1$	$-\dfrac{1}{m-1}$		
		$m-0.5$	$\dfrac{1}{(m-1)m}$
m	$-\dfrac{1}{m}$		
		$m+0.5$	$\dfrac{1}{m(m+1)}$
$m+1$	$-\dfrac{1}{m+1}$		

The numerical differentiation of $F(x)$ is given in table 7.9 which shows that the sum given in equation (8) is the sum of the values listed under $\Delta F / \Delta x$. Then, in terms of the definite integral, the required sum is

$$\sum_{1}^{m+1} \frac{\Delta F}{\Delta x} \Delta x = \Big[F(x) \Big]_{1}^{m+1} = -\frac{1}{m+1} + \frac{1}{1} = \frac{m}{m+1}.$$

This leads to the conclusion

$$\sum_{i=1}^{m} \frac{1}{i(i+1)} = \frac{1}{1 \times 2} + \frac{1}{2 \times 3} + \cdots + \frac{1}{m(m+1)} = \frac{m}{m+1}. \quad (9)$$

For $m = 1$, equation (9) says

$$\frac{1}{1\times 2} = \frac{1}{1+1} = \frac{1}{2}.$$

For $m = 2$, equation (9) says

$$\frac{1}{1\times 2} + \frac{1}{2\times 3} = \frac{2}{2+1} = \frac{2}{3}.$$

For $m = 3$, equation (9) says that

$$\frac{1}{1\times 2} + \frac{1}{2\times 3} + \frac{1}{3\times 4} = \frac{1}{2} + \frac{1}{6} + \frac{1}{12} = \frac{9}{12}$$

is equal to

$$\frac{m}{m+1} = \frac{3}{3+1} = \frac{3}{4}.$$

All these statements are obviously true.

The above result is obtained directly form the definition of integration rather than from formal rules. The integrand is not even expressed as a function of the mid-point $\bar{x}$. If it were, it would be

$$f(\bar{x}) = \frac{1}{(\bar{x} - 0.5)(\bar{x} + 0.5)} = \frac{1}{(\bar{x})^2 - 0.25}$$

as shown in table 7.9. This function cannot be integrated by the rules developed in this chapter.

EXERCISES

1. (a) Find the indefinite integral $F(x)$ of the function

x	1.0	1.2	1.4	1.6	1.8	2.0
$f(x)$	8	10	4	−5	−3	12

by the standard method given in table 7.2b.

(b) Find the definite integrals of the function $f(x)$ for the following pairs of limits:

(i) $x = 1.1$ to $x = 1.9$

(ii) $x = 0.9$ to $x = 1.5$

(c) Plot graphs so that the definite integrals of part (b) are represented by areas.

(d) For the given data, evaluate the following quantities:

(i) $\left[F(x)\right]_{1.3}^{1.9}$ (ii) $\left[F(x)\right]_{1.5}^{2.1}$

(iii) $F(1.7)$ (iv) $F(0.9)$

2. (a) Find the indefinite integral $F(x)$ of the function

x	10	20	30	40	50	60	70	80	90
$f(x)$	9	4	−3	−7	1	8	11	18	25

by the standard method given in table 7.2b.

(b) Find the value of the definite integral from $x=15$ to $x=75$.

(c) Plot a graph so that the definite integral of part (b) is represented by an area.

(d) Evaluate the following quantities with the knowledge that the constant of integration is equal to 100.

(i) $F(25)$ (ii) $F(65)$

(iii) $\left[F(x)\right]_{35}^{85}$ (iv) $\left[F(x)\right]_{15}^{55}$

3. (a) Find the indefinite integral of the function

$$u(x) = x + 2$$

by the standard method for the range $x = 0$ to $x = 20$ with Δx being equal to 4. The mid-points of the five intervals are 2, 6, 10, 14 and 18.

(b) Integrate the same function by rule, and see if the integral obtained remains the same.

(c) Evaluate the definite integral of the given function from $x = 4$ to $x = 16$.

4. Repeat exercise 3 for the function

$$v(x) = 5x^2.$$

5. Repeat exercise 3 for the function

$$w(x) = x^3$$

6. Repeat exercise 3 for the function

$$f(x) = x^3 - 5x^2 + x + 2$$

7. The relation among the integrands of exercises 3 to 6 is

$$f(x) = w(x) - v(x) + u(x).$$

Through the indefinite integrals of these exercises, show that

$$F(x) = W(x) - V(x) + U(x)$$

where W, V and U are the indefinite integrals of w, v and u respectively.

8. Show that the sum of the first m odd integers is equal to the square of m, or

$$1 + 3 + 5 + \cdots + (2m - 1) = m^2,$$

by means of the rules of integration. Then plot a graph showing the definite integral

$$1 + 3 + 5 + 7 + 9 = 25$$

as an area.

9. Show that the sum of the squares of the first m odd integers is equal to

$$1^2 + 3^2 + 5^2 + \cdots + (2m - 1)^2 = \frac{1}{3}m(2m - 1)(2m + 1)$$

by means of rules of integration. Then plot a graph showing the definite integral

$$1^2 + 3^2 + 5^2 + 7^2 = 84$$

as an area.

10. Find the sum of first m terms of the sequence

$$1 \times 2 \quad 3 \times 4 \quad 5 \times 6 \quad 7 \times 8 \quad \cdots$$

by means of integration.

CHAPTER 8

INTEGRATION—INFINITESIMAL INTERVAL

This chapter is a continuation of the preceding one. The topic is still integral calculus, but the emphasis is on the limiting value of the integral as Δx approaches zero.

8.1 Limiting Value of Integral

The magnitude of Δx in an integration is determined by the integrand $f(x)$. In evaluating the sum

$$\sum_{i=1}^{m} i^2 = 1^2 + 2^2 + 3^2 + \cdots + m^2$$

in section 7.9, the integrand used is

$$f(x) = x^2$$

and the length of the interval is automatically

$$\Delta x = 1$$

because the integrand $f(x)$ is defined only for the positive integers

$$1 \quad 2 \quad 3 \quad \cdots \quad m.$$

However, if the function $f(x)$ were defined at the x-values

$$1.0 \quad 1.5 \quad 2.0 \quad 2.5 \quad 3.0 \quad \cdots \quad m,$$

the Δx would be 0.5. This is to illustrate that the magnitude of Δx is determined by the integrand at hand.

For an integrand $f(x)$ which is defined for every value of x between the limits a and b, the range from a to b would have to be divided into infinitely many intervals, each with a length of zero. In such a case, the integral

$$\sum_{a}^{b} f(\bar{x})\Delta x = \Delta x \sum_{a}^{b} f(\bar{x})$$

can no longer be directly evaluated. At first it appears to be equal to zero, because the common factor Δx is equal to that value. But, when Δx is equal to zero, there will be infinitely many intervals

261

each of which has a value of $f(\bar{x})$. The sum of these infinitely many values of $f(\bar{x})$ would be equal to ∞, which is the symbol for infinity. Then the integral becomes $(0)(\infty)$ which is indeterminate.

To overcome this difficulty, the integral of a function $f(x)$, which is defined for every value of x, is defined as the limiting value of the sum of the products $f(\bar{x})\Delta x$ as Δx approaches zero. Integration of such a function is to find the limiting value of $(0)(\infty)$ which cannot be directly evaluated. This is similar to the situation where differentiation of such a function is to find the limiting value of $0/0$ which cannot be directly evaluated either.

TABLE 8.1a

INTEGRATION OF $f(x) = 3x^2$ WITH $\Delta x = 1.0$

$\bar{x}$	$f(\bar{x}) = 3(\bar{x})^2$	$f(\bar{x})\Delta x$	x	$F(x)$	x^3	$\frac{x}{4}(\Delta x)^2$
			0	$F(0)$	0.00	0.00
0.5	0.75	0.75				
			1	$F(0) + 0.75$	1.00	0.25
1.5	6.75	6.75				
			2	$F(0) + 7.50$	8.00	0.50

TABLE 8.1b

INTEGRATION OF $f(x) = 3x^2$ WITH $\Delta x = 0.5$

$\bar{x}$	$f(\bar{x}) = 3(\bar{x})^2$	$f(\bar{x})\Delta x$	x	$F(x)$	x^3	$\frac{x}{4}(\Delta x)^2$
			0.0	$F(0)$	0.00000	0.00000
0.25	0.1875	0.09375				
			0.5	$F(0) + 0.09375$	0.12500	0.03125
0.75	1.6875	0.84375				
			1.0	$F(0) + 0.93750$	1.00000	0.06250
1.25	4.6875	2.34375				
			1.5	$F(0) + 3.28125$	3.37500	0.09375
1.75	9.1875	4.59375				
			2.0	$F(0) + 7.87500$	8.00000	0.12500

TABLE 8.1c

INTEGRATION OF $f(x) = 3x^2$ WITH $\Delta x = 0.2$

$\bar{x}$	$f(\bar{x}) = 3(\bar{x})^2$	$f(\bar{x})\Delta x$	x	$F(x)$	x^3	$\dfrac{x}{4}(\Delta x)^2$
			0.0	$F(0)$	0.000	0.000
0.1	0.03	0.006				
			0.2	$F(0) + 0.006$	0.008	0.002
0.3	0.27	0.054				
			0.4	$F(0) + 0.060$	0.064	0.004
0.5	0.75	0.150				
			0.6	$F(0) + 0.210$	0.216	0.006
0.7	1.47	0.294				
			0.8	$F(0) + 0.504$	0.512	0.008
0.9	2.43	0.486				
			1.0	$F(0) + 0.990$	1.000	0.010
1.1	3.63	0.726				
			1.2	$F(0) + 1.716$	1.728	0.012
1.3	5.07	1.014				
			1.4	$F(0) + 2.730$	2.744	0.014
1.5	6.75	1.350				
			1.6	$F(0) + 4.080$	4.096	0.016
1.7	8.67	1.734				
			1.8	$F(0) + 5.814$	5.832	0.018
1.9	10.83	2.166				
			2.0	$F(0) + 7.980$	8.000	0.020

The idea of the limiting value of an integral is illustrated by the integration of the function

$$f(x) = 3x^2 \tag{1}$$

for the range from $x = 0$ to $x = 2$. Increasingly smaller values of Δx are used in integrating the given function, and the resulting integrals are given in tables 8.1a, 8.1b and 8.1c. In these tables the values of Δx are equal to 1.0, 0.5 and 0.2 respectively.

The integrals $F(x)$ given in the three tables are not the same, even though the integrand is the same function $3(\bar{x})^2$. The purpose of these tables is to show that the integral $F(x)$ is a function of x as well as Δx. Of course, this is a foregone conclusion, because it is known that the integral of $3(\bar{x})^2$ is (rule 7, section 7.7)

$$F(x) = x^3 - \frac{x}{4}(\Delta x)^2 \tag{2}$$

which is unquestionably a function of x and Δx. In fact, the values of $F(x)$ in tables 8.1a, 8.1b and 8.1c can be obtained by substituting values of x into the above equation. For $\Delta x = 1$, the values of $F(x)$ are

$$F(0) = 0^3 - \frac{0}{4}(1) = 0.00$$

$$F(1) = 1^3 - \frac{1}{4}(1) = 0.75$$

$$F(2) = 2^3 - \frac{2}{4}(1) = 7.50$$

which are the same values given in table 8.1a.

As Δx approaches zero, the limiting value of the integral of $3(\bar{x})^2$ is x^3. This can be seen from equation (2). As Δx approaches zero, the limiting value of $\bar{x}$ becomes

$$\lim_{\Delta x \to 0} \bar{x} = \lim_{\Delta x \to 0} \left(x + \frac{1}{2}\Delta x \right) = x$$

and that of the integrand becomes $3x^2$. At the same time, the limiting value of $F(x)$ becomes

$$\lim_{\Delta x \to 0} F(x) = \lim_{\Delta x \to 0} \left[x^3 - \frac{x}{4}(\Delta x)^2 \right] = x^3 .$$

So the discrepancy between the integral $F(x)$ of $3(\bar{x})^2$ with a positive Δx and its limiting value x^3 as Δx approaches zero is

$$x^3 - F(x) = \frac{x}{4}(\Delta x)^2 \tag{3}$$

whose limiting value is zero as Δx approaches zero.

The fact that the limiting value of the discrepancy is zero, as Δx approaches zero, can be observed in tables 8.1a, 8.1b and 8.1c. In each table the values of the discrepancy are listed in the last column. As Δx decreases and approaches zero, the values of the discrepancy are also getting closer to zero. As a result, the integral $F(x)$ is getting closer to x^3. For example, at $x = 2$, the values of $F(x)$ for different values of Δx are

$$F(2) = 7.500 \qquad \text{for } \Delta x = 1.0$$

$$F(2) = 7.875 \qquad \text{for } \Delta x = 0.5$$

$$F(2) = 7.980 \qquad \text{for } \Delta x = 0.2$$

which are getting closer to 2^3 or 8 as Δx approaches zero.

In the common usage of the terms, the limiting value of an integral, as Δx approaches zero, is simply called an *integral*. Thus $x^3 + C$ is called the integral of $3x^2$. What is called an integral in the preceding chapter is usually called a *sum*, which is the sum of a number of products $f(\bar{x})\Delta x$. Thus an integral is the limiting value of the sum $\sum f(\bar{x})\Delta x$ as Δx approaches zero.

The cumbersome equation

$$\lim_{\Delta x \to 0} \sum_{a}^{x} 3(\bar{x})^2 \Delta x = x^3 + C \tag{4}$$

is usually streamlined into

$$\int_{a}^{x} 3x^2 dx = x^3 + C \tag{5}$$

or simply as

$$\int 3x^2 dx = x^3 + C \tag{6}$$

without indicating the limits of integration. To indicate that the integral is a limiting value, as Δx approaches zero, the sum $\sum$ is replaced by the elongated S and the difference Δ is replaced by the letter d. But both $\sum$ and $\int$ are derived from the word *sum*, and both Δ and d come from *difference*. The symbols $\sum$ and Δ are used in connection with integrals or sums with positive Δx, while $\int$ and d are used in connection with their limiting values as Δx approaches zero.

The quantity dx and dy are called *differentials*, in contrast to Δx and Δy which are called differences. The differential of x is an interval of x with an infinitesimal length, and that of y is

$$dy = \frac{dy}{dx}dx. \tag{7}$$

For example, the differential of x^2 is equal to

$$d(x^2) = 2x\ dx.$$

As a practice of using the new symbols, one may consider the definite integral of $3x^2$ from $x = 0$ to $x = 2$ for various values of Δx. From table 8.1a where Δx is equal to 1, the definite integral obtained is

$$3\sum_0^2 (\bar{x})^2 \Delta x = F(2) - F(0) = 7.500.$$

From table 8.1b where Δx is equal to 0.5, the definite integral obtained is

$$3\sum_0^2 (\bar{x})^2 \Delta x = F(2) - F(0) = 7.875.$$

From table 8.1c where Δx is equal to 0.2, the definite integral obtained is

$$3\sum_0^2 (\bar{x})^2 \Delta x = F(2) - F(0) = 7.980.$$

But the limiting value of the same definite integral is

$$\int_0^2 3x^2 dx = \left[x^3 \right]_0^2 = 2^3 - 0^3 = 8.000.$$

The idea of the limiting value of an integral can also be expressed geometrically. Each of the four definite integrals given above is represented in figure 8.1 as an area which consists of a number of rectangles. The height of each rectangle is $f(\bar{x})$ and the width is Δx (tables 8.1a, b, c). As Δx decreases and approaches zero, the number of rectangles increases. But the product of the two numbers

$$p\,\Delta x = 2$$

is a constant, where p is the number of intervals or rectangles. For $\Delta x = 1$, the product is

$$p\,\Delta x = 2(1) = 2.$$

For $\Delta x = 0.5$, the product is

$$p\,\Delta x = 4(0.5) = 2.$$

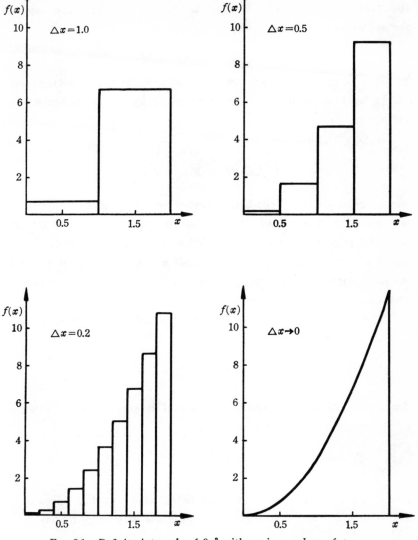

FIG. 8.1. Definite integrals of $3x^2$ with various values of Δx.

For $\Delta x = 0.2$, the product is also equal to

$$p\,\Delta x \;=\; 10(0.2) \;=\; 2\,.$$

In each case, the total area of the p rectangles is the definite integral

$$\sum_0^2 f(\bar{x})\Delta x \;=\; F(2) - F(0)$$

which increases from 7.500 to 7.875 and then to 7.980 as Δx assumes the values 1.0, 0.5 and 0.2. As Δx approaches zero, the top of rectangles becomes the curve

$$f(x) = 3x^2$$

as given in the lower-right graph of figure 8.1 and the limiting value of the area is 8.000 which is represented by the area under the curve.

In general, the integral

$$\int_a^b f(x)\, dx = F(b) - F(a)$$

can be represented by the area bounded by the curve $f(x)$ on the top, x axis on the bottom, the vertical line located at $x = a$ on the left, and another vertical line located at $x = b$ on the right. In an indefinite integral where the upper limit is the independent variable x, the vertical line at the right is not fixed but moves with the changing value of x.

The integral of $3x^2$ can also be obtained from the derivative (equation 6, section 6.2)

$$\frac{d}{dx}(x^3 + C) = 3x^2.$$

Since integration is the inverse operation of differentiation, the integral of the derivative of $x^3 + C$ must be

$$\int 3x^2 dx = \int\left[\frac{d}{dx}(x^3 + C)\right]dx = \int d(x^3 + C) = x^3 + C$$

itself. Here one can see the neutralizing effect of the operators $\int$ and d which react to each other in the same way as Σ and Δ do.

8.2 Integration by Formula

The definite integral of $f(x)$ from $x = a$ to $x = b$ is

$$\int_a^b f(x)\, dx = \lim_{\Delta x \to 0} \sum_a^b f(\bar{x})\Delta x,$$

and the indefinite integral of $f(x)$ is

$$\int f(x)\, dx = \int_a^x f(x)\, dx = \lim_{\Delta x \to 0} \sum_a^x f(\bar{x})\Delta x.$$

These are definitions, but the operation is done by formulas whenever possible.

The formulas can be obtained either by finding the limiting value of

$$F(x) = \sum_{a}^{x} f(\bar{x}) \Delta x$$

as Δx approaches zero or by reversing the formulas of differentiation. Some of these formulas are given below:

(1) $\int dx = x + C$

(2) $\int dU = U + C$

(3) $\int k \, dx = kx + C$

(4) $\int ku \, dx = k \int u \, dx$

(5) $\int (u + v) \, dx = \int u \, dx + \int v \, dx$

(6) $\int x \, dx = \frac{1}{2} x^2 + C$

(7) $\int x^2 \, dx = \frac{1}{3} x^3 + C$

(8) $\int x^3 \, dx = \frac{1}{4} x^4 + C$

(9) $\int x^n \, dx = \frac{1}{n+1} x^{n+1} + C \qquad n \neq -1$

(10) $\int v^n \, dv = \frac{1}{n+1} v^{n+1} + C \qquad n \neq -1.$

The first eight formulas of the above list are the limiting values of those given in section 7.7 as Δx approaches zero. As a result, the operators Σ and Δ are replaced by $\int$ and d. Furthermore, the mid-point

$$\bar{x} = x - \frac{1}{2} \Delta x$$

becomes x as Δx approaches zero.

The ninth formula originates from

$$\frac{\Delta}{\Delta x}x^n = nx^{n-1} + g(x)(\Delta x)^2$$

given in equation (6) of section 5.4. As Δx approaches zero, the derivative of x^n becomes

$$\frac{d}{dx}x^n = nx^{n-1}$$

or that of x^{n+1} becomes

$$\frac{d}{dx}x^{n+1} = (n+1)x^n.$$

Integrating both sides of the above equation, one obtains

$$x^{n+1} + C_1 = (n+1)\int x^n dx$$

or

$$\int x^n dx = \frac{1}{n+1}x^{n+1} + C$$

where C is equal to $C_1/(n+1)$. The above equation is formula no. 9, but it is also formula nos. 1, 6, 7 and 8 when n is equal to 0, 1, 2 and 3 respectively.

The tenth formula is derived from the ninth one. When the independent variable x in the ninth formula is replaced by the function $v(x)$, the result is

$$\int v^n dv = \frac{1}{n+1}v^{n+1} + C \qquad n \neq -1.$$

In both formulas, no. 9 and no. 10, the number n cannot be equal to -1, for otherwise division by zero would occur. The method of integrating v^{-1} is discussed in section 10.6.

The remaining formulas of integration can also be obtained from those of differentiation. For example, from the derivative

$$\frac{d}{dx}(U+C) = \frac{dU}{dx} + 0 = \frac{dU}{dx}$$

one can obtain the integral

$$U + C = \int \left(\frac{dU}{dx} \right) dx = \int dU$$

which is formula no. 2.

The integration of a polynomial can be readily accomplished by using the formulas in concert. The integration of the function

$$f(x) = 4x^3 - 3x^2 + 2x - 1$$

is used here as an illustration. By formula 5, the function can be integrated term by term. Then each term can be integrated by formulas 4 and 9. The integral thus obtained is

$$F(x) + C = x^4 - x^3 + x^2 - x + C.$$

The integrand $f(x)$ given above is the same one given in equation (1) of section 7.8 and the integral $F(x) + C$ is the limiting value of the integral given in equation (2) of the same section or the integral is

$$F(x) + C = \lim_{\Delta x \to 0} \left[x^4 - x^3 + x^2 - x - \frac{1}{4}(\Delta x)^2 (2x^2 + x) + C \right]$$

$$= x^4 - x^3 + x^2 - x + C.$$

From this example, one can see that the integral of a polynomial is even easier to find if one is only interested in its limiting value.

When Δx approaches zero, the limiting value of a definite integral of a polynomial is just as easy to obtain. For example, the definite integral of the given function $f(x)$ from $x = 1$ to $x = 3$ is

$$\int_1^3 f(x)\, dx = \left[x^4 - x^3 + x^2 - x \right]_1^3 = 60 - 0 = 60$$

which take considerably less time to evaluate than the numerical process.

As a practice of using the formulas of integration, one may find the definite integral of

$$f(x) = x^3 - 2x^2 + 4x - 5$$

from $x = 1$ to $x = 4$. The indefinite integral of $f(x)$ is

$$F(x) + C = \frac{x^4}{4} - \frac{2x^3}{3} + \frac{4x^2}{2} - 5x + C,$$

and the definite integral is

$$\int_1^4 f(x)dx = F(4) - F(1) = \frac{100}{3} - \frac{-41}{12} = 36.75 \,.$$

The application of formula no. 10 may be illustrated by the integration of the function

$$f(x) = x(x^2 + 1)^2$$

from $x = 1$ to $x = 5$. Here the quantity $x^2 + 1$ may be regarded as the function $v(x)$. Then derivative of v is

$$\frac{dv}{dx} = \frac{d}{dx}(x^2 + 1) = 2x$$

or the differential of v is (equation 7, section 8.1)

$$dv = 2x\,dx\,.$$

In terms of v, the integral of $f(x)$ is

$$\int x(x^2 + 1)^2 dx = \frac{1}{2}\int (x^2 + 1)^2(2x\,dx) = \frac{1}{2}\int v^2 dv = \frac{1}{6}v^3 + C \,.$$

At the same time, the limits $x = 1$ and $x = 5$ become $v = 2$ and $v = 26$ because $v = x^2 + 1$. Then the definite integral becomes

$$\int_1^5 f(x)\,dx = \frac{1}{6}\Big[v^3\Big]_2^{26} = \frac{1}{6}(17{,}576 - 8) = 2{,}928 \,.$$

Of course, the integral can be expressed as a function of x before evaluation; that is,

$$\int_1^5 f(x)\,dx = \frac{1}{6}\Big[(x^2 + 1)^3\Big]_1^5 = 2{,}928 \,.$$

But the result remains the same.

For the given example, formula no. 10 can be avoided. The integrand $f(x)$ can be expressed as

$$x(x^2 + 1)^2 = x(x^4 + 2x^2 + 1) = x^5 + 2x^3 + x$$

which is a polynomial in x. After integration term by term, the indefinite integral is

$$F(x) + C = \int f(x)\,dx = \frac{1}{6}x^6 + \frac{2}{4}x^4 + \frac{1}{2}x^2 + C$$

and the definite integral is

$$\int_1^5 f(x)\,dx \;=\; F(5) - F(1) \;=\; \frac{17{,}575}{6} - \frac{7}{6} \;=\; 2{,}928$$

which is the same result obtained through the integration of v.

An integral is a function of its limits. The definite integral of a function $f(x)$ may or may not be a function of x. It all depends on the limits of the integral. For example, the definite integral

$$\int_0^1 2x\,dx \;=\; \Big[\,x^2\,\Big]_0^1 \;=\; 1$$

is not a function of x but the constant 1. If one prefers, he may write the simple number 1 in this fancy fashion.

The integral can be a function of another variable t, even if the integrand is a function of x. For example, the integral

$$\int_0^t 2x\,dx \;=\; \Big[\,x^2\,\Big]_0^t \;=\; t^2$$

is a function of t.

Only when one of the limits of an integral is x, the integral itself is a function of x. For example, the integral

$$\int_1^x 2x\,dx \;=\; \Big[\,x^2\,\Big]_1^x \;=\; x^2 - 1$$

is a function of x. So is the integral

$$\int_x^5 2x\,dx \;=\; \Big[\,x^2\,\Big]_x^5 \;=\; 25 - x^2.$$

When the limits are equal, the integral is equal to zero. For example, the integral

$$\int_b^b 2x\,dx \;=\; \Big[\,x^2\,\Big]_b^b \;=\; b^2 - b^2 \;=\; 0.$$

One can always express the simple number 0 in this impressive way.

All these points about the definite integral are discussed in section 7.3. They are brought up here again to emphasize the fact that an integral is a function of its limits.

8.3 Area under Curve

The geometric interpretation of the integral or the sum

$$\sum_a^b f(\bar{x})\Delta x \;=\; F(b) - F(a)$$

is that it is the total area of a number of rectangles each of which has $f(\bar{x})$ as the height and Δx as the width. As Δx approaches zero, the limiting value

$$\int_a^b f(x)\,dx = \lim_{\Delta x \to 0} \sum_a^b f(\bar{x})\Delta x$$

becomes the area under the curve

$$y = f(x)$$

as shown in figure 8.1. Three examples are given in this section to demonstrate that the integration can be used in finding an area of a geometric figure which is not a rectangle.

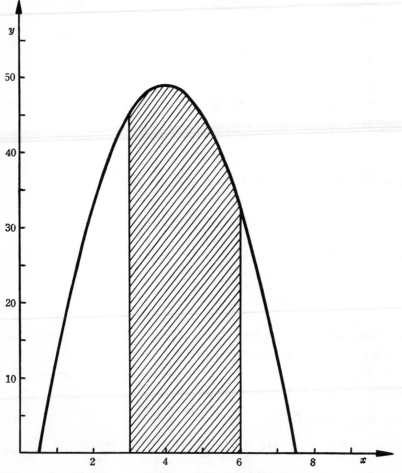

Fig. 8.3a. Geometric interpretation of integral of $y = f(x) = -4x^2 + 32x - 15$ from $x = 3$ to $x = 6$.

The first example is to find the area bounded by the curve

$$y = f(x) = -4x^2 + 32x - 15 \tag{1}$$

on the top, the x axis on the bottom, the vertical line $x = 3$ on the left, and another vertical line $x = 6$ on the right. This is the shaded area shown in figure 8.3a. The technic of finding the area of such an irregular figure is to divide the range from $x = 3$ to $x = 6$ into p intervals with the length of each interval being

$$\Delta x = \frac{6-3}{p} = \frac{3}{p}.$$

Then the value of $f(\bar{x})$ is computed for the mid-point $\bar{x}$ of each of the p intervals. The total area of the p rectangles is approximately equal to the area desired. However, as p increases with bound, or as Δx approaches zero, the limiting value

$$\lim_{\Delta x \to 0} \sum_{3}^{6} f(\bar{x})\Delta x = \int_{3}^{6} f(x)\, dx$$

becomes the area desired. This is demonstrated at the end of section 8.1.

By means of the formulas, the integral of $f(x)$ can be found as

$$F(x) + C = \frac{-4x^3}{3} + \frac{32x^2}{2} - 15x + C.$$

The desired area obtained from the above integral is

$$\frac{1}{3}\left[-4x^3 + 48x^2 - 45x \right]_{3}^{6} = \frac{1}{3}(594 - 189) = 135 \tag{2}$$

which is the size of the shaded area of figure 8.3a.

The second example is to find the area bounded by the curve

$$y = g(x) = x^3 - 10x^2 + 27x - 18 \tag{3}$$

and the x axis. This is the shaded area shown in figure 8.3b. The area above the x axis is positive and that below it is negative, because a positive value of $g(x)$ is plotted above the x axis and a negative value plotted below it.

The first step of solving this problem is to find the zeroes of $g(x)$ so that one would know where the curve crosses the x axis. Solving the equation

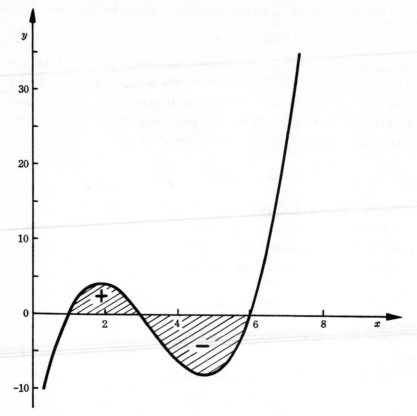

Fɪɢ. 8.3b. Integral of $y = g(x) = x^3 - 10x^2 + 27x - 18$ showing
positive and negative areas.

$$g(x) = x^3 - 10x^2 + 27x - 18 = 0,$$

one obtains 1, 3 and 6 as the roots. These roots furnish the limits
of the integral of $g(x)$.

The second step is to find the area

$$\int_1^3 g(x)dx = \left[\frac{x^4}{4} - \frac{10x^3}{3} + \frac{27x^2}{2} - 18x \right]_1^3 = \frac{16}{3}$$

and the area

$$\int_3^6 g(x)dx = \left[\frac{x^4}{4} - \frac{10x^3}{3} + \frac{27x^2}{2} - 18x \right]_3^6 = -\frac{63}{4}$$

separately. Then the total area enclosed by the curve $y = g(x)$ and
the x axis is the sum of the numerical values of the two integrals;

that is,

$$\frac{16}{3} + \frac{63}{4} = \frac{253}{12} = 21.08.$$

However, if the function $g(x)$ were integrated from $x = 1$ to $x = 6$ all at once, the integral would be

$$\int_1^6 g(x)dx = \left[\frac{x^4}{4} - \frac{10x^3}{3} + \frac{27x^2}{2} - 18x\right]_1^6 = -\frac{125}{12}$$

which is equal to

$$\int_1^3 g(x)dx + \int_3^6 g(x)dx = \frac{16}{3} - \frac{63}{4} = -\frac{125}{12}.$$

This integral is as correct as can be, but it is not the area being sought.

The third example is to find the area bounded by the curves

$$y = f(x) = -4x^2 + 32x - 15$$

and

$$y = h(x) = x^2 - 8x + 20.$$

This is the shaded area shown in figure 8.3c.

In finding the enclosed area, one can visualize the irregular figure is cut into long and narrow rectangles each with a height of $f(\bar{x}) - h(\bar{x})$ and a width of Δx. The total area of the rectangles is approximately equal to the area of the irregular figure. But, as Δx approaches zero, the limiting value

$$\lim_{\Delta x \to 0} \sum_a^b [f(\bar{x}) - h(\bar{x})]\Delta x = \int_a^b [f(x) - h(x)]dx$$

is the area sought.

The first step in solving the problem at hand is to determine the limits of integration. It can be seen in figure 8.3c that the limits are the values of x where the curves meet or where $f(x)$ is equal to $h(x)$. Solving the equation

$$f(x) - h(x) = -5x^2 + 40x - 35 = 0,$$

one obtains 1 and 7 as the roots. So the enclosed area starts from $x = 1$ and ends at $x = 7$. These values become the limits of integration.

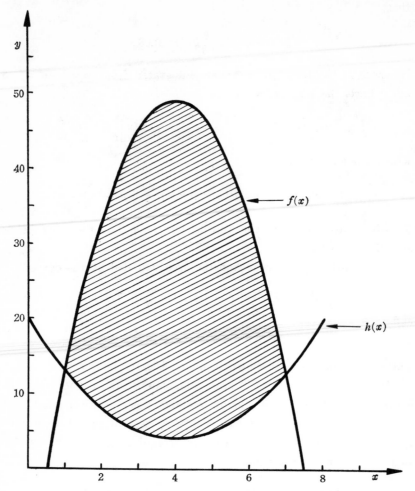

Fig. 8.3c. Enclosed area by $y = f(x) = -4x^2 + 32x - 15$ and
$y = h(x) = x^2 - 8x + 20$.

The second step is to evaluate the integral

$$\int_1^7 [f(x) - h(x)]dx = \int_1^7 (-5x^2 + 40x - 35)dx.$$

By means of the formulas of integration, it can be found that the integral is equal to

$$\left[-\frac{5x^3}{3} + \frac{40x^2}{2} - \frac{35x}{1} \right]_1^7 = 180.$$

All the three examples of application of integration given in this section illustrate the fact that the basic area is that of a rectangle. When confronted with any figure other than a rectangle, one divides the figure into a number of rectangles and finds the total area of the rectangles as the approximate area of the irregular figure. If an exact area is desired, one finds the limiting value of the total area as the width Δx approaches zero. This is the basic idea of finding the area of a geometric figure by means of integral calculus.

When one finds the area of a geometric figure through calculus, he is not necessarily interested in the area as such. He can be interested in anything that can be interpreted as an area. Since curves are so commonly used in so many fields of human endeavor, or so many diversified problems are translated into geometry, perhaps the reader can find applications of integral calculus in his own field of interest through geometry.

8.4 Volume of Solid of Revolution

The solid of revolution is the solid generated by revolving a plane surface about an axis. Figure 8.4a shows that the triangle AOB generates a cone when it revolves about the x axis. Figure 8.4b shows that a circle generates a sphere in the same way. This section is devoted to the evaluation of the volumes of such solids.

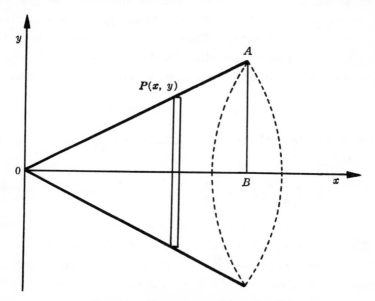

Fig. 8.4a. Cone generated by triangle.

The first example of the volume of a solid of revolution is that of a cone whose height is equal to h and whose radius at the base is equal to r. The volume of such a cone is

$$V_c = \frac{1}{3}\pi r^2 h \tag{1}$$

as given in high-school geometry. Here, as a practice of the application of integration, the volume is determined from the very beginning.

As the first step, the triangle AOB is constructed as shown in figure 8.4a. The coordinates of the vertices are $A(h, r)$, $O(0, 0)$ and $B(h, 0)$ so that the cone generated by the triangle revolving about the x axis will have a height h and a radius r at the base. With these coordinates assigned, the equation of the straight line OA necessarily becomes

$$y = \frac{r}{h}x \tag{2}$$

as explained in section 4.3.

The second step is to visualize the cone as a pile of circular discs with the bottom one having the radius r and the top one radius zero. The volume of the cone is approximately equal to the total volume of the discs. It can be observed in figure 8.4a that the circular disc at the point $P(x, y)$ has a radius y, thickness Δx, and consequently a volume $\pi y^2 \Delta x$. Then the approximate volume of the cone is the sum of such quantities, and the exact volume V_c of the cone is the limiting value of this sum, as Δx approaches zero, or

$$V_c = \lim_{\Delta x \to 0} \sum_0^h \pi y^2 \Delta x = \int_0^h \pi y^2 dx . \tag{3}$$

By means of the formulas of integration, the volume V_c can be determined as

$$\int_0^h \pi \left(\frac{r}{h}x\right)^2 dx = \frac{\pi r^2}{h^2}\left[\frac{x^3}{3}\right]_0^h = \frac{1}{3}\pi r^2 h \tag{4}$$

which is the well-known result given in equation (1).

The second example of the volume of a solid of revolution is that of a sphere whose radius is equal to r. The sphere can be generated by revolving the circle (section 4.8)

$$x^2 + y^2 = r^2 \tag{5}$$

about the x axis as shown in figure 8.4b. To find the volume of the sphere, one visualizes the solid as a stack of circular discs. The radius of the disc increases from zero at the point $A(-r, 0)$ to r at the origin, and then decreases from there to zero again at the point $B(r, 0)$. The volume of the sphere is approximately equal to the total volume of the discs.

The disc at a point $P(x, y)$ on the circle has a radius y, thickness Δx, and consequently a volume $\pi y^2 \Delta x$. The limiting value of the sum of $\pi y^2 \Delta x$, as Δx approaches zero, is the exact volume

$$V_s = \lim_{\Delta x \to 0} \sum_{-r}^{r} \pi y^2 \Delta x = \int_{-r}^{r} \pi y^2 dx. \qquad (6)$$

With the aid of the formulas of integration, the volume can be determined as

$$\int_{-r}^{r} \pi (r^2 - x^2) dx = \pi \left[r^2 x - \frac{x^3}{3} \right]_{-r}^{r} = \frac{4}{3} \pi r^3 \qquad (7)$$

which is the volume of a sphere.

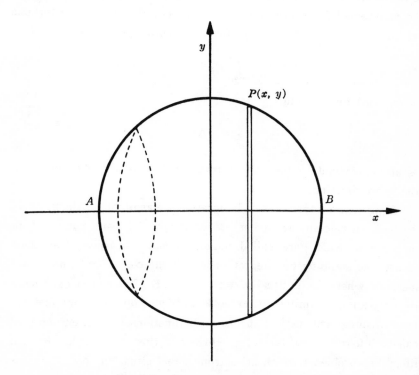

Fig. 8.4b. Sphere generated by circle.

The purpose of this section is not to introduce the volume of a cone and that of a sphere, but to illustrate the possible applications of integration. Since a definite integral is the limiting value of the sum of a number of elements such as $\pi y^2 \Delta x$, the first step in an application of integration is to determine the elements. After this is done, one can evaluate the definite integral as a process of finding the limiting value of the sum of these elements, as Δx approaches zero.

8.5 Standard Method of Integration

The formulas of integration introduced so far are good only for polynomials in x. For positive Δx, the rules of integration are summarized in section 7.7 and their applications are demonstrated in section 7.9. For infinitesimal Δx, the formulas of integration are given in section 8.2 and their applications are demonstrated in sections 8.3 and 8.4. The line of demarcation between these two cases is quite clear. However, this distinction between the cases cannot always be maintained for every kind of integrand. Whenever the formula of integration cannot be found for the function $f(x)$, the integral

$$\int_a^b f(x)\,dx$$

is replaced by the sum

$$\sum_a^b f(\bar{x})\Delta x$$

as an approximate value. Of course, smaller is the Δx; closer is the approximation.

Long lists of formulas of integration are available. Almost every textbook on calculus has a list. Much longer lists are published in monographs which are called *integral tables*. In spite of all these efforts, the stand-by of integration is still the collection of numerical methods where Δx is usually small but finite. When one's experience in integration is limited to textbook problems, one does not feel the need of numerical methods because all functions he ever encountered can be integrated by formulas. However, this is not true in real life. For problems which arise from a real situation, one often has to rely upon numerical methods which use Δx rather than dx.

One of the numerical methods of integration is the standard method given in table 7.2b. This method is repeatedly used in chapter 7 as a means of presenting the principles of integration. Now its use is demonstrated in a different light. Here the sum

$$\sum_{a}^{b} f(\bar{x})\Delta x$$

is looked upon as an approximation of the integral

$$\int_{a}^{b} f(x)dx .$$

The first example of the use of the standard method as a means of approximation is the integration of the linear function

$$f(x) \;=\; 2x$$

from $x = 1$ to $x = 9$. The details of the computation are shown in table 8.5a. The range 1 to 9 is divided into four intervals with Δx equal to 2. At the mid-point $\bar{x}$ of each interval, the value of $2\bar{x}$ is calculated. The sum of $f(\bar{x})\Delta x$ is equal to

TABLE 8.5a

INTEGRATION OF $f(x) = 2x$ BY STANDARD METHOD

x	$\bar{x}$	$f(\bar{x})$
1		
	2	4
3		
	4	8
5		
	6	12
7		
	8	16
9		
	Sum	40
$\Delta x \; \Sigma f(\bar{x}) = 2(40) = 80$		

$$\sum_1^9 f(\bar{x})\Delta x \;=\; \Delta x \sum_1^9 f(\bar{x}) \;=\; 2(40) \;=\; 80\,.$$

But the same integral obtained by formula is also

$$\int_1^9 2x\,dx \;=\; \Big[\,x^2\,\Big]_1^9 \;=\; 81-1 \;=\; 80.$$

This is to demonstrate that the standard method and the integration by formula yield an identical result if the integrand is a linear function.

The reason why the standard method of integration yields the same result as that obtained by formula in the case of a linear integrand is shown graphically in figure 8.5a. The integral

$$\int_1^9 2x\,dx \;=\; 80$$

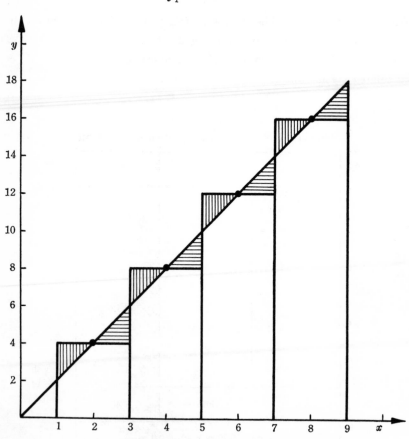

Fɪɢ. 8.5a. Standard method of integrating $2x$.

represents the area bounded by the straight line

$$y = 2x$$

on the top, x axis on the bottom, the vertical line at $x = 1$ on the left, and another vertical line at $x = 9$ on the right; while the sum

$$\sum_1^9 f(\bar{x})\Delta x = 80$$

represents the total area of the four rectangles. When the standard method is used in integration, the area under the curve

$$y = f(x) = 2x$$

is replaced by those of the rectangles. In so doing, some areas are gained and others are lost. The areas gained are shaded by vertical lines in figure 8.5a, and those lost by horizontal ones. It can be proven by plane geometry that the total area gained is exactly equal to that lost if the integrand is a straight line. This is the reason why the standard method yields the exact definite integral for the given example.

If the integrand is not linear, the standard method does not yield the same value as the corresponding integral. This is illustrated by the integration of the function

$$f(x) = 3x^2$$

from $x = 1$ to $x = 9$. The details of the computation are shown in table 8.5b. In that table, the range 1 to 9 is divided into four intervals with Δx equal to 2. For the mid-point $\bar{x}$ of each interval, the value of $3(\bar{x})^2$ is calculated. The approximate integral is equal to

$$\sum_1^9 f(\bar{x})\Delta x = \Delta x \sum_1^9 3(\bar{x})^2 = 2(360) = 720.$$

But the integral of $3x^2$ obtained by formula is

$$\int_1^9 3x^2 dx = \left[x^3\right]_1^9 = 729 - 1 = 728.$$

Then the discrepancy or error is

$$720 - 728 = -8.$$

TABLE 8.5b

INTEGRATION OF $f(x) = 3x^2$ BY STANDARD METHOD

x	$\bar{x}$	$f(\bar{x})$
1		
	2	12
3		
	4	48
5		
	6	108
7		
	8	192
9		
	Sum	360
$\Delta x \sum f(\bar{x}) = 2(360) = 720$		

The reason why the standard method does not yield the exact integral for the function $3x^2$ can be seen graphically from figure 8.5b. The exact integral is the area under the curve from $x = 1$ to $x = 9$, and the approximate integral is the total area of the four rectangles. When the exact integral is replaced by the approximate integral, the areas gained do not entirely compensate those lost. However, the discrepancy should decrease if the Δx is reduced in magnitude.

The approximate integral produced by the standard method can be made as close to the exact integral as one wishes by using small enough Δx or large enough number of intervals. The error -8 of the given example is a direct consequence of the number of intervals used in the integration. From rule 7 of section 7.7 it can be established that

$$\sum_{a}^{x} 3(\bar{x})^2 \Delta x = x^3 - \frac{x}{4}(\Delta x)^2 + C.$$

Then the approximate integral obtained by the standard method is simply

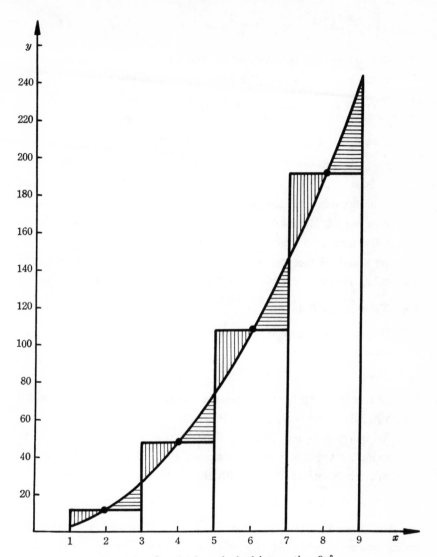

F<small>IG</small>. 8.5b. Standard method of integrating $3x^2$.

$$\left[x^3 - \frac{x}{4}(\Delta x)^2\right]_1^9 = \left[729 - \frac{9}{4}(2)^2\right] - \left[1 - \frac{1}{4}(2)^2\right] = 720.$$

But the exact integral is

$$\left[x^3\right]_1^9 = 729 - 1 = 728.$$

So the error has to be

$$\left[-\frac{x}{4}(\Delta x)^2\right]_1^9 = -\frac{9-1}{4}(\Delta x)^2 = -\frac{9-1}{4}(2)^2 = -8.$$

However, when Δx is reduced in magnitude, the error decreases. For example, if Δx is 0.01, the error is reduced to

$$-\frac{9-1}{4}(\Delta x)^2 = -0.0002.$$

In this case, the number of intervals becomes

$$\frac{9-1}{0.01} = 800.$$

Then the amount of computation will be increased considerably. One does not obtain more accurate result for nothing. The price to pay is the increased amount of computation.

The standard method is one among many numerical methods. Two other methods are given in the following sections.

8.6   Trapezoidal Rule

The *trapezoidal rule* is a numerical method of integration. To integrate the function

$$y = f(x)$$

from $x = a$ to $x = b$ by this rule, the range a to b is first divided into p equal intervals by $p+1$ points with x_1 being equal to a and x_{p+1} being equal to b. Then for each of the $p+1$ values of x, the corresponding value of y or $f(x)$ is calculated. So, by the trapezoidal rule, one starts the operation with the following $p+1$ points:

$$P_1(x_1, y_1) \quad P_2(x_2, y_2) \quad \cdots \quad P_{p+1}(x_{p+1}, y_{p+1})$$

The process of the trapezoidal rule is illustrated in figure 8.6a which shows an example of p being equal to 4. The $p+1$ or 5 points are shown in that figure as dots and are designated by P_1, P_2, P_3, P_4 and P_5. Then the straight lines P_1P_2, P_2P_3, P_3P_4 and P_4P_5 are drawn to join the adjacent points. Thus p or 4 trapezoids are formed. The trapezoidal rule is to use the total area of the p trapezoids as an approximation of the integral

$$\int_a^b f(x)\,dx = \int_a^b y\,dx$$

which is the area under the curve $y = f(x)$.

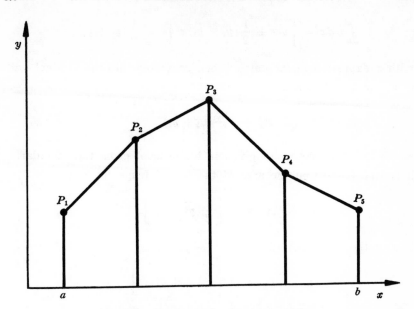

FIG. 8.6a. Trapezoidal rule of integration.

The area of a trapezoid can be found through the equation of the straight line connecting two adjacent points. To simplify the algebra involved, the first pair of points are given the coordinates $P_1(0, y_1)$ and $P_2(1, y_2)$ so that the length of the interval becomes

$$\Delta x = x_2 - x_1 = 1 - 0 = 1.$$

This is to say that the independent variable is now using Δx as the unit of measurement.

The equation of the straight line connecting the points $P_1(0, y_1)$ and P_2 $(1, y_2)$ is (equation 5, section 4.4)

$$\frac{y - y_1}{x - x_1} = \frac{y_2 - y_1}{x_2 - x_1}$$

or

$$\frac{y - y_1}{x} = y_2 - y_1$$

or

$$y = y_1 + (y_2 - y_1)x.$$

Then the area of the first trapezoid is

$$\int_0^1 y \, dx = \left[y_1 x + \frac{1}{2}(y_2 - y_1)x^2 \right]_0^1 = \frac{1}{2}(y_1 + y_2)$$

with x expressed in Δx unit. When converted into the original unit of x, the area becomes

$$A_1 = \frac{\Delta x}{2}(y_1 + y_2)$$

which is a familiar result given in high-school geometry. Similarly, it can be found that the area of the second trapezoid is

$$A_2 = \Delta x \left[\frac{1}{2}(y_2 + y_3) \right],$$

that of the ith trapezoid is

$$A_i = \Delta x \left[\frac{1}{2}(y_i + y_{i+1}) \right], \tag{1}$$

and that of the pth or the last trapezoid is

$$A_p = \Delta x \left[\frac{1}{2}(y_p + y_{p+1}) \right].$$

Thus the total area of the p trapezoids is

$$\sum_{i=1}^{p} A_i = \Delta x \left[\frac{1}{2} y_1 + y_2 + \cdots + y_p + \frac{1}{2} y_{p+1} \right]$$

$$= \Delta x \left[\frac{1}{2} f(x_1) + f(x_2) + \cdots + f(x_p) + \frac{1}{2} f(x_{p+1}) \right] \tag{2}$$

which is an approximation of the integral

$$\int_a^b f(x) \, dx$$

with the limits being $a = x_1$ and $b = x_{p+1}$.

The definite integral by trapezoidal rule can also be expressed as

$$\Delta x \sum_{i=1}^{p+1} W_i f(x_i) = \Delta x [W_1 f(x_1) + W_2 f(x_2) + \cdots + W_{p+1} f(x_{p+1})] \tag{3}$$

where p is the number of intervals and W_i the weight of $f(x_i)$. Thus the integral becomes Δx multiplied by the weighted sum of $f(x)$ with the weights being

$$0.5 \quad 1.0 \quad 1.0 \quad \cdots \quad 1.0 \quad 0.5.$$

TABLE 8.6a

INTEGRATION OF $f(x) = 2x$ BY TRAPEZOIDAL RULE

x	$f(x)$	W	$Wf(x)$
1	2	0.5	1
3	6	1.0	6
5	10	1.0	10
7	14	1.0	14
9	18	0.5	9
		Sum	40
$\Delta x \sum Wf(x) = 2(40) = 80$			

As a demonstration, the function

$$f(x) = 2x$$

is integrated by trapezoidal rule from $x = 1$ to $x = 9$ with p equal to 4 and Δx equal to 2. The details of computation are shown in table 8.6a. In that table, the range 1 to 9 is divided into 4 equal intervals. For each of the 5 end-points x, the value of $f(x)$ or $2x$ is calculated. Then each value of $f(x)$ is multiplied by the weight W. The integral by trapezoidal rule is

$$\Delta x \sum Wf(x) = 2(40) = 80$$

which is equal to the exact integral

$$\int_1^9 2x \, dx = \left[x^2 \right]_1^9 = 81 - 1 = 80.$$

This is to be expected, because the integrand is a linear function and the lines joining adjacent points of the trapezoidal rule are straight lines.

As another demonstration, the function

$$f(x) = 3x^2$$

is integrated by the trapezoidal rule from $x = 1$ to $x = 9$ with p equal to 4 and Δx equal to 2. The details of the computation are shown in table 8.6b. The total area of the 4 trapezoids is equal to

$$\Delta x \sum Wf(x) = 2(372) = 744$$

in contrast to the exact integral

$$\int_1^9 3x^2 dx = \left[x^3\right]_1^9 = 729 - 1 = 728.$$

The discrepancy or error for this example is

$$744 - 728 = 16,$$

but the error can be reduced by using a smaller Δx.

TABLE 8.6b

INTEGRATION OF $f(x) = 3x^2$ BY TRAPEZOIDAL RULE

x	$f(x)$	W	$Wf(x)$
1	3	0.5	1.5
3	27	1.0	27.0
5	75	1.0	75.0
7	147	1.0	147.0
9	243	0.5	121.5
		Sum	372.0
$\Delta x \sum Wf(x) = 2(372) = 744$			

The trapezoidal rule and the standard method of integration are similar in some ways and different in others. Both methods require the division of the range a to b into p equal intervals. By the trapezoidal rule, $p+1$ values of the integrand $f(x)$ are calculated at the end-points x of the p intervals and the integral is

$$\Delta x \left[\frac{1}{2}f(x_1) + f(x_2) + \cdots + f(x_p) + \frac{1}{2}f(x_{p+1})\right]$$

which is the total area of p trapezoids with Δx as the width. But, by the standard method, only p values of $f(\bar{x})$, which are evaluated at the mid-points $\bar{x}$ of the p intervals, are needed and the integral is

$$\Delta x \left[f(\bar{x}_1) + f(\bar{x}_2) + \cdots + f(\bar{x}_p)\right]$$

which is the total area of p rectangles with Δx as the width. In general, the results obtained by these two methods are not the same. The integral of $3x^2$ from $x = 1$ to $x = 9$ is evaluated in table 8.5b by

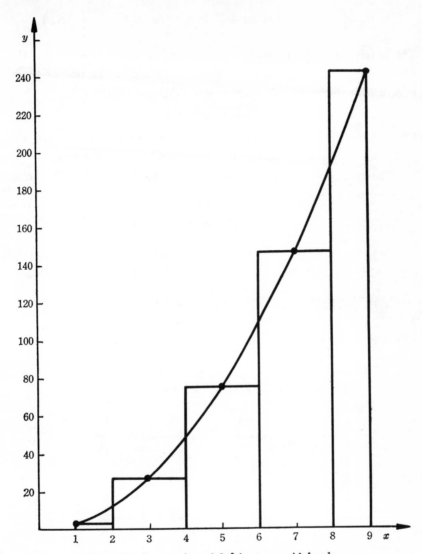

F<small>IG</small>. 8.6b. Integration of $3x^2$ by trapezoidal rule.

the standard method and again in table 8.6b by trapezoidal rule, with Δx equal to 2 in both tables. Yet the integral is 720 in the former table and 744 in the latter.

The total area of the p trapezoids

$$\Delta x\left[\frac{1}{2}f(x_1) + f(x_2) + \cdots + f(x_p) + \frac{1}{2}f(x_{p+1})\right]$$

may be expressed as that of $p + 1$ rectangles

$$f(x_1)\left(\frac{1}{2}\Delta x\right) + f(x_2)\Delta x + \cdots + f(x_p)\Delta x + f(x_{p+1})\left(\frac{1}{2}\Delta x\right).$$

The height of each rectangle is $f(x)$, but the width is $\frac{1}{2}\Delta x$ for the first and the last rectangle and Δx for each of the rest of them. Figure 8.6b shows five rectangles superimposed on the curve

$$y = 3x^2.$$

When this graph is compared with figure 8.5b, one can see the difference between the standard method and trapezoidal rule.

The trapezoidal rule is the standard method with $f(\bar{x})$ being replaced by

$$\bar{f}(x) = \frac{1}{2}\Big[f(x_i) + f(x_{i+1})\Big]$$

which is the average of two adjacent values of $f(x)$. This can be seen from the fact that the area of the ith trapezoid is (equation 1)

$$A_i = \Delta x\Big[\frac{1}{2}(y_i + y_{i+1})\Big] = \frac{1}{2}\Big[f(x_i) + f(x_{i+1})\Big]\Delta x = \bar{f}(x)\Delta x$$

which is a rectangle with $\bar{f}(x)$ as the height and Δx as the width.

TABLE 8.6c

INTEGRATION OF $f(x) = 3x^2$ BY TRAPEZOIDAL RULE

x	$f(x)$	$\bar{x}$	$\bar{f}(x)$
1	3		
		2	15
3	27		
		4	51
5	75		
		6	111
7	147		
		8	195
9	243		
		Sum	372
$\Delta x \Sigma \bar{f}(x) = 2(372) = 744$			

The integration of $3x^2$ from $x = 1$ to $x = 9$ is carried out from this point of view in table 8.6c. The mid-point $\bar{x}$ is found for each interval, but the values of $f(\bar{x})$ are not. Instead, the average of the two values of $f(x)$ at the end-points x of an interval is found for that interval, such as

$$\frac{3 + 27}{2} = 15$$

and

$$\frac{27 + 75}{2} = 51 .$$

The total area of four such rectangles

$$\Sigma[\bar{f}(x)\Delta x] = \Delta x \, \Sigma \bar{f}(x) = 2(372) = 744$$

is exactly equal to that of the four trapezoids given in table 8.6b.

The graphical presentation of table 8.6c is given in figure 8.6c. The four pairs of values of $\bar{x}$ and $\bar{f}(x)$ are plotted as dots. Then four rectangles are constructed with the values of $\bar{f}(x)$ as the heights and Δx as the width. Thus each of the four dots is located at the center of the horizontal line which constitutes the top of a rectangle. However, the dots are not located on the curve

$$y = 3x^2$$

which is the integrand, because $\bar{f}(x)$ is not equal to $f(\bar{x})$. The four values of $\bar{f}(x)$ are

$$15 \quad 51 \quad 111 \quad 195$$

as shown in table 8.6c; while those of $f(\bar{x})$ are

$$12 \quad 48 \quad 108 \quad 192$$

as shown in table 8.5b.

Now it can be concluded that the standard method and trapezoidal rule differ only in one respect—$f(\bar{x})$ is used in the former and $\bar{f}(x)$ in the latter as the height of a rectangle. The symbol $f(\bar{x})$ represents the value of the integrand $f(x)$ evaluated at the mid-point $\bar{x}$ which is the average value of two end-points of an interval; while $\bar{f}(x)$ is the average of two values of $f(x)$ evaluated at the end-points of an interval. This contrast can be seen by comparing

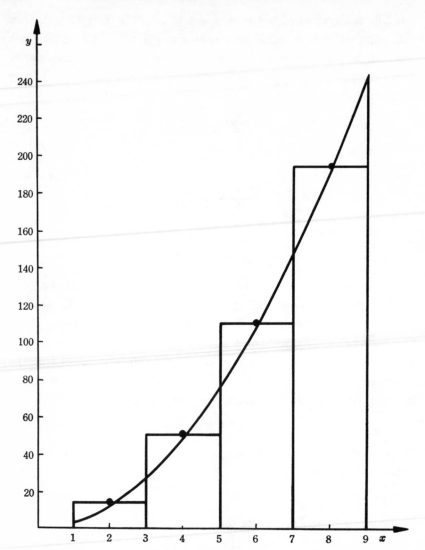

Fɪɢ. 8.6c. Integration of $3x^2$ by trapezoidal rule with trapezoids
being replaced by rectangles.

table 8.5b with table 8.6c. It can also be observed by comparing figure 8.5b with figure 8.6c.

8.7 Simpson's Rule

Simpson's rule is another numerical method of integration. As in trapezoidal rule, the range a to b is also divided into p equal intervals and the integration is carried out on the following $p+1$ points:

$$P_1(x_1, y_1) \quad P_2(x_2, y_2) \quad \cdots \quad P_{p+1}(x_{p+1}, y_{p+1})$$

But, in Simpson's rule, the number of intervals must be an even number such as 2, 4, 6, 8 and so forth; while, in trapezoidal rule, the number p can be either even or odd. In other words, the p intervals in Simpson's rule must occur in q pairs where p is equal to $2q$ and q is a positive integer.

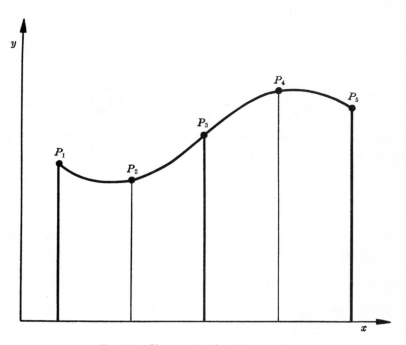

Fig. 8.7. Simpson's rule of integration.

The process of Simpson's rule is illustrated in figure 8.7 which shows an example of p being equal to 4 or q equal to 2. The $p+1$ or 5 points are shown in that figure as dots and are designated by P_1, P_2, P_3, P_4 and P_5. Then a parabola or second-degree polynomial is fitted to the three points of every double interval (section 4.7). For the given example, a parabola is fitted to the points P_1, P_2 and P_3 and another one is fitted to P_3, P_4 and P_5. This is the reason why the number of intervals has to be even. It takes three points or two intervals to fit a parabola. Simpson's rule is to use the total area under the $p/2$ or q parabolas as an approximation of the integral

$$\int_a^b f(x)\,dx = \int_a^b y\,dx$$

which is the area under the curve $y = f(x)$. For this reason, Simpson's rule is also called *parabolic rule* of integration. In contrast, trapezoidal rule should be called *linear rule* of integration.

The area under each parabola, which covers two intervals, can be found from the equation of the parabola. If the equation for the double interval from x_1 to x_3 is

$$y = b_0 + b_1 x + b_2 x^2,$$

the area under the parabola is

$$\int_{x_1}^{x_3} y\,dx = \left[b_0 x + \frac{1}{2} b_1 x^2 + \frac{1}{3} b_2 x^3 \right]_{x_1}^{x_3}.$$

Simpson's rule of integration is to use the sum of q such areas as an approximation of the definite integral desired.

The equation of the parabola passing three given points, such as $P_1(x_1,\ y_1)$, $P_2(x_2,\ y_2)$ and $P_3(x_3,\ y_3)$, can be determined by the method given in section 4.7. To simplify the algebra involved, the three x-values are replaced by -1, 0 and 1 so that the length of the interval becomes

$$\Delta x = x_3 - x_2 = x_2 - x_1 = 1.$$

This is to say that the independent variable is now using Δx as the unit of measurement.

To determine the values of b_0, b_1 and b_2 of the equation

$$y = b_0 + b_1 x + b_2 x^2,$$

each of the points $P_1(-1,\ y_1)$, $P_2(0,\ y_2)$ and $P_3(1,\ y_3)$ are substituted into the above equation. The three equations thus obtained are:

$$y_1 = b_0 - b_1 + b_2$$

$$y_2 = b_0$$

$$y_3 = b_0 + b_1 + b_2$$

The solutions of the above system of linear equations are:

$$b_0 = y_2$$

$$b_1 = \frac{1}{2}(y_3 - y_1)$$

$$b_2 = \frac{1}{2}(y_1 - 2y_2 + y_3)$$

Thus the equation of the parabola passing through the points P_1, P_2 and P_3 is

$$y = y_2 + \frac{1}{2}(y_3 - y_1)x + \frac{1}{2}(y_1 - 2y_2 + y_3)x^2.$$

Then the area under the parabola for the first pair of intervals is

$$\int_{-1}^{1} y\, dx = \left[y_2 x + \frac{1}{4}(y_3 - y_1)x^2 + \frac{1}{6}(y_1 - 2y_2 + y_3)x^3 \right]_{-1}^{1}$$

$$= 2y_2 + \frac{1}{3}(y_1 - 2y_2 + y_3)$$

$$= \frac{1}{3}(y_1 + 4y_2 + y_3)$$

with x expressed in Δx unit. When converted to the original unit of x, the area becomes

$$A_1 = \frac{\Delta x}{3}(y_1 + 4y_2 + y_3).$$

Similarly, it can be determined that the area under the parabola for the second pair of intervals is

$$A_2 = \frac{\Delta x}{3}(y_3 + 4y_4 + y_5),$$

that for the third pair is

$$A_3 = \frac{\Delta x}{3}(y_5 + 4y_6 + y_7),$$

and that for the qth or the last pair of intervals is

$$A_q = \frac{\Delta x}{3}(y_{p-1} + 4y_p + y_{p+1}).$$

By Simpson's rule, the approximate integral is the sum of these q areas which can be expressed as

$$\sum_{i=1}^{q} A_i = \frac{\Delta x}{3}[y_1 + 4y_2 + 2y_3 + 4y_4 + 2y_5 + \cdots + 4y_p + y_{p+1}]. \quad (1)$$

Like trapezoidal rule (equation 3, section 8.6), Simpson's rule is basically the weighted sum of y_i or $f(x_i)$. When the values

$$1 \quad 4 \quad 2 \quad 4 \quad 2 \quad \cdots \quad 4 \quad 1$$

are assigned to the weights W_i, the integral by Simpson's rule can be expressed as

$$\frac{\Delta x}{3} \sum_{i=1}^{p+1} W_i f(x_i) = \frac{\Delta x}{3} [W_1 f(x_1) + W_2 f(x_2) + \cdots + W_{p+1} f(x_{p+1})]. \qquad (2)$$

Comparing the above equation with equation (3) of section 8.6, one will see two differences between trapezoidal rule and Simpson's rule. First, the weights are different. The former rule uses

$$0.5 \quad 1.0 \quad 1.0 \quad 1.0 \quad 1.0 \quad \cdots \quad 1.0 \quad 0.5$$

as the weights, and the latter uses

$$1 \quad 4 \quad 2 \quad 4 \quad 2 \quad \cdots \quad 4 \quad 1.$$

Second, the common factor of the former rule is Δx and that of the latter is $\Delta x/3$. These are the characteristics which distinguish the two rules.

TABLE 8.7a

INTEGRATION OF $f(x) = 3x^2$ BY SIMPSON'S RULE

x	$f(x)$	W	$W f(x)$
1	3	1	3
3	27	4	108
5	75	2	150
7	147	4	588
9	243	1	243
		Sum	1,092

$$\frac{\Delta x}{3} \sum W f(x) = \frac{2}{3}(1,092) = 728$$

As a demonstration, Simpson's rule is used in integrating the function

$$f(x) = 3x^2$$

from $x = 1$ to $x = 9$. The details of computation is given in table 8.7a which shows that p is equal to 4, q is equal to 2 and Δx is equal to 2. The integral obtained in that table is 728 which is equal to the integral

$$\int_1^9 3x^2 dx = \left[x^3 \right]_1^9 = 729 - 1 = 728.$$

This is to be expected, because the integrand $3x^2$ itself is a second-degree polynomial and Simpson's rule passes parabolas or second-degree polynomials through the $p+1$ points.

Despite the fact that Simpson's rule uses parabolas to connect the $p+1$ points, the rule yields an exact integral even if the integrand is a third-degree polynomial. As a demonstration, the function

$$f(x) = 4x^3$$

is integrated by Simpson's rule from $x = 1$ to $x = 9$. The details of computation are given in table 8.7b. The integral obtained in that

TABLE 8.7b

INTEGRATION OF $f(x) = 4x^3$ BY SIMPOSON'S RULE

x	$f(x)$	W	$Wf(x)$
1	4	1	4
3	108	4	432
5	500	2	1,000
7	1,372	4	5,488
9	2,916	1	2,916
		Sum	9,840
$\dfrac{\Delta x}{3} \sum Wf(x) = \dfrac{2}{3}(9,840) = 6,560$			

table is 6,560 which is equal to the exact integral

$$\int_1^9 4x^3 dx = \left[x^4 \right]_1^9 = 6,561 - 1 = 6,560.$$

In fact, the same result can be obtained by using only one pair of intervals by letting x be equal to 1, 5 and 9 and Δx be equal to 4. The integral for this one pair of intervals is (table 8.7b)

$$\frac{\Delta x}{3}[f(1) + 4f(5) + f(9)] = \frac{4}{3}[4 + 4(500) + 2,916] = 6,560$$

which is also the value of the exact integral.

To show that Simpson's rule yields the exact integral for a third-degree polynomial, one only need to show that the rule yields the exact integral of x^3. To make the case general, the three points $P_1(x_1, y_1)$, $P_2(x_2, y_2)$ and $P_3(x_3, y_3)$ are expressed as

$$P_1[(x - \Delta x), (x - \Delta x)^3] \quad P_2[x, x^3] \quad P_3[(x + \Delta x), (x + \Delta x)^3].$$

By Simpson's rule, the integral is equal to

$$\frac{\Delta x}{3}[(x - \Delta x)^3 + 4x^3 + (x + \Delta x)^3] = 2x^3(\Delta x) + 2x(\Delta x)^3$$

because

$$(x - \Delta x)^3 = x^3 - 3x^2(\Delta x) + 3x(\Delta x)^2 - (\Delta x)^3$$

and

$$(x + \Delta x)^3 = x^3 + 3x^2(\Delta x) + 3x(\Delta x)^2 + (\Delta x)^3.$$

By formula, the integral is also equal to

$$\int_{x-\Delta x}^{x+\Delta x} x^3 dx = \frac{1}{4}\left[x^4\right]_{x-\Delta x}^{x+\Delta x} = 2x^3(\Delta x) + 2x(\Delta x)^3$$

because

$$(x + \Delta x)^4 = x^4 + 4x^3(\Delta x) + 6x^2(\Delta x)^2 + 4x(\Delta x)^3 + (\Delta x)^4$$

$$(x - \Delta x)^4 = x^4 - 4x^3(\Delta x) + 6x^2(\Delta x)^2 - 4x(\Delta x)^3 + (\Delta x)^4$$

and

$$(x + \Delta x)^4 - (x - \Delta x)^4 = 8x^3(\Delta x) + 8x(\Delta x)^3.$$

Simpson's rule does not yield the exact integral when the integrand is a polynomial of a degree higher than three. This is demonstrated by integrating $5x^4$ from $x = 1$ to $x = 9$ as shown in table 8.7c. The integral obtained in that table is 59,133.33, but the exact integral is

$$\int_1^9 5x^4 dx = \left[x^5\right]_1^9 = 59,049 - 1 = 59,048$$

which is a different value.

TABLE 8.7c

INTEGRATION OF $f(x) = 5x^4$ BY SIMPSON'S RULE

x	$f(x)$	W	$Wf(x)$
1	5	1	5
3	405	4	1,620
5	3,125	2	6,250
7	12,005	4	48,020
9	32,805	1	32,805
		Sum	88,700

$$\frac{\Delta x}{3} \sum Wf(x) = \frac{2}{3}(88,700) = 59,133.33$$

Despite the fact that Simpson's rule does not require much more computation than trapezoidal rule, the former method yields a smaller error than the latter in integrating the same function with the same magnitude of Δx. One is good for a third-degree polynomial, and the other is good only for a linear function. So Simpson's rule is a highly recommended method of numerical integration. However, this rule does require some advance planning so that the number of intervals is even and never odd.

A polynomial in x never requires numerical integration, because the exact integral can be so readily obtained through formulas of integration. The reason why polynomials are used as illustrations in presenting the numerical methods is that the polynomial is the only kind of function introduced so far. The numerical methods are designed for functions which cannot be integrated by formulas.

EXERCISES

1. Demonstrate numerically that the limiting value of the integral of $2x$, as Δx approaches zero, is $x^2 + C$ by letting Δx be equal to 1.0, 0.2 and 0.04 for the range from $x = 0$ to $x = 1$ (tables 8.1a, b, c).

2. Integrate the following functions by formula:
   (a) $f(x) = 0$ (b) $f(x) = 1$
   (c) $f(x) = x$ (d) $f(x) = x + 1$

3. Evaluate the following integrals:

(a) $\int_0^x x^2 dx$ (b) $\int_0^y x^2 dx$ (c) $\int_0^t x^2 dx$

(d) $\int_0^3 x^2 dx$ (e) $\int_3^6 x^2 dx$

The purpose of this exercise is to demonstrate that an integral is a function of its limits.

4. Evaluate the following integrals:

(a) $\int_0^2 (x^4 - 3x^2 + 6) dx$ (b) $\int_1^4 (x^3 + 2x - 1) dx$

5. Find the area under the curve

$$y = x^3$$

from $x = 4$ to $x = 8$ through integration by formula.

6. Find the area bounded by the curve

$$y = x^2 - 4x$$

and the x axis through integration by formula.

7. Find the area bounded by the curves

$$y = x^2$$

and

$$y = x^4$$

through integration by formula.   Plot the curves.

8. Repeat exercise 5 by Simpson's rule and show that the result obtained remains the same regardless of the magnitude of Δx.

9. Repeat exercise 6 by Simpson's rule and show that the result obtained remains the same regardless of the magnitude of Δx.

10. Repeat exercise 5 by trapezoidal rule with Δx equal to 1.   Integrate again with Δx equal to 0.5.   Show that the integral obtained through the smaller Δx is closer to the true area, even though neither result is exactly equal to the true area.

CHAPTER 9

EXPONENTIAL AND LOGARITHMIC FUNCTIONS

The exponential function $y = f(x)$ is a function in which the rate of change of y with respect to x is proportional to the value of y. This function is necessarily more complicated than the linear function whose rate of change is a constant. However, the introduction of the new topic begins with exponent and logarithm which are usually covered in high-school mathematics. Along with the exponential function, its inverse function—the logarithmic function—is also presented in this chapter.

9.1 Exponent

The whole idea of exponent is based on the shorthand that the product of n equal quantities B is expressed as B^n or

$$BBB \cdots B = B^n$$

such as

$$BBB = B^3.$$

The number n of the expression B^n is called the *exponent* and B the *base*. This is indeed a shorthand. A quantity like

$$2 \times 2 \times 2 \times 2 \times 2 \times 2 \times 2 \times 2 \times 2 \times 2 = 1{,}024$$

can be simply expressed as

$$2^{10} = 1{,}024.$$

From the basic definition of the exponents come the laws of operations. The first is

$$B^m B^n = B^{m+n} \tag{1}$$

where B, m and n are all numbers. When $B = 2$, $m = 3$, and $n = 4$, the law says

$$2^3 2^4 = 2^{3+4} = 2^7$$

which is obviously true. In longhand the quantity $2^3 2^4$ is equal to

305

$$(2 \times 2 \times 2)(2 \times 2 \times 2 \times 2) = 2 \times 2 \times 2 \times 2 \times 2 \times 2 \times 2$$

which may be expressed as 2^7 by the definition of exponent.

So far an exponent is a positive integer, but it can also be zero. The value of B^0 can be derived from equation (1). When n is equal to 0, that equation becomes

$$B^m B^0 = B^{m+0} = B^m \qquad (2)$$

which implies that

$$B^0 = 1 \qquad B \neq 0. \qquad (3)$$

So the quantity B^0 is defined as 1 so that the law given in equation (1) can be extended to include the zero exponent. However, it is understood that the quantity B itself is not equal to zero. Even though equation (2) indicates that B^0 is equal to 1, the fact that

$$0^3 = 0 \times 0 \times 0 = 0$$

$$0^2 = 0 \times 0 = 0$$

$$0^1 = 0$$

also indicates that 0^0 should be equal to 0. To avoid this ambiguity, the quantity 0^0 is excluded from equation (3) and left undefined.

The second law of exponent is

$$\frac{B^m}{B^n} = B^{m-n} \qquad (4)$$

which can be explained in terms of numbers. When $B = 2$, $m = 4$, and $n = 3$, the above equation says

$$\frac{2^4}{2^3} = \frac{2 \times 2 \times 2 \times 2}{2 \times 2 \times 2} = 2^{4-3} = 2^1 = 2$$

which is obviously true.

This law leads to the definition of a negative exponent. When $B = 2$, $m = 3$, and $n = 6$, equation (4) becomes

$$\frac{2^3}{2^6} = 2^{3-6} = 2^{-3}.$$

But the same expression is equal to

$$\frac{2 \times 2 \times 2}{2 \times 2 \times 2 \times 2 \times 2 \times 2} = \frac{1}{2 \times 2 \times 2}.$$

Then it follows that

$$2^{-3} = \frac{1}{2 \times 2 \times 2} = \frac{1}{2^3}$$

or, in general,

$$B^{-n} = \frac{1}{B^n} \qquad B \neq 0. \qquad (5)$$

Here again it is understood that B is not equal to zero, because that number cannot be used as a divisor.

The third law of exponent is

$$(B^m)^n = B^{mn} \qquad (6)$$

such as

$$(2^3)^4 = 2^{12}.$$

This is obviously true, because by the definition of exponent the quantity $(2^3)^4$ is equal to

$$2^3 \times 2^3 \times 2^3 \times 2^3 = 2^{3+3+3+3} = 2^{12}.$$

This law leads to the definition of a fractional exponent. The nth power of the nth root of a number B is equal to that number itself or

$$(\sqrt[n]{B})^n = B.$$

If one wishes to expresses the nth root of B in the exponential form as

$$\sqrt[n]{B} = B^x,$$

one has to determine the value of x so that the law of exponent would apply. To make the equation

$$(\sqrt[n]{B})^n = (B^x)^n = B^{xn} = B$$

come true, the value of x has to be equal to $1/n$. So the nth root of B is defined as B with the exponent $1/n$ or

$$\sqrt[n]{B} = B^{\frac{1}{n}}. \qquad (7)$$

From equation (6), it follows that

$$(\sqrt[n]{B})^m = B^{\frac{1}{n}} B^{\frac{1}{n}} \cdots B^{\frac{1}{n}} = B^{m\left(\frac{1}{n}\right)} = B^{\frac{m}{n}} \qquad (8)$$

which is the definition of a fractional exponent.

The (m/n)th power of a number B can be found in two different ways. It may be looked upon as the nth root of the mth power of B or the mth power of the nth root of the same number. Both methods give the same result. In symbolic form, the equivalence of the methods can be expressed as

$$B^{\frac{m}{n}} = \sqrt[n]{B^m} = (\sqrt[n]{B})^m.$$

As an example, one can see that $5^{\frac{2}{3}}$ is equal to

$$(\sqrt[3]{5})^2 = (1.7099759)^2 = 2.924018$$

or

$$\sqrt[3]{5^2} = \sqrt[3]{25} = 2.924018$$

which are the same value. As another example, one can see that $5^{\frac{3}{2}}$ is equal to

$$(\sqrt{5})^3 = (2.2360680)^3 = 11.180340$$

or

$$\sqrt{5^3} = \sqrt{125} = 11.180340$$

which are also identical numbers.

Now the exponent is defined in fractions and integers as well as in positive and negative numbers. The three laws given in equations (1), (4) and (6) are equally applicable to all these kinds of exponents.

9.2 Logarithm

If the number N is equal to B^n where B is a positive number different from 1, the exponent n is called the *logarithm* of N and B the *base* of that logarithm. In symbolic form, the logarithm of N is expressed as

$$\log_B N = n$$

if

$$N = B^n .$$

Diagrammatically, the relation among the three elements—number, base and logarithm—can be expressed as

$$\text{number} = (\text{base})^{\text{logarithm}}$$

where the base is a positive number different from 1.

From the given definition, the logarithms of many numbers can be found. The logarithm of 16 to the base 4 is

$$\log_4 16 = 2$$

because

$$16 = 4^2.$$

When the base is changed from 4 to 2, the logarithm of the same number becomes

$$\log_2 16 = 4$$

because

$$16 = 2^4.$$

The logarithm of 81 to the base 3 is

$$\log_3 81 = 4$$

because

$$81 = 3^4.$$

When the base is changed from 3 to 9, the logarithm of the same number becomes

$$\log_9 81 = 2$$

because

$$81 = 9^2.$$

The negative and fractional logarithms come from the exponents with such properties. The logarithm of 0.125 to the base 2 is

$$\log_2 0.125 = -3$$

because

$$0.125 = \frac{1}{8} = \frac{1}{2^3} = 2^{-3}.$$

The logarithm of 2 to the base 16 is

$$\log_{16} 2 = \frac{1}{4} = 0.25$$

because

$$2 = \sqrt[4]{16} = 16^{\frac{1}{4}} = 16^{0.25}.$$

The logarithm of 0.4472136 to the base 5 is

$$\log_5(0.4472136) = -0.5$$

because

$$0.4472136 = \frac{1}{\sqrt{5}} = 5^{-\frac{1}{2}} = 5^{-0.5}.$$

Many consequences can be derived from the definition of logarithm. The logarithm of the base B is equal to 1, or

$$\log_B B = 1 \tag{1}$$

because

$$B = B^1.$$

The logarithm of 1 is equal to 0, or

$$\log_B 1 = 0 \tag{2}$$

because

$$1 = B^0.$$

A more obvious consequence is

$$N = B^{\log N} \tag{3}$$

because the exponent n of the equation

$$N = B^n$$

is, by definition, the logarithm of the number N to the base B.

From the definition of logarithm come the laws of operations. The first one is

$$\log_B(MN) = \log_B M + \log_B N \tag{4}$$

which says that the logarithm of the product of two numbers is equal to the sum of the logarithms of those two numbers regardless of the base used. The logarithms

$$\log_B M = m$$

and

$$\log_B N = n$$

imply

$$M = B^m$$

and

$$N = B^n .$$

Then the product of M and N is equal to

$$MN = B^m B^n = B^{m+n} .$$

Consequently, the logarithm of the product MN is

$$\log_B(MN) = m + n = \log_B M + \log_B N .$$

As an illustration of this law, one may consider the equation

$$\log_2(4 \times 8) = \log_2 4 + \log_2 8 .$$

The logarithm of 4×8 or 32 to the base 2 is

$$\log_2 32 = 5$$

because

$$32 = 2^5 .$$

The logarithms of 4 and 8 to the same base are

$$\log_2 4 = 2$$

and

$$\log_2 8 = 3$$

respectively. The law says

$$5 = 2 + 3$$

which is obviously true.

The second law of logarithm is

$$\log_B\left(\frac{M}{N}\right) = \log_B M - \log_B N \tag{5}$$

which says that the logarithm of a fraction is equal to the logarithm of the numerator minus that of the denominator. When the numbers

M and N are expressed as

$$M = B^m$$

and

$$N = B^n,$$

the fraction itself can be expressed as

$$\frac{M}{N} = \frac{B^m}{B^n} = B^{m-n}.$$

Then, by definition, the logarithms of the fraction and its numerator and denominator are

$$\log_B M = m$$

$$\log_B N = n$$

and

$$\log_B\left(\frac{M}{N}\right) = m - n.$$

Therefore, the relation among the three logarithms is

$$\log_B\left(\frac{M}{N}\right) = \log_B M - \log_B N.$$

As an illustration of this law, one may consider the equation

$$\log_3\left(\frac{243}{9}\right) = \log_3 243 - \log_3 9.$$

The logarithm of 243/9 or 27 to the base 3 is

$$\log_3 27 = 3$$

because

$$27 = 3^3;$$

that of 243 to the same base is

$$\log_3 243 = 5$$

because

$$243 = 3^5;$$

and that of 9 is

$$\log_3 9 = 2$$

because

$$9 = 3^2.$$

The law says that

$$\log_3\left(\frac{243}{9}\right) = \log_3 27 = \log_3 243 - \log_3 9$$

or

$$3 = 5 - 2$$

which is obviously true.

The third law of logarithm is

$$\log_B M^n = n \log_B M \tag{6}$$

which can also be derived from the laws of exponent. When the number M is expressed as

$$M = B^m,$$

its nth power must be

$$M^n = B^m B^m \cdots B^m = B^{nm}.$$

Then, by definition, the logarithm of M is

$$\log_B M = m$$

and that of M^n is

$$\log_B M^n = nm.$$

When the number m is replaced by $\log_B M$, the result is that given in equation (6).

This law can be illustrated by the example

$$\log_2(4^5) = 5\log_2 4.$$

The 5th power of 4 is equal to 1,024, and the logarithm of this number to the base 2 is

$$\log_2(4^5) = \log_2(1,024) = 10$$

because

$$1,024 = 2^{10}.$$

Since the logarithm of 4 to the base 2 is

$$\log_2 4 = 2,$$

it is obviously true that

$$10 = 5(2)$$

which is what the law says.

The third law of logarithm given above also includes the fourth law

$$\log_B \sqrt[r]{M} = \frac{\log_B M}{r} \tag{7}$$

as a special case. The rth root of M can be expressed as

$$\sqrt[r]{M} = M^{\frac{1}{r}} = M^n.$$

Therefore, equation (7) is a special case of equation (6) with

$$n = 1/r.$$

This law can be illustrated by the example

$$\log_5 \sqrt[3]{125} = \frac{1}{3} \log_5 (125).$$

Since the cube root of 125 is equal to 5, the logarithm of the root to the base 5 is

$$\log_5 \sqrt[3]{125} = \log_5 5 = 1.$$

The law says that this number is equal to one third of the logarithm of 125. This is obviously true, because

$$\log_5 125 = 3$$

on account of the fact that

$$125 = 5^3.$$

9.3 Common Logarithm

The base of the logarithm can be selected to suit the convenience of the user, but one of the most commonly used base is 10. When this base is selected, the logarithm of a number is called the *common logarithm* of that number.

The common logarithm of any number which is an integral power of 10 can be immediately established from its definition. Some of such logarithms are given as follows:

Number	0.001	0.01	0.1	1	10	100	1,000
Logarithm	-3	-2	-1	0	1	2	3

The fact that the common logarithm of 0.001 is −3 comes from the equation

$$0.001 \ = \ \frac{1}{1,000} \ = \ \frac{1}{10^3} \ = \ 10^{-3}$$

and that of 1,000 is 3 from

$$1,000 \ = \ 10^3 \,.$$

The common logarithm of a number N is simply expressed as $\log N$ with the base 10 omitted from the symbol. This is not a universally accepted practice, but it is the one being followed all through this text. In terms of this abbreviated notation, the logarithms given in the above table can be expressed as follows:

$$\log 0.001 \ = \ -3$$
$$\log 0.01 \ = \ -2$$
$$\log 0.1 \ = \ -1$$
$$\log 1 \ = \ 0$$
$$\log 10 \ = \ 1$$
$$\log 100 \ = \ 2$$
$$\log 1,000 \ = \ 3$$

The above list suggests that the logarithm of a negative number is not defined. When a positive number is getting closer to zero, its logarithm becomes a larger negative number.

The common logarithms of numbers between 1 and 10 are given in table 1 of the appendix. This table consists of 18 pages, each of which has 50 rows and 10 columns. Each row is identified by a three-digit number and each column by a one-digit number. Thus every five-digit number given in this long table is uniquely identified. For example, the number given at row 123 and column 4 is 09132. This is understood to mean that the common logarithm of 1.234 is equal to 0.09132 or

$$\log 1.234 = 0.09132.$$

The three-digit number which identifies a row is the first three digits of the number N, and the one-digit number which identifies the column is the fourth digit. The decimal point between the first and second digit of N is omitted from the table. So is the decimal point in front of the five-digit logarithm of N. With this understanding, one can find from the table that the logarithms of 1.800, 2.908, 7.950 and 1.000 are

$$\log 1.800 = 0.25527$$

$$\log 2.908 = 0.46359$$

$$\log 7.950 = 0.90037$$

$$\log 1.000 = 0.00000.$$

When the common logarithm

$$n = \log N$$

is known, one can determine the value of N from the table. The number N is sometimes called the *antilogarithm* of n, but it is simply 10^n. The four equations given above can be expressed as

$$1.800 = 10^{0.25527}$$

$$2.908 = 10^{0.46359}$$

$$7.950 = 10^{0.90037}$$

$$1.000 = 10^{0.00000}.$$

Table 1 lists only the common logarithms of numbers between 1 and 10. Since

$$\log 1 = 0$$

and

$$\log 10 = 1,$$

the tabulated logarithms have to be between 0 and 1. However, through the first law of logarithm

$$\log (MN) = \log M + \log N$$

given in equation (4) of section 9.2, the common logarithm of any number can be found by expressing that number as the product of M and N, where M is an integral power of 10 and N a number between 1 and 10. In finding the common logarithm of 123.4, the number can be expressed as

$$123.4 = 100 \times 1.234.$$

Then the common logarithm of 123.4 becomes

$$\log 123.4 = \log 100 + \log 1.234$$
$$= 2 + 0.09132$$
$$= 2.09132$$

with the value of $\log 100$ obtained from the definition of the common logarithm and that of $\log 1.234$ obtained from table 1 of the appendix. Similarly, one can see that the common logarithm of 1,234 is equal to

$$\log 1,234 = \log 1,000 + \log 1.234 = 3.09132$$

and that of 12,340 is equal to 4.09132.

The integral part of the common logarithm is called the *characteristic* and the decimal part the *mantissa* of the logarithm. The characteristic is determined by the definition of the common logarithm and the mantissa is obtained from the table. In the logarithm

$$\log 1,234 = 3.09132,$$

the number 3 is the characteristic and 0.09132 the mantissa.

The common logarithm of a number between 0 and 1 can also be obtained by determining the characteristic and the mantissa separately through the second law of logarithm

$$\log \left(\frac{M}{N} \right) = \log M - \log N.$$

In finding the common logarithm of 0.01234, the number is expressed as the fraction

$$0.01234 = 1.234/100.$$

Then the logarithm of 0.01234 becomes

$$\log 0.01234 \;=\; \log 1.234 - \log 100$$

$$= 0.09132 - 2$$

$$= -1.90868 .$$

Similarly, the logarithm of 0.001234 is

$$\log 0.001234 \;=\; 0.09132 - 3 \;=\; -2.90868 .$$

It should be noted that -3 is the characteristic of the above logarithm and 0.09132 the mantissa, even though the logarithm is equal to -2.90868. In other words, the mantissa is always positive.

To find the value of

$$10^n \;=\; N$$

with a negative value of n from the logarithm table, the decimal part of n has first to be made positive. This can be done by adding 1 to the decimal part of n and subtracting the same numher from the integral part. For example, to find the value of

$$10^{-2.90868} \;=\; N ,$$

the logarithm should be expressed as

$$-2.90868 \;=\; -2 - 0.90868$$

$$= (-2 - 1) + (1 - 0.90868)$$

$$= -3 + 0.09132$$

before the table can be used. Then the value of N is

$$10^{-2.90868} \;=\; 10^{-3} \times 10^{0.09132} \;=\; \frac{1.234}{1{,}000} \;=\; 0.001234 .$$

Before computing machines were invented, the logarithm table was frequently used as a computing tool. It enables one to replace a multiplication by an addition, and a division by a subtraction. To find the product

$$37 \times 48 \;=\; 1{,}776 ,$$

one first finds the logarithms

$$\log 37 \;=\; 1.56820$$

and

$$\log 48 \ = \ 1.68124$$

whose sum is 3.24944. From this logarithm, one can find from the table

$$10^{3.24944} \ = \ 10^3 \times 10^{0.24944}$$

$$= \ 1,000 \times 1.776$$

$$= \ 1,776 \,.$$

By this process a multiplication is converted into an addition, but the price paid for this convenience is the inconvenience of looking up the logarithm table three times. In these days of desk calculators and electronic computers, it is doubtfully that this process is still being used except as classroom exercises.

The logarithm table is still useful in evaluating the root or power of a number, even though it is no longer useful in carrying out multiplications and divisions. The evaluation of the quantity

$$N \ = \ \sqrt[9]{(512)^{10}} \ = \ 512^{\frac{10}{9}}$$

may be used as an illustration. The common logarithm of N is equal to

$$\frac{10}{9} \log 512 \ = \ \frac{10}{9}(2.70927) \ = \ 3.01030 \,.$$

From this logarithm, one can find from the table that

$$N \ = \ 10^{3.01030} \ = \ 10^3 \times 10^{0.01030} \ = \ 1,000 \times 1.024 \ = \ 1,024 \,.$$

The five-place logarithm table given in the appendix is good enough for teaching purposes. When it is found to be inadequate for practical uses, one may consult a ten-place table. However, with availability of computers, the days of logarithm tables are numbered. The logarithms needed in computation are frequently generated in the machines rather than obtained from tables. On account of this development, it becomes more important to understand the principles of logarithm than to acquire the proficiency of using the tables. However, one should not confuse the tables with the principles. The tables may be obsolete, but the principles are still going strong.

The logarithm of a number N to any base B can be converted into the common logarithm or vice versa. The fact that the logarithm of N to the base B is equal to

$$\log_B N = n$$

implies

$$N = B^n .$$

By finding the common logarithms of both sides of the above equation, one has

$$\log N = n \log B = (\log_B N)(\log B) \qquad (1)$$

or

$$\log_B N = \frac{\log N}{\log B} \qquad (2)$$

Equation (1) can be used in converting the logarithm of N to any base B into the common logarithm. The logarithm of 32 to the base 2 is 5, because 32 is equal to 2^5. To convert this logarithm into the common logarithm, one simply multiplies this logarithm by

$$\log 2 = 0.30103$$

and obtains

$$\log 32 = (\log_2 32)(\log 2)$$

$$= 5(0.30103)$$

$$= 1.50515$$

which is the value given in the logarithm table as it should be.

Equation (2) can be used in converting the common logarithm of N into a logarithm to any base. The common logarithm

$$\log 81 = 1.90849$$

may be converted into the logarithm to the base 3 by dividing the above value by

$$\log 3 = 0.47712 .$$

The result obtained is

$$\log_3 81 = \frac{\log 81}{\log 3} = \frac{1.90849}{0.47712} = 4.0000$$

which is the value expected because 81 is equal to 3^4.

9.4   Natural Logarithm

The natural logarithm of a number is the logarithm of that number to the base e, where e is the limiting value of

$$f(p) = \left(1 + \frac{1}{p}\right)^p \tag{1}$$

as p increases without bound. When $p = 1$, 2 and 3, the values of $f(p)$ are

$$f(1) = \left(1 + \frac{1}{1}\right)^1 = 2$$

$$f(2) = \left(1 + \frac{1}{2}\right)^2 = 1.5^2 = 2.25$$

$$f(3) = \left(1 + \frac{1}{3}\right)^3 = \left(\frac{4}{3}\right)^3 = 2.370370$$

which indicate that $f(p)$ increases with p. Additional values of $f(p)$ given in table 9.4 confirms this trend. However, the rate of increase of $f(p)$ slows down for larger values of p. The rate of increase at the interval $p = 2$ to $p = 3$ is

$$\frac{2.370370 - 2.250000}{3 - 2} = \frac{0.120370}{1} = 0.120370.$$

By the time $f(p)$ reaches the interval $p = 100$ to $p = 1,000$, its rate of increase slows down to

$$\frac{2.716924 - 2.704814}{1,000 - 100} = \frac{0.012110}{900} = 0.000013.$$

For larger values of p, the rate of increase of $f(p)$ slows down even more. On account of its ever slower rate of increase, $f(p)$ cannot reach beyond a certain limit no matter how large is the value of p. This ceiling of $f(p)$ is expressed as

$$e = \lim_{p \to \infty} \left(1 + \frac{1}{p}\right)^p \tag{2}$$

whose numerical value is

$$e = 2.718282 \tag{3}$$

which is also listed in table 9.4.   The symbol ∞ (infinity), which is given in that table and also in equation (2), stands for an unlimited large value.

TABLE 9.4

VALUES OF $f(p) = (1 + 1/p)^p$

p	$f(p)$	p	$f(p)$
2	2.250000	10	2.593742
3	2.370370	100	2.704814
4	2.441406	1,000	2.716924
5	2.488320	∞	2.718282

At this stage it appears that nothing is more unnatural than the natural logarithm which uses the number e as its base. However, the base e does have its advantages.   The natural logarithm facilitates the operations in calculus, even though it is not a particularly desirable computing tool.

The natural logarithm of a number is defined in the same way as any other logarithm.   If a number is equal to

$$N = e^x,$$

x is called the natural logarithm of N.   A brief table of the values of e^x and e^{-x} is given in table 2 of the appendix.   For example,

$$e^{4.3} = 73.700$$

is listed in that table.   By definition, the natural logarithm of 73.700 is equal to 4.3.

The product of e^x and e^{-x} is equal to 1, because

$$e^x e^{-x} = e^{x-x} = e^0 = 1.$$

For example, the values

$$e^{1.5} = 4.4817$$

and

$$e^{-1.5} = 0.22313$$

are given in table 2. The product of these two numbers is equal to

$$(4.4817)(0.22313) = 1.00000.$$

The value of e^x and e^{-x} can still be obtained even if the value of x is beyond the range of table 2. For example, e^8 can be expressed as

$$e^4 e^4 = (54.598)^2 = 2,981.$$

Then, by definition, 8 is the natural logarithm of 2,981.

A table of common logarithms can also be used in evaluating e^x whether x is positive or negative. The evaluation of e^8 may be used as an example. The common logarithm of e^8 is equal to

$$\log e^8 = 8 \log e = 8(0.43429) = 3.47432.$$

Then the value of e^8 must be

$$10^{3.47432} = 2,981$$

which is the same value obtained from the table of e^x.

The evaluation of $e^{0.06}$ may be used as another example. The common logarithm of $e^{0.06}$ is equal to

$$\log e^{0.06} = 0.06(0.43429) = 0.02606.$$

Then the value of $e^{0.06}$ must be

$$10^{0.02606} = 1.062.$$

A brief table of the natural logarithms is given in the appendix as table 3 which occupies only two pages. For example, the natural logarithms of 1.01, 1.50, 1.89 and 3.00 are

$$\log_e 1.01 = 0.00995$$

$$\log_e 1.50 = 0.40547$$

$$\log_e 1.89 = 0.63658$$

$$\log_e 3.00 = 1.09861$$

as shown in the table.

The natural logarithm of a number beyond the range of table 3 can be obtained by the law

$$\log_e MN = \log_e M + \log_e N.$$

For example, the natural logarithm of

$$73.7 = (7.37)(10)$$

is equal to

$$\log_e 73.7 = \log_e 7.37 + \log_e 10$$

$$= 1.99742 + 2.30259$$

$$= 4.30001.$$

The combination of the value

$$\log_e 73.7 = 4.30001$$

obtained from table 3 and the value

$$e^{4.3} = 73.700$$

obtained from table 2 illustrates the relation

$$e^{\log N} = N$$

where the symbol log in the above equation stands for the natural logarithm. This is not a new equation. It is a special case of equation (3) of section 9.2 with the base B being specified.

The natural logarithm can be converted into the common logarithm, or vice versa, by the methods given in equations (1) and (2) of section 9.3. The natural logarithm

$$\log_e N = x$$

implies

$$N = e^x.$$

Finding the common logarithms of both sides of the above equation, one has

$$\log N = x \log e = (\log_e N)(\log e) \tag{4}$$

through which the natural logarithm of a number N can be converted into the common logarithm of that number. To convert the common logarithm into the natural logarithm, one can rely on the relation

$$\log_e N = \frac{\log N}{\log e} \tag{5}$$

which is derived from equation (4).

The above equation can be expressed in another way. The fact

$$\log N = n$$

implies

$$N = 10^n .$$

Finding the natural logarithms of both sides of the above equation, one has

$$\log_e N = n \log_e 10 = (\log N)(\log_e 10) . \tag{6}$$

Comparison of equations (5) and (6) leads to the conclusion that $\log_e 10$ is the reciprocal of $\log e$, or

$$\frac{1}{\log e} = \log_e 10 \tag{7}$$

or

$$(\log e)(\log_e 10) = 1 . \tag{8}$$

From the fact that

$$\log e = \log (2.718282) = 0.4342945 , \tag{9}$$

it can be established that

$$\log_e 10 = \frac{1}{0.4342945} = 2.302585 \tag{10}$$

which is given as 2.30259 in table 3 of the appendix. Now the conversion of the common and natural logarithms can be summarized as follows:

$$\log_e N = (2.302585)(\log N) \tag{11}$$

$$\log N = (0.4342945)(\log_e N) \tag{12}$$

Equation (11) may be used in converting the common logarithm of a number into the natural logarithm of that number. For example, the common logarithm of 2.34 is

$$\log 2.34 = 0.36922$$

and the natural logarithm of the same number is equal to

$$\log_e 2.34 = (2.302585)(0.36922) = 0.85016.$$

The corresponding value given in the table of natural logarithms is 0.85015. The discrepancy is due to the round-off errors of the tabulated values.

Equation (12) may be used in converting the natural logarithm of a number into the common logarithm of that number. For example, the natural logarithm of 5.67 is given in table 3 as

$$\log_e 5.67 = 1.73519$$

and the common logarithm of the same number is

$$\log 5.67 = (0.4342945)(1.73519) = 0.75358.$$

This is the same value given in the table of common logarithms.

Extensive tables are available for the values of $\log_e N$ as well as e^x. For practical computation, such tables may be used in obtaining these values. However, if a computer is used, it may even be more convenient to generate these values in the machine. The methods of obtaining the values of $\log_e N$ and e^x from the table of common logarithms are given in this section mainly for the purpose of demonstrating the relation between logarithms with different bases. They are too tedious to be of practice use, especially when large numbers of such values are needed.

9.5 Geometric Progression

A sequence of numbers such as

$$1 \quad 2 \quad 4 \quad 8 \quad 16$$

is called a *geometric progression*, the characteristic of which is that the ratio of any two adjacent terms is a constant. The *common ratio* of the given example is 2; that is, every term except the first one can be obtained by multiplying the preceding term by the common ratio. As another example, one can see that the common ratio of the progression

$$1 \quad \frac{1}{2} \quad \frac{1}{4} \quad \frac{1}{8} \quad \frac{1}{16}$$

is 1/2. Here every term, except the first one, can be obtained by multiplying the preceding one by 1/2.

Symbolically, the geometric progression can be expressed as

$$A \qquad A R \qquad A R^2 \qquad \cdots \qquad A R^{n-1}$$

where A is the first term, R the common ratio, and n the number of terms of the progression. This sequence clearly shows that every term is R times the preceding term. When $A = 2$, $R = 3$, and $n = 4$, the progression is

$$2 \qquad 2 \times 3 \qquad 2 \times 3^2 \qquad 2 \times 3^3$$

or

$$2 \qquad 6 \qquad 18 \qquad 54 \,.$$

When $A = 1$, $R = 10$, $n = 5$, the progression is

$$1 \qquad 1 \times 10 \qquad 1 \times 10^2 \qquad 1 \times 10^3 \qquad 1 \times 10^4$$

or

$$1 \qquad 10 \qquad 100 \qquad 1{,}000 \qquad 10{,}000 \,.$$

The ith term of a geometric progression can be expressed as

$$G_i = A R^{i-1} \qquad i = 1, 2, \cdots, n \,. \tag{1}$$

When the values of i are substituted into G_i, the result is the geometric progression

$$A R^0 \qquad A R^1 \qquad A R^2 \qquad \cdots \qquad A R^{n-1}$$

because R^0 is equal to 1 and AR^0 is equal to A.

The sum of the n terms of a geometric progression is equal to

$$\sum_{i=1}^{n} G_i = \frac{A(R^n - 1)}{R - 1} \qquad R \neq 1 \,. \tag{2}$$

This result can be seen by writing out all the n terms of the sum as

$$\sum G_i = A + AR + AR^2 + \cdots + AR^{n-2} + AR^{n-1}$$

and also R times the same sum as

$$R \sum G_i = AR + AR^2 + AR^3 + \cdots + AR^{n-1} + AR^n \,.$$

Then the difference between the above two equations is

$$R \sum G_i - \sum G_i = - A + AR^n$$

or

$$(R - 1)\sum G_i = A(R^n - 1).$$

Dividing both sides of the above equation by $R - 1$, one obtains equation (2). From this formula, one can find that the sum of the geometric progression

$$2 \quad 6 \quad 18 \quad 54$$

is

$$\frac{2(3^4 - 1)}{3 - 1} = 80$$

which is exactly equal to

$$2 + 6 + 18 + 54 = 80.$$

Using the same formula, one can find that the sum of the geometric progression

$$1 \quad \frac{1}{2} \quad \frac{1}{4} \quad \frac{1}{8} \quad \frac{1}{16}$$

is

$$\frac{1[(0.5)^5 - 1]}{0.5 - 1} = \frac{0.03125 - 1}{0.5 - 1} = \frac{-0.96875}{-0.5} = 1.9375$$

which is exactly equal to

$$1 + \frac{1}{2} + \frac{1}{4} + \frac{1}{8} + \frac{1}{16} = \frac{16 + 8 + 4 + 2 + 1}{16} = \frac{31}{16} = 1.9375.$$

The formula for the sum of the n terms of a geometric progression given in equation (2) works for all values of R except 1. When the common ratio R is equal to 1, the division by zero is encountered and the sum cannot be determined. However, this is not a situation which would cause any trouble. When R is equal to 1, the geometric progression becomes

$$A \quad A \quad \cdots \quad A$$

whose sum is evidently

$$A + A + \cdots + A = n A.$$

The logarithms of the terms of a geometric progression constitute an arithmetic progression. The terms of a geometric progression are

$$A \qquad A R \qquad A R^2 \qquad \cdots \qquad A R^{n-1}$$

where A is the first term and R the common ratio. The logarithms of these terms to any base are

$$\log A \quad \log A + \log R \quad \log A + 2 \log R \quad \cdots \quad \log A + (n - 1) \log R$$

which constitute an arithmetic progression with $\log A$ being the first term and $\log R$ being the common difference. For example, the common logarithms of the geometric progression

$$1 \qquad 2 \qquad 4 \qquad 8 \qquad 16$$

are

$$0.00000 \quad 0.30103 \quad 0.60206 \quad 0.90309 \quad 1.20412$$

which constitute an arithmetic progression with $\log 1$ as the first term and

$$\log 2 = 0.30103$$

as the common difference, where 2 is the common ratio of the original geometric progression.

9.6 Compound Interest

The worth of a bank account which draws a compound interest constitutes a geometric progression at the end of a number of consecutive years. If the principal is $100, drawing an interest of 6% compounded annually, the amount grows to

$$\$100.00 \quad \$106.00 \quad \$112.36 \quad \$119.10$$

at the end of the zeroth, first, second and third year respectively. The first term of the above progression is the principal. The second term is the principal plus one year of interest, or

$$\$100 + \$100(0.06) = \$100(1.06) = \$106.00$$

where the number 0.06 is the interest rate. Now the principal has grown from $100 to $106. For the following year, the entire amount of $106 is drawing interest. So the third term is the new principal plus one year of interest on this new principal, or

$$\$106 + \$106(0.06) \ = \ \$106(1.06) \ = \ \$112.36$$

which is equal to

$$\$100(1.06)(1.06) \ = \ \$100(1.06)^2 .$$

Similarly, the fourth term is

$$\$100(1.06)^3 \ = \ \$119.1016 .$$

Thus the amounts accumulated at the end of the three consecutive years, which may be expressed as

$$\$100(1.06)^0 \quad \$100(1.06)^1 \quad \$100(1.06)^2 \quad \$100(1.06)^3 ,$$

form a geometric progression with the principal $100 as the first term and the number 1.06 as the common ratio. In general, the amount M accumulated at the end of the nth year with the interest compounded annually is

$$M \ = \ A(1+r)^n \tag{1}$$

where A is the principle and r is the annual rate of interest. However, this is the $(n+1)$st term of the geometric progression because the principle A is the first term. The nth term of the geometric progression is

$$G_n \ = \ A(1+r)^{n-1}$$

which is the amount accumulated at the end of the $(n-1)$st year. This relation can be illustrated by the following diagram:

first year	second year		$(n-1)$st year	nth year	
first term	second term	third term	$(n-1)$st term	nth term	$(n+1)$st term

The principal A, which draws an interest at the annual rate of r compounded k times a year, is worth the amount

$$M \ = \ A\left(1 + \frac{r}{k}\right)^{kn} \tag{2}$$

at the end of n years. This equation is derived from equation (1) with k being the only new element. If $k = 2$, the interest is compounded semi-annually. If $k = 4$, the interest is compounded quarterly. If $k = 12$, the interest is compounded monthly. The element k divides each year into k periods. Thus an annual interest rate of r becomes r/k for each period, and the n years becomes kn periods. When the letters r and n of equation (1) are replaced by r/k and kn respectively, the result is equation (2).

For the given example where $A = \$100$ and $r = 0.06$, the worth of the account at the end of the zeroth, first, second and third year is

$$\$100 \qquad \$100(1.03)^2 \qquad \$100(1.03)^4 \qquad \$100(1.03)^6$$

if the interest is compounded semi-annually. These amounts

$$\$100.00 \qquad \$106.09 \qquad \$112.55 \qquad \$119.41$$

which are obtained by compounding the interest semi-annually are larger than the corresponding amounts

$$\$100.00 \qquad \$106.00 \qquad \$112.36 \qquad \$119.10$$

which are obtained by compounding the interest only once a year. Of course, the first term being the principal is the same for both progressions. In general, the amount

$$M = A\left(1 + \frac{r}{k}\right)^{kn}$$

becomes larger as k increases or the interest is compounded more frequently.

In comparing the geometric progression

$$A \qquad A(1 + r) \qquad A(1 + r)^2 \qquad A(1 + r)^3$$

when the interest is compounded annually with

$$A \qquad A\left(1 + \frac{r}{k}\right)^k \qquad A\left(1 + \frac{r}{k}\right)^{2k} \qquad A\left(1 + \frac{r}{k}\right)^{3k}$$

when the interest is compounded k times a year, one can see that the common ratio of the former is

$$R_1 = 1 + r$$

and that of the latter is

$$R_k = \left(1 + \frac{r}{k}\right)^k \tag{3}$$

which increases with k.

As k increases without bound, the limiting value of R_k is equal to

$$\lim_{k \to \infty} \left(1 + \frac{r}{k}\right)^k = e^r. \tag{4}$$

To show that this is true, one may let k be equal to pr or

$$\frac{1}{p} = \frac{r}{k}. \tag{5}$$

After this change of symbols, the common ratio R_k becomes

$$\left(1 + \frac{r}{k}\right)^k = \left(1 + \frac{1}{p}\right)^{pr}. \tag{6}$$

As k increases without bound, so will the quantity p because of the fact that k is equal to pr and r is a constant. But as p increases without bound, the limiting value of R_k becomes

$$\lim_{p \to \infty} \left(1 + \frac{1}{p}\right)^{pr} = e^r \tag{7}$$

because of the fact that

$$\lim_{p \to \infty} \left(1 + \frac{1}{p}\right)^p = e$$

as given in equation (2) of section 9.4.

Now it is established that equation (2) becomes

$$M = Ae^{rn} \tag{8}$$

as k increases without bound or the interest is compounded continuously. This equation says that the principal A grows to the amount M after n years at an annual interest rate of r compounded continuously. For the example where $A = \$100$ and $r = 6\% = 0.06$, the account is worth

$$\$100 \qquad \$100\, e^{0.06} \qquad \$100\, e^{0.12} \qquad \$100\, e^{0.18}$$

or

$$\$100.00 \qquad \$106.18 \qquad \$112.74 \qquad \$119.71$$

at the end of the zeroth, first, second and third year. This is evidently
a geometric progression with the common ratio being

$$R_\infty = e^r = e^{0.06} = 1.0618$$

which can be evaluated with the aid of the table of common logarithms.

Equations (1), (2) and (8) can also be used in determining the
value of a property which depreciates at a constant percentage rate.
In this case, the rate of growth r is a negative one. For example,
a piece of equipment is purchased for $10,000 and depreciates each
year at the rate of 10% of its value. At the end of the first year,
it is worth

$$\$10,000 - \$10,000(0.1) = \$10,000(1 - 0.1) = \$9,000.$$

At the end of the second year, it is worth

$$\$9,000 - \$9,000(0.1) = \$9,000(1 - 0.1) = \$8,100.$$

At the end of the third year, it is worth

$$\$8,100 - \$8,100(0.1) = \$8,100(1 - 0.1) = \$7,290.$$

Thus the value of the equipment is

$$\$10,000 \qquad \$9,000 \qquad \$8,100 \qquad \$7,290$$

at the end of the zeroth, first, second and third year. This sequence
which can be written as

$$\$10,000 \qquad \$10,000(1 - 0.1) \qquad \$10,000(1-0.1)^2 \qquad \$10,000(1 - 0.1)^3$$

is a geometric progression with the original worth of the equipment
as the first term and the number

$$R = 1 + r = 1 - 0.1 = 0.9$$

as the common ratio, where $r = -0.1$ is the rate of depreciation or
a negative rate of interest.

The rate of interest and that of depreciation given in the above
examples are both represented by the letter r, because in both cases
r is the percentage rate of change. In the example of interest, r is
equal to 0.06 which is the rate of growth. But in the example of
depreciation, r is equal to -0.1 which is also the rate of growth but
a negative one. Thus equations (1), (2) and (8) may be used for

either interest or depreciation provided that the percentage rate of change is a constant.

Examples of interest and depreciation are also given in connection with the arithmetic progression in section 4.5. There the constant rate of change is an absolute amount such as $6 a year, which is the common difference D. But here in this section the constant rate of change is based on the percentage of the preceding term. For a constant percentage rate of r, the common ratio of the geometric progression is

$$R = 1 + r.$$

In the arithmetic progression, a term is obtained by *adding* to the preceding term the constant difference D which may be either positive or negative. While in the geometric progression, a term is obtained by multiplying the preceding term by the constant ratio

$$R = 1 + r$$

which may be either greater than or less than 1 depending whether the constant percentage-rate r is positive or negative.

The problems of interest and depreciation are brought up here only incidentally as illustrations of the geometric progression. Readers who are interested in this subject may consult a text on the mathematics of finance.

9.7 Exponential Equation

An equation such as

$$2^x = 8$$

where the unknown quantity x appears in the exponent is called an *exponential equation*. For this particular example, the root of the equation is 3 because 2^3 is equal to 8.

The general method of solving an exponential equation is to find the common logarithms of both sides of the equation. For the given example, the logarithms are

$$x \log 2 = \log 8$$

or

$$x(0.30103) = 0.90309$$

from which the root

$$x = \frac{0.90309}{0.30103} = 3$$

is determined.

The solution of an exponential equation is not a new topic. To solve the equation

$$2^x = 8$$

is merely to find the logarithm of 8 to the base 2. The method suggested here is an application of equation (2) of section 9.3.

The general method of solving the exponential equation may be relied upon regardless of the base. For the solution of the equation

$$e^{-0.01x} = 0.5,$$

one may find the common logarithms of both sides and obtains

$$-0.01 \, x \log e = \log 0.5$$

or

$$-0.01 \, x \, (0.43429) = -1 + 0.69897$$

or

$$x = \frac{-0.30103}{-0.0043429} = 69.315$$

which is the root of the equation.

As another example of the exponential equation, one may return to the problem of compound interest of the preceding section. One wishes to know the time required for the principal of A dollars to double itself if the interest rate is 6% compounded annually. Through equation (1) of section 9.6, the given condition can be translated into the equation

$$A(1 + r)^n = 2A$$

or

$$(1.06)^n = 2.$$

Then the problem is to determine the value of n. Finding the common logarithms of both sides of the equation, one obtains

$$n \log 1.06 = \log 2$$

or

$$n = \frac{0.30103}{0.02531} = 11.89 \,.$$

From this value of n, one can tell that it takes 12 years for an amount to double itself. By that time, the principle A is worth

$$A(1.06)^{12} = 2.01219647 \, A$$

or the principal of one million dollars is worth \$2,012,196.47 in 12 years.

The above example is a demonstration of the solution of an exponential equation. For practical problems of this kind, the logarithm table is seldom used because the values of $(1 + r)^n$ are extensively tabulated for various values of r and n.

9.8   Exponential Function

The equation of the *exponential function* of x is

$$y = f(x) = A \, e^{rx} \tag{1}$$

where A and r are constants. This function, which is equation (8) of section 9.6 with n and M replaced by x and y, is frequently called the *growth curve*. The quantity A, which grows continuously at the constant percentage-rate r, reaches the quantity y after x periods of time. The graph of the equation

$$y = e^{0.5x}$$

which is the exponential function with A equal to 1 and r equal to 0.5 is shown in figure 9.8a. The values of y in that graph are obtained from table 2 of the appendix.

When A, r and x of the exponential equation are given, the quantity y can be determined. For example, the population of a country is 10 million now. If it grows at the constant rate of 2% per year, in 10 years it will be

$$y = 10,000,000 \, e^{0.02(10)}$$

$$= 10,000,000 \, e^{0.2}$$

$$= 12,214,000$$

which is more than a 20% increase.

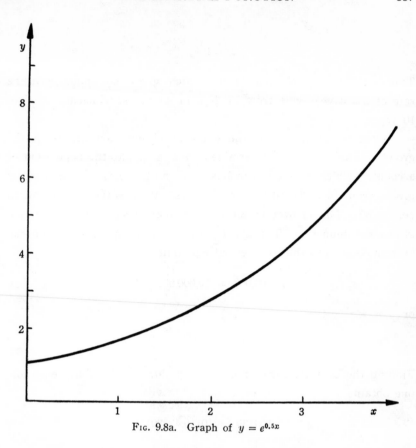

Fɪɢ. 9.8a. Graph of $y = e^{0.5x}$

When A, r and y of the exponential equation are given, the quantity x can be determined. For example, one may wish to know the number of years for the population of a country to grow by 20% if it grows at the rate of 2% a year. The answer is not 10 years, because the population grows continuously. Through equation (1), the given condition can be translated into the exponential equation

$$A e^{0.02x} = 1.2 A$$

or

$$e^{0.02x} = 1.2.$$

Finding the common logarithms of both sides of the above equation, one obtains

$$0.02 x (0.43429) = 0.07918$$

or

$$x = 9.1 \,.$$

This is to say that the population which grows continuously at the rate of 2% a year will grow by 20% in 9.1 years, which is less than 10 years.

When A, x and y of the exponential equation are given, the growth rate r can be determined. For example, the population of a country which grows continuously at the percentage rate of r has grown from 10 to 11 million in 10 years. What is the rate of growth per year? The answer is not 1% per year, because the population grows continuously. Through equation (1), the given condition can be translated into the exponential equation

$$11{,}000{,}000 = 10{,}000{,}000\, e^{10r}$$

or

$$1.1 = e^{10r} \,.$$

Finding the common logarithms of both sides of the above equation, one obtains

$$0.04139 = 10r(0.43429)$$

or

$$r = 0.00954$$

which indicates that the population has grown at the rate of 0.954% a year, which is less than 1%.

In the exponential function, the growth rate r can also be a negative number. For example, a chemical may decompose continuously at the rate of 1% a day. Here the rate r is equal to -0.01. However, the amount left in 30 days is not 70% of the original amount but

$$y = A\, e^{-0.01(30)} = A\, e^{-0.3} = 0.7408\, A$$

or 74.08% of the original amount. The graph of the above equation is given in figure 9.8b.

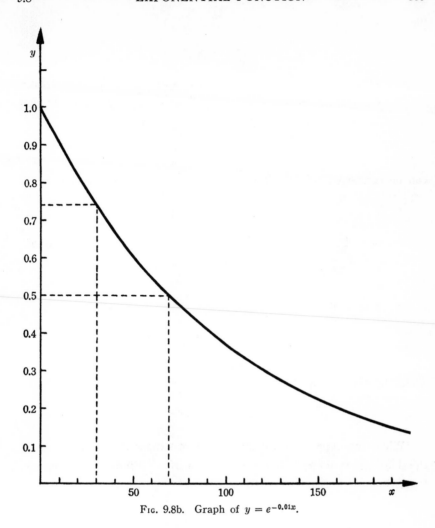

Fɪɢ. 9.8b.   Graph of $y = e^{-0.01x}$.

To determine the half-life of a chemical is to determine the number of periods of time required for the chemical to decompose one half of its original amount. For the above example where the rate of decomposition is 1% per day, the half-life of the chemical can be determined by solving the exponential equation

$$A\, e^{-0.01x} = 0.5\, A$$

or

$$e^{-0.01x} = 0.5\,.$$

The root

$$x = 69.3$$

indicates that only one half of the chemical still remains after 69.3 days.

An exponential equation with any base can be converted to that of base e. The function

$$y = (10)2^x$$

can be converted into the form

$$y = A e^{rx}$$

by letting A be equal to 10 and e^r equal to 2. From the equation

$$e^r = 2,$$

it can be determined that

$$r = \frac{\log 2}{\log e} = \frac{0.30103}{0.43429} = 0.69315.$$

Then the given function becomes

$$y = (10)2^x = 10\, e^{0.69315x}.$$

When the dependent variable y is an exponential function of x, the logarithm of y is a linear function of x. Finding the common logarithms of both sides of the equation

$$y = A e^{rx},$$

one obtains

$$\log y = \log A + r x \log e = \log A + (r \log e)x$$

which is a linear equation with $\log A$ as the intercept and $r \log e$ as the slope. The graph of

$$y = e^{0.5x}$$

given in figure 9.8a becomes the straight line

$$\log y = 0.5(0.43429)x = 0.217145\, x$$

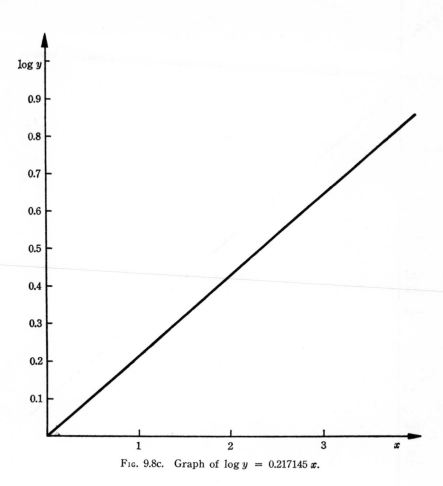

Fɪɢ. 9.8c.   Graph of $\log y \;=\; 0.217145\, x$.

in figure 9.8c where y is expressed in the logarithmic scale. Similarly the graph of

$$y \;=\; e^{-0.01x}$$

of figure 9.8b becomes the straight line

$$\log y \;=\; -\,0.01(0.43429)x \;=\; -\,0.0043429\, x$$

of figure 9.8d.

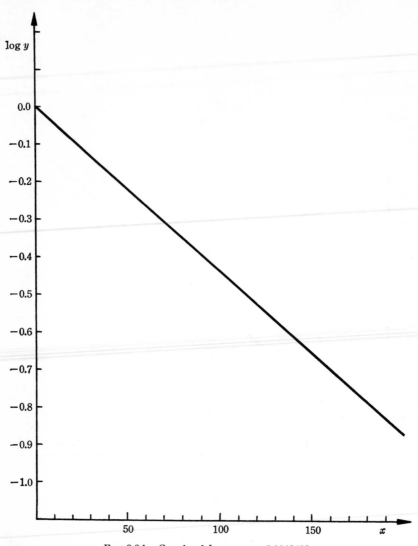

Fig. 9.8d. Graph of $\log y = -0.0043429\, x$.

9.9 Logarithmic Function

The linear function of the logarithm of the independent variable x such as

$$y = b_0 + b_1 \log_B x \tag{1}$$

is called the *logarithmic function* of x. The base B of the logarithm can be any positive value different from 1. When $b_0 = 0$, $b_1 = 1$, and $B = 10$, the function is

$$y = \log x$$

which is the simplest logarithmic function of x. The graph of this equation is given in figure 9.9, and the values of x and $\log x$ for this graph are obtained from the table of common logarithms.

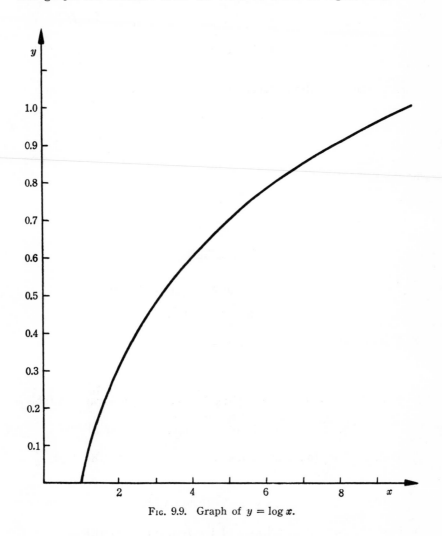

Fig. 9.9. Graph of $y = \log x$.

The logarithmic function is the inverse of the exponential function. If x is an exponential function of y, the variable y is the logarithmic function of x. The exponential function of y is

$$x = A e^{ry}.$$

Finding the natural logarithms of both sides of the above equation, one obtains

$$\log_e x = \log_e A + r y$$

or

$$y = \frac{1}{r}(\log_e x - \log_e A)$$

which is the logarithmic function of x given in equation (1) with

$$b_0 = -(\log_e A)/r$$

$$b_1 = 1/r$$

and

$$B = e.$$

EXERCISES

1. Find the logarithms of the following quantities to the base 2:

(a) 1   (b) 2   (c) 64   (d) 0.25

2. Evaluate the following quantities:

(a) $10^{\log 2}$ (b) $10^{\log 5}$

3. Evaluate the following quantities by means of the logarithm table:

(a) $\sqrt[10]{9,729}$ (b) $(1.06)^{20}$ (c) $e^{2.5}$ (d) $10^{0.30103}$

4. Evaluate the following quantities by means of the logarithm table:

(a) 125×64 (b) $12/1,728$

5. Find the natural logarithms of the following quantities:

(a) 2.5   (b) 100   (c) 1/2   (d) 0.1

6. (a) Find the fourth and the fifth term of the following geo-metric progression:

$$10 \quad 50 \quad \cdots$$

(b) Find the sum of the first five terms of the above progression by equation (2) of section 9.5 and check your result by adding the five terms together.

7. (a) Find the first six terms of the following geometric progression:

$$1,024 \quad 512 \quad \cdots$$

(b) Find the sum of the six terms of the above progression by equation (2) of section 9.5 and check your result by adding the six terms together.

8. Find the common logarithms of the six terms of the geometric progression of exercise 7 and show that the result is an arithmetic progression by identifying its first term and common difference.

9. The values of x

$$0 \quad 1 \quad 2 \quad 3 \quad 4$$

constitute an arithmetic progression with the first term being equal to 0 and the common difference equal to 1. Find the five values of 10^x and show that these values constitute a geometric progression by identifying its first term and common ratio.

10. Find the worth of $200 after 5 years if the rate of interest is 6% a year

(a) compounded annually

(b) compounded quarterly

(c) compounded monthly

and

(d) compounded continuously.

11. Find the annual rate of interest which enables $200 to double itself in 10 years if the interest is compounded semi-annually.

12. Solve the following equations:

$$(a)\ 3^x\ =\ 20$$

$$(b)\ e^{0.2x}\ =\ 7.389$$

13. Plot the graph of $y\ =\ e^x$ from $x\ =\ -1$ to $x\ =\ 2$. Use as many points as necessary. Obtain the values of y from table 2 of the appendix.

14. Plot the graph of $y\ =\ \log_e x$ from $x\ =\ 0.1$ to $x\ =\ 3.0$. Use as many points as necessary. Obtain the values of y from table 3 of the appendix.

CHAPTER 10

CALCULUS OF EXPONENTIAL AND LOGARITHMIC FUNCTIONS

The exponential and logarithmic functions are introduced in the preceding chapter. The differentiation and integration of these functions are discussed in this one.

10.1 Differentiation of Exponential Function

The rate of change of the exponential function B^x for the interval from x to $x+\Delta x$ is, by definition, equal to

$$\frac{\Delta}{\Delta x} B^x = \frac{B^{x+\Delta x} - B^x}{\Delta x} = \frac{B^x B^{\Delta x} - B^x}{\Delta x} = B^x \frac{B^{\Delta x} - 1}{\Delta x}. \quad (1)$$

According to this rule, the differentiation of B^x only involves the evaluation of the constant

$$K = \frac{B^{\Delta x} - 1}{\Delta x}. \quad (2)$$

The derivative of B^x can be obtained by multiplying B^x by the constant K.

TABLE 10.1a

DIFFERENTIATION OF $y = 4^x$

x	y	Δx	Δy	$\bar{x}$	$\dfrac{\Delta y}{\Delta x}$
0.0	1				
		0.5	1	0.25	2
0.5	2				
		0.5	2	0.75	4
1.0	4				
		0.5	4	1.25	8
1.5	8				
		0.5	8	1.75	16
2.0	16				

The numerical demonstration of this rule of differentiation is given in table 10.1a. The base B used in that example is 4, and the length of interval is 0.5. The differentiation is carried out in the usual way, and the values of $\bar{x}$ and their corresponding values of $\Delta y/\Delta x$ constitute the derivative of the function 4^x.

The purpose of this demonstration is to show that the same result can be obtained through evaluation of K which is equal to

$$\frac{B^{\Delta x} - 1}{\Delta x} = \frac{4^{0.5} - 1}{0.5} = \frac{2 - 1}{0.5} = 2 .$$

According to equation (1), the derivative of the given function is twice the function itself or

$$\frac{\Delta}{\Delta x} 4^x = (2)4^x .$$

This relation can be observed in table 10.1a. The values of

$$y = 4^x$$

at the lower end-points of the four intervals are

$$1 \quad 2 \quad 4 \quad 8;$$

while the rates of change of these intervals are

$$2 \quad 4 \quad 8 \quad 16$$

which are twice as large as y.

TABLE 10.1b

DIFFERENTIATION OF $y = A R^x$

x	y	$\bar{x}$	$\Delta y = \dfrac{\Delta y}{\Delta x}$
0	A		
		0.5	$AR - A \quad = A \quad (R - 1)$
1	AR		
		1.5	$AR^2 - AR = AR \ (R - 1)$
2	AR^2		
		2.5	$AR^3 - AR^2 = AR^2 \ (R - 1)$
3	AR^3		
		3.5	$AR^4 - AR^3 = AR^3 \ (R - 1)$
4	AR^4		

The rule given in equation (1) can be directly applied to the differentiation of the geometric progression as shown in table 10.1b. The exponential function

$$y = A R^x \tag{3}$$

yields the geometric progression given in that table when the values 0, 1, 2, 3 and 4 are assigned to x. The difference Δy is equal to the derivative $\Delta y/\Delta x$ because Δx is equal to 1. The result shows that the value of $\Delta y/\Delta x$ for each interval is equal to $(R-1)$ times the value of y at the lower end-point of that interval. For example, the y-value at the lower end-point of the first interval is A and the derivative for that interval is $A(R-1)$.

The same result can be obtained from equation (1). According to that rule, the derivative of

$$y = A R^x$$

is

$$\frac{\Delta y}{\Delta x} = \frac{\Delta}{\Delta x} A R^x = A \frac{\Delta}{\Delta x} R^x = A R^x K$$

where

$$K = \frac{R^{\Delta x} - 1}{\Delta x} = \frac{R^1 - 1}{1} = R - 1$$

because Δx is equal to 1.

The physical meaning of the constant

$$K = \frac{B^{\Delta x} - 1}{\Delta x}$$

can be seen from the problem of compound interest (section 9.6). If the principle is $100, drawing an interest of 6% compounded annually, the amount grows to

$$\$100(1.06)^0 \quad \$100(1.06)^1 \quad \$100(1.06)^2 \quad \$100(1.06)^3$$

at the end of the zeroth, first, second and third year as shown in table 10.1c. This sequence of values can be represented by the exponential function

$$y = 100(1.06)^x$$

TABLE 10.1c

DIFFERENTIATION OF $y = 100(1.06)^x$

x	y	$\Delta y = \dfrac{\Delta y}{\Delta x}$	$0.06\, y$
0	100.0000		6.0000
		6.0000	
1	106.0000		6.3600
		6.3600	
2	112.3600		6.7416
		6.7416	
3	119.1016		

for $x = 0$, 1, 2 and 3. According to the rule of differentiation given in equation (1), the derivative of y is

$$\frac{\Delta}{\Delta x}100(1.06)^x = 100(1.06)^x K$$

where

$$K = \frac{B^{\Delta x} - 1}{\Delta x} = \frac{1.06 - 1}{1} = 0.06$$

which is nothing but the interest rate. This can be seen in table 10.1c which shows that the value of $\Delta y/\Delta x$ of every interval is equal to 0.06 times the value of y at the beginning of that interval. Of course, this is a foregone conclusion to anyone who knows the meaning of the rate of interest.

When Δx is equal to 1, the constant

$$K = \frac{B^{\Delta x} - 1}{\Delta x}$$

becomes

$$K = B - 1$$

and the derivative of B^x becomes

$$\frac{\Delta}{\Delta x}B^x = \Delta B^x = B^x(B - 1). \tag{4}$$

If the base B is equal to 3 and Δx equal to 1, the derivative of B^x becomes

$$\Delta 3^x = 2(3^x).$$

If the base is equal to 2 and Δx equal to 1, equation (4) reduces to the neat formula

$$\Delta 2^x = 2^x. \tag{5}$$

This equation is demonstrated numerically in table 10.1d. The value of $\Delta y/\Delta x$ or $\Delta 2^x$ of every interval given in that table is equal to the value of y or 2^x at the lower end-point of that interval.

TABLE 10.1d

DIFFERENTIATION OF $y = 2^x$

x	y	$\bar{x}$	$\Delta y = \dfrac{\Delta y}{\Delta x}$
-2	0.25		
		-1.5	0.25
-1	0.50		
		-0.5	0.50
0	1.00		
		0.5	1.00
1	2.00		
		1.5	2.00
2	4.00		
		2.5	4.00
3	8.00		

So far the derivative of B^x is expressed as a function of the lower end-point x of the interval from x to $x+\Delta x$. However, it can also be expressed as that of the mid-point

$$\bar{x} = x + 0.5\Delta x.$$

When the exponent in the derivative given in equation (1) is expressed as

$$x = \bar{x} - 0.5\Delta x,$$

that equation becomes

$$\frac{\Delta}{\Delta x}B^x = B^{\bar{x}-0.5\Delta x}\left(\frac{B^{\Delta x}-1}{\Delta x}\right)$$

$$= B^{\bar{x}}B^{-0.5\Delta x}\left(\frac{B^{\Delta x}-1}{\Delta x}\right)$$

$$= B^{\bar{x}}\left(\frac{B^{\Delta x}-1}{\Delta x\sqrt{B^{\Delta x}}}\right)$$

$$= K'B^{\bar{x}} \tag{6}$$

where

$$K' = \frac{B^{\Delta x}-1}{\Delta x\sqrt{B^{\Delta x}}} \tag{7}$$

is a constant.

The meaning of the new constant K' may be clarified by a numerical example. In table 10.1a where $B = 4$, $\Delta x = 0.5$, and

$$B^{\Delta x} = (4)^{0.5} = \sqrt{4} = 2,$$

the value of the new constant is

$$K' = \frac{2-1}{0.5\sqrt{2}} = \frac{2}{\sqrt{2}} = \sqrt{2}.$$

At the mid-points

$$0.25 \qquad 0.75 \qquad 1.25 \qquad 1.75$$

of the four intervals given in that table, the corresponding values of $B^{\bar{x}}$ are

$$(4)^{0.25} \qquad (4)^{0.75} \qquad (4)^{1.25} \qquad (4)^{1.75}$$

or

$$\sqrt{2} \qquad 2\sqrt{2} \qquad 4\sqrt{2} \qquad 8\sqrt{2}.$$

When these values are multiplied by the new constant $\sqrt{2}$, the resulting products are

$$2 \quad 4 \quad 8 \quad 16$$

which are exactly the same values of $\Delta y/\Delta x$ given in the last column of table 10.1a.

10.2   Derivative of Exponential Function

The objective of this section is to find the derivative

$$\frac{d}{dx}B^x = \underset{\Delta x \to 0}{\text{limit}}\ \frac{\Delta}{\Delta x}B^x$$

of the function B^x. The rate of change of B^x for the interval from x to $x+\Delta x$ is known to be (equations 1 and 2, section 10.1)

$$\frac{\Delta}{\Delta x}B^x = B^x\frac{B^{\Delta x}-1}{\Delta x} = B^xK \tag{1}$$

for a positive Δx. However, when Δx is equal to zero, the constant K becomes

$$\frac{B^{\Delta x}-1}{\Delta x} = \frac{B^0-1}{0} = \frac{1-1}{0} = \frac{0}{0}$$

which is indeterminate. To overcome this difficulty, K is replaced by its limiting value as Δx approaches zero.

Before finding the limiting value of K, one may first select a convenient value for the base B so that the constant K is equal to 1. To do so, one may let the length of an interval be one-pth of a unit or

$$\Delta x = \frac{1}{p}. \tag{2}$$

When Δx is replaced by $1/p$, the constant K becomes

$$K = \frac{B^{1/p}-1}{\frac{1}{p}}.$$

To make the constant K equal to 1, one must fulfill the condition

$$B^{1/p}-1 = \frac{1}{p}$$

or

$$B^{1/p} = 1+\frac{1}{p}.$$

Raising both sides of the above equation to their pth power, one has

$$B = \left(1+\frac{1}{p}\right)^p \tag{3}$$

which is the condition that the constant K is equal to 1 or

$$\frac{\Delta}{\Delta x} B^x = B^x.$$

When p is equal to 1 or

$$\Delta x = \frac{1}{p} = \frac{1}{1} = 1,$$

the required base to make K equal to 1 is

$$B = \left(1 + \frac{1}{p}\right)^p = \left(1 + \frac{1}{1}\right)^1 = 2.$$

This leads to the neat formula

$$\frac{\Delta}{\Delta x} 2^x = 2^x$$

which is equation (5) of section 10.1.

When Δx approaches zero or p approaches infinity, the required base to make K equal to 1 is e. This can be seen from equation (3). As p approaches infinity, the limiting value of B becomes (equation 2, section 9.4)

$$\lim_{p \to \infty} \left(1 + \frac{1}{p}\right)^p = e.$$

This leads to the conclusion that the derivative of e^x is

$$\frac{d}{dx} e^x = e^x. \tag{4}$$

This is the reason why the strange number e is chosen as the base of the natural logarithm.

Equation (4) can be generalized. If the exponent of e is a function of x such as $v(x)$, the derivative is (rule 11, section 5.7)

$$\frac{d}{dx} e^v = \frac{d}{dv} e^v \frac{dv}{dx} = e^v \frac{dv}{dx}. \tag{5}$$

For example, the derivative of

$$y = e^{2x}$$

is

$$\frac{dy}{dx} = e^{2x} \frac{d}{dx}(2x) = 2 e^{2x}$$

and that of

$$y = 3\,e^{-x^2}$$

is

$$\frac{dy}{dx} = 3\,\frac{d}{dx}e^{-x^2}$$

$$= 3\,e^{-x^2}\frac{d}{dx}(-x^2)$$

$$= 3\,e^{-x^2}(-2x)$$

$$= -\,6\,x\,e^{-x^2}.$$

TABLE 10.2a

DIFFERENTIATION OF $y = e^{2x}$

x	y	Δx	Δy	$\bar{x}$	$\dfrac{\Delta y}{\Delta x}$	$2\,e^{2\bar{x}}$
0.0	1.0000					
		0.1	0.2214	0.05	2.214	2.210
0.1	1.2214					
		0.1	0.2704	0.15	2.704	2.700
0.2	1.4918					
		0.1	0.3303	0.25	3.303	3.297
0.3	1.8221					
		0.1	0.4034	0.35	4.034	4.028
0.4	2.2255					

The numerical demonstration of the derivative

$$\frac{d}{dx}e^{2x} = 2\,e^{2x} \tag{6}$$

for the range from $x = 0.0$ to $x = 0.4$ is given in table 10.2a. The chosen Δx of 0.1 fixes the values of x at 0.0, 0.1, $\cdots$, 0.4. The corresponding values of

$$y = e^{2x}$$

are obtained from table 2 of the appendix. The differentiation is carried out in the usual way. The resulting values of the mid-points $\bar{x}$ and their corresponding values of $\Delta y/\Delta x$ constitute the derivative of y.

To demonstrate the validity of equation (6), the values of $2\,e^{2x}$ are computed at the mid-points $\bar{x}$ and are listed in the last column of table 10.2a. Comparing the numbers in the last two columns of that table, one will note that the values of $\Delta y/\Delta x$ are approximately equal to those of $2\,e^{2\bar{x}}$. When rounded off to two decimal places, both sets of values are equal to

$$2.21 \qquad 2.70 \qquad 3.30 \qquad 4.03\,.$$

The discrepancy stems from the fact that the Δx used in the demonstration is 0.1 while the dx in the formula is an infinitesimal quantity. The discrepancy is expected to reduce in magnitude if a smaller Δx is used. The purpose of this demonstration is to reveal the meaning of equation (5) in general and to show the validity of equation (6) in particular.

Now it can be shown that the characteristic of the exponential function (equation 1, section 9.8)

$$y \ = \ A\,e^{rx} \tag{7}$$

is that the rate of change of y is proportional to y or

$$\frac{dy}{dx} \ = \ r\,y\,. \tag{8}$$

The above derivative can be obtained by the known rules of differentiation. It should be

$$\frac{dy}{dx} \ = \ A\,\frac{d}{dx}e^{rx}$$

$$= \ A\,e^{rx}\frac{d}{dx}(rx)$$

$$= \ A\,e^{rx}\,r$$

$$= \ r\,y\,.$$

This derivative shows that the percentage rate of growth of y is the constant

$$\frac{\dfrac{dy}{dx}}{y} \ = \ r\,.$$

The derivative of B^x for any base can be derived from equation (5). When the base is expressed as

$$B = e^m$$

or

$$\log_e B = m,$$

the function becomes

$$B^x = e^{mx}$$

and its derivative becomes

$$\frac{d}{dx}B^x = \frac{d}{dx}e^{mx} = e^{mx}\frac{d}{dx}mx = e^{mx}m = B^x(\log_e B).$$

The newly obtained formula of differentiation

$$\frac{d}{dx}B^x = (\log_e B)B^x \tag{9}$$

is a generalized version of equation (4). When the base B is e, the natural logarithm of B becomes 1 and consequently equation (9) becomes equation (4).

Equation (9) can be further generalized. If the exponent x of B is a function of x such as $v(x)$, the derivative is

$$\frac{d}{dx}B^v = \frac{d}{dv}B^v\frac{dv}{dx} = (\log_e B)\,B^v\,\frac{dv}{dx}. \tag{10}$$

For example, the derivative of

$$y = 3^{2x}$$

is equal to

$$\frac{dy}{dx} = (\log_e 3)\,3^{2x}\frac{d}{dx}(2x)$$

$$= 2(\log_e 3)3^{2x}.$$

If the same function is expressed as

$$y = 3^{2x} = 9^x,$$

the derivative becomes

$$\frac{dy}{dx} = (\log_e 9)9^x$$

which is the same expression because

$$\log_e 9 = 2 \log_e 3$$

and

$$9^x = 3^{2x}.$$

TABLE 10.2b

DIFFERENTIATION OF $y = 3^{2x}$

x	y	Δx	Δy	$\bar{x}$	$\dfrac{\Delta y}{\Delta x}$	$(2.19722)3^{2\bar{x}}$
0.0	1.000					
		0.1	0.246	0.05	2.46	2.45
0.1	1.246					
		0.1	0.306	0.15	3.06	3.05
0.2	1.552					
		0.1	0.381	0.25	3.81	3.81
0.3	1.933					
		0.1	0.475	0.35	4.75	4.74
0.4	2.408					

The numerical demonstration of the derivative

$$\frac{d}{dx} 3^{2x} = 2(\log_e 3)3^{2x}$$

for the range from $x = 0.0$ to $x = 0.4$ is given in table 10.2b. The chosen Δx of 0.1 fixes the values of x at 0.0, 0.1, $\cdots$, 0.4. The corresponding values of

$$y = 3^{2x}$$

are computed with the aid of the table of common logarithms. For example, when x is equal to 0.1, y is equal to $3^{0.2}$ and the common logarithm of y is

$$\log y = 0.2 \log 3 = 0.2(0.47712) = 0.095424.$$

From the logarithm table, it can be found that y is equal to 1.246 which is listed in table 10.2b.

After the values of y are computed, the differentiation is carried out in the usual way. The values of $\Delta y/\Delta x$ for the four intervals and those of

$$2(\log_e 3)\, 3^{2x} = (2.19722)\, 3^{2x}$$

evaluated at the mid-points $\bar{x}$ of the intervals are listed side by side in the last two columns of table 10.2b. One column of numbers is approximately equal to the other. The discrepancy, of course, comes from the fact that the Δx in the demonstration is 0.1 and the dx in the formula is an infinitesimal quantity. The purpose of this demonstration is to reveal the meaning of equation (10).

10.3   Derivative of Logarithmic Function

The derivative of the natural logarithm of the independent variable x is

$$\frac{d}{dx}\log_e x = \frac{1}{x} = x^{-1}. \tag{1}$$

This result can be derived from equation (4) of section 10.2 which says

$$\frac{d}{dy}e^y = e^y.$$

If e^y is represented by x, the above equation becomes

$$\frac{dx}{dy} = x.$$

But the representation

$$x = e^y$$

implies

$$y = \log_e x.$$

Then the combination of the two derivatives

$$\frac{dy}{dx} = \frac{d}{dx}\log_e x$$

and

$$\frac{dx}{dy} = x$$

leads to the conclusion

$$\frac{d}{dx}\log_e x = \frac{1}{x}$$

because

$$\frac{dy}{dx} = \frac{1}{\dfrac{dx}{dy}}.$$

TABLE 10.3a

DIFFERENTIATION OF $y = \log_e x$

x	y	Δx	Δy	$\bar{x}$	$\dfrac{\Delta y}{\Delta x}$	$\dfrac{1}{\bar{x}}$
1.0	0.00000					
		0.1	0.09531	1.05	0.9531	0.9524
1.1	0.09531					
		0.1	0.08701	1.15	0.8701	0.8696
1.2	0.18232					
		0.1	0.08004	1.25	0.8004	0.8000
1.3	0.26236					
		0.1	0.07411	1.35	0.7411	0.7407
1.4	0.33647					
		0.1	0.06900	1.45	0.6900	0.6897
1.5	0.40547					

The numerical demonstration of equation (1) is given in table 10.3a which shows the differentiation of the function

$$y = \log_e x$$

for the range from $x = 1.0$ to $x = 1.5$. The chosen Δx is 0.1 which fixes the values of x at 1.0, 1.1, $\cdots$, 1.5. The corresponding values of y are obtained from table 3 of the appendix. After the values of x and y are determined, the differentiation is carried out in the usual way. The resulting values of $\bar{x}$ and $\Delta y/\Delta x$ constitute the derivative of the natural logarithm of x.

To demonstrate the validity of equation (1), the values of $1/\bar{x}$ are computed at the mid-points $\bar{x}$ of the intervals. These values, which are listed in the last column of table 10.3a, are approximately equal to the corresponding values of $\Delta y/\Delta x$ given in that table. The largest discrepancy occurs in the first interval whose error is

$$0.9531 - 0.9524 = 0.0007 \,.$$

The purpose of this demonstration is to reveal the meaning of the derivative

$$\frac{d}{dx}\log_e x = \frac{1}{x} \,.$$

The discrepancy shown in table 10.3a is due to the fact that the Δx used in the demonstration is 0.1 while the dx in the formula is an infinitesimal quantity.

The derivative given in equation (1) can be generalized. If the independent variable x is replaced by a function of x such as $v(x)$, the derivative of

$$y = \log_e v$$

becomes

$$\frac{dy}{dx} = \frac{dy}{dv} \cdot \frac{dv}{dx}$$

or

$$\frac{d}{dx}\log_e v = \frac{1}{v} \cdot \frac{dv}{dx} \,. \tag{2}$$

For example, the derivative of

$$y = \log_e (x^2 + 1)^3 = 3\log_e (x^2 + 1) \tag{3}$$

is

$$\frac{dy}{dx} = 3\,\frac{d}{dx}\log_e (x^2 + 1)$$

$$= \frac{3}{x^2 + 1} \cdot \frac{d}{dx}(x^2 + 1)$$

$$= \frac{6x}{x^2 + 1} \,. \tag{4}$$

The numerical demonstration of the above derivative is given in table 10.3b which shows the differentiation of the function

$$y = \log_e(x^2 + 1)^3 = 3\log_e(x^2 + 1)$$

for the range from $x = 0.0$ to $x = 0.4$. The chosen Δx is 0.1 which fixes the values of x at 0.0, 0.1, $\cdots$, 0.4. The corresponding values of y are obtained with the aid of table 3 of the appendix. For example, the value of y at $x = 0.4$ is

$$\log_e[(0.4)^2 + 1]^3 = 3\log_e(1.16) = 3(0.14842) = 0.44526.$$

After the values of y are computed, the differentiation is carried out in the usual way. The values of the mid-points $\bar{x}$ and their corresponding values of $\Delta y/\Delta x$ constitute the derivative of the given function.

TABLE 10.3b

DIFFERENTIATION OF $y = \log_e(x^2 + 1)^3$

x	y	Δx	Δy	$\bar{x}$	$\dfrac{\Delta y}{\Delta x}$	$\dfrac{6\bar{x}}{(\bar{x})^2 + 1}$
0.0	0.00000					
		0.1	0.02985	0.05	0.2985	0.2993
0.1	0.02985					
		0.1	0.08781	0.15	0.8781	0.8802
0.2	0.11766					
		0.1	0.14088	0.25	1.4088	1.4118
0.3	0.25854					
		0.1	0.18672	0.35	1.8672	1.8708
0.4	0.44526					

To demonstrate the validity of the equation

$$\frac{d}{dx}\log_e(x^2 + 1)^3 = \frac{6x}{x^2 + 1},$$

the values of $6x/(x^2 + 1)$ are computed at the mid-points $\bar{x}$ and are listed in the last column of table 10.3b. For example, the last value of that column is

$$\frac{6(0.35)}{(0.35)^2 + 1} = \frac{2.10}{1.1225} = 1.8708.$$

The similarity of the corresponding numbers of the last two columns of table 10.3b demonstrates that equation (2) does hold true. When rounded off to two decimal places, both sets of numbers are equal to

$$0.30 \quad 0.88 \quad 1.41 \quad 1.87 \,.$$

The discrepancy, of course, comes from the fact the Δx used in the demonstration is 0.1 and the dx in equation (2) is an infinitesimal quantity.

The derivative of the logarithm of x to the base B can be obtained from equation (1). Since the logarithm of x to the base B is equal to (equation 4, section 9.4)

$$\log_B x = (\log_B e) \log_e x,$$

its derivative must be

$$\frac{d}{dx} \log_B x = (\log_B e) \frac{d}{dx} \log_e x = \frac{\log_B e}{x} \,. \tag{5}$$

Similarly, it can be derived that the derivative of $\log_B v$ is

$$\frac{d}{dx} \log_B v = \frac{\log_B e}{v} \cdot \frac{dv}{dx} \,. \tag{6}$$

For example, if the base B is 10, the derivative of the function

$$y = \log(x^2 + 1)^3 = 3 \log(x^2 + 1) \tag{7}$$

is

$$\frac{d}{dx} \log (x^2 + 1)^3 = \frac{3 \log e}{x^2 + 1} 2x = \frac{0.43429(6x)}{x^2 + 1} \,. \tag{8}$$

TABLE 10.3c

DIFFERENTIATION OF $y = \log(x^2 + 1)^3$

x	y	Δx	Δy	$\bar{x}$	$\dfrac{\Delta y}{\Delta x}$	$\dfrac{0.43429(6\bar{x})}{(\bar{x})^2 + 1}$
0.0	0.00000					
		0.1	0.01296	0.05	0.1296	0.1300
0.1	0.01296					
		0.1	0.03813	0.15	0.3813	0.3823
0.2	0.05109					
		0.1	0.06120	0.25	0.6120	0.6131
0.3	0.11229					
		0.1	0.08109	0.35	0.8109	0.8125
0.4	0.19338					

The numerical demonstration of the above equation is given in table 10.3c. This table is similar to table 10.3b in every way except that the table of common logarithms is used in finding the value of y instead of that of the natural logarithms. The fact that the numbers of the last two columns of table 10.3c can be rounded off to

$$0.13 \quad 0.38 \quad 0.61 \quad 0.81$$

indicates that equation (8) holds true.

The difference between equations (2) and (6) are clearly shown in tables 10.3b and 10.3c. In both tables, the function $v(x)$ is

$$v = (x^2 + 1)^3$$

and the only difference between the two tables is the base of the logarithm of $v(x)$. The fact that

$$\log v = (\log e) \log_e v = 0.43429 \, (\log_e v)$$

is indicated by the y-values of table 10.3c being 0.43429 times as large as those of table 10.3b. Because of this, the derivative given in table 10.3c is also 0.43429 times that of table 10.3b. This is how equation (6) is derived from equation (2). The basic principle is that of common factor.

10.4   Sum of Exponential Function

The integral of the function B^x can be obtained from the derivative (equations 6 and 7, section 10.1)

$$\frac{\Delta}{\Delta x} B^x = K' B^{\bar{x}}$$

of that function. When both sides of the above equation are integrated with respect to x, the result is

$$B^x + C_1 = K' \sum_a^x B^{\bar{x}} \Delta x .$$

From the above equation, it can be seen that the integral of B^x is equal to

$$\sum_a^x B^{\bar{x}} \Delta x = \frac{1}{K'} B^x + \frac{1}{K'} C_1 = \frac{B^x}{K'} + C \tag{1}$$

where (equation 7, section 10.1)

$$\frac{1}{K'} = \frac{\Delta x \sqrt{B^{\Delta x}}}{B^{\Delta x} - 1} \cdot \qquad (2)$$

TABLE 10.4a

INTEGRATION OF $f(x) = 16^x$

$\bar{x}$	$f(\bar{x})$	$f(\bar{x}) \, \Delta x$	x	$F(x)$	$16^x/3$
			0.0	$F(0)$	$\dfrac{1}{3} = \dfrac{1}{3}$
0.25	2	1			
			0.5	$F(0) + 1$	$\dfrac{4}{3} = \dfrac{1}{3} + 1$
0.75	8	4			
			1.0	$F(0) + 5$	$\dfrac{16}{3} = \dfrac{1}{3} + 5$
1.25	32	16			
			1.5	$F(0) + 21$	$\dfrac{64}{3} = \dfrac{1}{3} + 21$
1.75	128	64			
			2.0	$F(0) + 85$	$\dfrac{256}{3} = \dfrac{1}{3} + 85$

The numerical demonstration of equation (1) is given in table 10.4a where the function

$$f(x) = 16^x$$

is integrated from $x = 0$ to $x = 2$. The chosen Δx is 0.5 which fixes the mid-points $\bar{x}$ of the intervals at 0.25, 0.75, 1.25 and 1.75. At these points, the value of

$$f(\bar{x}) = 16^{\bar{x}}$$

are

$$(16)^{0.25} = \sqrt[4]{(16)^1} = \quad 2$$
$$(16)^{0.75} = \sqrt[4]{(16)^3} = \quad 8$$
$$(16)^{1.25} = \sqrt[4]{(16)^5} = \quad 32$$
$$(16)^{1.75} = \sqrt[4]{(16)^7} = 128$$

as shown in table 10.4a. After the values of $f(\bar{x})$ are computed, the integration is carried out by the standard method. The values of the end-points x and their corresponding values of $F(x)$ constitute the integral of 16^x.

To demonstrate the validity of equation (1), the value of $1/K'$ has to be computed. For the given example where the base is

$$B = 16$$

and the length of an interval is

$$\Delta x = 0.5,$$

the value of the constant is

$$\frac{1}{K'} = \frac{0.5\sqrt{(16)^{0.5}}}{(16)^{0.5} - 1} = \frac{0.5(2)}{4 - 1} = \frac{1}{3}.$$

If equation (1) is true, the integral of 16^x must be

$$F(x) = \frac{16^x}{3}.$$

This is indeed the case as shown by the numbers of the last two columns of table 10.4a. From that table, it can be established that

$$F(x) - F(0) = \frac{16^x}{3} - \frac{1}{3}$$

or

$$F(x) = \frac{16^x}{3}$$

because

$$F(0) = \frac{16^0}{3} = \frac{1}{3}.$$

The definite integral of 16^x from $x = 0$ to $x = 2$ is

$$\sum_{0}^{2} 16^{\bar{x}} \Delta x = \left[\frac{16^x}{3} \right]_0^2 = \frac{256}{3} - \frac{1}{3} = 85.$$

Of course, this integral is simply the sum

$$\sum f(\bar{x}) \, \Delta x = 1 + 4 + 16 + 64 = 85$$

as shown in table 10.4a.

The sum of the n terms of a geometric progression

$$\sum_{i=1}^{n} G_i = A + AR + AR^2 + \cdots + AR^{n-1}$$

can be evaluated by equation (1). The function

$$f(x) = AR^x$$

generates the geometric progression

$$A \quad AR \quad AR^2 \quad \cdots \quad AR^{n-1}$$

if the values $0, 1, 2, \cdots, n-1$ are assigned to x. To find the sum of the n terms is to integrate the function $f(x)$ from

$$x = 0 - 0.5 = -0.5$$

to

$$x = (n-1) + 0.5 = n - 0.5$$

as shown in table 10.4b.

TABLE 10.4b

INTEGRATION OF $f(x) = AR^x$

$\bar{x}$	$f(\bar{x})$	x	$F(x)$
		-0.5	$F(-0.5)$
0	A		
		0.5	$F(-0.5) + A$
1	AR		
		1.5	$F(-0.5) + A + AR$
2	AR^2		
		2.5	$F(-0.5) + A + AR + AR^2$
$\cdots$	$\cdots$		
		$\cdots$	$\cdots$
$n-1$	AR^{n-1}		
		$n - 0.5$	$F(-0.5) + \sum_{i=1}^{n} A R^{i-1}$

According to equation (1), the indefinite integral of AR^x is

$$\sum_a^x A R^{\bar{x}} \Delta x = A \sum_a^x R^{\bar{x}} \Delta x = \frac{A}{K'} R^x + C.$$

Since $\Delta x = 1$ and $B = R$, the constant multiplier is

$$\frac{1}{K'} = \frac{\sqrt{R}}{R-1}.$$

Then the definite integral of AR^x from -0.5 to $n-0.5$ must be

$$\frac{A\sqrt{R}}{R-1}\Big[R^x\Big]_{-0.5}^{n-0.5} = \frac{A\sqrt{R}}{R-1}\Big(\frac{R^n}{\sqrt{R}} - \frac{1}{\sqrt{R}}\Big) = \frac{A(R^n - 1)}{R-1}$$

which is the same expression given in equation (2) of section 9.5.

As a further illustration of equation (1), one may consider the sum

$$\sum_{i=1}^{5} 3^i = 3 + 3^2 + 3^3 + 3^4 + 3^5$$

$$= 3 + 9 + 27 + 81 + 243$$

$$= 363.$$

This sum is the integral of the function 3^x with x being equal to 1, 2, 3, 4 and 5. According to equation (1), the integral is equal to

$$\sum_{0.5}^{5.5} 3^x \Delta x = \Big[\frac{3^x}{K'}\Big]_{0.5}^{5.5}$$

with the constant multiplier being equal to

$$\frac{1}{K'} = \frac{\sqrt{3}}{3-1} = \frac{\sqrt{3}}{2}$$

because the base is

$$B = 3$$

and the length of an interval is

$$\Delta x = 1.$$

After substitutions, the integral is equal to

$$\frac{\sqrt{3}}{2}(3^{5.5} - 3^{0.5}) = \frac{1}{2}(3^6 - 3^1) = \frac{1}{2}(729 - 3) = 363$$

which is the value expected.

The purpose of this example is to illustrate the principles of integration in general and equation (1) in particular. The simplest way of obtaining the sum 363 is still the addition of the five given numbers. However, one may also compute the sum by formula because the given numbers

$$3 \quad 3^2 \quad 3^3 \quad 3^4 \quad 3^5$$

constitute a geometric progression with the first term being

$$A = 3$$

and the common ratio being

$$R = 3.$$

Then the sum of the first five terms of this progression is (equation 2, section 9.5)

$$\frac{A(R^n - 1)}{R - 1} = \frac{3(3^5 - 1)}{3 - 1} = \frac{3}{2}(243 - 1) = 363$$

which is the same number obtained by addition.

10.5 Integral of Exponential Function

The objective of this section is to find the limiting value of the integral of the exponential function as Δx approaches zero. The integral of the function e^x can be obtained from the equation (equation 4, section 10.2)

$$\frac{d}{dx}e^x = e^x.$$

When both sides of the above equation are integrated with respect to x, the result is

$$e^x + C = \int e^x \, dx$$

or

$$\int e^x \, dx = e^x + C. \tag{1}$$

The numerical demonstration of equation (1) is given in table 10.5a which shows the integration of the function

$$f(x) = e^x$$

from $x = 0.0$ to $x = 0.8$. With the chosen Δx being equal to 0.2, the mid-points $\bar{x}$ are automatically fixed at 0.1, 0.3, 0.5 and 0.7. The corresponding values of $f(\bar{x})$ for these points are obtained from table 2 of the appendix. After the values of $\bar{x}$ and $f(\bar{x})$ are determined, the integration is carried out by the standard method. The resulting integral is represented by the two columns of numbers labeled x and $F(x)$. When the values of $F(x)$ and e^x given in the last two columns of table 10.5a are compared, one will note that $F(x) - F(0)$ is approximately equal to $e^x - 1$ for every value of x. This is to demonstrate that the integral of e^x is

$$F(x) = e^x$$

because

$$F(0) = e^0 = 1.$$

TABLE 10.5a

INTEGRATION OF $f(x) = e^x$ BY STANDARD METHOD

$\bar{x}$	$f(\bar{x})$	$f(\bar{x}) \Delta x$	x	$F(x)$	e^x
			0.0	$F(0)$	1.0000
0.1	1.1052	0.22104			
			0.2	$F(0) + 0.2210$	1.2214
0.3	1.3499	0.26998			
			0.4	$F(0) + 0.4910$	1.4918
0.5	1.6487	0.32974			
			0.6	$F(0) + 0.8208$	1.8221
0.7	2.0138	0.40276			
			0.8	$F(0) + 1.2235$	2.2255

According to equation (1), the definite integral of e^x from $x = 0.0$ to $x = 0.8$ is

$$\int_{0.0}^{0.8} e^x \, dx = \left[e^x \right]_{0.0}^{0.8} = 2.2255 - 1.0000 = 1.2255. \tag{2}$$

But, from table 10.5a, the same integral is equal to

$$F(0.8) - F(0.0) = [F(0) + 1.2235] - F(0) = 1.2235.$$

Of course, the discrepancy

$$1.2235 - 1.2255 = -0.0020 \tag{3}$$

comes from the fact that the integral obtained from table 10.5a is the sum

$$\sum_{0.0}^{0.8} f(\bar{x})\, \Delta x \;=\; \sum_{0.0}^{0.8} e^{\bar{x}}\, \Delta x$$

and that obtained from equation (1) is the limiting value of this sum as Δx approaches zero. The discrepancy is expected to reduce in magnitude if a smaller Δx is used in such a demonstration.

The standard method of integration given in table 10.5a is used to illustrate the principles of integration, but it is not a good method of computation. The evaluation of the definite integral given in equation (2) does not need a numerical method. However, if it did, Simpson's rule (section 8.7) should be used because it offers an improved accuracy. As a demonstration, the definite integral of equation (2) is evaluated by Simpson's rule with the details of computation given in table 10.5b. The result obtained is 1.2255 whose deviation from the true value given in equation (2) is

$$1.2255 - 1.2255 \;=\; 0.0000 .$$

This discrepancy is definitely smaller than that of the standard method given in equation (3) even though the Δx used is 0.2 in both methods.

TABLE 10.5b

INTEGRATION OF $f(x) \;=\; e^{x}$ BY SIMPSON'S RULE

x	$f(x)$	W	$Wf(x)$
0.0	1.0000	1	1.0000
0.2	1.2214	4	4.8856
0.4	1.4918	2	2.9836
0.6	1.8221	4	7.2884
0.8	2.2255	1	2.2255
		Sum	18.3831
$\dfrac{\Delta x}{3}\sum Wf(x) \;=\; \dfrac{0.2}{3}(18.3831) \;=\; 1.2255$			

Equation (1) can be generalized. If the exponent x of the base e is replaced by a function of x such as $v(x)$, the integral of e^{v} is

$$\int e^v \, dv \ = \ e^v + C \, . \tag{4}$$

For example, in integrating the function

$$f(x) \ = \ 6 \, e^{2x+1}$$

with respect to x, one may regard the exponent of e as

$$v \ = \ 2x + 1 \, .$$

Then it follows that the differential of v is equal to

$$dv \ = \ 2 \, dx$$

or the differential of x is equal to

$$dx \ = \ \frac{1}{2} \, dv \, .$$

With these substitutions, the integral of the given function becomes

$$\int 6 \, e^{2x+1} \, dx \ = \ 3 \int e^v \, dv$$

$$= \ 3(e^v + C_1)$$

$$= \ 3 \, e^{2x+1} + C \, . \tag{5}$$

TABLE 10.5c

INTEGRATION OF $f(x) \ = \ 6 \, e^{2x+1}$ BY STANDARD METHOD

$\bar{x}$	$f(\bar{x})$	$f(\bar{x}) \, \Delta x$	x	$F(x)$	$3 \, e^{2x+1}$	$3 \, e^{2x+1} - 3 \, e$
			0.0	$F(0)$	8.1549	0.0000
0.05	18.0252	1.80252				
			0.1	$F(0) + 1.8025$	9.9603	1.8054
0.15	22.0158	2.20158				
			0.2	$F(0) + 4.0041$	12.1656	4.0107
0.25	26.8902	2.68902				
			0.3	$F(0) + 6.6931$	14.8590	6.7041
0.35	32.8434	3.28434				
			0.4	$F(0) + 9.9775$	18.1488	9.9939

The numerical demonstration of equation (5) is given in table 10.5c which shows the integration of the function

$$f(x) = 6\,e^{2x+1}$$

from $x = 0.0$ to $x = 0.4$. With the chosen Δx being equal to 0.1, the mid-points $\bar{x}$ of the intervals are automatically fixed at 0.05, 0.15, 0.25 and 0.35. The corresponding values of $f(\bar{x})$ are computed with the aid of table 2 of the appendix. After the values of $\bar{x}$ and $f(\bar{x})$ are determined, the integration is carried out by the standard method. The resulting integral is represented by the two columns of numbers labeled x and $F(x)$.

To demonstrate the validity of equation (5), the values of

$$3\,e^{2x+1} - 3\,e = 3\,e^{2x+1} - 8.1549$$

are computed for every end-points x of the intervals. These values are listed in the last column of table 10.5c. When they are compared with those of the integral $F(x)$, one will note that the equation

$$F(x) - F(0) = 3\,e^{2x+1} - 3\,e$$

holds approximately for every value of x. Both sets of numbers can be rounded off to

$$1.8 \quad 4.0 \quad 6.7 \quad 10.0\,.$$

This is to demonstrate that the integral of the function

$$f(x) = 6\,e^{2x+1}$$

is

$$F(x) = 3\,e^{2x+1}$$

because $F(0)$ is equal to $3e$.

The definite integral of the function

$$f(x) = 6\,e^{2x+1}$$

from $x = 0.0$ to $x = 0.4$ may be evaluated in two ways. One is through the variable x. By this method, the integral is

$$\int_{0.0}^{0.4} 6\,e^{2x+1}dx = 3\left[\,e^{2x+1}\,\right]_{0.0}^{0.4} = 3\,(e^{1.8} - e^{1.0})$$

$$= 3(6.0496 - 2.7183) = 9.9939 \tag{6}$$

which is the value given at the lower right corner of table 10.5c. The other way is through the transformed variable

$$v = 2x + 1.$$

By this method, the limits of integration become

$$2(0.0) + 1 = 1.0$$

and

$$2(0.4) + 1 = 1.8$$

and the definite integral becomes

$$3\int_{1.0}^{1.8} e^v \, dv = \left[3\, e^v \right]_{1.0}^{1.8} = 3\,(e^{1.8} - e^{1.0}) = 9.9939.$$

These two methods of evaluation always yield the same result.

The definite integral of the same function obtained from table 10.5c is a slightly different value. The integral obtained from that table is

$$F(0.4) - F(0.0) = [F(0) + 9.9775] - F(0) = 9.9775.$$

The deviation of this value from the true value given in equation (6) is

$$9.9775 - 9.9939 = -0.0164. \tag{7}$$

This discrepancy, of course, comes from the difference between the Δx of the numerical demonstration and the dx in the formula of integration.

This is another opportunity to demonstrate the superiority of Simpson's rule over the standard method as a numerical method of integration. The definite integral of equation (6) is evaluated by Simpson's rule in table 10.5d, and the result is 9.9941 whose deviation from the true value given in equation (6) is only

$$9.9941 - 9.9939 = 0.0002.$$

This discrepancy is much smaller than that of the standard method given in equation (7), even though the Δx used is 0.1 in both methods.

TABLE 10.5d

INTEGRATION OF $f(x) = 6\,e^{2x+1}$ BY SIMPSON'S RULE

x	$2x + 1$	e^{2x+1}	$f(x) = 6\,e^{2x+1}$	W	$Wf(x)$
0.0	1.0	2.7183	16.3098	1	16.3098
0.1	1.2	3.3201	19.9206	4	79.6824
0.2	1.4	4.0552	24.3312	2	48.6624
0.3	1.6	4.9530	29.7180	4	118.8720
0.4	1.8	6.0496	36.2976	1	36.2976
				Sum	299.8242

$$\frac{\Delta x}{3} \sum Wf(x) = \frac{0.1}{3}(299.8242) = 9.9941$$

The integral of B^x is

$$\int B^x\,dx = \frac{B^x}{\log_e B} + C. \qquad (8)$$

This result can be obtained from equation (9) of section 10.2 which says

$$\frac{d}{dx}B^x = (\log_e B)B^x.$$

Integrating both sides of the above equation, one obtains

$$B^x + C_1 = (\log_e B)\int B^x\,dx$$

or

$$\int B^x\,dx = \frac{B^x}{\log_e B} + C$$

which is equation (8).

The numerical demonstration of equation (8) is given in table 10.5e which shows the integration of the function

$$f(x) = 2^x$$

from $x = 1.00$ to $x = 1.08$. The chosen Δx is 0.02 which fixes the mid-points $\bar{x}$ at 1.01, 1.03, 1.05 and 1.07. The corresponding values of $f(\bar{x})$ are computed with the aid of a logarithm table. For example,

TABLE 10.5e

INTEGRATION OF $f(x) = 2^x$

$\bar{x}$	$f(\bar{x})$	$f(\bar{x}) \Delta x$	x	$F(x)$	$\dfrac{2^x}{0.69315}$	$\dfrac{2^x - 2}{0.69315}$
			1.00	$F(1)$	2.885	0.000
1.01	2.014	0.04028				
			1.02	$F(1) + 0.040$	2.926	0.041
1.03	2.042	0.04084				
			1.04	$F(1) + 0.081$	2.966	0.081
1.05	2.071	0.04142				
			1.06	$F(1) + 0.123$	3.008	0.123
1.07	2.099	0.04198				
			1.08	$F(1) + 0.165$	3.050	0.165

the common logarithm of the last value of $f(\bar{x})$ given in table 10.5e
is

$$\log(2^{1.07}) = 1.07 \log 2 = 1.07(0.30103) = 0.32210$$

which yields the value of $f(\bar{x})$ as 2.099.

After the values of $\bar{x}$ and $f(\bar{x})$ are determined, the integration
is carried out by the standard method. The result shows that the
equation

$$F(x) - F(1) = \frac{2^x}{0.69315} - \frac{2}{0.69315}$$

holds for every value of x. The constant 0.69315 in the above
equation is the value of

$$\log_e B = \log_e 2$$

which is given in table 3 of the appendix. The purpose of this
demonstration is to show that the integral of 2^x is equal to

$$F(x) = \frac{2^x}{\log_e 2}$$

because

$$F(1) = \frac{2}{\log_e 2}.$$

The integral of B^v is

$$\int B^v \, dv = \frac{B^v}{\log_e B} + C.$$ (9)

This is simply equation (8) with the independent variable x replaced by the function $v(x)$. This formula may be illustrated by the integration of the function

$$f(x) = x(3)^{x^2}.$$ (10)

The integral of $f(x)$, in terms of

$$v = x^2$$

and

$$dv = 2x \, dx,$$

is

$$\int x \, (3)^{x^2} \, dx = \frac{1}{2} \int 3^v \, dv.$$

Then the integral can be expressed as

$$\frac{3^v}{2 \log_e 3} + C = \frac{3^{x^2}}{2.19722} + C.$$ (11)

TABLE 10.5f

PRELIMILARY CALCULATION FOR INTEGRATION

x	x^2	$x^2 \log 3$	3^{x^2}	$x \, (3)^{x^2}$	$\dfrac{3^{x^2}}{2.19722}$
0.0	0.00	0.00000	1.000		0.4551
0.1	0.01	0.00477	1.011	0.1011	
0.2	0.04	0.01908	1.045		0.4756
0.3	0.09	0.04294	1.104	0.3312	
0.4	0.16	0.07634	1.192		0.5425
0.5	0.25	0.11928	1.316	0.6580	
0.6	0.36	0.17176	1.485		0.6759
0.7	0.49	0.23379	1.713	1.1991	
0.8	0.64	0.30536	2.020		0.9193

TABLE 10.5g

INTEGRATION OF $f(x) = x\,(3)^{x^2}$

$\bar{x}$	$f(\bar{x})$	$f(\bar{x})\,\Delta x$	x	$F(x)$	$\dfrac{3^{x^2}-1}{2.19722}$
			0.0	$F(0)$	0.00
0.1	0.1011	0.02022			
			0.2	$F(0) + 0.02$	0.02
0.3	0.3312	0.06624			
			0.4	$F(0) + 0.09$	0.09
0.5	0.6580	0.13160			
			0.6	$F(0) + 0.22$	0.22
0.7	1.1991	0.23982			
			0.8	$F(0) + 0.46$	0.46

The numerical demonstration of the integral

$$\int x\,(3)^{x^2}\,dx = \frac{3^{x^2}}{2.19722} + C$$

is given in tables 10.5f and 10.5g. The prelimilary calculation is given in the former table, and the integration is shown in the latter. The result shows that the equation

$$F(x) - F(0) = \frac{3^{x^2}}{2.19722} - \frac{1}{2.19722}$$

holds for every value of x. This is to say that the integral is equal to

$$F(x) = \frac{3^{x^2}}{2\log_e 3}$$

because $F(0)$ is equal to 1/2.19722.

10.6 Integral of Reciprocal of Function

The integral of the reciprocal of x is

$$\int \frac{1}{x}\,dx = \log_e x + C. \tag{1}$$

This formula can be derived from equation (1) of section 10.3 which says

$$\frac{d}{dx}\log_e x = \frac{1}{x}.$$ (2)

From the above equation, it can be seen that the differential of the function $\log_e x$ is

$$d(\log_e x) = \frac{1}{x}dx.$$

Integration of both sides of the above equation leads to the integral

$$\log_e x + C = \int \frac{1}{x}\,dx$$

which is the formula given in equation (1).

TABLE 10.6a

INTEGRATION OF $f(x) = x^{-1}$ BY STANDARD METHOD

$\bar{x}$	$f(\bar{x})$	$f(\bar{x})\,\Delta x$	x	$F(x)$	$\log_e x$	$\log_e x - \log_e 2$
			2.00	$F(2)$	0.69315	0.00000
2.01	0.49751	0.0099502				
			2.02	$F(2) + 0.00995$	0.70310	0.00995
2.03	0.49261	0.0098522				
			2.04	$F(2) + 0.01980$	0.71295	0.01980
2.05	0.48780	0.0097560				
			2.06	$F(2) + 0.02956$	0.72271	0.02956
2.07	0.48309	0.0096618				
			2.08	$F(2) + 0.03922$	0.73237	0.03922
2.09	0.47847	0.0095694				
			2.10	$F(2) + 0.04879$	0.74194	0.04879
2.11	0.47393	0.0094786				
			2.12	$F(2) + 0.05827$	0.75142	0.05827

The numerical demonstration of equation (1) is given in table 10.6a which shows the integration of the function

$$f(x) = \frac{1}{x} = x^{-1}$$

from $x = 2.00$ to $x = 2.12$. The chosen Δx is equal to 0.02 which fixes the mid-points $\bar{x}$ at 2.01, 2.03, $\cdots$, 2.11. The corresponding values of the integrand are those of

$$f(\bar{x}) = \frac{1}{\bar{x}}$$

which can be readily computed. After the values of $\bar{x}$ and $f(\bar{x})$ are determined, the integration is carried out by the standard method. The values of the end-points x and their corresponding values of $F(x)$ given in table 10.6a constitute the integral of the function $1/x$.

To demonstrate the validity of equation (1), the values of $\log_e x$ at the end-points x are obtained from table 3 of the appendix and are listed in table 10.6a. From that table, one can see that the equation

$$F(x) - F(2) = \log_e x - \log_e 2 \tag{3}$$

holds for every value of x or that the integral of $1/x$ is

$$F(x) = \log_e x$$

because $F(2)$ is equal to $\log_e 2$. The reason why equation (3) holds for every value of x given in table 10.6a is that the length

$$\Delta x = 0.02$$

of an interval is so short that the discrepancy is too small to show in five decimal places.

The formula of integration given in equation (1) may be generalized. If the independent variable x is replaced by a function of x such as $v(x)$, that equation becomes

$$\int \frac{1}{v} \, dv = \log_e v + C. \tag{4}$$

This formula can be used in integrating the reciprocal of $v(x)$. For example, in integrating the function

$$f(x) = \frac{x}{x^2 + 1}$$

with respect to x, one may regard $x^2 + 1$ as the function $v(x)$. Then the differential of v becomes

$$dv = 2x \, dx$$

from which the equation

$$x \, dx = \frac{1}{2} \, dv$$

can be derived. With these substitutions, the integral of $f(x)$ becomes

$$\int \frac{x\,dx}{x^2+1} = \frac{1}{2}\int \frac{dv}{v}$$

$$= \frac{1}{2}\log_e v + C$$

$$= \frac{1}{2}\log_e(x^2+1) + C. \tag{5}$$

TABLE 10.6b

INTEGRATION OF $f(x) = \dfrac{x}{x^2+1}$ BY STANDARD METHOD

$\bar{x}$	$(\bar{x})^2+1$	$f(\bar{x})$	$f(\bar{x})\,\Delta x$	x	$F(x)$	$s=$ x^2+1	$\frac{1}{2}\log_e s$
				0.0	$F(0)$	1.00	0.00000
0.05	1.0025	0.049875	0.0049875				
				0.1	$F(0) + 0.00499$	1.01	0.00498
0.15	1.0225	0.146699	0.0146699				
				0.2	$F(0) + 0.01966$	1.04	0.01961
0.25	1.0625	0.235294	0.0235294				
				0.3	$F(0) + 0.04319$	1.09	0.04309
0.35	1.1225	0.311804	0.0311804				
				0.4	$F(0) + 0.07437$	1.16	0.07421
0.45	1.2025	0.374220	0.0374220				
				0.5	$F(0) + 0.11179$	1.25	0.11157
0.55	1.3025	0.422265	0.0422265				
				0.6	$F(0) + 0.15402$	1.36	0.15374

The numerical demonstration of equation (5) is given in table 10.6b where the function

$$f(x) = \frac{x}{x^2+1}$$

is integrated from $x = 0.0$ to $x = 0.6$. With the chosen Δx being 0.1, the values of the mid-points $\bar{x}$ are automatically fixed at 0.05, 0.15, $\cdots$, 0.55. The corresponding values of $f(\bar{x})$ are computed from the above equation. After the values of $\bar{x}$ and $f(\bar{x})$ are determined, the integration is carried out by the standard method. The values of x and their corresponding values of $F(x)$ constitute the integral of $f(x)$.

To demonstrate the validity of equation (5), the values of

$$\frac{1}{2}\log_e(x^2+1) = \log_e \sqrt{x^2+1}$$

are computed with the aid of table 3 of the appendix. From table 10.6b, it can be seen that these values are approximately equal to $F(x) - F(0)$. Both sets of values can be rounded off to

$$0.005 \quad 0.020 \quad 0.043 \quad 0.074 \quad 0.112 \quad 0.154.$$

This is to demonstrate that the integral of $x/(x^2+1)$ is

$$F(x) = \frac{1}{2}\log_e(x^2+1)$$

because $F(0)$ is equal to zero.

The purpose of this numerical demonstration is to reveal the meaning of equation (5), but the standard method is not a good method of integration. The definite integral of the given function from $x = 0$ to $x = 0.6$ is

$$\int_{0.0}^{0.6}\frac{x\,dx}{x^2+1} = \frac{1}{2}\Big[\log_e(x^2+1)\Big]_{0.0}^{0.6}$$

$$= \frac{1}{2}\Big[\log_e(1.36) - \log_e 1\Big]$$

$$= \frac{1}{2}(0.30748 - 0)$$

$$= 0.15374$$

which is the value at the lower right corner of table 10.6b. But the same integral obtained from the standard method as shown in the same table is

$$F(0.6) - F(0) = 0.15402$$

with an error of

$$0.15402 - 0.15374 = 0.00028.$$

However, the same definite integral obtained by Simpson's rule, with the same Δx, is 0.15375 with an error of only

$$0.15375 - 0.15374 = 0.00001$$

as shown in table 10.6c. However, in spite of the advantage of Simpson's rule, the standard method of integration is used in every numerical demonstration in this text. The reason for this is that the standard method shows the indefinite integral as well as the definite integral of a given function.

TABLE 10.6c

INTEGRATION OF $f(x) = \dfrac{x}{x^2 + 1}$ BY SIMPSON'S RULE

x	$x^2 + 1$	$f(x)$	W	$W f(x)$
0.0	1.00	0.000000	1	0.000000
0.1	1.01	0.099010	4	0.396040
0.2	1.04	0.192308	2	0.384616
0.3	1.09	0.275229	4	1.100916
0.4	1.16	0.344828	2	0.689656
0.5	1.25	0.400000	4	1.600000
0.6	1.36	0.441176	1	0.441176
			Sum	4.612404

$$\frac{\Delta x}{3} \sum W f(x) = \frac{0.1}{3}(4.612404) = 0.15375$$

Equation (1) supplements the formula (formula 9, section 8.2)

$$\int x^n \, dx = \frac{1}{n+1} x^{n+1} + C \qquad n \neq -1.$$

In the above formula, the exponent n can be any constant except -1. When n is equal to -1, the integrand becomes

$$x^n = x^{-1} = \frac{1}{x}$$

and the integral of this function becomes that of equation (1). For the same reason, equation (4) supplements the formula (formula 10, section 8.2).

$$\int v^n \, dv = \frac{1}{n+1} v^{n+1} + C \qquad n \neq -1.$$

Now, with the gap $n = -1$ being filled, the functions x^n and v^n can be integrated for any value of n.

10.7   Power of x

A power of x such as x^n is not to be confused with the exponential function B^x. In x^n, the base x is a variable and the exponent n is a constant. But in B^x, the base B is a constant and the exponent x is a variable. They are not the same function of x at all.

The formula of differentiation (equation 7, section 6.2)

$$\frac{d}{dx} v^n = n v^{n-1} \tag{1}$$

and that of integration (formula 10, section 8.2)

$$\int v^n \, dv = \frac{1}{n+1} v^{n+1} + C \qquad n \neq -1 \tag{2}$$

apply for all values of n, positive or negative, fractional or integral, even though in chapters 6 and 8 the exponent n is restricted to positive integers. Now the negative and fractional exponents are defined. This restriction can be removed.

Equation (1) may be illustrated by a few examples. The derivative of

$$y = \frac{1}{\sqrt{x^3}} = x^{-1.5} \tag{3}$$

is

$$\frac{dy}{dx} = -1.5 \, x^{-2.5} = \frac{-1.5}{\sqrt{x^5}}. \tag{4}$$

The derivative of

$$y = \sqrt{v} = \sqrt{x^2 + 2x - 1} = (x^2 + 2x - 1)^{0.5} \tag{5}$$

is

$$\frac{dy}{dx} = \frac{dy}{dv} \cdot \frac{dv}{dx}$$

$$= 0.5(x^2 + 2x - 1)^{-0.5}(2x + 2)$$

$$= \frac{x + 1}{\sqrt{x^2 + 2x - 1}}. \tag{6}$$

And the derivative of

$$y = x^3 \sqrt{x^2 + 1} = u\,v \tag{7}$$

is (equation 5, section 6.2)

$$\frac{dy}{dx} = u\,\frac{dv}{dx} + v\,\frac{du}{dx}$$

$$= x^3 \frac{d}{dx}\sqrt{x^2 + 1} + \sqrt{x^2 + 1}\,\frac{d}{dx}x^3$$

$$= x^3\,(x^2 + 1)^{-0.5}(2x) + \sqrt{x^2 + 1}\,(3x^2)$$

$$= \frac{2x^4}{\sqrt{x^2 + 1}} + 3x^2\sqrt{x^2 + 1}$$

$$= \frac{2x^4 + 3x^2(x^2 + 1)}{\sqrt{x^2 + 1}}$$

$$= \frac{5x^4 + 3x^2}{\sqrt{x^2 + 1}}\,. \tag{8}$$

The meaning of the last example is numerically demonstrated in tables 10.7a, 10.7b and 10.7c. In the first table, the values of y are computed according to equation (7). In the second table, the differentiation of y with respect to x is carried out. And in the third table, the values of the derivative are computed at the midpoints $\bar{x}$ of the intervals according to equation (8). The last two columns of table 10.7b shows that the derivative obtained by the numerical method is approximately equal to that obtained by formulas. The discrepancy is

$$\frac{\Delta y}{\Delta x} - \frac{dy}{dx} = 0.0001$$

for every value of $\bar{x}$.

The formula of integration of v^n given in equation (2) may be illustrated by examples. The integral of the function

$$f(x) = \frac{1}{\sqrt{x}} = x^{-0.5} \tag{9}$$

is

$$\int x^{-0.5}dx = \frac{1}{-0.5 + 1}\,x^{-0.5 + 1} + C = 2\sqrt{x} + C, \tag{10}$$

TABLE 10.7a
CALCULATION OF $y = x^3\sqrt{x^2 + 1}$

x	x^2	$x^2 + 1$	$\sqrt{x^2 + 1}$	x^3	y
0.00	0.0000	1.0000	1.0000 0000	0.000000	0.0000 0000
0.02	0.0004	1.0004	1.0001 9998	0.000008	0.0000 0800
0.04	0.0016	1.0016	1.0007 9968	0.000064	0.0000 6405
0.06	0.0036	1.0036	1.0017 9838	0.000216	0.0002 1639
0.08	0.0064	1.0064	1.0031 9490	0.000512	0.0005 1364
0.10	0.0100	1.0100	1.0049 8756	0.001000	0.0010 0499

TABLE 10.7b
DIFFERENTIATION OF $y = x^3\sqrt{x^2 + 1}$

x	y	Δx	Δy	$\bar{x}$	$\dfrac{\Delta y}{\Delta x}$	$\dfrac{dy}{dx}$
0.00	0.0000 0000					
		0.02	0.0000 0800	0.01	0.0004	0.0003
0.02	0.0000 0800					
		0.02	0.0000 5605	0.03	0.0028	0.0027
0.04	0.0000 6405					
		0.02	0.0001 5234	0.05	0.0076	0.0075
0.06	0.0002 1639					
		0.02	0.0002 9725	0.07	0.0149	0.0148
0.08	0.0005 1364					
		0.02	0.0004 9135	0.09	0.0246	0.0245
0.10	0.0010 0499					

TABLE 10.7c
CALCULATION OF $\dfrac{dy}{dx} = \dfrac{5x^4 + 3x^2}{\sqrt{x^2 + 1}}$ AT MID-POINTS

x	x^2	$\sqrt{x^2 + 1}$	x^4	$5x^4 + 3x^2$	$\dfrac{dy}{dx}$
0.01	0.0001	1.0000 5000	0.0000 0001	0.0003 0005	0.0003 0003
0.03	0.0009	1.0004 4990	0.0000 0081	0.0027 0405	0.0027 0283
0.05	0.0025	1.0012 4922	0.0000 0625	0.0075 3125	0.0075 2185
0.07	0.0049	1.0024 4701	0.0000 2401	0.0148 2005	0.0147 8387
0.09	0.0081	1.0040 4183	0.0000 6561	0.0246 2805	0.0245 2891

and that of the function

$$f(x) = x\sqrt{x^2 + 4} \tag{11}$$

is

$$\int (x^2 + 4)^{0.5} x \, dx = \frac{1}{2} \int (x^2 + 4)^{0.5} d(x^2 + 4)$$

$$= \frac{1}{2} \cdot \frac{1}{1.5} (x^2 + 4)^{1.5} + C$$

$$= \frac{1}{3} \sqrt{(x^2 + 4)^3} + C. \tag{12}$$

TABLE 10.7d

CALCULATION OF $f(x) = x\sqrt{x^2 + 4}$

x	x^2	$x^2 + 4$	$\sqrt{x^2 + 4}$	$x\sqrt{x^2 + 4}$
2.01	4.0401	8.0401	2.8355 0701	5.6993 6909
2.03	4.1209	8.1209	2.8497 1928	5.7849 3014
2.05	4.2025	8.2025	2.8640 0070	5.8712 0144
2.07	4.2849	8.2849	2.8783 5022	5.9581 8496
2.09	4.3681	8.3681	2.8927 6684	6.0458 8270

TABLE 10.7e

INTEGRATION OF $f(x) = x\sqrt{x^2 + 4}$

$\bar{x}$	$f(\bar{x})$	$f(\bar{x}) \Delta x$	x	$F(x)$	$\frac{1}{3}\sqrt{(x^2 + 4)^3} - \frac{1}{3}\sqrt{8^3}$
			2.00	$F(2)$	0.000000
2.01	5.6993 6909	0.1139 8738			
			2.02	$F(2)+0.113987$	0.113988
2.03	5.7849 3014	0.1156 9860			
			2.04	$F(2)+0.229686$	0.229687
2.05	5.8712 0144	0.1174 2403			
			2.06	$F(2)+0.347110$	0.347112
2.07	5.9581 8496	0.1191 6370			
			2.08	$F(2)+0.466274$	0.466276
2.09	6.0458 8270	0.1209 1765			
			2.10	$F(2)+0.587191$	0.587194

TABLE 10.7f

CALCULATION OF $\frac{1}{3}\sqrt{(x^2 + 4)^3}$

x	x^2	$x^2 + 4$	$\sqrt{x^2 + 4}$	$\sqrt{(x^2 + 4)^3}$	$\frac{1}{3}\sqrt{(x^2 + 4)^3}$
2.00	4.0000	8.0000	2.8284 2712	22.6274 1696	7.5424 7232
2.02	4.0804	8.0804	2.8426 0444	22.9693 8092	7.6564 6031
2.04	4.1616	8.1616	2.8568 5141	23.3164 7847	7.7721 5949
2.06	4.2436	8.2436	2.8711 6701	23.6687 5236	7.8895 8412
2.08	4.3264	8.3264	2.8855 5021	24.0262 4527	8.0087 4842
2.10	4.4100	8.4100	2.9000 0000	24.3890 0000	8.1296 6667

The meaning of the integral given in equation (12) is numerically demonstrated in tables 10.7d, 10.7e and 10.7f. In the first table, the values of the integrand $f(x)$ are computed according to equation (11). In the second table, the function $f(x)$ is integrated by the standard method with Δx being equal to 0.02. In the third table, the integral is computed according to equation (12) for every end-point x of the intervals. The last two columns of table 10.7e shows that $F(x) - F(2)$ is approximately equal to

$$\frac{1}{3}\sqrt{(x^2 + 4)^3} - \frac{1}{3}\sqrt{(2^2 + 4)^3} = \frac{1}{3}\sqrt{(x^2 + 4)^3} - 7.54247232$$

whose values are obtained from table 10.7f. The equation

$$F(x) - F(2) = \frac{1}{3}\sqrt{(x^2 + 4)^3} - \frac{1}{3}\sqrt{8^3}$$

demonstrates that the integral of the function

$$f(x) = x\sqrt{(x^2 + 4)}$$

is

$$F(x) = \frac{1}{3}\sqrt{(x^2 + 4)^3}$$

because $F(2)$ is equal to

$$\frac{1}{3}\sqrt{8^3} = 7.54247232.$$

10.8 Infinite Limit of Definite Integral

The limits of a definite integral may not always be finite quantities. In case they are not, the lower limit being $-\infty$ implies that the definite integral is equal to

$$\int_{-\infty}^{b} f(x)\, dx \;=\; \lim_{a \to -\infty} \int_{a}^{b} f(x)\, dx \tag{1}$$

and the upper limit being ∞ implies that the definite integral is equal to

$$\int_{a}^{\infty} f(x)\, dx \;=\; \lim_{b \to \infty} \int_{a}^{b} f(x)\, dx \tag{2}$$

provided that these limits exist.

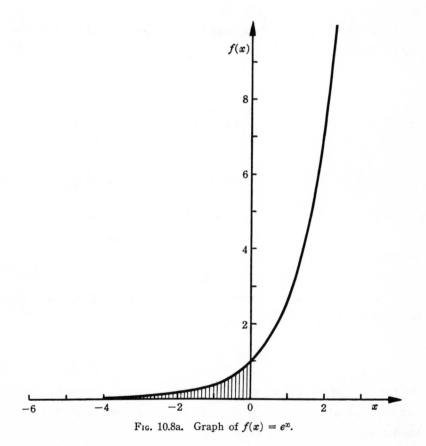

Fig. 10.8a. Graph of $f(x) = e^{x}$.

Equation (1) may be illustrated by the integration of the function (figure 10.8a)

$$f(x) = e^x$$

from $x = -\infty$ to $x = 0$. The definite integral of $f(x)$ for this range is

$$\int_a^0 e^x \, dx = \Big[e^x \Big]_a^0 = e^0 - e^a = 1 - e^a.$$

But as the lower limit a approaches $-\infty$, the quantity e^a approaches

$$e^{-\infty} = \frac{1}{e^\infty} = 0.$$

Therefore, the definite integral is equal to 1 which is geometrically represented by the shaded area in figure 10.8a.

Equation (2) may be illustrated by the integration of the function (figure 10.8b)

$$f(x) = \frac{1}{x^2} = x^{-2}$$

from $x = 2$ to $x = \infty$. The definite integral of the given function for this range is

$$\int_2^b x^{-2} \, dx = \Big[\frac{1}{-1} x^{-1} \Big]_2^b = \Big[\frac{-1}{x} \Big]_2^b = -\frac{1}{b} + \frac{1}{2}.$$

But as b approaches ∞, the quantity $1/b$ approaches 0. So the definite integral is equal to 0.5 which is geometrically represented by the shaded area in figure 10.8b.

The range of integration of the above example is purposely chosen. If the lower limit were changed from $x = 2$ to $x = 0$, the definite integral would be

$$\lim_{a \to 0} \Big[\frac{-1}{x} \Big]_a^b = -\frac{1}{b} + \lim_{a \to 0} \frac{1}{a}.$$

As a approaches 0, the quantity $1/a$ increases without bound or does not approach any finite value as a limit. In a case like this one, the integral is said not to exist.

The definite integral

$$\int_0^1 \frac{dx}{x} = \Big[\log_e x\Big]_0^1 = 0 - \mathop{\text{limit}}_{x \to 0} \log_e x$$

also does not exist. As x approaches zero, its logarithm is negative but its numerical value becomes larger and larger. Therefore, the definite integral does not exist.

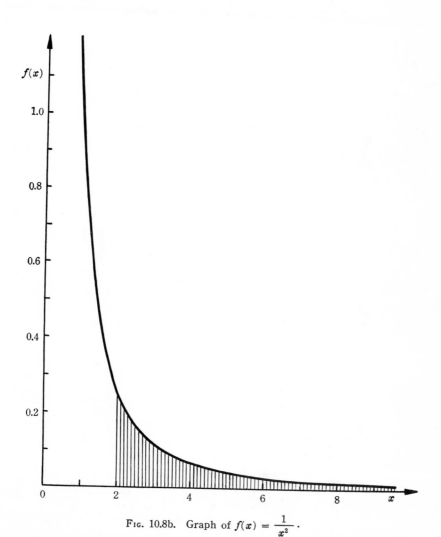

Fig. 10.8b. Graph of $f(x) = \dfrac{1}{x^2}$.

10.9 Summary of Rules

The rules of differentiation and integration of the exponential and logarithmic functions are summarized in the following list:

(A) Differentiation—finite interval

(1) $\dfrac{\Delta}{\Delta x}B^x = B^x\!\left(\dfrac{B^{\Delta x}-1}{\Delta x}\right)$ $\Delta x > 0$

(2) $\dfrac{\Delta}{\Delta x}B^x = B^{\bar{x}}\!\left(\dfrac{B^{\Delta x}-1}{\Delta x\sqrt{B^{\Delta x}}}\right)$ $\Delta x > 0$

(3) $\dfrac{\Delta}{\Delta x}B^x = B^x(B-1)$ $\Delta x = 1$

(4) $\dfrac{\Delta}{\Delta x}2^x = 2^x$ $\Delta x = 1$

(B) Differentiation—infinitesimal interval

(5) $\dfrac{d}{dx}e^x = e^x$

(6) $\dfrac{d}{dx}e^v = e^v\,\dfrac{dv}{dx}$

(7) $\dfrac{d}{dx}B^x = (\log_e B)B^x$

(8) $\dfrac{d}{dx}B^v = (\log_e B)B^v\,\dfrac{dv}{dx}$

(9) $\dfrac{d}{dx}\log_e x = \dfrac{1}{x}$

(10) $\dfrac{d}{dx}\log_e v = \dfrac{1}{v}\cdot\dfrac{dv}{dx}$

(11) $\dfrac{d}{dx}\log_B x = \dfrac{\log_B e}{x}$

(12) $\dfrac{d}{dx}\log_B v = \dfrac{\log_B e}{v}\cdot\dfrac{dv}{dx}$

(C) Integration—finite interval

(13) $\sum\limits_{a}^{x}B^{\bar{x}}\Delta x = \dfrac{\Delta x\sqrt{B^{\Delta x}}}{B^{\Delta x}-1}\,B^x + C$ $\Delta x > 0$

(14) $\sum\limits_{a}^{x}B^{\bar{x}}\Delta x = \dfrac{\sqrt{B}}{B-1}\,B^x + C$ $\Delta x = 1$

(D)   Integration—infinitesimal interval

(15) $\displaystyle\int e^x\, dx = e^x + C$

(16) $\displaystyle\int e^v\, dv = e^v + C$

(17) $\displaystyle\int B^x\, dx = \frac{B^x}{\log_e B} + C$

(18) $\displaystyle\int B^v\, dv = \frac{B^v}{\log_e B} + C$

(19) $\displaystyle\int \frac{dx}{x} = \log_e x + C$

(20) $\displaystyle\int \frac{dv}{v} = \log_e v + C$

The formulas of differentiation given in part B of the above list should be used in concert with those given in section 6.2. For example, the derivative of

$$y = x^2 e^{-x}$$

is

$$\frac{dy}{dx} = x^2 \frac{d}{dx} e^{-x} + e^{-x} \frac{d}{dx} x^2$$
$$= x^2 e^{-x}(-1) + e^{-x} 2x$$
$$= e^{-x}(2x - x^2)$$

and that of

$$y = x^3 \log_e(x^2 + 4)$$

is

$$\frac{dy}{dx} = x^3 \frac{d}{dx} \log_e(x^2 + 4) + \left[\log_e(x^2 + 4)\right] \frac{d}{dx} x^3$$
$$= x^3 \frac{2x}{x^2 + 4} + \left[\log_e(x^2 + 4)\right] 3x^2$$
$$= \frac{2x^4}{x^2 + 4} + 3x^2 \log_e(x^2 + 4).$$

The formulas of integration given in part D of the list should be used in concert with those given in section 8.2. For example, the integral of

$$f(x) = (e^x + 1)^2 = e^{2x} + 2e^x + 1$$

is

$$\int f(x)\, dx = \frac{1}{2}e^{2x} + 2e^x + x + C$$

and that of

$$f(x) = \frac{x^3 - 2x^2 + x - 5}{x + 1} = x^2 - 3x + 4 - \frac{9}{x + 1}$$

is

$$\int f(x)\, dx = \frac{x^3}{3} - \frac{3x^2}{2} + 4x - 9\log_e(x + 1) + C$$

$$= \frac{1}{6}(2x^3 - 9x^2 + 24x) - 9\log_e(x + 1) + C.$$

EXERCISES

1. Differentiate the geometric progression

$$64 \quad 32 \quad 16 \quad 8 \quad 4 \quad 2$$

by the numerical process as well as by equation (1) of section 10.1, and see if the derivatives thus obtained are the same.

2. Differentiate the function 4^x for the range -2 to 0 with Δx equal to 0.5 (table 10.1a), and differentiate the same function again by equation (1) of section 10.1. See if the derivatives thus obtained are the same.

3. Demonstrate numerically (table 10.2a) the relation

$$\frac{d}{dx}e^{2x} = 2\,e^{2x}$$

for the range -0.6 to 0.0 with Δx being equal to 0.1.

4. Demonstrate numerically the relation

$$\frac{d}{dx}9^x = (\log_e 9)9^x$$

for the range $x = 0.0$ to $x = 0.4$ with Δx being equal to 0.1. Why is your result identical to that of table 10.2b?

5. Differentiate the function

$$y = \log_e(2x + 1)$$

by formula, and verify the derivative numerically for the range $x = 1.00$ to 1.05 with Δx being equal to 0.01 (table 10.3b).

6. Repeat exercise 5 with the function

$$y = \log_{10}(2x + 1).$$

7. Obtain the sum

$$\sum_{i=1}^{4}\left(\frac{1}{2}\right)^{i} = \frac{1}{2} + \frac{1}{4} + \frac{1}{8} + \frac{1}{16} = \frac{15}{16}$$

by integration. Use equation (1) of section 10.4 as well as the numerical integration (table 10.4a).

8. Repeat exercise 7 with the sum

$$\sum_{i=1}^{3} 5^{i} = 5 + 25 + 125 = 155.$$

9. Demonstrate the integral

$$\int e^{x}\, dx = e^{x} + C$$

numerically (table 10.5a) for the range $x = 1.0$ to $x = 2.2$ with Δx being equal to 0.2.

10. Evaluate the definite integral

$$\int_{1.0}^{2.2} e^{x}\, dx$$

by formula. Then evaluate the same integral by Simpson's rule with Δx equal to 0.1. What is the error of Simpson's rule?

11. Integrate the function

$$f(x) = \frac{1}{2x + 1}$$

by formula, and demonstrate the meaning of the integration numerically for the range $x = 0.00$ to $x = 0.08$ with Δx being equal to 0.02.

12. Evaluate the definite integral

$$\int_{0.00}^{0.08} \frac{dx}{2x + 1}$$

by formula. Then evaluate the same integral by Simpson's rule with Δx equal to 0.01. What is the error of the numerical method?

13. Differentiate the function

$$y = \sqrt{x^2 + 1}$$

by formula, and demonstrate the derivative numerically for the range $x = 0.00$ to $x = 0.10$ with Δx being equal to 0.02. Take advantage of the results given in tables 10.7a and 10.7c.

14. Demonstrate the integral

$$\int \frac{dx}{\sqrt{x}} = 2\sqrt{x} + C$$

numerically for the range $x = 1.01$ to $x = 1.09$ with Δx being equal to 0.02.

15. Evaluate the definite integral

$$\int_{0.01}^{0.09} \frac{dx}{\sqrt{x}}$$

by formula, and verify the result by Simpson's rule with Δx being equal to 0.01.

16. Evaluate the following definite integrals by formula:

(a) $\int_1^\infty \frac{dx}{x^3}$ (b) $\int_0^\infty e^{-2x}\, dx$ (c) $\int_0^\infty 2^{-x}\, dx$

17. Differentiate the following functions by formula:

(a) $y = x^3\, 2^x$ (b) $y = x^2 \log_e x$

(c) $y = x\, e^{-2x}$ (d) $y = (x^2 + 4) \log_e (x + 1)$

18. Evaluate the following definite integrals by formula:

(a) $\int_0^1 \frac{dx}{x + 2}$ (b) $\int_1^2 \frac{x^2 + 3x - 4}{x}\, dx$

CHAPTER 11

TRIGONOMETRIC FUNCTIONS

The trigonometric functions are introduced in this chapter. The emphasis is entirely on the circular functions, and the solution of triangles are not even mentioned. Readers who are interested in the solution of triangles may consult any textbook on trigonometry.

11.1 Functions of Acute Angle

It is generally known that a right angle is divided into 90 degrees, a degree into 60 minutes, and a minute into 60 seconds. An angle θ with 29 degrees 14 minutes and 15 seconds may be written as

$$\theta = 29° 14' 15''.$$

The same angle may be expressed in term of seconds as

$$\theta = 29 \times 60 \times 60'' + 14 \times 60'' + 15'' = 105{,}255'',$$

or in terms of minutes as

$$\theta = 29 \times 60' + 14' + \frac{15'}{60} = 1{,}754.25',$$

or in terms of degrees as

$$\theta = 29° + \frac{14°}{60} + \frac{15°}{60 \times 60} = 29° + \frac{14.25°}{60} = 29.2375°.$$

All these different ways of expressing the magnitude of an angle may be used. One may select the unit to suit his convenience.

An angle has six functions, all of which can be defined in terms of a right-angled triangle such as the one shown in figure 11.1a. The trigonometric functions are the ratios of the sides of such a triangle. The sine of angle A is equal to

$$\sin A = \frac{\text{opposite side}}{\text{hypotenuse}} = \frac{a}{c}. \tag{1}$$

The cosine of angle A is equal to

$$\cos A = \frac{\text{adjacent side}}{\text{hypotenuse}} = \frac{b}{c}. \tag{2}$$

The tangent of angle A is equal to

$$\tan A = \frac{\text{opposite side}}{\text{adjacent side}} = \frac{a}{b}. \tag{3}$$

The cotangent of angle A is equal to

$$\cot A = \frac{\text{adjacent side}}{\text{opposite side}} = \frac{b}{a}. \tag{4}$$

The secant of angle A is equal to

$$\sec A = \frac{\text{hypotenuse}}{\text{adjacent side}} = \frac{c}{b}. \tag{5}$$

The cosecant of angle A is equal to

$$\csc A = \frac{\text{hypotenuse}}{\text{opposite side}} = \frac{c}{a}. \tag{6}$$

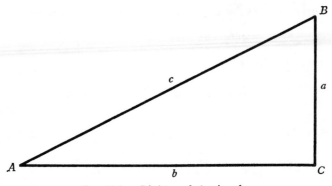

Fɪɢ. 11.1a. Right-angled triangle.

Many consequences can be derived from the definitions of the trigonometric functions. The reciprocal of the sine of an angle is equal to the cosecant of that angle, or

$$\frac{1}{\sin A} = \frac{c}{a} = \csc A. \tag{7}$$

The reciprocal of the cosine of an angle is equal to the secant of that angle, or

$$\frac{1}{\cos A} = \frac{c}{b} = \sec A. \tag{8}$$

The reciprocal of the tangent of an angle is equal to the cotangent of that angle, or

$$\frac{1}{\tan A} = \frac{b}{a} = \cot A. \tag{9}$$

Furthermore, the tangent of an angle is equal to the sine of that angle divided by the cosine of that angle, or

$$\tan A = \frac{a}{b} = \frac{a/c}{b/c} = \frac{\sin A}{\cos A}. \tag{10}$$

It follows that the cotangent of an angle, being the reciprocal of the tangent of that angle, must be equal to

$$\cot A = \frac{\cos A}{\sin A}. \tag{11}$$

The relations given in equations (7) to (11) enable one to express all trigonometric functions of an angle in terms of the sine and cosine of that angle. As a result, the sine and cosine of an angle are much more commonly used than the other four functions.

The cofunctions of an angle such as cosine, cotangent and cosecant are the functions of the complement of that angle. In figure 11.1a the complement of angle A is angle B, or

$$A + B = 90°.$$

The cosine of angle A is, by definition, equal to

$$\cos A = \frac{b}{c}.$$

But it is also the sine of angle B, because the sine of angle B is equal to

$$\sin B = \frac{\text{opposite side}}{\text{hypotenuse}} = \frac{b}{c}.$$

Thus the relation

$$\cos A = \sin(90° - A) \tag{12}$$

is established. The relation

$$\cot A = \tan(90° - A) \tag{13}$$

can also be readily seen, because the cotangent of angle A is equal to

$$\cot A = \frac{b}{a}$$

and the tangent of its complement is equal to

$$\tan B = \tan(90° - A) = \frac{\text{opposite side}}{\text{adjacent side}} = \frac{b}{a}$$

which is the same quantity. Similarly, the relation

$$\csc A = \sec(90° - A) \qquad\qquad (14)$$

can be established, because the cosecant of angle A is equal to

$$\csc A = \frac{c}{a}$$

and the secant of its complement is equal to

$$\sec B = \sec(90° - A) = \frac{\text{hypotenuse}}{\text{adjacent side}} = \frac{c}{a}$$

which is the same quantity.

The table of trigonometric functions is given in table 4 of the appendix. That table lists four functions—sine, cosine, tangent and cotangent—of angles ranges from 0 to 90 degrees. For angles between 0 and 45 degrees, the number of degrees is given at the top of the table, and the number of minutes at the left-hand margin. For example, the functions of 20° 12′ are listed as follows:

sin	cos	tan	cot
0.34530	0.93849	0.36793	2.7179

For angles between 45 and 90 degrees, the number of degrees is given at the bottom of the table, and the number of minutes at the right-hand margin. For example, the functions of 69° 48′ are listed as follows:

0.34530	0.93849	0.36793	2.7179
cos	sin	cot	tan

The above examples show that the same four tabulated values are associated with 20° 12′ as well as its complement 69° 48′. The reason why the table can be made this way is that a cofunction of an angle is equal to the corresponding function of the complement of that angle. This is the reason that each tabulated value is associated with two angles such as

$$0.34530 \ = \ \sin(20° \ 12') \ = \ \cos(69° \ 48')$$

$$0.93849 \ = \ \cos(20° \ 12') \ = \ \sin(69° \ 48')$$

$$0.36793 \ = \ \tan(20° \ 12') \ = \ \cot(69° \ 48')$$

and

$$2.7179 \ = \ \cot(20° \ 12') \ = \ \tan(69° \ 48') \ .$$

To clarify the meaning of the trigonometry table, one may consider the functions of 0 degree. The tabulated functions of this angle are listed as follows:

sin	cos	tan	cot
0.00000	1.0000	0.00000	—

These values can be obtained from the definitions of these functions. If angle A of figure 11.1a is equal to zero, the triangle degenerates into a straight line. Then it follows that

$$a = 0$$

and

$$b = c \, .$$

From equations (1) to (4), one can see that the functions of 0 degree are

$$\sin A \ = \ \frac{a}{c} \ = \ \frac{0}{c} \ = \ 0$$

$$\cos A \ = \ \frac{b}{c} \ = \ \frac{c}{c} \ = \ 1$$

and

$$\tan A \ = \ \frac{a}{b} \ = \ \frac{0}{b} \ = \ 0 \, .$$

But the cotangent of 0 degree

$$\cot A \ = \ \frac{b}{a} \ = \ \frac{b}{0} \, ,$$

which requires the division by 0, is not defined and is represented by a dash in the table.

To further clarify the meaning of the trigonometry table, one may consider the four functions of 30 degrees. The tabulated values

sin	cos	tan	cot
0.50000	0.86603	0.57735	1.7321

can be obtained from figure 11.1b. All the three sides of the triangle *ABD* in that figure are 2 units long. Then the three angles *A*, *B* and *D* are all equal to 60 degrees. The line *AC* in that figure is perpendicular to line *BD* and bisects angle *A*. The length of the line *AC* is necessarily

$$\sqrt{2^2 - 1^2} = \sqrt{3}$$

because *ABC* is a right-angled triangle.

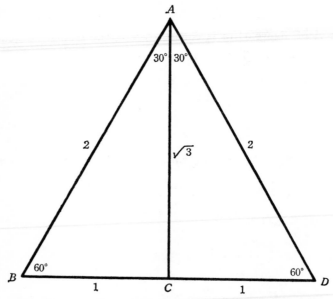

Fɪɢ. 11.1b. Equilateral triangle with sides equal to 2 units.

The trigonometric functions of 30 degrees can be obtained from the right-angled triangle *ABC*. The sine of angle *A* is equal to

$$\sin 30° = \frac{1}{2} = 0.50000.$$

The cosine of angle A is equal to

$$\cos 30° = \frac{\sqrt{3}}{2} = \frac{1.7320508}{2} = 0.86603 \,.$$

The tangent of angle A is equal to

$$\tan 30° = \frac{1}{\sqrt{3}} = \frac{1}{1.7320508} = 0.57735 \,.$$

The cotangent of angle A is equal to

$$\cot 30° = \frac{\sqrt{3}}{1} = 1.7320508 = 1.7321 \,.$$

These are the same values given in the trigonometry table.

These same four tabulated values are also associated with 60 degrees. From figure 11.1b, it can be seen that the functions of 60 degrees are

$$\cos 60° = \frac{1}{2} = 0.50000$$

$$\sin 60° = \frac{\sqrt{3}}{2} = 0.86603$$

$$\cot 60° = \frac{1}{\sqrt{3}} = 0.57735$$

$$\tan 60° = \frac{\sqrt{3}}{1} = 1.7321 \,.$$

These are exactly the tabulated functions

0.50000	0.86603	0.57735	1.7321
cos	sin	cot	tan

of 60 degrees as shown in the trigonometry table.

11.2   Circular Functions

Any angle, positive or negative, can be defined in terms of the circle (section 4.8)

$$x^2 + y^2 = 1$$

whose center is at the origin $(0,0)$ and whose radius is equal to 1. The graph of the circle is given in figure 11.2a. The point $Q(1,0)$

is a fixed point, and the point $P(x, y)$ is a moving one. The starting point of P is $Q(1, 0)$. When P is in this position, the angle θ is equal to zero. As P moves from Q counterclockwise along the circumference of the circle, the angle θ thus generated is positive. As P moves clockwise, the angle is negative.

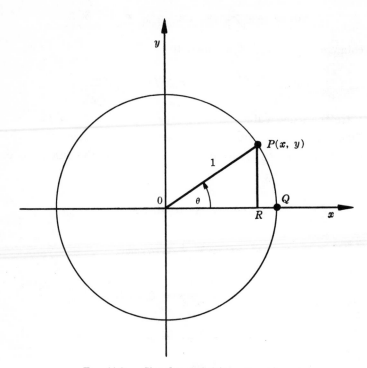

Fɪɢ. 11.2a. Circular definition of angle.

The position of the moving point alone cannot determine the angle. The direction in which the point moves is also an important factor. For example, the fact that the moving point P (figure 11.2a) reaches the halfway point of the circumference of the circle does not necessarily mean that the angle θ is 180 degrees. It may be either 180 degrees or -180 degrees depending on the direction in which the point P moves. If that position is reached by moving counterclockwise, the angle is 180 degrees; otherwise, -180 degrees.

The functions of the angle θ of figure 11.2a can be expressed in terms of the coordinates of the moving point P. The sine of θ is equal to

$$\sin \theta \ = \ \frac{RP}{OP} \ = \ \frac{y}{1} \ = \ y.$$
(1)

The cosine of θ is equal to

$$\cos \theta \ = \ \frac{OR}{OP} \ = \ \frac{x}{1} \ = \ x.$$
(2)

The tangent of θ is equal to

$$\tan \theta \ = \ \frac{RP}{OR} \ = \ \frac{y}{x}.$$
(3)

The cotangent of θ is equal to

$$\cot \theta \ = \ \frac{OR}{RP} \ = \ \frac{x}{y}.$$
(4)

The secant of θ is equal to

$$\sec \theta \ = \ \frac{OP}{OR} \ = \ \frac{1}{x}.$$
(5)

The cosecant of θ is equal to

$$\csc \theta \ = \ \frac{OP}{RP} \ = \ \frac{1}{y}.$$
(6)

Through the coordinates of the moving point P, the trigonometric functions of an angle ϕ larger than 90 degrees can be expressed as the corresponding functions of an acute angle θ. Thus the trigonometry table, which shows the functions of only acute angles, can be used for any angle. The basic method of doing this is to express the angle ϕ as $0° \pm \theta$ or $180° \pm \theta$ as shown in figure 11.2b. If the terminal point of P is in the first quadrant, ϕ is simply θ. In the second quadrant, ϕ is expressed as $180° - \theta$. In the third quadrant, ϕ is expressed as $180° + \theta$. In the fourth quadrant, ϕ is expressed as $0° - \theta$ or $360° - \theta$. If the coordinates of P_1 of figure 11.2b are

$$(x, y) \ = \ (\alpha, \beta) \ = \ (\cos \theta, \sin \theta),$$
(7)

those of P_2 must be

$$(x, y) \ = \ (-\alpha, \beta) \ = \ (-\cos \theta, \sin \theta),$$
(8)

those of P_3 must be

$$(x, y) \ = \ (-\alpha, -\beta) \ = \ (-\cos \theta, -\sin \theta),$$
(9)

and those of P_4 must be

$$(x, y) = (\alpha, -\beta) = (\cos\theta, -\sin\theta). \qquad (10)$$

Thus the trigonometric functions of any angle ϕ can be expressed as those of an acute angle θ.

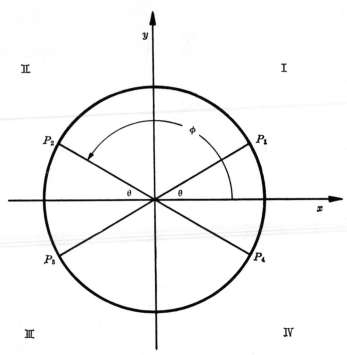

Fɪɢ. 11.2b. Functions of any angle.

The method of expressing the functions of any angle ϕ in terms of those of an acute angle θ may be illustrated by numerical examples. If the angle ϕ is in the second quadrant and is equal to

$$150° = 180° - 30°,$$

the sine of ϕ is equal to (equation 8)

$$\sin 150° = \sin 30°$$

and the cosine of ϕ is equal to (equation 8)

$$\cos 150° = -\cos 30°.$$

The tangent of ϕ, being the ratio of $\sin\phi$ to $\cos\phi$, must be equal to

$$\tan 150° = \frac{\sin 150°}{\cos 150°} = \frac{\sin 30°}{-\cos 30°} = -\tan 30°.$$

The cotangent of ϕ, being the reciprocal of tan ϕ, must be equal to

$$\cot 150° = \frac{1}{\tan 150°} = \frac{1}{-\tan 30°} = -\cot 30°.$$

The secant of ϕ, being the reciprocal of cos ϕ, must be equal to

$$\sec 150° = \frac{1}{\cos 150°} = \frac{1}{-\cos 30°} = -\sec 30°.$$

The cosecant of ϕ, being the reciprocal of sin ϕ, must be equal to

$$\csc 150° = \frac{1}{\sin 150°} = \frac{1}{\sin 30°} = \csc 30°.$$

Similarly, the functions of

$$200° = 180° + 20°,$$

which is in the third quadrant, can be determined. They are (equation 9):

$$\sin 200° = -\sin 20°$$

$$\cos 200° = -\cos 20°$$

$$\tan 200° = \frac{\sin 200°}{\cos 200°} = \frac{-\sin 20°}{-\cos 20°} = \tan 20°$$

$$\cot 200° = \frac{1}{\tan 200°} = \frac{1}{\tan 20°} = \cot 20°$$

$$\sec 200° = \frac{1}{\cos 200°} = \frac{1}{-\cos 20°} = -\sec 20°$$

$$\csc 200° = \frac{1}{\sin 200°} = \frac{1}{-\sin 20°} = -\csc 20°$$

As an example of an angle in the fourth quadrant, one may consider the functions of the angle

$$350° = 360° - 10°.$$

The functions of this angle can be obtained from equation (10). They are:

$$\sin 350° = -\sin 10°$$

$$\cos 350° = \cos 10°$$

$$\tan 350° = \frac{\sin 350°}{\cos 350°} = \frac{-\sin 10°}{\cos 10°} = -\tan 10°$$

$$\cot 350° = \frac{1}{\tan 350°} = \frac{1}{-\tan 10°} = -\cot 10°$$

$$\sec 350° = \frac{1}{\cos 350°} = \frac{1}{\cos 10°} = \sec 10°$$

$$\csc 350° = \frac{1}{\sin 350°} = \frac{1}{-\sin 10°} = -\csc 10°$$

These examples demonstrate that the functions of any angle can be found in the trigonometry table, even though it lists only the functions of acute angles.

11.3 Circular Measure of Angle

Another way of measuring an angle is the circular one. The unit in this system is the *radian* which is the magnitude of an angle subtended at the center of a circle by an arc whose length is equal to the radius of that circle. This definition is illustrated in figure 11.3 which shows a circle with radius equal to r. The length of the arc QP of that circle is made equal to the radius r. Then the angle QOP subtended by the arc QP is equal to one radian.

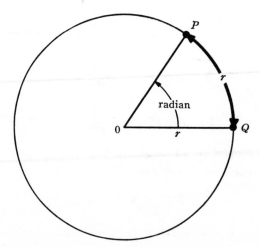

Fig. 11.3. Definition of radian.

The advantage of the radian measure is that an angle and its subtending arc of an unit circle are equal. If the angle is θ radians, the length of the corresponding arc of the circle is θr (figure 11.3). When the radius r of the circle is made equal to 1, the angle in radian unit and the length of the subtending arc are both equal to θ. This advantage will show up in the following chapter where the calculus of trigonometric functions is discussed.

One system of measure of an angle can be readily converted into the other. Since the circumference of a circle is equal to $2\pi r$, it must subtend an angle of 2π radians. At the same time, it is known that such an angle is equal to 360 degrees. Then the relation between the two systems is

$$360° = 2\pi = 2(3.14159) = 6.28318 \tag{1}$$

radians. The number 6.28318 is also the length of the circumference, if the radius of the circle is equal to 1.

Numerous consequences can be derived from this basic relation. For example, 180 degrees is equal to π radians; 90 degrees is equal to $\pi/2$ radians; one degree is equal to

$$\frac{2\pi}{360} = \frac{6.28318}{360} = 0.0174533 \tag{2}$$

radian; and one radian is approximately equal to

$$\frac{360°}{2\pi} = 57.2958° = 57° \, 17' \, 45''. \tag{3}$$

11.4 Graphs of Functions

The graphs of the sine and cosine of θ are given in this section. The purpose of presenting these graphs is to show that these functions are periodic ones.

The graph of $y = \sin\theta$ is given in figure 11.4a. The variables y and θ in that graph are the same ones used in figure 11.2a. As the point $P(x, y)$ moves counterclockwise along the circumference of the circle

$$x^2 + y^2 = 1,$$

both angle θ and ordinate y change in value. Figure 11.4a shows ordinate y of point P as a function of angle θ.

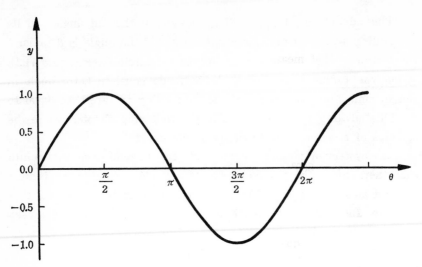

F𝗜𝗚. 11.4a.   Graph of $y = \sin \theta$.

The graph of $y = \sin \theta$ is plotted with the aid of the trigonometry table. The horizontal axis is first marked with degrees. For θ between 0 and 90 degrees, the values of $\sin \theta$ can be obtained directly from the table. For θ between 90 and 360 degrees, equations (8), (9) and (10) of section 11.2 are used to find the values of $\sin \theta$. Beyond 360°, $\sin \theta$ repeats itself in value because the ordinate y or $\sin \theta$ is the same whether the angle is θ or $360° + \theta$. After the graph is plotted, the unit of the horizontal axis is converted from degrees into radians. The advantage of using the circular unit is that the value θ is also the length of the arc of the unit circle which subtends the angle θ at the center. So the horizontal axis of figure 11.4a represents the angle in radian unit as well as the length of the arc of the circle

$$x^2 + y^2 = 1.$$

The graph of $x = \cos \theta$ is given in figure 11.4b. The variables x and θ in that graph are the same ones used in figure 11.2a. As the angle θ increases, the abscissa x of the moving point $P(x, y)$ changes with θ. Figure 11.4b shows the abscissa x of the point P as a function of the angle θ. If such a graph is represented by the equation

$$y = \cos x,$$

one should know that x is the angle or the arc, and y is the abscissa of the moving point P of figure 11.2a.

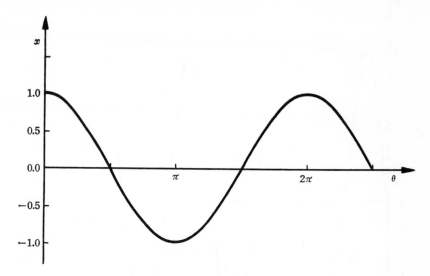

Fig. 11.4b. Graph of $x = \cos \theta$.

The generalized version of the sine curve is that of

$$y \;=\; A \sin m\theta. \tag{1}$$

The graph of the equation

$$y \;=\; 2 \sin 3\theta, \tag{2}$$

which is a special case of equation (1), is given in figure 11.4c.

The effect of the multiplier

$$A \;=\; 2$$

on the sine curve is the change in the range of the values of y. In figure 11.4a where the graph of

$$y \;=\; \sin \theta$$

is shown, the values of y range from -1 to 1. In figure 11.4c where the graph of

$$y \;=\; 2 \sin 3\theta$$

is shown, the values of y range from -2 to 2. This is the effect of A, and the multiplier A is called the *amplitude* of the function.

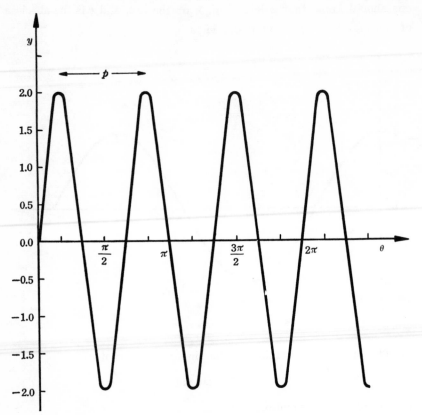

Fɪɢ. 11.4c. Graph of $y = 2 \sin 3\theta$.

The effect of the multiplier

$$m = 3$$

on the sine curve is the change in the number of cycles of that curve within a fixed distance. Comparing figures 11.4a and 11.4c which are drawn to the same scale, one will note that the curve of

$$y = \sin \theta$$

completes one cycle while θ changes from 0 to 2π and the curve of

$$y = 2 \sin 3\theta$$

completes m or 3 cycles while θ covers the same distance.   This is the effect of m on the sine curve.

The range within which the function

$$y = A \sin m\theta$$

completes one cycle is called the *period* of the function. To complete one cycle is to let $m\theta$ change 2π or to let θ changes $2\pi/m$. This number

$$p = \frac{2\pi}{m}$$

is called the *period*. For the given example where m is equal to 3, the period is $2\pi/3$. This can be observed in figure 11.4c where the horizontal axis is marked every $\pi/6$. It is at the point where θ is equal to

$$4\left(\frac{\pi}{6}\right) = \frac{2\pi}{3}$$

that one cycle of the sine curve is completed. Of course, the period p is also the distance between two adjacent peaks of the curve as shown in figure 11.4c.

The reciprocal of the period is called the *frequency*, which is

$$f = \frac{1}{p} = \frac{m}{2\pi}.$$

The frequency is the number of cycles or periods completed in one unit of θ, which is one radian in terms of the angle, or one-unit length in terms of the arc which subtends the angle. For the given example, the frequency is

$$f = \frac{3}{2\pi} = 0.4775.$$

Only that fraction of a cycle of the sine curve is completed in one unit of θ.

The above discussion about the sine curve is equally applicable to the cosine curve

$$y = A \cos m\theta.$$

The constant A is the amplitude, and m is the number of cycles of the curve completed in 2π units of θ.

The technical terms introduced in this section are amplitude, period and frequency. They are used here in connection with trigonometry. When some of these terms are used in other fields of science, their definitions may or may not be the same.

11.5 Inverse Functions

The trigonometric functions have their inverse functions. If the function is

$$y = \sin \theta, \tag{1}$$

its inverse function is

$$\theta = \arcsin y. \tag{2}$$

The above equation says that θ is the angle whose sine is equal to y. For example,

$$0.5 = \sin 30°, \tag{3}$$

then

$$30° = \arcsin 0.5. \tag{4}$$

However, it is true that sine of 30 degrees is 0.5, but the arc sine of 0.5 can also be other values besides 30 degrees. It can be (equations 7 and 8, section 11.2)

$$180° - 30° = 150°$$

$$360° + 30° = 390°$$

$$540° - 30° = 510°$$

and many other values. But at most two values lie between 0 and 360 degrees. These values are called *principal values*. For the given example, the principal values of $\arcsin 0.5$ are 30 and 150 degrees.

The above discussion about the inverse sine is equally applicable to the inverses of other trigonometric functions. For example,

$$\tan 45° = 1$$

and

$$45° = \arctan 1.$$

The other principal value of arc tan 1 is (equation 9, section 11.2)

$$180° + 45° = 225°.$$

The inverse sine

$$\theta = \text{arc sin } y \tag{5}$$

is the angle θ of figure 11.2a expressed as a function of the ordinate y of the moving point $P(x, y)$. Since the radius of the circle is equal to 1, the angle θ in radian unit is equal to the length of the arc QP. At the same time, the ordinate y is the length of the line RP. As the point P moves along the circumference of the circle

$$x^2 + y^2 = 1,$$

both θ and y change in value. The inverse sine function expresses θ as a function of y. The equations

$$\text{arc sin } 0.5 = 30° = \frac{\pi}{6} = 0.5236 \tag{6}$$

and

$$\text{arc sin } 0.5 = 150° = \frac{5\pi}{6} = 2.6180 \tag{7}$$

say that, when the length of the line RP of figure 11.2a is equal to 0.5, the length of the arc QP can be either 0.5236 or 2.6180.

11.6 Identity and Equation

A trigonometric identity is an equation holds for all values of θ. The equation (equation 10, section 11.1)

$$\tan \theta = \frac{\sin \theta}{\cos \theta} \tag{1}$$

is a trigonometric identity, because it holds for all values of θ. For example, the tangent of 24 degrees is equal to

$$\tan 24° = \frac{\sin 24°}{\cos 24°} = \frac{0.40674}{0.91355} = 0.44523$$

which can be verified by the trigonometry table.

Another commonly known identity is

$$\sin^2 \theta + \cos^2 \theta = 1. \tag{2}$$

For θ equal to 24 degrees, the above equation becomes

$$(0.40674)^2 + (0.91355)^2 = 0.1654 + 0.8346 = 1.0000.$$

The fact that equation (2) holds for any angle can be seen from equations (1) and (2) of section 11.1. From those equations, one can see that the equation

$$\sin^2 A + \cos^2 A = \frac{a^2}{c^2} + \frac{b^2}{c^2} = \frac{a^2 + b^2}{c^2} = 1$$

is true because a and b are the two sides and c the hypotenuse of a right-angled triangle ABC as shown in figure 11.1a.

The identity given in equation (2) can also be observed from figure 11.2a. The coordinates of the moving point P are

$$x = \cos \theta$$

and

$$y = \sin \theta,$$

and the equation of the circle is

$$x^2 + y^2 = 1.$$

This leads to the equation

$$\cos^2 \theta + \sin^2 \theta = 1.$$

A trigonometric equation is an equation who holds only for some values of θ but does not hold for all values of θ. For example,

$$\sin \theta = \cos \theta \tag{3}$$

is a trigonometric equation because it does not hold for all values of θ. The value of θ for which the equation holds is called the *solution* of that equation.

The basic technic of solving a trigonometric equation is to change different trigonometric functions in an equation into a single function and treat that function as an unknown quantity in that equation. For example, the equation

$$\sin \theta = \cos \theta$$

involves two functions of θ. However, when both sides of the equation is divided by $\cos \theta$, the resulting equation becomes

$$\tan \theta = 1.$$

To solve this equation is to find the arc tangents of 1 which are 45 and 225 degrees. Converted into radian unit or the arc length of the unit circle, they are $\pi/4$ and $5\pi/4$.

As another example of solving trigonometric equations, one may consider

$$16 \cos^2 \theta - 47 \tan^2 \theta + 44 \sec^2 \theta = 0. \tag{4}$$

The three trigonometric functions can be expressed in terms of $\cos \theta$ alone. Utilizing the identities given in equations (1) and (2), one can convert the above equation into

$$16 \cos^2 \theta - \frac{47 \sin^2 \theta}{\cos^2 \theta} + \frac{44}{\cos^2 \theta} = 0$$

or

$$16 \cos^4 \theta - 47(1 - \cos^2 \theta) + 44 = 0$$

or

$$16 \cos^4 \theta + 47 \cos^2 \theta - 3 = 0.$$

Now the problem is to solve the above equation with $\cos \theta$ as the unknown quantity. For such chore, one can depend on the method of successive approximation (section 4.10) knowing beforehand that $\cos \theta$ can only be somewhere between -1 and 1. The roots of the equation are

$$\cos \theta = + 0.25000$$

and

$$\cos \theta = - 0.25000.$$

With the aid of the trigonometry table and equations (7) to (10) of section 11.2, one can determine the angle θ. When $\cos \theta$ is equal to 0.25000, the angle θ is approximately equal to

$$75° \, 31' \qquad \text{or} \qquad 360° - 75° \, 31'.$$

When $\cos \theta$ is equal to $- 0.25000$, the angle θ is approximately equal to

$$180° - 75° \, 31' \qquad \text{or} \qquad 180° + 75° \, 31'.$$

When the four values of θ are converted into radian unit or into the arc length of the unit circle, they are

$$1.318 \qquad 1.824 \qquad 4.460 \qquad 4.965$$

which are the solutions of equation (4). This example demonstrates the general method of solving trigonometric equations.

EXERCISES

1. Find the six functions of the following angles:

    (a) 15° 16'   (b) 42° 14'

    (c) 63° 15'   (d) 74° 39'

2. Construct a right-angled triangle whose sides are both equal to 1. Find the length of the hypotenuse. From this triangle determine the sine, cosine, tangent and cotangent of 45 degrees. Check the values thus obtained against those given in the trigonometry table.

3. Find the six functions of the following angles:

    (a) 125° 16'   (b) 170° 25'

    (c) 220° 40'   (d) 249° 42'

    (e) 340° 26'   (f) 310° 48'

4. Convert the six angles of exercise 3 into radian unit.

5. Convert the following angles, which are given in radian unit, into degrees and minutes:

    (a) $\pi/6$ (b) $\pi/4$

    (c) $\pi/3$ (d) $3\pi/2$

    (e) $10\pi/6$ (f) $5\pi/6$

6. Plot the graph of $y = 3\cos 2x$ for the range $x = 0$ to $x = 2\pi$.

7. Find the principal values of θ in radian unit for the following equations:

    (a) $\theta = \text{arc sin } 0.58779$ (b) $\theta = \text{arc cos } 0.95106$

    (c) $\theta = \text{arc tan } 1.3764$ (d) $\theta = \text{arc cot } 0.32492$

8. Prove the identity

$$1 - \sin\theta - \tan\theta + \sec\theta = \frac{(1 + \cos\theta)(1 - \sin\theta)}{\cos\theta}.$$

9. Solve the equation

$$\tan\theta = \cot\theta.$$

10. Solve the equation

$$2\sin^2\theta = 3\cos\theta.$$

CHAPTER 12

CALCULUS OF TRIGONOMETRIC FUNCTIONS

The calculus of the six trigonometric functions is discussed in this chapter. Formulas of differentiation and integration are introduced. In addition, the meaning of the formulas is demonstrated numerically.

12.1 Derivative of Sine

The derivative of $\sin x$ with respect to x is equal to

$$\frac{d}{dx}\sin x = \cos x \qquad (1)$$

with x being the arc θ of the preceding chapter. No attempt is made here to prove this theorem, but its meaning is to be demonstrated numerically. Readers who are interested in a mathematical proof may consult another text on calculus.

The numerical demonstration of equation (1) is given in table 12.1a. The independent variable x is an angle measured in radians or in the arc length of a unit circle which subtends the angle at the center. But, for the convenience of finding the values of

TABLE 12.1a

DIFFERENTIATION OF $y = \sin x$

x	y	Δx	Δy	$\bar{x}$	$\dfrac{\Delta y}{\Delta x}$	$\cos \bar{x}$
10°	0.17365					
		0.017453	0.01716	10.5°	0.9832	0.9833
11°	0.19081					
		0.017453	0.01710	11.5°	0.9798	0.9799
12°	0.20791					
		0.017453	0.01704	12.5°	0.9763	0.9763
13°	0.22495					
		0.017453	0.01697	13.5°	0.9723	0.9724
14°	0.24192					

$$y = \sin x$$

from the trigonometry table, x is first expressed in degrees and then changed into radians at the stage of the determination of Δx. The length of the interval in this demonstration is

$$\Delta x = 1° = \frac{2\pi}{360} = 0.017453$$

as shown in table 12.1a.

The differentiation of $\sin x$ is carried out in the usual way, and the values of $\bar{x}$ and their corresponding values of $\Delta y / \Delta x$ given in table 12.1a constitute the derivative of $\sin x$. To demonstrate the validity of equation (1), the values of $\cos \bar{x}$ are found from the trigonometry table and are listed in the last column of that table. The fact that the values of $\Delta y / \Delta x$ and those of $\cos \bar{x}$ can be both rounded off to

$$0.983 \qquad 0.980 \qquad 0.976 \qquad 0.972$$

demonstrates that the derivative of $\sin x$ with respect to x is equal to $\cos x$.

The derivative of the function

$$y = \sin v,$$

where v is a function of x, is equal to

$$\frac{dy}{dx} = \frac{d}{dx}\sin v = \cos v \, \frac{dv}{dx} \, .$$

The derivative of y with respect to v is (equation 1)

$$\frac{dy}{dv} = \frac{d}{dv}\sin v = \cos v \, .$$

Then the derivative of y with respect to x must be

$$\frac{dy}{dx} = \frac{dy}{dv} \cdot \frac{dv}{dx}$$

or

$$\frac{d}{dx}\sin v = \cos v \, \frac{dv}{dx} \, . \tag{2}$$

As an example of equation (2), one may consider the function

$$y = 5 \sin 2x$$

where $2x$ is the function v. According to equation (2), its derivative should be

$$\frac{dy}{dx} = 5\frac{d}{dx}\sin 2x = 5\cos 2x \frac{d}{dx}2x$$

or

$$\frac{d}{dx}5\sin 2x = 10\cos 2x . \qquad (3)$$

The numerical demonstration of the above derivative is given in table 12.1b. The values of x in that table are

$$10° \qquad 11° \qquad 12° \qquad 13° \qquad 14° ,$$

and those of $\sin 2x$ are the sines of

$$20° \qquad 22° \qquad 24° \qquad 26° \qquad 28°$$

given in the trigonometry table. The values of y are 5 times of those of $\sin 2x$.

TABLE 12.1b

DIFFERENTIATION OF $y = 5\sin 2x$

x	$\sin 2x$	y	Δx	Δy	$\bar{x}$	$\dfrac{\Delta y}{\Delta x}$	$10\cos 2\bar{x}$
10°	0.34202	1.71010					
			0.017453	0.16295	10.5°	9.3363	9.3358
11°	0.37461	1.87305					
			0.017453	0.16065	11.5°	9.2046	9.2050
12°	0.40674	2.03370					
			0.017453	0.15815	12.5°	9.0613	9.0631
13°	0.43837	2.19185					
			0.017453	0.15550	13.5°	8.9095	8.9101
14°	0.46947	2.34735					

After the values of x and y are determined, the differentiation is carried out in the usual way. The fact that the values of $\Delta y/\Delta x$ and those of $10\cos 2\bar{x}$ can both be rounded off to

$$9.34 \quad 9.20 \quad 9.06 \quad 8.91$$

demonstrates the validity of equation (3).

The numerical demonstrations of this section cannot be carried out effectively with a shorter interval as long as one depends on the five-place trigonometry table. At first, it may appear that the Δx can be made equal to two minutes instead of one degree. But, if such a Δx is used, the corresponding Δy has so few significant figures that the accuracy of $\Delta y/\Delta x$ is impaired. As an illustration, one may consider the interval

$$x_1 = 40° 10'$$

to

$$x_2 = 40° 12'$$

with its length being

$$\Delta x = x_2 - x_1 = 2' = \frac{2\pi}{360 \times 30} = 0.000581776.$$

The corresponding values of y are

$$y_1 = \sin 40° 10' = 0.64501$$

and

$$y_2 = \sin 40° 12' = 0.64546.$$

According to equation (1), the rate of change

$$\frac{\Delta y}{\Delta x} = \frac{y_2 - y_1}{x_2 - x_1} = \frac{0.00045}{0.000581776} = 0.77349$$

for the given interval should be approximately equal to

$$\cos 40° 11' = 0.76398.$$

These numbers have an agreement of only one significant figure, because both of them can be rounded off to 0.8. The reason for this is that

$$\Delta y = 0.00045$$

has too few significant figures and not that the Δx is too large. If a ten-place trigonometry table were used, Δy would have seven significant figures. Then equation (1) can be very effectively demonstrated by a Δx of two minutes.

12.2 Derivative of Cosine

The derivative of $\cos x$ with respect to x is equal to

$$\frac{d}{dx}\cos x = -\sin x. \tag{1}$$

This result can be obtained from the identity (equation 2, section 11.6)

$$\sin^2 x + \cos^2 x = 1.$$

Differentiating the above equation term by term, one obtains

$$2\sin x \frac{d}{dx}\sin x + 2\cos x \frac{d}{dx}\cos x = 0$$

or

$$2\sin x \cos x + 2\cos x \frac{d}{dx}\cos x = 0$$

or

$$\frac{d}{dx}\cos x = -\sin x$$

which is equation (1).

The numerical demonstration of equation (1) is given in table 12.2a. The fact that the values of $\Delta y/\Delta x$ are approximately equal to those of $-\sin \bar{x}$ demonstrates that the derivative of $\cos x$ is equal to $-\sin x$.

TABLE 12.2a

DIFFERENTIATION OF $y = \cos x$

x	y	Δx	Δy	$\bar{x}$	$\dfrac{\Delta y}{\Delta x}$	$-\sin \bar{x}$
20°	0.93969					
		0.017453	− 0.00611	20.5°	− 0.350	− 0.350
21°	0.93358					
		0.017453	− 0.00640	21.5°	− 0.367	− 0.367
22°	0.92718					
		0.017453	− 0.00668	22.5°	− 0.383	− 0.383
23°	0.92050					
		0.017453	− 0.00695	23.5°	− 0.398	− 0.399
24°	0.91355					

The derivative of the function

$$y = \cos v,$$

where v is a function of x, is equal to

$$\frac{d}{dx}\cos v = -\sin v \frac{dv}{dx}$$ (2)

because

$$\frac{dy}{dx} = \frac{dy}{dv} \cdot \frac{dv}{dx}.$$

For example, the derivative of the function

$$y = 4\cos 3x$$

is equal to

$$\frac{dy}{dx} = 4\frac{d}{dx}\cos 3x = 4(-\sin 3x)\frac{d}{dx}3x$$

or

$$\frac{d}{dx}4\cos 3x = -12\sin 3x.$$ (3)

The numerical demonstration of equation (3) is given in table 12.2b. The fact that the values of $\Delta y/\Delta x$ are equal to those of $-12\sin 3\bar{x}$ demonstrates the validity of that equation.

TABLE 12.2b

DIFFERENTIATION OF $y = 4\cos 3x$

x	$\cos 3x$	y	Δx	Δy	$\bar{x}$	$\dfrac{\Delta y}{\Delta x}$	$-12\sin 3\bar{x}$
20°	0.50000	2.00000					
			0.017453	−0.18404	20.5°	−10.55	−10.55
21°	0.45399	1.81596					
			0.017453	−0.18900	21.5°	−10.83	−10.83
22°	0.40674	1.62696					
			0.017453	−0.19348	22.5°	−11.09	−11.09
23°	0.35837	1.43348					
			0.017453	−0.19740	23.5°	−11.31	−11.31
24°	0.30902	1.23608					

This section is almost a carbon copy of the preceding one. One section deals with the derivative of $\sin x$ being $\cos x$, and the other section deals with the derivative of $\cos x$ being $-\sin x$. These results are some of the characteristics of trigonometric functions in the same sense that the identities

$$\tan x = \frac{\sin x}{\cos x}$$

and

$$\sin^2 x + \cos^2 x = 1$$

are characteristics of trigonometric functions.

12.3   Derivatives of Tangent and Cotangent

The derivative of $\tan x$ with respect to x is equal to

$$\frac{d}{dx}\tan x = \sec^2 x. \tag{1}$$

This result can be derived from the identity

$$\tan x = \frac{\sin x}{\cos x}.$$

Differentiating $\tan x$ as a quotient, one obtains (equation 7, section 6.2)

$$\frac{d}{dx}\tan x = \frac{\cos x \dfrac{d}{dx}\sin x - \sin x \dfrac{d}{dx}\cos x}{\cos^2 x}.$$

But, on account of the fact that

$$\frac{d}{dx}\sin x = \cos x$$

$$\frac{d}{dx}\cos x = -\sin x$$

and

$$\cos^2 x + \sin^2 x = 1,$$

the numerator is nothing but 1. Furthermore, $\cos x$ is the reciprocal of $\sec x$. Then the derivative of $\tan x$ must be equal to $\sec^2 x$.

The numerical demonstration of equation (1) is given in table 12.3a. The values of y are directly obtained from the trigonometry table, and those of $\sec \bar{x}$ are obtained from $\cos \bar{x}$ by the relation

$$\sec x = \frac{1}{\cos x}.$$

The fact that the values of $\Delta y/\Delta x$ are approximately equal to those of $\sec^2 \bar{x}$ demonstrates that the derivative of $\tan x$ is equal to $\sec^2 x$.

TABLE 12.3a

DIFFERENTIATION OF $y = \tan x$

x	y	Δx	Δy	$\bar{x}$	$\dfrac{\Delta y}{\Delta x}$	$\cos \bar{x}$	$\sec \bar{x}$	$\sec^2 \bar{x}$
20°	0.36397							
		0.017453	0.01989	20.5°	1.140	0.93667	1.0676	1.140
21°	0.38386							
		0.017453	0.02017	21.5°	1.156	0.93042	1.0748	1.155
22°	0.40403							
		0.017453	0.02044	22.5°	1.171	0.92388	1.0824	1.172
23°	0.42447							
		0.017453	0.02076	23.5°	1.189	0.91706	1.0904	1.189
24°	0.44523							

The derivative of $\tan v$ with respect to x, where v is a function of x, is equal to

$$\frac{d}{dx}\tan v = \sec^2 v \frac{dv}{dx}. \qquad (2)$$

For example, the derivative of the function

$$y = 4 \tan 5x$$

is equal to

$$\frac{dy}{dx} = 4 \sec^2 5x \frac{d}{dx} 5x = 20 \sec^2 5x.$$

The derivative of $\cot x$ with respect to x is equal to

$$\frac{d}{dx}\cot x = -\csc^2 x. \qquad (3)$$

This result can be obtained by differentiating the identity

$$\cot x = \frac{\cos x}{\sin x}$$

with respect to x. The derivative thus obtained is

$$\frac{d}{dx}\cot x = \frac{\sin x \dfrac{d}{dx}\cos x - \cos x \dfrac{d}{dx}\sin x}{\sin^2 x}$$

$$= \frac{\sin x(-\sin x) - (\cos x)(\cos x)}{\sin^2 x}$$

$$= \frac{-1}{\sin^2 x}$$

$$= -\csc^2 x.$$

The numerical demonstration of equation (3) is given in table 12.3b. The fact that the values of $\Delta y/\Delta x$ are approximately equal to those of $-\csc^2\bar{x}$ demonstrates that the derivative of $\cot x$ is equal to $-\csc^2 x$.

TABLE 12.3b

DIFFERENTIATION OF $y = \cot x$

x	y	Δx	Δy	$\bar{x}$	$\dfrac{\Delta y}{\Delta x}$	$\sin \bar{x}$	$\csc x$	$-\csc^2\bar{x}$
20°	2.7475							
		0.017453	− 0.1424	20.5°	− 8.159	0.35021	2.8554	− 8.153
21°	2.6051							
		0.017453	− 0.1300	21.5°	− 7.449	0.36650	2.7285	− 7.445
22°	2.4751							
		0.017453	− 0.1192	22.5°	− 6.830	0.38268	2.6131	− 6.828
23°	2.3559							
		0.017453	− 0.1099	23.5°	− 6.297	0.39875	2.5078	− 6.289
24°	2.2460							

The derivative of $\cot v$ with respect to x, where v is a function of x, is equal to

$$\frac{d}{dx}\cot v = -\csc^2 v \frac{dv}{dx}. \tag{4}$$

For example, the derivative of the function

$$y = 2 \cot 5x$$

is equal to

$$\frac{dy}{dx} = 2(-\csc^2 5x)5 = -10\csc^2 5x.$$

12.4   Derivatives of Secant and Cosecant

The derivative of $\sec x$ with respect to x is equal to

$$\frac{d}{dx}\sec x = \sec x \tan x. \tag{1}$$

This result can be derived from the identity

$$\sec x = \frac{1}{\cos x} = (\cos x)^{-1}.$$

Differentiating the above equation with respect to x, one obtains

$$\frac{d}{dx}\sec x = -1(\cos x)^{-2}\frac{d}{dx}\cos x$$

$$= \frac{(-1)(-\sin x)}{\cos^2 x}$$

$$= \frac{1}{\cos x}\cdot\frac{\sin x}{\cos x}$$

$$= \sec x \tan x$$

which is the expression given in equation (1).

The numerical demonstration of equation (1) is given in table 12.4a. The fact that the values of $\Delta y/\Delta x$ are equal to those of $\sec \bar{x} \tan \bar{x}$ demonstrates that the derivative of $\sec x$ is equal to the product of $\sec x$ and $\tan x$.

The derivative of $\sec v$ with respect to x, where v is a function of x, is equal to

$$\frac{d}{dx}\sec v = \sec v \tan v \frac{dv}{dx}. \tag{2}$$

For example, the derivative of the function

$$y = 2 \sec 4x$$

is equal to

$$\frac{dy}{dx} = 2 \sec 4x \tan 4x \frac{d}{dx} 4x$$

$$= 8 \sec 4x \tan 4x .$$

TABLE 12.4a

DIFFERENTIATION OF $y = \sec x$

x	y	Δx	Δy	$\bar{x}$	$\dfrac{\Delta y}{\Delta x}$	$\sec \bar{x}$	$\tan \bar{x}$	$\sec \bar{x} \tan \bar{x}$
20°	1.0642							
		0.017453	0.0069	20.5°	0.40	1.0676	0.37388	0.40
21°	1.0711							
		0.017453	0.0074	21.5°	0.42	1.0748	0.39391	0.42
22°	1.0785							
		0.017453	0.0079	22.5°	0.45	1.0824	0.41421	0.45
23°	1.0864							
		0.017453	0.0082	23.5°	0.47	1.0904	0.43481	0.47
24°	1.0946							

The derivative of $\csc x$ with respect to x is equal to

$$\frac{d}{dx} \csc x = - \csc x \cot x . \tag{3}$$

This result can be derived from the identity

$$\csc x = \frac{1}{\sin x} = (\sin x)^{-1} .$$

Differentiating the above equation with respect to x, one obtains

$$\frac{d}{dx} \csc x = - 1 (\sin x)^{-2} \frac{d}{dx} \sin x$$

$$= \frac{-1 \cos x}{\sin^2 x}$$

$$= \frac{-1}{\sin x} \cdot \frac{\cos x}{\sin x}$$

$$= - \csc x \cot x$$

which is the expression given in equation (3).

The numerical demonstration of equation (3) is given in table 12.4b. The fact that the values of $\Delta y / \Delta x$ and those of $- \csc \bar{x} \cot \bar{x}$ can both be rounded off to

$$- 7.64 \quad - 6.93 \quad - 6.31 \quad - 5.77$$

demonstrates the validity of that equation.

TABLE 12.4b

DIFFERENTIATION OF $y = \csc x$

x	y	Δx	Δy	$\bar{x}$	$\dfrac{\Delta y}{\Delta x}$	$\csc \bar{x}$	$\cot \bar{x}$	$- \csc \bar{x} \cot \bar{x}$
20°	2.9238							
		0.017453	− 0.1334	20.5°	− 7.643	2.8554	2.6746	− 7.637
21°	2.7904							
		0.017453	− 0.1210	21.5°	− 6.933	2.7285	2.5386	− 6.927
22°	2.6694							
		0.017453	− 0.1101	22.5°	− 6.308	2.6131	2.4142	− 6.309
23°	2.5593							
		0.017453	− 0.1007	23.5°	− 5.770	2.5078	2.2998	− 5.767
24°	2.4586							

The derivative of $\csc v$ with respect to x, where v is a function of x, is equal to

$$\frac{d}{dx} \csc v = - \csc v \cot v \frac{dv}{dx}. \tag{4}$$

For example, the derivative of the function

$$y = 3 \csc 2x$$

is equal to

$$\frac{dy}{dx} = 3(- \csc 2x \cot 2x) \frac{d}{dx} 2x$$

$$= - 6 \csc 2x \cot 2x.$$

12.5 Integral of Sine

The integral of $\sin x$ is equal to

$$\int \sin x \, dx = - \cos x + C. \tag{1}$$

This result is obtained from the derivative (equation 1, section 12.2)

$$\frac{d}{dx}\cos x = -\sin x.$$

When both sides of the above equation is integrated with respect to x, the resulting equation is

$$\cos x = -\int \sin x \, dx + C$$

which is equation (1).

The numerical demonstration of equation (1) is given in table 12.5 where the function

$$f(x) = \sin x$$

is integrated from $x = 20°$ to $x = 24°$ with the length of the interval being equal to

$$\Delta x = 1° = \frac{2\pi}{360} = 0.0174533.$$

The mid-points $\bar{x}$ are

$$20.5° \quad 21.5° \quad 22.5° \quad 23.5°$$

TABLE 12.5

INTEGRATION OF $f(x) = \sin x$

$(\Delta x = 1° = 0.0174533)$

$\bar{x}$	$f(\bar{x})$	$f(\bar{x})\Delta x$	x	$F(x)$	$-\cos x$	$-\cos x + 0.93969$
			$20°$	$F(20°)$	-0.93969	0.00000
$20.5°$	0.35021	0.00611				
			$21°$	$F(20°) + 0.00611$	-0.93358	0.00611
$21.5°$	0.36650	0.00640				
			$22°$	$F(20°) + 0.01251$	-0.92718	0.01251
$22.5°$	0.38268	0.00668				
			$23°$	$F(20°) + 0.01919$	-0.92050	0.01919
$23.5°$	0.39875	0.00696				
			$24°$	$F(20°) + 0.02615$	-0.91355	0.02614

and their corresponding value of $f(\bar{x})$ are the sines of these angles. The fact that the equation

$$F(x) - F(20°) = -\cos x - (-0.93969)$$

holds approximately for every value of x demonstrates that the integral of $\sin x$ is equal to

$$F(x) = -\cos x$$

because, at x equal to 20 degrees, $F(x)$ is equal to -0.93969.

Tables 12.2a and 12.5 jointly demonstrate that integration is the inverse operation of differentiation and vice versa. The former table shows that the derivative of $\cos x$ is equal to $-\sin x$, and the latter table shows that the integral of $\sin x$ is equal to $-\cos x$. The values of x, $\bar{x}$ and Δx are identical in both tables. The values of

$$y \qquad \Delta y \qquad \frac{\Delta y}{\Delta x}$$

of the former table are those of

$$F(x) \qquad f(\bar{x})\Delta x \qquad f(\bar{x})$$

of the latter table with the signs changed.

The definite integral of $\sin x$ from a to b is

$$\int_a^b \sin x \, dx = \left[-\cos x \right]_a^b = \cos a - \cos b \qquad (2)$$

with the limits a and b measured in radians, because x is measured in radians. However, the limits can be converted into degrees for the convenience of using the trigonometry table. For example, table 12.5 shows that the definite integral of $\sin x$ from

$$a = 20° = \frac{20(2\pi)}{360} = 0.349$$

to

$$b = 24° = \frac{24(2\pi)}{360} = 0.419$$

is equal to

$$F(24°) - F(20°) = 0.02615$$

by the standard method of integration. But, by formula, the same integral is equal to

$$\int_{0.349}^{0.419} \sin x \, dx = \cos 20° - \cos 24° = 0.02614$$

which is approximately the same value.

As another example of the definite integral of $\sin x$, one may consider the interval from 0 to 1 degree. When every other items of the first column of the trigonometry table, such as

$$\sin 01' = 0.00029$$

$$\sin 03' = 0.00087$$

$$\sin 05' = 0.00145$$

$$\cdots$$

$$\sin 57' = 0.01658$$

$$\sin 59' = 0.01716,$$

are added together, the sum of the 30 items is equal to

$$\sum \sin \bar{x} = 0.26179.$$

The length of the interval is equal to

$$\Delta x = 2' = \frac{2\pi}{360 \times 30} = 0.000581776.$$

The definite integral obtained by the standard method is

$$\sum \sin \bar{x} \, \Delta x = (0.26179)(0.000581776) = 0.00015.$$

But, by formula, the same integral is equal to

$$\cos 0° - \cos 1° = 1.00000 - 0.99985 = 0.00015$$

which is the same value. This is the meaning of equation (2).

The meaning of equation (2) can also be demonstrated by trapezoidal rule. The sum of the 61 items of the first column of the trigonometry table is equal to

$$\sum \sin x = 0.53231.$$

But trapezoidal rule requires only one half of the first and the last values of $f(x)$ or $\sin x$. Thus the sum of $\sin x$ required is

$$0.53231 - 0.5(0.00000) - 0.5(0.01745) = 0.52358.$$

The length of the interval in this integration is

$$\Delta x = 1' = \frac{2\pi}{360 \times 60} = 0.000290888 \, .$$

Then the definite integral of $\sin x$ from 0 to 1 degree is equal to

$$(0.52358)(0.000290888) = 0.00015$$

which is also equal to

$$\cos 0° - \cos 1° = 1.00000 - 0.99985 = 0.00015 \, .$$

The definite integral

$$\int_0^{\pi/2} \sin x \, dx = -\Big[\cos x\Big]_0^{\pi/2} = -(0-1) = 1$$

can be demonstrated by the trapezoidal rule. The length of the interval may be made equal to

$$\Delta x = 1' = \frac{2\pi}{360 \times 60} = \frac{\pi}{10,800} = 0.000290888 \, .$$

Then the $90 \times 60 + 1$ or 5,401 items of $\sin x$ from 0 to 90 degrees are added together. This sum is designated by $\sum \sin x$. The required definite integral should be equal to

$$\Delta x \, [\sum \sin x - 0.5(0) - 0.5(1)] = \Delta x (\sum \sin x - 0.5) = 1.00000 \, .$$

An ambitious reader may like to find the sum of the 5,401 items of $\sin x$ given in the trigonometry table. But, in doing so, he should be careful not to add the duplicate items. For example, $\sin 0° \, 60'$ and $\sin 1° \, 0'$ are the same entry and one of them should be eliminated.

The generalized version of the integral of sine is

$$\int \sin v \, dv = -\cos v + C \tag{3}$$

where v is a function of x. For example, the integral of

$$f(x) = 12 \sin 3x$$

is equal to

$$\int f(x) \, dx = 4 \int \sin 3x \, d(3x) = -4 \cos 3x + C \, .$$

The numerical demonstration of this integral is not necessary. It is the inverse operation of table 12.2b where the function $4 \cos 3x$ is differentiated.

12.6 Integral of Cosine

The integral of $\cos x$ is equal to

$$\int \cos x \, dx = \sin x + C \tag{1}$$

which can be obtained by integrating the derivative

$$\frac{d}{dx}\sin x = \cos x$$

given in equation (1) of section 12.1. The numerical demonstration of this integral is given in table 12.6 where the function

$$f(x) = \cos x$$

is integrated from 10 to 14 degrees with the length of the interval being equal to

$$\Delta x = 1° = 0.0174533 .$$

The result that the equation

$$F(x) - F(10°) = \sin x - 0.17365$$

holds for every value of x demonstrates that the integral of $\cos x$ is

$$F(x) = \sin x$$

TABLE 12.6

INTEGRATION OF $f(x) = \cos x$

$(\Delta x = 1° = 0.0174533)$

$\bar{x}$	$f(\bar{x})$	$f(\bar{x}) \, \Delta x$	x	$F(x)$	$\sin x$	$\sin x - 0.17365$
			10°	$F(10°)$	0.17365	0.00000
10.5°	0.98325	0.01716				
			11°	$F(10°) + 0.01716$	0.19081	0.01716
11.5°	0.97992	0.01710				
			12°	$F(10°) + 0.03426$	0.20791	0.03426
12.5°	0.97630	0.01704				
			13°	$F(10°) + 0.05130$	0.22495	0.05130
13.5°	0.97237	0.01697				
			14°	$F(10°) + 0.06827$	0.24192	0.06827

because the sine of 10 degrees is equal to 0.17365. Incidentally, tables 12.1a and 12.6 jointly demonstrate that integration is the inverse operation of differentiation and vice versa.

The definite integral of $\cos x$ from a to b is

$$\int_a^b \cos x \, dx = \Big[\sin x \Big]_a^b = \sin b - \sin a \tag{2}$$

with x being measured in radians. From table 12.6, it can be seen that the definite integral of $\cos x$ from

$$a = 10° = \frac{10(2\pi)}{360} = 0.174533$$

to

$$b = 14° = \frac{14(2\pi)}{360} = 0.244346$$

is equal to

$$F(14°) - F(10°) = 0.06827 \,.$$

But, by equation (2), the same integral is equal to

$$\int_{0.174533}^{0.244346} \cos x \, dx = \sin 14° - \sin 10° = 0.06827$$

which is the same value.

The meaning of equation (2) can also be demonstrated through the trapezoidal rule by integrating $\cos x$ from 20 to 21 degrees. The 61 items

$$\cos 20° \, 00' = 0.93969$$

$$\cos 20° \, 01' = 0.93959$$

$$\cos 20° \, 02' = 0.93949$$

$$\cdots$$

$$\cos 20° \, 59' = 0.93368$$

$$\cos 21° \, 00' = 0.93358$$

are added together, and the sum is equal to

$$\sum \cos x = 57.13620 \,.$$

But the trapezoidal rule requires only one half of the first and the last values of $f(x)$ or $\cos x$. Thus the sum required is

$$57.13620 - 0.5(0.93969) - 0.5(0.93358) = 56.19956 .$$

The length of the interval of this integration is

$$\Delta x = 1' = 0.000290888 .$$

Then the definite integral of $\cos x$ from 20 to 21 degrees, by trapezoidal rule, is

$$(56.19956)(0.000290888) = 0.01635 .$$

But, by equation (2), the same integral is equal to

$$\sin 21° - \sin 20° = 0.35837 - 0.34202 = 0.01635$$

which is the same value. This, again, demonstrates that formulas of differentiation and integration are short cuts of computation.

The generalized version of the integral of cosine is

$$\int \cos v \, dv = \sin v + C \tag{3}$$

where v is a function of x. For example, the integral of

$$f(x) = 10 \cos 2x$$

is equal to

$$\int f(x) \, dx = 5 \int \cos 2x \, d(2x) = 5 \sin 2x + C .$$

The numerical demonstration of the above integral is not presented here. It is simply the inverse operation of table 12.1b where the function $5 \sin 2x$ is differentiated.

12.7 Integrals of Tangent and Cotangent

The integral of $\tan x$ is equal to

$$\int \tan x \, dx = - \log_e \cos x + C . \tag{1}$$

This result can be derived from the identity

$$\tan x = \frac{\sin x}{\cos x}$$

and the differential

$$d(\cos x) = -\sin x \, dx.$$

After these substitutions are made, the integral of $\tan x$ becomes

$$\int \frac{\sin x}{\cos x} dx = -\int (\cos x)^{-1} d(\cos x) = -\log_e \cos x + C$$

which is the expression given in equation (1).

The numerical demonstration of equation (1) is given in table 12.7a where the function

$$f(x) = \tan x$$

is integrated from 20 to 24 degrees with the length of the interval being

$$\Delta x = 1° = 0.0174533.$$

The values of x and $F(x)$ given in that table constitute the integral of $\tan x$.

TABLE 12.7a

INTEGRATION OF $f(x) = \tan x$

$$(\Delta x = 1° = 0.0174533)$$

$\bar{x}$	$f(\bar{x})$	$f(\bar{x}) \Delta x$	x	$F(x)$	$-\log_e \cos x - 0.06219$
			20°	$F(20°)$	0.00000
20.5	0.37388	0.00653			
			21°	$F(20°) + 0.00653$	0.00652
21.5	0.39391	0.00687			
			22°	$F(20°) + 0.01340$	0.01340
22.5	0.41421	0.00723			
			23°	$F(20°) + 0.02063$	0.02066
23.5	0.43481	0.00759			
			24°	$F(20°) + 0.02822$	0.02823

To demonstrate the validity of equation (1), the values of $-\log_e \cos x$ are calculated with the details of computation given in table 12.7b. The last two columns of table 12.7a show that

$$F(x) - F(20°) = -\log_e \cos x - 0.06219$$

holds approximately for every value of x. This is to demonstrate that the integral of $\tan x$ is equal to

$$F(x) = -\log_e \cos x$$

because, at x equal to 20 degrees, $F(x)$ is equal to

$$-\log_e \cos 20° = 0.06219.$$

TABLE 12.7b

CALCULATION OF $-\log_e \cos x$

x	$\cos x$	$\log \cos x$	$-\log \cos x$	$-\log_e \cos x$	$-\log_e \cos x - 0.06219$
20°	0.93969	$-1 + 0.97299$	0.02701	0.06219	0.00000
21°	0.93358	$-1 + 0.97016$	0.02984	0.06871	0.00652
22°	0.92718	$-1 + 0.96717$	0.03283	0.07559	0.01340
23°	0.92050	$-1 + 0.96402$	0.03598	0.08285	0.02066
24°	0.91355	$-1 + 0.96073$	0.03927	0.09042	0.02823

The computation of table 12.7b requires the trigonometry table as well as the logarithm table. First, the values of $\cos x$ are found from the trigonometry table. Second, the common logarithms of $\cos x$ are found from the logarithm table. Third, the natural logarithms of $\cos x$ are obtained by multiplying each common logarithm of $\cos x$ by (equation 10, section 9.4)

$$\log_e 10 = 2.302585.$$

The definite integral of $\tan x$ from a to b is equal to

$$\int_a^b \tan x \, dx = -\left[\log_e \cos x\right]_a^b$$

$$= -\log_e \cos b + \log_e \cos a$$

$$= \log_e\left(\frac{\cos a}{\cos b}\right). \tag{2}$$

From table 12.7a, it can be seen that the definite integral of $\tan x$ from 20 to 24 degrees is equal to

$$F(24°) - F(20°) = 0.02822.$$

But, by equation (2), the same integral is equal to

$$\log_e\left(\frac{\cos 20°}{\cos 24°}\right) = \log_e\left(\frac{0.93969}{0.91355}\right) = \log_e 1.0286$$

or

$$(2.302585)(0.01225) = 0.02821 .$$

The same quantity obtained from table 12.7b is

$$- \log_e \cos 24° + \log_e \cos 20° = 0.09042 - 0.06219 = 0.02823 .$$

The discrepancy among these numbers comes from the round-off errors in computation.

The generalized version of the integral of tangent is

$$\int \tan v \, dv = - \log_e \cos v + C \tag{3}$$

where v is a function of x. For example, the integral of $\tan 2x$ is equal to

$$\int \tan 2x \, dx = \frac{1}{2}\int \tan 2x \, d(2x) = -\frac{1}{2}\log_e \cos 2x + C .$$

The integral of $\cot x$ is equal to

$$\int \cot x \, dx = \log_e \sin x + C . \tag{4}$$

This result can be derived from the identity

$$\cot x = \frac{\cos x}{\sin x}$$

and the differential

$$d(\sin x) = \cos x \, dx .$$

After these substitutions are made, the integral of $\cot x$ becomes

$$\int \frac{\cos x}{\sin x}dx = \int \frac{d(\sin x)}{\sin x} = \log_e \sin x + C$$

which is the expression given in equation (4). The numerical demonstration of the integral of $\cot x$, which is similar to that of $\tan x$, is left to the reader as an exercise.

The generalized version of the integral of cotangent is

$$\int \cot v \, dv = \log_e \sin v + C \tag{5}$$

where v is a function of x. For example, the integral of $\cot 3x$ is

$$\int \cot 3x \, dx = \frac{1}{3} \int \cot 3x \, d(3x) = \frac{1}{3} \log_e \sin 3x + C.$$

12.8 Integrals of Secant and Cosecant

The integral of $\sec x$ is equal to

$$\int \sec x \, dx = \log_e (\sec x + \tan x) + C. \qquad (1)$$

This result can be derived from the identity

$$\sec x = \sec x \frac{\sec x + \tan x}{\sec x + \tan x} = \frac{\sec x \tan x + \sec^2 x}{\sec x + \tan x}$$

and the differential (equation 1, section 12.4; equation 1, section 12.3)

$$d(\sec x + \tan x) = (\sec x \tan x + \sec^2 x) dx.$$

After these substitutions are made, the integral of $\sec x$ becomes

$$\int \frac{d(\sec x + \tan x)}{\sec x + \tan x} = \log_e (\sec x + \tan x) + C$$

which is the expression given in equation (1).

The numerical demonstration of equation (1) is given in table 12.8a where the function

TABLE 12.8a

INTEGRATION OF $f(x) = \sec x$

$(\Delta x = 1° = 0.0174533)$

$\bar{x}$	$\cos \bar{x}$	$f(\bar{x})$	$f(\bar{x}) \Delta x$	x	$F(x)$	$\log_e(\sec x + \tan x)$ -0.3563
				20°	$F(20°)$	0.0000
20.5	0.93667	1.06761	0.01863			
				21°	$F(20°) + 0.0186$	0.0187
21.5	0.93042	1.07478	0.01876			
				22°	$F(20°) + 0.0374$	0.0378
22.5	0.92388	1.08239	0.01889			
				23°	$F(20°) + 0.0563$	0.0565
23.5	0.91706	1.09044	0.01903			
				24°	$F(20°) + 0.0753$	0.0755

$$f(x) = \sec x$$

is integrated from 20 to 24 degrees with the length of the interval being

$$\Delta x = 1° = 0.0174533 .$$

The values of $f(\bar{x})$ given in that table are the reciprocals of the values of $\cos \bar{x}$, where $\bar{x}$ is the mid-point of an interval. The integration is carried out in the usual way, and the values of x and $F(x)$ constitute the integral of $\sec x$.

TABLE 12.8b

CALCULATION OF $\log_e (\sec x + \tan x) = \log_e T$

x	$\cos x$	$\sec x$	$\tan x$	T	$\log T$	$\log_e T$	$\log_e T - 0.3563$
20°	0.93969	1.06418	0.36397	1.42815	0.15473	0.3563	0.0000
21°	0.93358	1.07115	0.38386	1.45501	0.16286	0.3750	0.0187
22°	0.92718	1.07854	0.40403	1.48257	0.17114	0.3941	0.0378
23°	0.92050	1.08637	0.42447	1.51084	0.17926	0.4128	0.0565
24°	0.91355	1.09463	0.44523	1.53986	0.18752	0.4318	0.0755

To demonstrate the validity of equation (1), the values of

$$\operatorname{leg}_e (\sec x + \tan x) - 0.3563$$

are calculated with the details of computation given in table 12.8b. The last two columns of table 12.8a shows that the equation

$$F(x) - F(20°) = \log_e(\sec x + \tan x) - 0.3563$$

holds approximately for every value of x. This is to demonstrate that the integral of $\sec x$ is equal to

$$F(x) = \log_e(\sec x + \tan x)$$

because, at x equal to 20 degrees, $F(x)$ is equal to 0.3563 as shown in table 12.8b.

The new symbol T used in table 12.8b is of no particular importance. It is used here to represent $\sec x + \tan x$ to save space. The symbol log used in that table, as usual, stands for the common logarithm, and $\log_e$ stands for the natural logarithm.

The meaning of the definite integral

$$\int_a^b \sec x \, dx = \Big[\log_e(\sec x + \tan x) \Big]_a^b$$

can be demonstrated numerically. For the limits

$$a = 20° = 0.349$$

and

$$b = 24° = 0.419,$$

the integral is equal to

$$F(24°) - F(20°) = 0.0753$$

as shown in table 12.8a. By formula, the same integral is equal to

$$\int_{0.349}^{0.419} \sec x \, dx = 0.4318 - 0.3563 = 0.0755$$

as shown in table 12.8b.

As a review of Simpson's rule, one may also find the same definite integral by that method. The details of computation are given in table 12.8c. The values of $f(x)$ are obtained from table 12.8b and the weights W are those of Simpson's rule. The sum of products of W and $f(x)$ is equal to

TABLE 12.8c

INTEGRATION OF $f(x) = \sec x$ BY SIMPSON'S RULE

$(\Delta x = 1° = 0.0174533)$

x	$f(x)$	W	$W f(x)$
20°	1.06418	1	1.06418
21°	1.07115	4	4.28460
22°	1.07854	2	2.15708
23°	1.08637	4	4.34548
24°	1.09463	1	1.09463
		Sum	12.94597
$\frac{\Delta x}{3} \sum W f(x) = 0.0753$			

$$\Sigma \, W f(x) \; = \; 12.94597$$

and the length of the interval is

$$\Delta x \; = \; 1° \; = \; 0.0175433 \,.$$

Thus the value of the definite integral is

$$\frac{\Delta x}{3} \, \Sigma \, W f(x) \; = \; 0.0753$$

which is the same value obtained by the standard method.

The generalized version of the integral of secant is

$$\int \sec v \, dv \; = \; \log_e (\sec v \, + \, \tan v) \, + \, C \qquad\qquad (2)$$

where v is a function of x. For example, the integral of $\sec 4x$ is

$$\int \sec 4x \, dx \; = \; \frac{1}{4} \int \sec 4x \, d(4x)$$

$$= \; \frac{1}{4} \log_e (\sec 4x \, + \, \tan 4x) \, + \, C \,.$$

The integral of $\csc x$ is equal to

$$\int \csc x \, dx \; = \; \log_e (\csc x \, - \, \cot x) \, + \, C \,. \qquad\qquad (3)$$

This result can be derived from the identity

$$\csc x \; = \; \csc x \, \frac{\csc x \, - \, \cot x}{\csc x \, - \, \cot x} \; = \; \frac{- \csc x \cot x \, + \, \csc^2 x}{\csc x \, - \, \cot x}$$

and the differential (equation 3, section 12.4; equation 3, section 12.3)

$$d(\csc x \, - \, \cot x) \; = \; (- \csc x \cot x \, + \, \csc^2 x) dx \,.$$

After these substitutions are made, the integral of $\csc x$ becomes

$$\int \frac{d(\csc x \, - \, \cot x)}{\csc x \, - \, \cot x} \; = \; \log_e (\csc x \, - \, \cot x) \, + \, C$$

which is the expression given in equation (3). The numerical demonstration of the integral of $\csc x$, which is similar to that of $\sec x$, is left to the reader as an exercise.

The generalized version of the integral of cosecant is

$$\int \csc v \, dv \; = \; \log_e (\csc v \, - \, \cot v) \, + \, C \qquad\qquad (4)$$

where v is a function of x. For example, the integral of $\csc 4x$ is equal to

$$\int \csc 4x \, dx = \frac{1}{4} \int \csc 4x \, d(4x)$$

$$= \frac{1}{4} \log_e (\csc 4x - \cot 4x) + C.$$

12.9   Summary of Formulas

The formulas for differentiating and integrating the six trigonometric functions are summarized as follows:

(1) $\dfrac{d}{dx} \sin v = \cos v \, \dfrac{dv}{dx}$

(2) $\dfrac{d}{dx} \cos v = - \sin v \, \dfrac{dv}{dx}$

(3) $\dfrac{d}{dx} \tan v = \sec^2 v \, \dfrac{dv}{dx}$

(4) $\dfrac{d}{dx} \cot v = - \csc^2 v \, \dfrac{dv}{dx}$

(5) $\dfrac{d}{dx} \sec v = \sec v \tan v \, \dfrac{dv}{dx}$

(6) $\dfrac{d}{dx} \csc v = - \csc v \cot v \, \dfrac{dv}{dx}$

(7) $\int \sin v \, dv = - \cos v + C$

(8) $\int \cos v \, dv = \sin v + C$

(9) $\int \tan v \, dv = - \log_e \cos v + C$

(10) $\int \cot v \, dv = \log_e \sin v + C$

(11) $\int \sec v \, dv = \log_e (\sec v + \tan v) + C$

(12) $\int \csc v \, dv = \log_e (\csc v - \cot v) + C$

The numerical demonstrations given in this chapter are used to explain the meaning of these formulas. At the same time, the demonstrations also show that these formulas are short cuts because they can replace a great deal of computation. However, each formula is a one-purpose gadget. It works beautifully if the occassion calls for it. On the other hand, the numerical methods are general-purpose methods. They can be used for any kind of function. The results are the same whether they are obtained by formulas or by numerical methods, if sufficiently small Δx is used.

It is not true that the formulas yield exact values while the numerical methods give only approximate ones. For example, the definite integral

$$\int_a^b \cot x \, dx = \Big[\log_e \sin x \Big]_a^b = \log_e \Big(\frac{\sin b}{\sin a} \Big)$$

is as exact as can be. But it is exact, because it is unfinished. At the very moment when numerical values are assigned to the limits, the values of $\sin a$ and $\sin b$ and their logarithms become approximate no matter how many decimal places are computed for these values. So the difference between formulas and numerical methods does not lie in the exactness of the results but in the stage at which computation begins and consequently the amount of computation involved. In general, the formulas are used as much as possible because they can save a great deal of computation.

EXERCISES

1. Demonstrate the derivatives of the functions

(a) $\sin x$ (b) $\cos x$

(c) $\tan x$ (d) $\cot x$

(e) $\sec x$ (f) $\csc x$

numerically for the range 30 to 40 degrees with Δx being equal to 2 degrees.

2. Demonstrate the indefinite integrals of the functions

(a) $\sin x$ (b) $\cos x$

(c) $\tan x$ (d) $\cot x$

(e) $\sec x$ (f) $\csc x$

numerically for the range 30 to 33 degrees with Δx being equal to 30 minutes. Then find the definite integrals of the same functions for the same range by the standard method.

3. Find the definite integrals of

(a) $\sin x$ (b) $\cos x$

(c) $\tan x$ (d) $\cot x$

(e) $\sec x$ (f) $\csc x$

for the range 30 to 33 degrees by trapezoidal rule with Δx being equal to 30 minutes. Compare the values thus obtained with those obtained by formulas of integration.

4. Find the definite integrals of

(a) $\sin x$ (b) $\cos x$

(c) $\tan x$ (d) $\cot x$

(e) $\sec x$ (f) $\csc x$

for the range 30 to 33 degrees by Simpson's rule with Δx being equal to 30 minutes. Compare the values thus obtained with those obtained by formulas of integration.

5. Find the minimum and maximum points of the curve

$$y = \sin x$$

within the range $x = 0$ to $x = 2\pi$. Check your answers against figure 11.4a, and see if they are correct.

6. Find the area bounded by the first cycle of the curve (figure 11.4a)

$$y = \sin x$$

and the x axis with all areas being counted as positive.

7. Find the minimum and maximum points of the curve

$$y = 2 \sin 3x$$

within the range $x = 0$ to $x = 2\pi$.   Check your answers against figure 11.4c, and see if they are correct.

8. Find the area bounded by the curve (figure 11.4c)

$$y = 2 \sin 3x$$

and the x axis, within the range $x = 0$ and $x = 2\pi$, with all areas being counted as positive.

CHAPTER 13

SERIES

The methods of computing the exponential, logarithmic and trigonometric functions are discussed in this chapter. In addition, the practice of approximating a function by a polynomial is justified.

13.1 Definitions

A *sequence* is a succession of terms which are formed according to a set of rules. For example, the arithmetic progression (section 4.5)

$$A \quad A+D \quad A+2D \quad \cdots \quad A+(n-1)D$$

is a sequence. So is the geometric progression (section 9.5)

$$A \quad AR \quad AR^2 \quad \cdots \quad AR^{n-1}.$$

A *series* is the sum of the first n terms of a sequence. The sum

$$A + (A+D) + (A+2D) + \cdots + [A+(n-1)D]$$

of the first n terms of the arithmetic sequence is called the *arithmetic series*. The sum

$$A + AR + AR^2 + \cdots + AR^{n-1}$$

is called the *geometric series*.

A series may be either *finite* or *infinite*. If the number of terms is limited, the series is said to be finite. If it is unlimited, the series is infinite. The arithmetic and geometric series discussed in sections 4.5 and 9.5 such as the arithmetic series

$$3 + 5 + 7 + 9 + 11 = 35$$

and the geometric series

$$1 + 2 + 4 + 8 + 16 = 31$$

are all finite series. The corresponding infinite series are expressed as

$$3 + 5 + 7 + \cdots + [3+(n-1)2] + \cdots$$

and

$$1 + 2 + 4 + \cdots + 2^{n-1} + \cdots$$

respectively.

An infinite series may be either *convergent* or *divergent*. As the number of terms of a series increases without bound, the infinite series may or may not approach a finite value as a limit. If it does, the series is said to be convergent. Otherwise, the series is divergent. For example, the arithmetic series

$$3 + 5 + 7 + \cdots + (2n+1) + \cdots$$

is a divergent one because the sum does not approach a finite value as the number of terms increases without bound. Another example of the divergent series is

$$2 - 2 + 2 - 2 + \cdots$$

the sum of which oscillates between 2 and 0 rather than converges to a single value.

The geometric series (equation 2, section 9.5)

$$A + AR + AR^2 + \cdots + AR^{n-1} = \frac{A(R^n - 1)}{R - 1} \tag{1}$$

is a convergent one, if the absolute value of the common ratio R is less than 1. Under the condition $|R| < 1$, the quantity R^n decreases as n increases. When n increases without bound, R^n approaches 0 as a limit. Then the infinite geometric series itself approaches

$$\frac{A(0 - 1)}{R - 1} = \frac{A}{1 - R} \tag{2}$$

as a limit. The range

$$-1 < R < 1$$

within which the geometric series converges is called the *interval of convergence* of the series.

The geometric series is divergent outside its interval of convergence. When R is equal to -1, the series becomes

$$A - A + A - A + \cdots + (-1)^{n+1}A + \cdots$$

which oscillates between A and 0 rather than converges to a single value. When R is equal to 1, the series becomes

$$A + A + A + \cdots + A + \cdots$$

which does not approach a limit as n increases without bound. When $|R|$ is greater than 1, R^n increases with n and the series again does not converge to a finite value.

The convergence and divergence of a series cannot always be determined by a casual observation. Several formal methods are available for this purpose, but none of them is discussed in this text. Readers who are interested in this topic are referred to a text on advanced calculus.

13.2   Factorial Number

The product of n successive integers, beginning with 1, is called n *factorial*. Symbolically, it is expressed as

$$n! = 1 \times 2 \times 3 \times \cdots \times n \tag{1}$$

or

$$\lfloor n = 1 \times 2 \times 3 \times \cdots \times n. \tag{2}$$

Both $n!$ and $\lfloor n$ are commonly used symbols for n factorial.

From the definition of the factorial number, it follows that

$$1! = 1$$
$$2! = 1 \times 2 = 2$$
$$3! = 1 \times 2 \times 3 = 6$$
$$4! = 1 \times 2 \times 3 \times 4 = 24$$

and so forth. It is understood that the number n in the expression $n!$ is a positive integer.

The product of successive integers, beginning with any number, can be expressed as the ratio of two factorial numbers. For example, the product

$$4 \times 5 \times 6 = 120$$

can be expressed as

$$\frac{1 \times 2 \times 3 \times 4 \times 5 \times 6}{1 \times 2 \times 3} = \frac{6!}{3!}.$$

In general, the product of k successive integers, beginning with $r + 1$, can be expressed as

$$(r+1)(r+2)\cdots(r+k) = \frac{(r+k)!}{r!}. \tag{3}$$

The successive differentiation of the function

$$F(x) = x^n \tag{4}$$

can lead to factorial numbers. The first derivative of $F(x)$ is

$$F'(x) = nx^{n-1} = \frac{n!}{(n-1)!}\, x^{n-1}\, ;$$

the second derivative of $F(x)$ is

$$F''(x) = n(n-1)x^{n-2} = \frac{n!}{(n-2)!}\, x^{n-2}\, ;$$

and the third derivative of $F(x)$ is

$$F'''(x) = n(n-1)(n-2)x^{n-3} = \frac{n!}{(n-3)!}\, x^{n-3}.$$

Now the pattern is clear. The kth derivative of $F(x)$ must be

$$F^{(k)}(x) = \frac{n!}{(n-k)!}\, x^{n-k} \tag{5}$$

where k is less than or equal to n.

The nth derivative of x^n leads to zero factorial. When k and n of equation (5) are equal, the nth derivative of x^n becomes

$$F^{(n)}(x) = \frac{n!}{(n-n)!}\, x^{n-n} = \frac{n!}{0!}$$

because x^0 is equal to 1. Now a value has to be assigned to 0! so that equation (5) can be used for the case where k is equal to n.

To investigate the value of 0!, one may start with a special case, such as $F(x) = x^2$. The first derivative of x^2 is $2x$, and the same derivative obtained from equation (5) is also equal to

$$\frac{2!}{(2-1)!}\, x^{2-1} = 2x.$$

The second derivative of x^2 is 2, and the same derivative obtained from equation (5) is

$$\frac{2!}{(2-2)!}\, x^{2-2} = \frac{2!}{0!} = \frac{2}{0!}.$$

This leads to the conclusion

$$\frac{2}{0!} = 2$$

or the necessary definition

$$0! = 1 \tag{6}$$

so that equation (5) can include the case where k is equal to n.

For the general case where

$$F(x) = x^n,$$

the nth derivative obtained by successive differentiation is

$$F^{(n)}(x) = n(n-1)(n-2)\cdots(3)(2)(1) = n!,$$

and that obtained by equation (5) is

$$\frac{n!}{(n-n)!} x^{n-n} = \frac{n!}{0!}.$$

These two numbers must be equal. So, for the convenience of symbolism, 0! is given the value 1.

The reason for bringing up the factorial number in this section is that it is useful in studying the series.

13.3 Maclaurin's Series

The infinite series

$$b_0 + b_1 x + b_2 x^2 + \cdots + b_n x^n + \cdots$$

is called a *power series*. It is a polynomial in x, but its degree is not n but infinity.

Maclaurin's series is a power series used in representing a given function $F(x)$. If the function $F(x)$ can be represented by a power series, the problem is to determine the values of the coefficients in the expression

$$F(x) = b_0 + b_1 x + b_2 x^2 + b_3 x^3 + b_4 x^4 + \cdots + b_n x^n + \cdots \tag{1}$$

which is an infinite series.

The coefficients in the power series are obtained by evaluating the successive derivatives at $x = 0$. By setting x equal to 0 in equation (1), one immediately obtains the zeroth coefficient

$$b_0 = F(0).$$

Differentiating equation (1) term by term, one obtains the first derivative

$$F'(x) = b_1 + 2b_2 x + 3b_3 x^2 + 4b_4 x^3 + \cdots + n b_n x^{n-1} + \cdots$$

whose value at $x = 0$ is

$$F'(0) = b_1$$

which implies that the first coefficient is

$$b_1 = F'(0).$$

Differentiating the first derivative, one obtains the second derivative

$$F''(x) = (2)(1)b_2 + (3)(2)b_3 x + (4)(3)b_4 x^2 + \cdots + n(n-1)b_n x^{n-2} + \cdots$$

whose value at $x = 0$ is

$$F''(0) = (2)(1)b_2$$

which implies that the second coefficient is

$$b_2 = \frac{F''(0)}{2!}.$$

Differentiating the second derivative, one obtains the third derivative

$$F'''(x) = (3)(2)(1)b_3 + (4)(3)(2)b_4 x + \cdots + n(n-1)(n-2)b_n x^{n-3} + \cdots$$

whose value at $x = 0$ is

$$F'''(0) = (3)(2)(1)b_3$$

which implies that the third coefficient is

$$b_3 = \frac{F'''(0)}{3!}.$$

Now, from this pattern, one can deduce that the nth coefficient of the power series is

$$b_n = \frac{F^{(n)}(0)}{n!}.$$

Consequently the function can be expressed as

$$F(x) = F(0) + F'(0)x + \frac{F''(0)}{2!}x^2 + \cdots + \frac{F^{(n)}(0)}{n!}x^n + \cdots \quad (2)$$

which is called *Maclaurin's series*. In more abbreviated notation, the series can be expressed as

$$F(x) = \sum_{n=0}^{\infty} \frac{F^{(n)}(0)}{n!} x^n \qquad (3)$$

with the zeroth derivative of $F(x)$ being the function $F(x)$ itself.

As an illustration of Maclaurin's series, one may consider the function

$$F(x) = e^x.$$

Since the derivative of $F(x)$ is equal to

$$\frac{d}{dx} F(x) = \frac{d}{dx} e^x = e^x = F(x),$$

the successive derivatives of $F(x)$ are all equal to e^x. At the point $x = 0$, the values of these derivatives are

$$F(0) = F'(0) = F''(0) = \cdots = F^{(n)}(0) = \cdots = 1.$$

Then the function $F(x)$ can be represented by the Maclaurin's series as

$$e^x = 1 + x + \frac{x^2}{2!} + \frac{x^3}{3!} + \cdots + \frac{x^n}{n!} + \cdots \qquad (4)$$

which converges for all values of x.

Equation (4) provides a method of evaluating e^x. Table 13.3a shows the calculation of $e^{0.1}$ by Maclaurin's series. The result

$$e^{0.1} = 1.10517$$

agrees with the value 1.1052 given in table 2 of the appendix.

TABLE 13.3a

CALCULATION OF $e^{0.1}$ BY MACLAURIN'S SERIES

n	$n!$	x^n	$\dfrac{x^n}{n!}$
0	1	1	1.000000
1	1	0.1	0.100000
2	2	0.01	0.005000
3	6	0.001	0.000167
4	24	0.0001	0.000004
5	120	0.00001	0.000000
		Sum	1.105171

As another illustration of the application of Maclaurin's series, the quantity e is calculated. By setting x equal to 1 in equation (4), one obtains

$$1 + 1 + \frac{1}{2!} + \frac{1}{3!} + \cdots + \frac{1}{n!} + \cdots = \sum_{n=0}^{\infty} \frac{1}{n!}$$

as the value of e. The details of computation are given in table 13.3b, and the result is the familiar value 2.71828 for the constant e.

TABLE 13.3b

CALCULATION OF e BY MACLAURIN'S SERIES

n	$n!$	$\frac{1}{n!}$
0	1	1.000000
1	1	1.000000
2	2	0.500000
3	6	0.166667
4	24	0.041667
5	120	0.008333
6	720	0.001389
7	5,040	0.000198
8	40,320	0.000025
9	362,880	0.000003
10	3,628,800	0.000000
	Sum	2.718282

All the values of e^x and e^{-x} given in table 2 of the appendix can be obtained from the values

$$e^{0.1} = 1.10517$$

and

$$e = 2.71828$$

given in tables 13.3a and 13.3b. For example, the computed values

$$e^{0.2} = (1.10517)(1.10517) = 1.2214$$

$$e^{1.1} = (2.71828)(1.10517) = 3.0042$$

$$e^{1.2} = (2.71828)(1.10517)^2 = 3.3201$$

$$e^{2.1} = (2.71828)^2(1.10517) = 8.1662$$

$$e^{2.2} = (2.71828)^2(1.10517)^2 = 9.0250$$

are equal to those listed in the table. The values of e^{-x} given in the table are simply the reciprocals of those of e^x.

13.4   Taylor's Series

In addition to Maclaurin's series, a function can also be represented by the infinite series

$$F(x) = b_0 + b_1(x - c) + b_2(x - c)^2 + \cdots + b_n(x - c)^n + \cdots \qquad (1)$$

which is a power series in $(x - c)$ with c being a constant. The coefficients in the above series are determined in the same manner as those of Maclaurin's series. By setting x equal to c in equation (1), one immediately obtains the zeroth coefficient

$$b_0 = F(c).$$

By setting x equal to c in the first derivative of $F(x)$, one obtains the first coefficient

$$b_1 = F'(c).$$

In general, the nth coefficient is equal to

$$b_n = \frac{F^{(n)}(c)}{n!}$$

which is obtained by setting x equal to c in the nth derivative of $F(x)$. After these coefficients are substituted in equation (1), the resulting expression for the function is

$$F(x) = F(c) + \frac{F'(c)}{1!}(x - c) + \frac{F''(c)}{2!}(x - c)^2 + \cdots$$

$$+ \frac{F^{(n)}(c)}{n!}(x - c)^n + \cdots$$

$$= \sum_{n=0}^{\infty} \frac{F^{(n)}(c)}{n!}(x - c)^n \qquad (2)$$

which is called *Taylor's series*.

Maclaurin's series is a special case of Taylor's series. When c is equal to 0, equation (2) becomes Maclaurin's series. Taylor's series can be used in computing the value of $F(x)$ in the neighborhood of $x = c$, while Maclaurin's series is more suitable in the neighborhood of $x = 0$.

Taylor's series may be illustrated by the evaluation of e^x. Since all the successive derivatives of the function

$$F(x) = e^x$$

are equal to $F(x)$ itself, the Taylor's series for $F(x)$ must be

$$e^x = e^c + \frac{e^c}{1!}(x - c) + \frac{e^c}{2!}(x - c)^2 + \cdots + \frac{e^c}{n!}(x - c)^n + \cdots$$

$$= e^c \left[1 + \frac{(x - c)}{1!} + \frac{(x - c)^2}{2!} + \cdots + \frac{(x - c)^n}{n!} + \cdots \right]. \quad (3)$$

In evaluating e^x by the above series, the value of e^c must be known. In addition, $x - c$ should be close to 0 so that $(x - c)^n$ becomes negligibly small for a moderate n. For example, in evaluating $e^{2.1}$ the value 2.0 may be assigned to c because e^c is known to be

$$(2.71828)^2 = 7.38905$$

and

$$(x - c) = 2.1 - 2.0 = 0.1$$

is close to 0. With the constant c so designated, the value of $e^{2.1}$ becomes

$$e^2 \left[1 + 0.1 + \frac{(0.1)^2}{2!} + \cdots + \frac{(0.1)^n}{n!} + \cdots \right]$$

$$= (7.38905)(1.10517)$$

$$= 8.1662$$

which is the value listed in table 2 of the appendix. The details of the evaluation of the series in the bracket are the same as those given in table 13.3a.

Taylor's series may be illustrated by another example. The function

$$F(x) = \log_e x$$

cannot be represented by Maclaurin's series, because $F(0)$ is not a finite value. However, it can be represented by Taylor's series. The successive derivatives of $F(x)$ are

$$F'(x) = x^{-1} = \frac{1}{x}$$

$$F''(x) = (-1)x^{-2} = \frac{-1}{x^2}$$

$$F'''(x) = (-1)(-2)x^{-3} = \frac{(-1)(-2)}{x^3}$$

$$\cdots$$

$$F^{(n)}(x) = (-1)^{n-1}(n-1)!\, x^{-n} = \frac{(-1)^{n+1}(n-1)!}{x^n}$$

and the Taylor's series must be

$$\log_e x = \log_e c + \frac{x-c}{c} - \frac{(x-c)^2}{2\,c^2}$$

$$+ \cdots + (-1)^{n+1}\frac{(x-c)^n}{n\,c^n} + \cdots \qquad (4)$$

whose interval of convergence is $0 < x \leqq 2c$.

As an example, equation (4) is used in evaluating the natural logarithm of 1.1. For this operation, the value 1.0 may be assigned to c because the logarithm of 1 is known to be equal to 0. At the same time,

$$x - c = 1.1 - 1.0 = 0.1$$

is close to 0. When these quantities are substituted into equation (4), the natural logarithm of 1.1 becomes

$$\log_e 1.1 = 0 + \frac{0.1}{1} - \frac{(0.1)^2}{2} + \cdots + (-1)^{n+1}\frac{(0.1)^n}{n} + \cdots$$

$$= 0.09531$$

with the details of computation given in table 13.4. This is the same value given in table 3 of the appendix.

The series for the natural logarithm can also be expressed as

$$\log_e(c + u) = \log_e c + \frac{u}{c} - \frac{u^2}{2c^2} + \cdots + (-1)^{n+1}\frac{u^n}{nc^n} + \cdots \qquad (5)$$

TABLE 13.4

CALCULATION OF $\log_e 1.1$ BY TAYLOR'S SERIES

n	$(0.1)^n$	$(-1)^{n+1}\dfrac{(0.1)^n}{n}$
1	0.1	0.100000
2	0.01	−0.005000
3	0.001	0.000333
4	0.0001	−0.000025
5	0.00001	0.000002
6	0.000001	−0.000000
	Sum	0.095310

whose interval of convergence is $-c < u \leqq c$. This series is obtained from equation (4) by the transformation

$$x = c + u$$

or

$$u = x - c.$$

In using this new series, the natural logarithm of c must be known and the quantity u should be close to 0.

13.5 Operations with Infinite Series

Many of the operations of algebra and calculus can be carried out with convergent series. The sum of two functions

$$F(x) = b_0 + b_1 x + b_2 x^2 + \cdots + b_n x^n + \cdots$$

and

$$G(x) = a_0 + a_1 x + a_2 x^2 + \cdots + a_n x^n + \cdots$$

is equal to

$$F(x) + G(x) = (b_0 + a_0) + (b_1 + a_1)x + (b_2 + a_2)x^2$$
$$+ \cdots + (b_n + a_n)x^n + \cdots$$

which is obtained by adding the two series term by term. For example, the sum of the functions (equation 4, section 13.3)

$$e^x = 1 + x + \frac{x^2}{2!} + \frac{x^3}{3!} + \cdots + \frac{x^n}{n!} + \cdots$$

and

$$e^{-x} = 1 - x + \frac{x^2}{2!} - \frac{x^3}{3!} + \cdots + (-1)^n \frac{x^n}{n!} + \cdots$$

is

$$e^x + e^{-x} = 2\left[1 + \frac{x^2}{2!} + \frac{x^4}{4!} + \cdots + \frac{x^{2k}}{(2k)!} + \cdots\right]$$

where k is a positive integer and $2k$ an even number.

Multiplication can also be carried out among convergent series. The product of two functions

$$F(x) = b_0 + b_1 x + b_2 x^2 + \cdots + b_n x^n + \cdots$$

and

$$G(x) = a_0 + a_1 x + a_2 x^2 + \cdots + a_n x^n + \cdots$$

is equal to

$$F(x)G(x) = a_0 b_0 + (a_0 b_1 + a_1 b_0)x + (a_0 b_2 + a_1 b_1 + a_2 b_0)x^2 + \cdots$$

which is obtained by grouping the terms after multiplication. For example, the product

$$c^x e^{-x} = 1$$

can be carried out by the multiplication of the series

$$c^x = 1 + x + \frac{x^2}{2!} + \frac{x^3}{3!} + \cdots + \frac{x^n}{n!} + \cdots$$

and

$$e^{-x} = 1 - x + \frac{x^2}{2!} - \frac{x^3}{3!} + \cdots + \frac{(-x)^n}{n!} + \cdots.$$

The series of the product is

$$(1 \times 1) + (1 \times 1 - 1 \times 1)x + \left(1 \times \frac{1}{2!} - 1 \times 1 + \frac{1}{2!} \times 1\right)x^2 + \cdots$$

which is also equal to 1 because all the coefficients of x^n are equal to 0 for n larger than or equal to 1.

A power series may be differentiated term by term within the interval of convergence. For example, the derivative of e^x is known to be e^x. When the series

$$e^x = 1 + x + \frac{x^2}{2!} + \frac{x^3}{3!} + \cdots + \frac{x^n}{n!} + \cdots$$

is differentiated term by term, the derivative is equal to

$$\frac{d}{dx}e^x = 0 + 1 + x + \frac{x^2}{2!} + \cdots + \frac{x^{n-1}}{(n-1)!} + \cdots$$

which is the series for e^x.

As another example of the differentiation of a power series, one may consider the series

$$\log_e x = \log_e c + \frac{x-c}{c} - \frac{(x-c)^2}{2\,c^2} + \cdots + (-1)^{n+1}\frac{(x-c)^n}{n\,c^n} + \cdots$$

which is given in equation (4) of section 13.4. When the above series is differentiated term by term, the derivative is equal to

$$\frac{1}{x} = 0 + \frac{1}{c} - \frac{x-c}{c^2} + \frac{(x-c)^2}{c^3} + \cdots + (-1)^{n+1}\frac{(x-c)^{n-1}}{c^n} + \cdots$$

which is a geometric series with the first term being equal to

$$A = \frac{1}{c}$$

and the common ratio being equal to

$$R = -\frac{x-c}{c}.$$

Then the series should be equal to (equation 2, section 13.1)

$$\frac{A}{1-R} = \frac{\frac{1}{c}}{1+\frac{x-c}{c}} = \frac{1}{c+x-c} = \frac{1}{x}$$

which is exactly the derivative of the natural logarithm of x.

A power series can be integrated term by term if the limits lie within the interval of convergence. For example, the integral of e^x is

$$\int e^x\, dx = e^x + C.$$

When the series

$$e^x = 1 + x + \frac{x^2}{2!} + \cdots + \frac{x^n}{n!} + \cdots$$

is integrated term by term, the result is

$$x + \frac{x^2}{2!} + \frac{x^3}{3!} + \cdots + \frac{x^{n+1}}{(n+1)!} + \cdots = e^x - 1$$

which is the same integral with C being equal to -1.

As another example of the integration of a power series, one may consider the series

$$f(u) = \frac{1}{1+u} = 1 - u + u^2 - u^3 + \cdots + (-1)^n u^n + \cdots$$

which is obtained by long division. The integral of $f(u)$ is known to be (equation 4, section 10.6)

$$\int \frac{du}{1+u} = \log_e(1+u) + C.$$

When the series is integrated term by term with respect to u, the result is

$$u - \frac{u^2}{2} + \frac{u^3}{3} - \frac{u^4}{4} + \cdots + (-1)^n \frac{u^{n+1}}{n+1} + \cdots = \log_e(1+u)$$

which is equation (5) of section 13.4 with c being equal to 1.

13.6 Some Useful Series

The series which are used in making the tables in the appendix are listed below:

$$e^x = 1 + x + \frac{x^2}{2!} + \cdots + \frac{x^n}{n!} + \cdots \tag{1}$$

for all values of x

$$\log_e(c + x) = \log_e c + \frac{x}{c} - \frac{x^2}{2c^2} + \cdots + (-1)^{n+1}\frac{x^n}{nc^n} + \cdots \tag{2}$$

for $-c < x \leqq c$

$$\sin x = x - \frac{x^3}{3!} + \frac{x^5}{5!} + \cdots + \frac{(-1)^{n-1}x^{2n-1}}{(2n-1)!} + \cdots \tag{3}$$

for all values of x

$$\cos x = 1 - \frac{x^2}{2!} + \frac{x^4}{4!} + \cdots + \frac{(-1)^n x^{2n}}{(2n)!} + \cdots \tag{4}$$

for all values of x

The first series is derived in section 13.3, and the second one in section 13.4. The derivation of the remaining two series is left to the reader as exercises, but their applications are demonstrated in this section.

The calculation of the sine of 10 degrees is used as an illustration of the sine series. When the angle is 10 degrees, the length of the arc of the unit circle which subtends this angle is

$$x = \frac{10(2\pi)}{360} = 0.174533.$$

When this value is substituted into equation (3), the sum is equal to 0.17365 with the details of computation being shown in table 13.6a. This is the same value given in the trigonometry table.

TABLE 13.6a

CALCULATION OF sin 10° BY MACLAURIN'S SERIES

n	$2n-1$	$(2n-1)!$	$(0.174533)^{2n-1}$	$\dfrac{(-1)^{n-1}(0.174533)^{2n-1}}{(2n-1)!}$
1	1	1	0.174533	0.174533
2	3	6	0.005317	−0.000886
3	5	120	0.000162	0.000001
4	7	5,040	0.000005	−0.000000
			Sum	0.173648

TABLE 13.6b

CALCULATION OF cos 10° BY MACLAURIN'S SERIES

n	$2n$	$(2n)!$	$(0.174533)^{2n}$	$\dfrac{(-1)^{n}(0.174533)^{2n}}{(2n)!}$
0	0	1	1.000000	1.000000
1	2	2	0.030462	−0.015231
2	4	24	0.000928	0.000039
3	6	720	0.000028	−0.000000
			Sum	0.984808

The calculation of the cosine of 10 degrees is used as an illustration of the cosine series. When the value

$$x = 0.174533$$

is substituted into equation (4), the sum is equal to 0.98481 with the details of computation being shown in table 13.6b. This is the same value given in the trigonometry table.

With the sine and cosine of 10 degrees computed, the tangent and cotangent of the same angle can be obtained by trigonometric identities. The tangent of 10 degrees is

$$\tan 10° = \frac{\sin 10°}{\cos 10°} = \frac{0.173648}{0.984808} = 0.17633$$

and the cotangent of the same angle is

$$\cot 10° = \frac{\cos 10°}{\sin 10°} = \frac{0.984808}{0.173648} = 5.6713 \,.$$

These are the same values given in the trigonometry table.

13.7 Applications of Series

One of the applications of the power series is the computation of various functions. This is demonstrated in the preceding sections. The advantage of using the series in this manner is that the computation of exponential, logarithmic, trigonometric and many other functions can be carried out by arithmetical operations which can be handled by machines.

For a given degree of accuracy, the number of terms used in computation is always finite in spite of the name infinite series. None of the examples given in the preceding sections uses more than 10 terms; yet the degree of accuracy of the tables of the appendix is already reached. One should not take the word infinite too seriously. It only means that one may use as many terms as he desires, and the supply of terms is inexhaustible. At no time need one attempt to use them all.

Another application of series is the replacement of a function by the first few terms of its power series. This practice is called *approximation*. The first approximation of a function is

$$F(x) = F(0) + F'(0)x \,;$$

the second approximation is

$$F(x) = F(0) + F'(0) x + \frac{1}{2} F''(0) x^2 ;$$

and so forth. For example, the first approximation of the function e^x is

$$F(x) = 1 + x$$

which is a first-degree polynomial in x, and the second approximation of e^x is

$$F(x) = 1 + x + \frac{1}{2} x^2$$

which is a second-degree polynomial in x. In the neighborhood of $x = 0$, these are fairly close approximations of e^x. For $x = 0.1$, the first approximation is

$$1 + x = 1 + 0.1 = 1.1$$

which is the tabulated value 1.1052 rounded off to two significant figures. The second approximation

$$1 + x + \frac{1}{2} x^2 = 1 + 0.1 + \frac{1}{2}(0.1)^2 = 1.105$$

is the tabulated value 1.1052 rounded off to four significant figures. This is the justification of the practice of representing an unknown function by a polynomial (sections 4.6 and 4.7).

The first few terms of a Taylor's series may be used in representing a function in the neighborhood of $x = c$. The first approximation of the function $F(x)$ is

$$F(x) = F(c) + F'(c) (x - c) ;$$

the second approximation of $F(x)$ is

$$F(x) = F(c) + F'(c) (x - c) + \frac{F''(c)}{2} (x - c)^2 ;$$

and so forth. For example, the first approximation of the natural logarithm of a number in the neighborhood of 1 is (equation 4, section 13.4)

$$\log_e x = (x - 1).$$

At the point $x = 1.02$, the first approximation is

$$\log_e(1.02) = 1.02 - 1 = 0.02$$

which is the tabulated value 0.01980 rounded off to one significant figure. The second approximation of the same function is

$$\log_e x = (x - 1) - \frac{(x - 1)^2}{2}.$$

At the point $x = 1.02$, the approximation is

$$\log_e(1.02) = 0.02 - \frac{(0.02)^2}{2} = 0.0198$$

which is the tabulated value 0.01980 rounded off to three significant figures.

The use of Taylor's series as an approximation is equivalent to the use of a polynomial in x. For the given example of natural logarithm, the first approximation is

$$x - 1 = -1 + x$$

which is a first-degree polynomial in x, and the second approximation is

$$(x - 1) - \frac{(x - 1)^2}{2} = -1.5 + 2.0\,x - 0.5\,x^2$$

which is a second-degree polynomial in x. This further justifies the practice of representing an unknown function by a polynomial (sections 4.6 and 4.7). This representation is not limited to the neighborhood of $x = 0$.

EXERCISES

1. Evaluate the following infinite series:

(a) $\sum_{n=1}^{\infty} \frac{1}{2^n} = \frac{1}{2} + \frac{1}{4} + \frac{1}{8} + \frac{1}{16} + \cdots$

(b) $\sum_{n=1}^{\infty} \frac{1}{3^n} = \frac{1}{3} + \frac{1}{9} + \frac{1}{27} + \frac{1}{81} + \cdots$

Check your answers by actually compute the above series to an accuracy of four decimal places.

2. Evaluate the following quantities:

   (a)   5!   (b)   7!

   (c) $\dfrac{5!}{3!}$ (d) $\dfrac{4!}{5!}$

3. Express the following products in terms of factorial numbers:

   (a) $7 \times 8 \times 9$ (b) $2 \times 3 \times 4$

   (c) $n(n-1)(n-2)$ (d) $(n+k)(n+k+1)$

4. Expand the following functions by Maclaurin's series:

   (a) $\sin x$ (b) $\cos x$

   Check your results with equations (3) and (4) of section 13.6.
5. Differentiate the series for $\sin x$ term by term, and see if the resulting series is that of $\cos x$.
6. Differentiate the series for $\cos x$ term by term, and see if the resulting series is that of $-\sin x$.
7. Integrate the series of $\sin x$ term by term, and see if the resulting series is that of $-\cos x + C$.
8. Integrate the series of $\cos x$ term by term, and see if the resulting series is that of $\sin x + C$.
9. Expand the polynomial

$$F(x) = 1 + x - x^2$$

by Taylor's series with c being equal to 1. Then convert the resulting series into a polynomial in x, and see if the expression for $F(x)$ thus obtained is that of the given function.
10. Evaluate $e^{0.2}$ by Maclaurin's series, and check your result with the tabulated value.
11. Find the natural logarithm of 2 by equation (2) of section 13.6, and check your result with the tabulated value.
12. Calculate the values of the sine and cosine of 5 degrees by equations (3) and (4) of section 13.6, and check your results with the tabulated values.

CHAPTER 14

PARTIAL DIFFERENTIATION

The differentiation of a function of two independent variables is presented in this chapter. This is an extension of the discussion of the differentiation of a function of one independent variable x. In this chapter, the dependent variable is designated by z which is a function of two independent variables x and y.

14.1 Function of Two Variables

A function of two independent variables is a common occurrence. The comfort index (z) is a function of relative humidity (x) and temperature (y). The floor space (z) of a room is a function of its length (x) and its width (y). The volume (z) of a cylinder is a function of its radius (x) and its height (y). These are some of the examples of functions of two variables.

A function of two variables, like that of one variable, can be presented in three different ways. First, it can be presented as an equation. Second, it can be presented as a table of numbers. Third, it can be presented as a three-dimensional model.

The methods of presenting a function of two variables can be illustrated by the volume of a cone. The volume (z) is a function of the height (y) and the radius (x) of the base. This function can be expressed by the equation (equation 1, section 8.4)

$$z = \frac{1}{3} \pi x^2 y .$$

As the second method of presenting the function, a table of volumes can be computed for various combinations of heights and radii as shown in table 14.1a. When the radius (x) of the base is equal to 2 inches and the height (y) is equal to 3 inches, the volume (z) is equal to

$$\frac{1}{3} \pi (2)^2 3 = 4(3.1416) = 12.5664$$

cubic inches as shown in the table.

TABLE 14.1a

VOLUME OF CONE $z = \dfrac{1}{3} \pi x^2 y$

x \ y	1	2	3	4
1	1.0472	4.1888	9.4248	16.7552
2	2.0944	8.3776	18.8496	33.5104
3	3.1416	12.5664	28.2744	50.2656

As the third method of presenting the function, a three-dimensional model can be built for the function given in table 14.1a. A 1×1 block is placed at each point (x, y) with the height equal to the volume z given in the table. Thus the model for the function contains 4×3 or 12 blocks. The drawing of this model is given in figure 14.1a.

The three-dimensional model of a function of two independent variables is equivalent to the histogram of a function of one independent variable. The model of the function

$$z = f(x, y)$$

of two independent variables consists of a number of blocks, each of which has a height z and a rectangular base $(\Delta x)(\Delta y)$. The base of each block shown in figure 14.1a is of the dimensions 1×1, because both Δx and Δy are equal to 1 as shown in table 14.1a. On the other hand, the histogram of the function

$$y = F(x)$$

of one independent variable consists of a number of rectangles, each of which has a height y and a width Δx. Thus a model is simply a three-dimensional histogram, or a histogram is a two-dimensional model.

As another example of a function of two independent variables, one may consider the equation

$$z = 1 - 50 x^2 y.$$

The tubulated values of z for various combinations of x and y are given in table 14.1b. The drawing of the corresponding model is

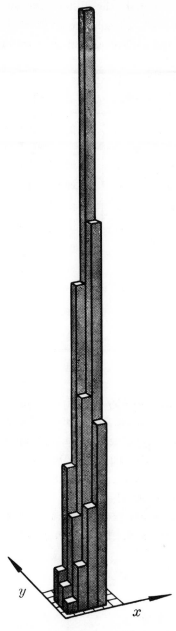

Fig. 14.1a.   Model of $z = \dfrac{1}{3}\pi x^2 y$.

shown in figure 14.1b. It is this function which is used extensively in later sections to illustrate the differentiation and integration of the function z. The row and column totals given in the table have no use until section 15.1 where partial integration is discussed.

TABLE 14.1b

VALUES OF $z = 1 - 50\,x^2\,y$

y \ x	-0.2	-0.1	0.0	0.1	0.2	Total
-0.3	1.60	1.15	1.00	1.15	1.60	6.50
-0.2	1.40	1.10	1.00	1.10	1.40	6.00
-0.1	1.20	1.05	1.00	1.05	1.20	5.50
0.0	1.00	1.00	1.00	1.00	1.00	5.00
0.1	0.80	0.95	1.00	0.95	0.80	4.50
0.2	0.60	0.90	1.00	0.90	0.60	4.00
0.3	0.40	0.85	1.00	0.85	0.40	3.50
0.4	0.20	0.80	1.00	0.80	0.20	3.00
0.5	0.00	0.75	1.00	0.75	0.00	2.50
Total	7.20	8.55	9.00	8.55	7.20	40.50

The increments Δx and Δy used in a table of values of $f(x,\,y)$ are determined by one's need. In table 14.1a where both x and y are positive integers, the values of Δx and Δy are both equal to 1. While in table 14.1b, both Δx and Δy are equal to 0.1. One can choose any pairs of values for these intervals to suit his need, and Δx does not have to be equal to Δy.

The number of z-values increases as Δx and Δy decrease, if the ranges of x and y are fixed. For example, in table 14.1a the range of x is

$$1 \leqq x \leqq 4$$

and that of y is

$$1 \leqq y \leqq 3\,.$$

If Δx is reduced to 0.1, the number of columns in that table will be increased from 4 to 31. If Δy is reduced to 0.05, the number of rows

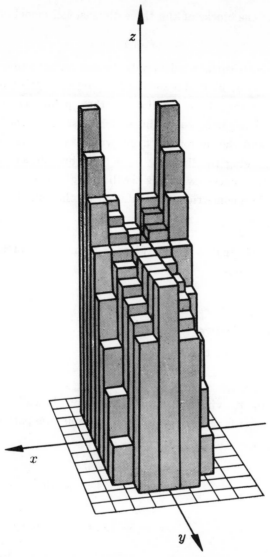

Fɪɢ. 14.1b. Model of $z = 1 - 50\,x^2 y$.

will be increased from 3 to 41. Then the total number of z-values will be increased from 12 to 31×41 or 1,271.

The number of z-values in a table is also the number of blocks in the corresponding model, because each block represents a tubulated value of z. Thus the number of blocks in figure 14.1a will also be increased from 12 to 1,271, if Δx is reduced from 1.0 to 0.1 and Δy from 1.0 to 0.05.

The top of the blocks of the three-dimensional model of a function

$$z = f(x, y)$$

becomes a smooth surface, when both Δx and Δy become infinitesimal. The coordinates (x, y) designate the location of a point on the floor, and z is the height of the ceiling at that point. Of course, this height can be a negative value, in which case the word ceiling is inappropriate and the bottom of a pit would be a better description.

A surface, being the limiting form of a three-dimensional model, is analogous to a curve which is the limiting form of a histogram. A surface is the geometric representation of the function

$$z = f(x, y)$$

in the same sense that a curve is the geometric representation of the function

$$y = F(x).$$

14.2 Partial Derivative

The derivative of the function

$$z = f(x, y)$$

with respect to x, while holding y constant, is called the *partial derivative* of z with respect to x. For example, the partial derivative of the function

$$z = 1 - 50\,x^2\,y \tag{1}$$

with respect to x is

$$\frac{\partial z}{\partial x} = -50(2\,x)y = -100\,x\,y \tag{2}$$

where y is being treated as a constant during the differentiation. The symbol ∂ is used here instead of d to indicate that the differentiation is partial.

The numerical demonstration of the partial differentiation of the function

$$z = 1 - 50\,x^2\,y$$

with respect to x is given in table 14.2a. The characteristic of the partial differentiation is that z is not a collection of numerical values but a sequence of functions of y. The partial derivative, which is represented by $\bar{x}$ and $\Delta z/\Delta x$ of that table, can be expressed as

$$\frac{\Delta z}{\Delta x} = -100\,\bar{x}\,y \tag{3}$$

which is the partial derivative given in equation (2). Here the slant delta Δ is used instead of the upright delta Δ to indicate that the derivative is a partial one.

Table 14.2a

PARTIAL DIFFERENTIATION OF $z = 1 - 50\,x^2\,y$ WITH RESPECT TO x

x	z	Δx	Δz	$\bar{x}$	$\dfrac{\Delta z}{\Delta x}$	$-100\,\bar{x}\,y$
-0.2	$1 - 2.0\,y$					
		0.1	$1.5\,y$	-0.15	$15\,y$	$15\,y$
-0.1	$1 - 0.5\,y$					
		0.1	$0.5\,y$	-0.05	$5\,y$	$5\,y$
0.0	1					
		0.1	$-0.5\,y$	0.05	$-5\,y$	$-5\,y$
0.1	$1 - 0.5\,y$					
		0.1	$-1.5\,y$	0.15	$-15\,y$	$-15\,y$
0.2	$1 - 2.0\,y$					

The procedure of partial differentiation is simple enough. If one can differentiate a function of x with respect to x, he can find the partial derivative of

$$z = f(x,\,y)$$

with respect to x. After all, z becomes nothing but a function of x when y is treated as a constant. However, the meaning of partial differentiation may not be at all clear. In fact, it appears to be inconsistent to first declare y a variable and then treat it as a constant during differentiation.

The meaning of the partial derivative can be demonstrated by the numerical values of

$$z = 1 - 50\,x^2\,y$$

given in table 14.1b. The partial derivative of z with respect to x is the derivative of each row of values of z with respect to x. The derivative of the first row is given in table 14.2b, and that of the second row in table 14.2c. For the values of z given in table 14.1b, one can differentiate z with respect to x nine times—once for each row. These nine derivatives, which collectively constitute the partial derivative of z with respect to x, are given in table 14.2d.

TABLE 14.2b

DIFFERENTIATION OF $z = 1 - 50\,x^2\,y$ WITH RESPECT TO x AT $y = -0.3$

x	z	Δx	Δz	$\bar{x}$	$\dfrac{\Delta z}{\Delta x}$	$-100\,\bar{x}\,y$
-0.2	1.60					
		0.1	-0.45	-0.15	-4.5	-4.5
-0.1	1.15					
		0.1	-0.15	-0.05	-1.5	-1.5
0.0	1.00					
		0.1	0.15	0.05	1.5	1.5
0.1	1.15					
		0.1	0.45	0.15	4.5	4.5
0.2	1.60					

TABLE 14.2c

DIFFERENTIATION OF $z = 1 - 50\,x^2\,y$ WITH RESPECT TO x AT $y = -0.2$

x	z	Δx	Δz	$\bar{x}$	$\dfrac{\Delta z}{\Delta x}$	$-100\,\bar{x}\,y$
-0.2	1.40					
		0.1	-0.30	-0.15	-3.0	-3.0
-0.1	1.10					
		0.1	-0.10	-0.05	-1.0	-1.0
0.0	1.00					
		0.1	0.10	0.05	1.0	1.0
0.1	1.10					
		0.1	0.30	0.15	3.0	3.0
0.2	1.40					

TABLE 14.2d

PARTIAL DERIVATIVE OF $z = 1 - 50\,x^2\,y$ WITH RESPECT TO x

y \ x	-0.15	-0.05	0.05	0.15
-0.3	-4.5	-1.5	1.5	4.5
-0.2	-3.0	-1.0	1.0	3.0
-0.1	-1.5	-0.5	0.5	1.5
0.0	0.0	0.0	0.0	0.0
0.1	1.5	0.5	-0.5	-1.5
0.2	3.0	1.0	-1.0	-3.0
0.3	4.5	1.5	-1.5	-4.5
0.4	6.0	2.0	-2.0	-6.0
0.5	7.5	2.5	-2.5	-7.5

For each row of values of z given in table 14.1b, the value of y is a constant. For the first row, y is equal to -0.3. For the second row, y is equal to -0.2. Then y is treated as a constant during partial differentiation for the simple reason that it actually is a constant.

To find the partial derivative of z with respect to x by differentiating each row of values of z can involve a tremendous amount of computation, if the number of rows is large. The obvious short cut is to use only one row of z-values to represent all of them by retaining y as a symbol during the differentiation as shown in table 14.2a. Then the derivative of each row of z-values can be obtained by substituting the appropriate values of y into the general form of the partial derivative. For example, at $y = -0.3$ the partial derivative given in table 14.2a is equal to

$$15(-0.3) \qquad 5(-0.3) \qquad -5(-0.3) \qquad -15(-0.3)$$

or

$$-4.5 \qquad -1.5 \qquad 1.5 \qquad 4.5$$

which is given in table 14.2b. At $y = -0.2$ the derivative is

$$15(-0.2) \qquad 5(-0.2) \qquad -5(-0.2) \qquad -15(-0.2)$$

or

$$-3.0 \qquad -1.0 \qquad 1.0 \qquad 3.0$$

which is given in table 14.2c. In fact, the complete set of values given in table 14.2d, which shows the partial derivative of z with respect to x, can be obtained this way.

The discussion of the partial derivative of z with respect to x can be summarized as this: A table of values of z can be computed as those shown in table 14.1b. Then each row of z-values is differentiated with respect to x. The resulting derivatives collectively constitute the partial derivative of z with respect to x. Or, if one prefers, he may retain y as a symbol and express all rows of z-values as one row of functions of y. Then this one row is differentiated with respect to x. The values of y are substituted into this derivative to obtain the complete partial derivative which covers all rows. This is the reason why the partial derivative of z with respect to x is obtained by differentiating z with respect to x, while treating y as a constant.

The simple operation of obtaining the partial derivative

$$\frac{\partial}{\partial x}(1 - 50\,x^2\,y) = -100\,x\,y$$

is equivalent to the derivation of table 14.2d from table 14.1b. The complete set of numerical values of the partial derivative listed in table 14.2d can be directly obtained from the above equation. For example, at the point $(x, y) = (0.05, 0.1)$, the partial derivative is equal to

$$\frac{\partial z}{\partial x} = -100(0.05)(0.1) = -0.5$$

which is the value listed in table 14.2d. This demonstrates that differentiation by formula is indeed a computing short cut. By this simple device, a number of tables can be bypassed.

The partial derivative of z with respect to y can be similarly demonstrated. The partial derivative of the function

$$z = 1 - 50\,x^2\,y$$

with respect to y is equal to

$$\frac{\partial z}{\partial y} = -50\,x^2. \tag{4}$$

TABLE 14.2e

PARTIAL DIFFERENTIATION OF $z = 1 - 50\,x^2\,y$ WITH RESPECT TO y

y	z	$\varDelta y$	$\varDelta z$	$\bar{y}$	$\dfrac{\varDelta z}{\varDelta y}$
-0.3	$1 + 15\,x^2$				
		0.1	$-5\,x^2$	-0.25	$-50\,x^2$
-0.2	$1 + 10\,x^2$				
		0.1	$-5\,x^2$	-0.15	$-50\,x^2$
-0.1	$1 + 5\,x^2$				
		0.1	$-5\,x^2$	-0.05	$-50\,x^2$
0.0	1				
		0.1	$-5\,x^2$	0.05	$-50\,x^2$
0.1	$1 - 5\,x^2$				
		0.1	$-5\,x^2$	0.15	$-50\,x^2$
0.2	$1 - 10\,x^2$				
		0.1	$-5\,x^2$	0.25	$-50\,x^2$
0.3	$1 - 15\,x^2$				
		0.1	$-5\,x^2$	0.35	$-50\,x^2$
0.4	$1 - 20\,x^2$				
		0.1	$-5\,x^2$	0.45	$-50\,x^2$
0.5	$1 - 25\,x^2$				

The numerical demonstration of this partial differentiation is given in table 14.2e. Since z is expressed as a sequence of functions of x, the derivative

$$\frac{\varDelta z}{\varDelta y} = -50\,x^2 \tag{5}$$

is also a sequence of functions of x as shown in the table. When the x-values

$$-0.2 \quad\quad -0.1 \quad\quad 0.0 \quad\quad 0.1 \quad\quad 0.2$$

are substituted into the derivative, the result is the partial derivative given in table 14.2f.

TABLE 14.2f

PARTIAL DERIVATIVE OF $z = 1 - 50 x^2 y$ WITH RESPECT TO y

x / y	-0.2	-0.1	0.0	0.1	0.2
-0.25	-2.0	-0.5	0.0	-0.5	-2.0
-0.15	-2.0	-0.5	0.0	-0.5	-2.0
-0.05	-2.0	-0.5	0.0	-0.5	-2.0
0.05	-2.0	-0.5	0.0	-0.5	-2.0
0.15	-2.0	-0.5	0.0	-0.5	-2.0
0.25	-2.0	-0.5	0.0	-0.5	-2.0
0.35	-2.0	-0.5	0.0	-0.5	-2.0
0.45	-2.0	-0.5	0.0	-0.5	-2.0

TABLE 14.2g

DIFFERENTIATION OF $z = 1 - 50x^2 y$ WITH RESPECT TO y AT $x = -0.2$

y	z	Δy	Δz	$\bar{y}$	$\dfrac{\Delta z}{\Delta y}$	$-50x^2$
-0.3	1.60					
		0.1	-0.2	-0.25	-2.0	-2.0
-0.2	1.40					
		0.1	-0.2	-0.15	-2.0	-2.0
-0.1	1.20					
		0.1	-0.2	-0.05	-2.0	-2.0
0.0	1.00					
		0.1	-0.2	0.05	-2.0	-2.0
0.1	0.80					
		0.1	-0.2	0.15	-2.0	-2.0
0.2	0.60					
		0.1	-0.2	0.25	-2.0	-2.0
0.3	0.40					
		0.1	-0.2	0.35	-2.0	-2.0
0.4	0.20					
		0.1	-0.2	0.45	-2.0	-2.0
0.5	0.00					

TABLE 14.2h

DIFFERENTIATION OF $z = 1 - 50\,x^2\,y$ WITH RESPECT TO y AT $x = -0.1$

y	z	Δy	Δz	$\bar{y}$	$\dfrac{\Delta z}{\Delta y}$	$-50x^2$
− 0.3	1.15					
		0.1	− 0.05	− 0.25	− 0.5	− 0.5
− 0.2	1.10					
		0.1	− 0.05	− 0.15	− 0.5	− 0.5
− 0.1	1.05					
		0.1	− 0.05	− 0.05	− 0.5	− 0.5
0.0	1.00					
		0.1	− 0.05	0.05	− 0.5	− 0.5
0.1	0.95					
		0.1	− 0.05	0.15	− 0.5	− 0.5
0.2	0.90					
		0.1	− 0.05	0.25	− 0.5	− 0.5
0.3	0.85					
		0.1	− 0.05	0.35	− 0.5	− 0.5
0.4	0.80					
		0.1	− 0.05	0.45	− 0.5	− 0.5
0.5	0.75					

The partial derivative of z with respect to y can also be obtained directly from the values of z given in table 14.1b by differentiating each column with respect to y. The differentiation of the first column is shown in table 14.2g, and that of the second column in table 14.2h. The derivatives of these columns are the same ones given in table 14.2f.

To obtain the partial derivative

$$\frac{\partial}{\partial y}(1 - 50\,x^2\,y) = -50\,x^2$$

by formula can eliminate many tables. The numerical values of the partial derivative given in table 14.2f can be directly obtained from the above equation.

It is not a coincidence that the function

$$z = 1 - 50\,x^2\,y$$

is used in illustrating the partial derivatives. It is chosen because the difference between Δx and dx does not affect the derivatives of this function.   Thus the numerical demonstrations are simplified. For the constant 1 in the function, the derivatives are both equal to zero or

$$\frac{\Delta}{\Delta x}\,1 = \frac{d}{dx}\,1 = 0\,.$$

For the variable y in the function, the derivatives are both equal to 1 or

$$\frac{\Delta}{\Delta y}\,y = \frac{d}{dy}\,y = 1\,.$$

Even for the term x^2 in the function, the derivatives

$$\frac{\Delta}{\Delta x}\,x^2 = 2\,\bar{x}$$

and

$$\frac{d}{dx}\,x^2 = 2\,x$$

are also equal when evaluated at the mid-point $\bar{x}$ of an interval.

14.3 Partial Derivative of Higher Order

The first partial derivatives

$$\frac{\partial z}{\partial x} = \frac{\partial}{\partial x}f(x,\,y)$$

and

$$\frac{\partial z}{\partial y} = \frac{\partial}{\partial y}f(x,\,y)$$

can be further differentiated to obtain the partial derivatives of z of a higher order. For example, the partial derivative of the partial derivative

$$\frac{\partial z}{\partial x} = \frac{\partial}{\partial x}(1 - 50\,x^2\,y) = -100\,x\,y$$

with respect to x is

$$\frac{\partial}{\partial x}\left(\frac{\partial z}{\partial x}\right) = \frac{\partial^2 z}{\partial x^2} = -100\,y \qquad (1)$$

and that with respect to y is

$$\frac{\partial}{\partial y}\left(\frac{\partial z}{\partial x}\right) = \frac{\partial^2 z}{\partial y\, \partial x} = -100\, x. \tag{2}$$

The meaning of equation (1) can be demonstrated numerically by differentiating each row of table 14.2d where the partial derivative

$$\frac{\varDelta z}{\varDelta x} = \frac{\varDelta}{\varDelta x}(1 - 50\, x^2\, y) = -100\, \bar{x}\, y$$

is given. The derivative of the first row is shown in table 14.3a, and that of the second row in table 14.3b. In these tables the $\bar{x}$ given in the above equation is replaced by x to conform with the format of the table of differentiation. But the values of x given in those tables are those of the mid-points of the original function given in table 14.1b. As a result, the values of the mid-points $\bar{x}$ given in those tables revert to those of the end-points x of the original data.

Each of the nine rows of table 14.2d can be differentiated in the same way. The nine resulting derivatives, which are given in table 14.3c, collectively constitute the second partial derivative of z with respect to x. The result shows that this derivative can be expressed as

$$\frac{\varDelta^2 z}{\varDelta x^2} = -100\, y$$

which agrees with equation (1).

TABLE 14.3a

DIFFERENTIATION OF $\dfrac{\varDelta z}{\varDelta x} = -100\, x\, y$ WITH RESPECT TO x AT $y = -0.3$

x	$\dfrac{\varDelta z}{\varDelta x}$	$\varDelta x$	$\varDelta \dfrac{\varDelta z}{\varDelta x}$	$\bar{x}$	$\dfrac{\varDelta^2 z}{\varDelta x^2}$	$-100\, y$
-0.15	-4.5					
		0.1	3.0	-0.1	30	30
-0.05	-1.5					
		0.1	3.0	0.0	30	30
0.05	1.5					
		0.1	3.0	0.1	30	30
0.15	4.5					

TABLE 14.3b

DIFFERENTIATION OF $\dfrac{\Delta z}{\Delta x} = -100\,x\,y$ WITH RESPECT TO x AT $y = -0.2$

x	$\dfrac{\Delta z}{\Delta x}$	Δx	$\Delta \dfrac{\Delta z}{\Delta x}$	$\bar{x}$	$\dfrac{\Delta^2 z}{\Delta x^2}$	$-100\,y$
-0.15	-3.0					
		0.1	2.0	-0.1	20	20
-0.05	-1.0					
		0.1	2.0	0.0	20	20
0.05	1.0					
		0.1	2.0	0.1	20	20
0.15	3.0					

TABLE 14.3c

VALUES OF $\dfrac{\Delta^2 z}{\Delta x^2} = -100\,y$

x ＼ y	-0.1	0.0	0.1
-0.3	30	30	30
-0.2	20	20	20
-0.1	10	10	10
0.0	0	0	0
0.1	-10	-10	-10
0.2	-20	-20	-20
0.3	-30	-30	-30
0.4	-40	-40	-40
0.5	-50	-50	-50

The meaning of equation (2) can be demonstrated numerically by differentiating each column of table 14.2d. The differentiation of the first column is shown in table 14.3d. Those of the other columns are not shown, but their derivatives are summarized in table 14.3e. The derivatives of all columns collectively constitute the desired partial derivative of the second order. The result shows that this derivative can be expressed as

$$\frac{\Delta}{\Delta y}\left(\frac{\Delta z}{\Delta x}\right) \;=\; \frac{\Delta^2 z}{\Delta y\,\Delta x} \;=\; -100\,x$$

which agrees with equation (2).

TABLE 14.3d

DIFFERENTIATION OF $\dfrac{\Delta z}{\Delta x} = -100\,x\,y$ WITH RESPECT TO y AT $x = -0.15$

y	$\dfrac{\Delta z}{\Delta x}$	Δy	$\Delta\dfrac{\Delta z}{\Delta x}$	$\bar{y}$	$\dfrac{\Delta^2 z}{\Delta y\,\Delta x}$	$-100\,x$
-0.3	-4.5					
		0.1	1.5	-0.25	15	15
-0.2	-3.0					
		0.1	1.5	-0.15	15	15
-0.1	-1.5					
		0.1	1.5	-0.05	15	15
0.0	0.0					
		0.1	1.5	0.05	15	15
0.1	1.5					
		0.1	1.5	0.15	15	15
0.2	3.0					
		0.1	1.5	0.25	15	15
0.3	4.5					
		0.1	1.5	0.35	15	15
0.4	6.0					
		0.1	1.5	0.45	15	15
0.5	7.5					

The partial derivative

$$\frac{\partial z}{\partial y} \;=\; \frac{\partial}{\partial y}(1 - 50\,x^2\,y) \;=\; -50\,x^2$$

can also be further differentiated to obtain

$$\frac{\partial}{\partial x}\left(\frac{\partial z}{\partial y}\right) \;=\; \frac{\partial^2 z}{\partial x\,\partial y} \;=\; -100\,x \qquad (3)$$

and

$$\frac{\partial}{\partial y}\left(\frac{\partial z}{\partial y}\right) = \frac{\partial^2 z}{\partial y^2} = 0.$$ (4)

The meaning of equation (3) can be demonstrated by differentiating each row of table 14.2f where the partial derivative

$$\frac{\Delta z}{\Delta y} = -50\,x^2$$

is shown. However, only the differentiation of one row is necessary because every row has the same numbers;

$$-2.0 \qquad -0.5 \qquad 0.0 \qquad -0.5 \qquad -2.0$$

The differentiation of the first row is given in table 14.3f, and the derivatives of all rows are summarized in table 14.3g. These derivatives collectively constitute the desired partial derivative of the second order. The result shows that this derivative can be expressed as

$$\frac{\Delta}{\Delta x}\left(\frac{\Delta z}{\Delta y}\right) = \frac{\Delta^2 z}{\Delta x\,\Delta y} = -100\,\bar{x}$$

which is equation (3) evaluated at the mid-point $\bar{x}$ of an interval.

TABLE 14.3e

VALUES OF $\dfrac{\Delta^2 z}{\Delta y\,\Delta x} = -100\,x$

x \ y	− 0.15	− 0.05	0.05	0.15
− 0.25	15	5	− 5	− 15
− 0.15	15	5	− 5	− 15
− 0.05	15	5	− 5	− 15
0.05	15	5	− 5	− 15
0.15	15	5	− 5	− 15
0.25	15	5	− 5	− 15
0.35	15	5	− 5	− 15
0.45	15	5	− 5	− 15

TABLE 14.3f

DIFFERENTIATION OF $\dfrac{\Delta z}{\Delta y} = -50\,x^2$ WITH RESPECT TO x AT $y = -0.25$

x	$\dfrac{\Delta z}{\Delta y}$	Δx	$\Delta \dfrac{\Delta z}{\Delta y}$	$\bar{x}$	$\dfrac{\Delta^2 z}{\Delta x\,\Delta y}$	$-100\,\bar{x}$
− 0.2	− 2.0					
		0.1	1.5	− 0.15	15	15
− 0.1	− 0.5					
		0.1	0.5	− 0.05	5	5
0.0	0.0					
		0.1	− 0.5	0.05	− 5	− 5
0.1	− 0.5					
		0.1	− 1.5	0.15	− 15	− 15
0.2	− 2.0					

TABLE 14.3g

VALUES OF $\dfrac{\Delta^2 z}{\Delta x\,\Delta y} = -100\,x$

x \ y	− 0.15	− 0.05	0.05	0.15
− 0.25	15	5	− 5	− 15
− 0.15	15	5	− 5	− 15
− 0.05	15	5	− 5	− 15
0.05	15	5	− 5	− 15
0.15	15	5	− 5	− 15
0.25	15	5	− 5	− 15
0.35	15	5	− 5	− 15
0.45	15	5	− 5	− 15

The meaning of equation (4) can be numerically demonstrated by differentiating each column of table 14.2f. Since all the numbers belonging to the same column are equal, the derivative of each column is a sequence of 0's. The derivatives of all five columns of that table are summarized in table 14.3h which is nothing but a matrix of 0's. These derivatives collectively constitute the desired partial derivative of the second order. The result shows that this derivative can be expressed as

$$\frac{\Delta}{\Delta y}\left(\frac{\Delta z}{\Delta y}\right) = \frac{\Delta^2 z}{\Delta y^2} = 0$$

which agrees with equation (4). It should be noted that the single 0 in equation (4) indicates that the second partial derivative of z with respect to y is equal to 0 at every point (x, y) and not just at a particular point.

TABLE 14.3h

VALUES OF $\dfrac{\Delta^2 z}{\Delta y^2} = 0$

x / y	-0.2	-0.1	0.0	0.1	0.2
-0.2	0	0	0	0	0
-0.1	0	0	0	0	0
0.0	0	0	0	0	0
0.1	0	0	0	0	0
0.2	0	0	0	0	0
0.3	0	0	0	0	0
0.4	0	0	0	0	0

The order of differentiating

$$z = f(x, y)$$

successively with respect to x and y is immaterial, or

$$\frac{\partial^2 z}{\partial y\,\partial x} = \frac{\partial^2 z}{\partial x\,\partial y}. \tag{5}$$

This is demonstrated by the similarity of equations (2) and (3). At the same time, the fact

$$\frac{\Delta^2 z}{\Delta y\,\Delta x} = \frac{\Delta^2 z}{\Delta x\,\Delta y} \tag{6}$$

is demonstrated by the similarity of tables 14.3e and 14.3g. When one traces back to the operations leading to these tables, he can see why these two second-order partial derivatives have to be equal.

Equation (5) reduces the number of partial derivatives of

$$z = f(x, y)$$

of the second order from 4 to 3. This group of derivatives originally includes the following members:

$$\frac{\partial^2 z}{\partial x^2} \qquad \frac{\partial^2 z}{\partial y \, \partial x} \qquad \frac{\partial^2 z}{\partial x \, \partial y} \qquad \frac{\partial^2 z}{\partial y^2}$$

Now the number of members is reduced to 3 on account of the fact that the two in the middle are equal.

14.4   Maximum and Minimum

One of the most important applications of the partial derivatives is the determination of the locations where the function

$$z = f(x, y)$$

may have maxima and minima. To simplify the problem, the variable y is first considered a constant. Thus z becomes a function of x only. Then the method of finding the maxima and minima of z becomes identical to that given in section 6.5. The method requires the solution of the equation

$$\frac{\partial z}{\partial x} = 0$$

whose roots are the critical values of x. The sign of the second partial derivative of z at a critical point determines whether the function z has a maximum or minimum at that point.

The same familiar function

$$z = 1 - 50 \, x^2 y$$

is used here as an illustration. First, the partial derivative

$$\frac{\partial z}{\partial x} = - 100 \, x \, y$$

is set equal to 0. The solution of the equation

$$- 100 \, x \, y = 0$$

is

$$x = 0$$

which is the critical value. Then the sign of the second partial derivative

$$\frac{\partial^2 z}{\partial x^2} = \frac{\partial}{\partial x}(-100\, x\, y) = -100\, y$$

is determined at the critical point. However, the sign of the second partial derivative depends on that of y. When y is negative,

$$\frac{\partial^2 z}{\partial x^2} > 0$$

and z has a minimum at $x = 0$. When y is equal to zero,

$$\frac{\partial^2 z}{\partial x^2} = 0$$

and z has neither a maximum nor a minimum at $x = 0$. When y is positive,

$$\frac{\partial^2 z}{\partial x^2} < 0$$

and z has a maximum at $x = 0$.

The physical meaning of these conclusions can be seen from table 14.1b where the numerical values of z are given. In each of the first three rows where y is negative, z does have a minimum at $x = 0.0$. In the fourth row where y is equal to 0.0, z has neither a minimum nor a maximum because all values of z in that row are equal to 1.00. In each of the remaining five rows where y is positive, z has a maximum at $x = 0.0$. When all the nine rows of z-values are considered at the same time, one reaches the conclusion that, along the vertical line

$$x = 0,$$

a valley and a ridge of z-values exist. When y is negative, a valley exists. When y is positive, a ridge exists. At the point $(0, 0)$ where the valley turns into a ridge, neither exists. This contour of z-values can be observed in table 14.1b as well as in figure 14.1b.

The lack of a maximum and a minimum in every column of the z-values of table 14.1b is reflected in the property of the partial derivative of z with respect to y. The derivative

$$\frac{\partial z}{\partial y} = \frac{\partial}{\partial y}(1 - 50\, x^2\, y) = -50\, x^2$$

cannot be equal to 0 for any value of y. Therefore, no critical value of y is in existence. Consequently, there is no maximum or minimum of z in any column of y with the possible exception of the middle column where x is equal to 0. But, in this column, the function

$$z = 1 - 50\,x^2\,y = 1 - 50(0)^2 y = 1$$

is a constant. Hence no maximum or minimum exists there either. This contour of z-values can also be observed in figure 14.1b.

A maximum or a minimum of a function of two independent variables does not refer to a ridge or a valley. Instead, a maximum is a peak and a minimum is a pit. For the function $f(x, y)$ to have a maximum at (x_0, y_0), $f(x_0, y_0)$ must be greater than its surrounding values of $f(x, y)$ in the neighborhood of (x_0, y_0); that is, the surface has a peak at (x_0, y_0) and its height is $f(x_0, y_0)$. For the function $f(x, y)$ to have a minimum at (x_0, y_0), $f(x_0, y_0)$ must be less than its surrounding values of $f(x, y)$ in the neighborhood of (x_0, y_0); that is, the surface has a pit at (x_0, y_0) and the elevation of the bottom is $f(x_0, y_0)$. At the critical point (x_0, y_0) where $f(x, y)$ may have a maximum or minimum, both partial derivatives must be equal to zero.

To locate the critical points (x_0, y_0) where the function

$$z = f(x, y)$$

may have maxima and minima, both partial derivatives are set equal to zero, or

$$\frac{\partial z}{\partial x} = 0$$

and

$$\frac{\partial z}{\partial y} = 0.$$

The solutions of the above simultaneous equations are the critical points. However, there is no assurance that a maximum or a minimum must exist at any one of the critical points. After the points are determined, each one of them has to be tested by comparing $f(x_0, y_0)$ with its surrounding values of $f(x, y)$.

The familiar function

$$z = 1 - 50\,x^2\,y$$

may be used as an illustration of the location of the maxima and minima of a function of two independent variables. The partial derivatives of z are

$$\frac{\partial z}{\partial x} = -100\, x\, y$$

and

$$\frac{\partial z}{\partial y} = -50\, x^2.$$

Setting both partial derivatives equal to zero, one obtains the simultaneous equations

$$-100\, x\, y = 0$$

$$-50\, x^2 = 0$$

whose solution is

$$(x_0,\ y_0) = (0,\ y).$$

This solution does not represent only one critical point but a whole sequence of them, because y can be any value as long as x is equal to 0. When the z-values are computed in the neighborhood of this sequence of critical points as those shown in table 14.1b, one can see a ridge and a valley. But no peak or pit is in sight. Then the conclusion is that the function

$$z = 1 - 50\, x^2 y$$

does not have a maximum or minimum.

As another illustration of the location of the maxima and minima of $f(x,\ y)$, one may consider the function

$$z = x^2 + y^2 + 4.$$

The partial derivatives of z are

$$\frac{\partial z}{\partial x} = 2\, x$$

and

$$\frac{\partial z}{\partial y} = 2\, y$$

Setting these partial derivatives equal to zero and solving the resulting simultaneous equations, one obtains

$$(x, y) = (0, 0)$$

as the solution. Now it is possible for a maximum or a minimum to exist at the critical point $(0, 0)$. But, at this point, the quantity $x^2 + y^2$ is equal to zero and it is positive everywhere else. Hence the function

$$z = x^2 + y^2 + 4$$

has a minimum at the point $(0, 0)$, and the minimum value of z is 4.

For most practical problems, the location of a maximum or a minimum of a function only involves the solution of the simultaneous equations. The subsequent comparison of $f(x_0, y_0)$ with its surrounding values of $f(x, y)$ is usually not necessary. This is due to the fact that, in a practical problem, one knows in advance what he is seeking. It is simply a matter of determining the location of the critical point. An example of such a problem is given in the following section.

14.5 Least Squares

The method of least squares is a device of fitting a curve to a given set of data (section 4.7). It is an extensive topic in mathematics. But, in this section, it is used as an illustration of the minimum of a function of two independent variables.

One of the simplest problems of least squares can be stated as this: The coordinates $P_1(x_1, y_1)$, $P_2(x_2, y_2)$, $\cdots$, $P_n(x_n, y_n)$ of n points are given. What are the values of a and b of the linear equation

$$y = a + bx$$

so that the sum of squares

$$z = \sum_{i=1}^{n} (y_i - y)^2 = \sum_{i=1}^{n} (y_i - a - bx_i)^2 \tag{1}$$

is a minimum?

The meaning of the problem can be clarified by means of a graph. Three points $P_1(1, 7)$, $P_2(2, 29)$ and $P_3(3, 27)$ are plotted in figure 14.5. The problem is to determine the equation of the straight line so that the sum of squares of the vertical distances of the points from the line is a minimum. From the graph one can see that the sum of squares has no maximum, because the line can be placed far above or far below the three points to increase the sum of squares.

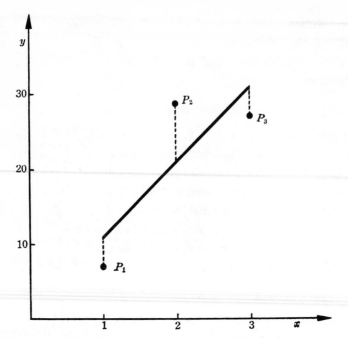

Fig. 14.5. Three points and their least-square line.

Many lines can be fitted to the three given points $P_1(1, 7)$, $P_2(2, 29)$ and $P_3(3, 27)$. For example, the line determined by P_1 and P_2, ignoring P_3, is

$$y = -15 + 22x.$$

For the given values of x

$$1 \quad 2 \quad 3,$$

the values of y computed from this equation are

$$7 \quad 29 \quad 51.$$

Then the sum of squares of the deviations of the given points from this line is

$$z = (7 - 7)^2 + (29 - 29)^2 + (27 - 51)^2 = 576.$$

As a further illustration, another line may be fitted to the data. The equation of the line determined by P_1 and P_3, ignoring P_2, is

$$y = -3 + 10x.$$

For the given values of x

$$1 \qquad 2 \qquad 3,$$

the values of y computed from this equation are

$$7 \qquad 17 \qquad 27.$$

Then the sum of squares is

$$z = (7 - 7)^2 + (29 - 17)^2 + (27 - 27)^2 = 144.$$

The purpose of fitting different lines to the same three points is to illustrate that z changes its value when a and b of the equation

$$y = a + bx$$

change theirs. In short, the purpose of finding these lines is to show that z is a function of a and b.

To express z as a function of a and b, one may start with the equation

$$y = a + bx$$

where both a and b are unknown. For the given values of x

$$1 \qquad 2 \qquad 3,$$

the values of y obtained from this equation are

$$a + b \qquad a + 2b \qquad a + 3b.$$

Then the sum of squares of the deviations of the given points $P_1(1, 7)$, $P_2(2, 29)$ and $P_3(3, 27)$ from this line must be

$$z = (7 - a - b)^2 + (29 - a - 2b)^2 + (27 - a - 3b)^2$$

even though the values of a and b are still unknown.

Now the problem is to determine the values of a and b so that z is a minimum. For this job, one obtains the partial derivatives

$$\frac{\partial z}{\partial a} = 2(7-a-b)(-1) + 2(29-a-2b)(-1) + 2(27-a-3b)(-1)$$

and

$$\frac{\partial z}{\partial b} = 2(7-a-b)(-1) + 2(29-a-2b)(-2) + 2(27-a-3b)(-3).$$

Setting both partial derivatives equal to zero, one obtains the simultaneous equations

$$-2(\ 63\ -\ 3\,a\ -\ \ 6\,b) = 0$$

$$-2(146\ -\ 6\,a\ -\ 14\,b) = 0$$

or

$$3\,a\ +\ 6\,b\ =\ 63 \qquad\qquad (2)$$

$$6\,a\ +\ 14\,b\ =\ 146 \qquad\qquad (3)$$

whose solutions are

$$(a,\ b)\ =\ (1,\ 10)\,.$$

Thus the required equation is

$$y = 1 + 10\,x \qquad\qquad (4)$$

which is plotted in figure 14.5. For the given values of x

$$1 \qquad 2 \qquad 3,$$

the values of y computed from this equation are

$$11 \qquad 21 \qquad 31\,.$$

Then the sum of squares of the deviations of the given points $P_1(1, 7)$, $P_2(2,\ 29)$ and $P_3(3,\ 27)$ from this line is

$$z = (7 - 11)^2 + (29 - 21)^2 + (27 - 31)^2 = 96\,.$$

This value of z is less than 576 and 144 which are computed from the lines

$$y = -15 + 22\,x$$

and

$$y = -3 + 10\,x$$

respectively. In fact, the z-value 96 is less than that computed from any line other than

$$y = 1 + 10\,x\,.$$

This line is the least-square line for the given points.

For the general case, the coordinates of the n points may be designated by

$$(x_1, y_1) \qquad (x_2, y_2) \qquad \cdots \qquad (x_n, y_n)$$

and the equation of the line by

$$y = a + bx.$$

At this stage, the values of x_i and y_i are known but those of a and b are to be determined. However, it is known that, for the given values of x

$$x_1 \qquad\qquad x_2 \qquad\qquad \cdots \qquad\qquad x_n ,$$

the values of y computed from this line must be

$$a + bx_1 \qquad a + bx_2 \qquad \cdots \qquad a + bx_n$$

which are functions of a and b. Then the sum of squares of the deviations of the given values of y_i from their corresponding ones computed from the line is

$$z = (y_1 - a - bx_1)^2 + (y_2 - a - bx_2)^2 + \cdots + (y_n - a - bx_n)^2$$

$$= \sum_{i=1}^{n} (y_i - a - bx_i)^2$$

which is the function of a and b given in equation (1).

Now the problem is to find a and b so that z is a minimum. For this job, one needs the partial derivatives

$$\frac{\partial z}{\partial a} = 2(y_1 - a - bx_1)(-1) + 2(y_2 - a - bx_2)(-1) + \cdots$$

$$+ 2(y_n - a - bx_n)(-1)$$

and

$$\frac{\partial z}{\partial b} = 2(y_1 - a - b_1x_1)(-x_1) + 2(y_2 - a - bx_2)(-x_2) + \cdots$$

$$+ 2(y_n - a - bx_n)(-x_n).$$

Setting both partial derivatives equal to zero, one obtains the simultaneous equations

$$-2[(y_1 + y_2 + \cdots + y_n) - na - b(x_1 + x_2 + \cdots + x_n)] = 0$$

$$-2[x_1y_1 + x_2y_2 + \cdots + x_ny_n - a(x_1 + x_2 + \cdots + x_n) - b(x_1^2 + x_2^2 + \cdots + x_n^2)] = 0$$

or simply

$$a\,n \;\; + b\sum x_i = \sum y_i \qquad\qquad (5)$$

$$a\sum x_i + b\sum x_i^2 = \sum x_i y_i . \qquad\qquad (6)$$

The solutions of these simultaneous equations are the values of a and b which minimize the function z given in equation (1).

The given numerical example may be used as an illustration of the new symbols. For the points

$$(1, 7) \qquad (2, 29) \qquad (3, 27),$$

the quantities in equations (5) and (6) are

$$n = 3$$

$$\sum x_i = 1 + 2 + 3 = 6$$

$$\sum y_i = 7 + 29 + 27 = 63$$

$$\sum x_i^2 = 1^2 + 2^2 + 3^2 = 14$$

$$\sum x_i y_i = 1 \times 7 + 2 \times 29 + 3 \times 27 = 146.$$

Thus the simultaneous equations are

$$3a + 6b = 63$$

$$6a + 14b = 146$$

which are identical to equations (2) and (3) as they should be.

The values of a and b may be expressed in terms of x_i and y_i. When equation (5) is multiplied by $\sum x_i$ and equation (6) by n, the resulting equations are

$$a n \sum x_i + b(\sum x_i)^2 = (\sum x_i)(\sum y_i) \qquad (7)$$

and

$$a n \sum x_i + b n \sum x_i^2 = n \sum x_i y_i. \qquad (8)$$

Subtracting equation (7) from equation (8), one obtains

$$b[n \sum x_i^2 - (\sum x_i)^2] = n \sum x_i y_i - (\sum x_i)(\sum y_i)$$

or

$$b = \frac{n \sum x_i y_i - (\sum x_i)(\sum y_i)}{n \sum x_i^2 - (\sum x_i)^2}. \qquad (9)$$

Now, with b known, one can obtain

$$a = \frac{\sum y_i - b \sum x_i}{n} \qquad (10)$$

from equation (5). For the given example, these quantities are

$$b = \frac{3(146) - (6)(63)}{3(14) - (6)(6)} = \frac{60}{6} = 10$$

and

$$a = \frac{63 - 10(6)}{3} = \frac{3}{3} = 1.$$

Thus the equation of the least-square line is

$$y = 1 + 10\,x$$

which is the same one given in equation (4) as it should be.

14.6 Total Differential

The total differential dz of the function

$$z = f(x,\,y)$$

is the differential of z produced by the change in both independent variables x and y, in contrast to the partial differential ∂z which is produced by the change in one independent variable only. However, before the total differential dz is considered, the total increment Δz should be examined first.

The total increment Δz is the sum of the partial increment Δz due to the change in x alone and the Δz due to the change in y alone. In symbolic form, it is equal to

$$\Delta z = \frac{\Delta z}{\Delta x}\Delta x + \frac{\Delta z}{\Delta y}\Delta y. \tag{1}$$

The total increment of z for the interval $(x,\,y)$ to $(x + \Delta x,\,y + \Delta y)$ is

$$\Delta z = f(x + \Delta x,\,y + \Delta y) - f(x,\,y) \tag{2}$$

which can be expressed as the sum of

$$\Delta z = f(x + \Delta x,\,y) - f(x,\,y) \tag{3}$$

and

$$\Delta z = f(x + \Delta x,\,y + \Delta y) - f(x + \Delta x,\,y). \tag{4}$$

Now one can see that equation (1) is an algebraic identity if the same length is chosen for Δx and Δx and also the same length for Δy and Δy.

The same symbol Δz represents two different quantities in equations (3) and (4). The Δz in equation (3) is the partial increment of z due to the change in x with the variable y being held constant at the lower limit y of the interval, but the Δz in equation (4) is the partial increment of z due to the change in y with the variable x being held constant at the upper limit $x + \Delta x$ of the interval.

The four equations given above can be illustrated by the familiar function

$$z = f(x, y) = 1 - 50\, x^2\, y. \tag{5}$$

Two points

$$z_1 = f(0.0,\ 0.2) = 1.00$$

and

$$z_2 = f(0.1,\ 0.3) = 0.85$$

are chosen from table 14.1b. For this example, the total increment of z is (equation 2)

$$\Delta z = z_2 - z_1 = 0.85 - 1.00 = -0.15\,;$$

the partial increment of z due to the change in x alone is (equation 3)

$$\Delta z = f(0.1,\ 0.2) - f(0.0,\ 0.2) = 0.90 - 1.00 = -0.10\,;$$

and the partial increment of z due to the change in y alone is (equation 4)

$$\Delta z = f(0.1,\ 0.3) - f(0.1,\ 0.2) = 0.85 - 0.90 = -0.05\,.$$

All equation (1) says is

$$0.85 - 1.00 = (0.90 - 1.00) + (0.85 - 0.90)$$

which is obviously true. The meaning of equation (1) should be even clearer if one cares to trace these numbers in table 14.1b.

Equation (1) can also be demonstrated numerically through the partial derivatives

$$\frac{\Delta z}{\Delta x} = \frac{\Delta}{\Delta x}(1 - 50\, x^2\, y) = -100\, \bar{x}\, y \tag{6}$$

and

$$\frac{\Delta z}{\Delta y} = \frac{\Delta}{\Delta y}(1 - 50\, x^2\, y) = -50\, x^2. \tag{7}$$

For the same two points

$$z_1 = f(0.0, 0.2) = 1.00$$

and

$$z_2 = f(0.1, 0.3) = 0.85,$$

equation (1) says

$$0.85 - 1.00 = [-100(0.05)(0.2)](0.1) + [-50(0.1)^2](0.1)$$

or

$$-0.15 = -0.10 - 0.05$$

which is obviously true. It should be noted that the partial derivative of z with respect to x is taken at $y = 0.2$ and that of z with respect to y is taken at $x+\Delta x = 0.1$. In terms of table 14.1b, Δz is obtained by moving right from $(0.0, 0.2)$ to $(0.1, 0.2)$ and then downwards to $(0.1, 0.3)$.

In terms of the numerical values of z given in table 14.1b one can see that, in order to produce a total increment $\Delta z = z_2 - z_1$, the two values z_1 and z_2 cannot be located in the same row or in the same column of that table. If the two values are in the same row, the difference between them is the partial increment of z due to the change in x alone. If they are in the same column, the difference is the partial increment of z due to the change in y alone. In order to produce a sequence of values of Δz, one must choose a path which is neither vertical nor horizontal.

TABLE 14.6a

TOTAL INCREMENT OF $z = 1 - 50\,x^2\,y$ ALONG PATH $y = x$

x	y	z	Δx	Δy	Δz	$\dfrac{\Delta z}{\Delta x}$	$\dfrac{\Delta z}{\Delta y}$	$\dfrac{\Delta z}{\Delta x}\Delta x + \dfrac{\Delta z}{\Delta y}\Delta y$
− 0.2	− 0.2	1.40						
			0.1	0.1	− 0.35	− 3.0	− 0.5	− 0.35
− 0.1	− 0.1	1.05						
			0.1	0.1	− 0.05	− 0.5	− 0.0	− 0.05
0.0	0.0	1.00						
			0.1	0.1	− 0.05	− 0.0	− 0.5	− 0.05
0.1	0.1	0.95						
			0.1	0.1	− 0.35	− 1.5	− 2.0	− 0.35
0.2	0.2	0.60						

Equation (1) is demonstrated for a sequence of intervals in table 14.6a. The function used for the demonstration is

$$z = 1 - 50 x^2 y,$$

and the path along which the values of z are obtained is

$$y = x.$$

The values of x, y and z along this path are reproduced from table 14.1b. For each interval (x, y) to $(x+\Delta x, y+\Delta y)$ along this path, the partial derivative of z with respect to x is equal to

$$\frac{\Delta z}{\Delta x} = - 100 \, \bar{x} \, y = - 100(x + \frac{1}{2}\Delta x)y$$

and that of z with respect to y is equal to

$$\frac{\Delta z}{\Delta y} = - 50 \, x^2$$

which becomes

$$\frac{\Delta z}{\Delta y} = - 50(x + \Delta x)^2$$

when evaluated at the upper limit $x+\Delta x$ of the interval. For the first interval of table 14.6a, the partial derivatives are

$$\frac{\Delta z}{\Delta x} = - 100(- 0.2 + 0.05)(- 0.2) = - 3.0$$

and

$$\frac{\Delta z}{\Delta y} = - 50(- 0.1)^2 = - 0.5.$$

Those for the other intervals are computed in the same way. The result shows that the equation

$$\Delta z = \frac{\Delta z}{\Delta x}\Delta x + \frac{\Delta z}{\Delta y}\Delta y$$

holds for every interval.

As another illustration of equation (1), a sequence of total increments of

$$z = 1 - 50 x^2 y$$

along the path

$$y = 2 x + 0.1$$

is shown in table 14.6b. The x-values are chosen from table 14.1b; the y-values are computed from the given path; and the corresponding z-values are reproduced from table 14.1b. The rest of the computation is done exactly the same way as in table 14.6a where the path is $y = x$. The result in table 14.6b shows that the equation

$$\Delta z = \frac{\Delta z}{\Delta x}\Delta x + \frac{\Delta z}{\Delta y}\Delta y$$

holds for every interval.

TABLE 14.6b

TOTAL INCREMENT OF $z = 1 - 50\,x^2\,y$ ALONG PATH $y = 2x + 0.1$

x	y	z	Δx	Δy	Δz	$\dfrac{\Delta z}{\Delta x}$	$\dfrac{\Delta z}{\Delta y}$	$\dfrac{\Delta z}{\Delta x}\Delta x + \dfrac{\Delta z}{\Delta y}\Delta y$
-0.2	-0.3	1.60						
			0.1	0.2	-0.55	-4.5	-0.5	-0.55
-0.1	-0.1	1.05						
			0.1	0.2	-0.05	-0.5	-0.0	-0.05
0.0	0.1	1.00						
			0.1	0.2	-0.15	-0.5	-0.5	-0.15
0.1	0.3	0.85						
			0.1	0.2	-0.85	-4.5	-2.0	-0.85
0.2	0.5	0.00						

The expression for the total differential dz can be obtained from equation (1) by letting all increments approach zero. When this happens, equation (1) approaches the limiting equation

$$dz = \frac{\partial z}{\partial x}dx + \frac{\partial z}{\partial y}dy \qquad (8)$$

which is the expression for the total differential of z. If the above equation is allowed to mix with equation (1), the result is the approximate equation

$$\Delta z = \frac{\partial z}{\partial x}\Delta x + \frac{\partial z}{\partial y}\Delta y \qquad (9)$$

which is valid for small Δx and Δy. It is this approximate equation which has many direct applications.

As an illustration of the application of the total differential, one may consider the floor space

$$z = x\,y$$

of a room whose width is x and whose length is y. The problem is to determine the difference in area between a 9×15 room and a 11×14 one. This is a simple problem of arithmetic. The difference is, of course,

$$11\times14 - 9\times15 = 154 - 135 = 19.$$

Now one may proceed to solve the same problem the hard way—through calculus. The partial derivatives of z are

$$\frac{\varDelta z}{\varDelta x} = \frac{\partial z}{\partial x} = y$$

and

$$\frac{\varDelta z}{\varDelta y} = \frac{\partial z}{\partial y} = x.$$

The two points are

$$(x,\,y) = (9,\,15)$$

and

$$(x + \varDelta x,\, y + \varDelta y) = (11,\,14).$$

By equation (1), the change in area is equal to

$$\varDelta z = \frac{\varDelta z}{\varDelta x}\varDelta x + \frac{\varDelta z}{\varDelta y}\varDelta y$$

$$= y\,\varDelta x + x\,\varDelta y$$

$$= 15(2) + 11(-1)$$

$$= 19$$

which is the same value obtained by simple arithmetic. Note that the partial derivative

$$\frac{\varDelta z}{\varDelta y} = x$$

is evaluated at $x+\varDelta x = 11$ and not at $x = 9$.

As a demonstration of the application of the approximate formula of Δz given in equation (9), the same problem is solved through that equation. By that equation, the difference in area between the two rooms is

$$\Delta z = \frac{\partial z}{\partial x}\Delta x + \frac{\partial z}{\partial y}\Delta y$$

$$= y\,\Delta x + x\,\Delta y$$

$$= 15(2) + 9(-1)$$

$$= 21$$

which is an approximation of the exact difference 19.

The approximation improves with smaller Δx and Δy. For example, one may wish to determine the error in area if a 9.02×14.99 room is regarded as 9 feet by 15 feet. The error is, of course,

$$9.02 \times 14.99 - 9 \times 15 = 0.2098$$

square feet. By equation (9), the approximate error is

$$\Delta z = y\,\Delta x + x\,\Delta y$$

$$= 15(0.02) + 9(-0.01)$$

$$= 0.21$$

which is the exact error 0.2098 square feet rounded off to two decimal places. The approximation is surely good enough.

As another illustration of the application of the total differential, one may consider the volume

$$z = \pi x^2 y$$

of a cylinder whose radius is x and whose height is y. The volume of a cylinder whose radius is 2 inches and whose height is 10 inches is

$$z_1 = \pi(2)^2 10 = 40\,\pi$$

cubic inches. The problem is to determine the increase in volume if the radius expands by 0.01 inch and the height expands by 0.02 inch. Again, this is a simple problem of arithmetic. The volume of the expanded cylinder is

$$z_2 = \pi(2.01)^2(10.02) = 40.481802\,\pi,$$

and the increase in volume is

$$\Delta z = z_2 - z_1 = 0.481802\,\pi = 1.5136$$

cubic inches.

Now the same problem can be solved by equation (1). The two points are

$$(x,\ y) = (2,\ 10)$$

and

$$(x + \Delta x,\ y + \Delta y) = (2.01,\ 10.02),$$

and the partial derivatives are

$$\frac{\Delta z}{\Delta x} = 2\,\pi\,\bar{x}\,y = 2\,\pi(x + \frac{1}{2}\Delta x)y$$

and

$$\frac{\Delta z}{\Delta y} = \pi\,x^2.$$

Since the latter derivative must be evaluated at the upper limit

$$x + \Delta x = 2.01,$$

it is equal to

$$\frac{\Delta z}{\Delta y} = \pi(x + \Delta x)^2 = \pi(2.01)^2.$$

Then, by equation (1), the increase in volume is

$$\Delta z = \frac{\Delta z}{\Delta x}\Delta x + \frac{\Delta z}{\Delta y}\Delta y$$

$$= [2\,\pi(2.005)(10)](0.01) + [\pi(2.01)^2](0.02)$$

$$= 0.401000\,\pi + 0.080802\,\pi$$

$$= 0.481802\,\pi$$

which is the exact value.

The same problem can be solved by equation (9), but the solution is an approximate one. The partial derivatives of z are

$$\frac{\partial z}{\partial x} = \frac{\partial}{\partial x} \pi x^2 y = 2 \pi x y$$

and

$$\frac{\partial z}{\partial y} = \frac{\partial}{\partial y} \pi x^2 y = \pi x^2 .$$

By equation (9), the approximate increase in volume is

$$\Delta z = 2 \pi x y \, \Delta x + \pi x^2 \, \Delta y$$
$$= [2 \pi (2)(10)](0.01) + [\pi(2)^2](0.02)$$
$$= 0.40 \pi + 0.08 \pi$$
$$= 0.48 \pi .$$

Thus the error in this approximation is

$$0.48 \pi - 0.481802 \pi = - 0.001802 \pi = - 0.0057 .$$

In other words, the approximation is only 0.0057 cubic inches off the exact value 1.5136 cubic inches. If the volume can only be measured to the accuracy of 0.01 cubic inch, the approximation has no error at all because both 1.5136 and

$$1.5136 - 0.0057 = 1.5079$$

can be rounded off to 1.51.

14.7　Total Derivative

The total derivative of z can be readily obtained from the total increment

$$\Delta z = \frac{\Delta z}{\Delta x} \Delta x + \frac{\Delta z}{\Delta y} \Delta y \tag{1}$$

which is given in equation (1) of section 14.6. When the above equation is divided by Δx, the result is

$$\frac{\Delta z}{\Delta x} = \frac{\Delta z}{\Delta x} + \frac{\Delta z}{\Delta y} \cdot \frac{\Delta y}{\Delta x} \tag{2}$$

which is the total derivative of z with respect to x. When the same equation is divided by Δy, the result is

$$\frac{\Delta z}{\Delta y} = \frac{\Delta z}{\Delta x} \cdot \frac{\Delta x}{\Delta y} + \frac{\Delta z}{\Delta y} \tag{3}$$

which is the total derivative of z with respect to y. Like the total differential, the total derivative of

$$z = f(x, y)$$

has to be taken along a path which is neither a vertical nor a horizontal line. For otherwise, the total derivative becomes a partial derivative.

TABLE 14.7a

TOTAL DERIVATIVE OF $z = 1 - 50\,x^2\,y$ WITH RESPECT TO x

ALONG PATH $y = 2\,x + 0.1$

x	y	z	$\dfrac{\Delta z}{\Delta x}$	$\dfrac{\Delta z}{\Delta y}$	$\dfrac{\Delta y}{\Delta x}$	$\dfrac{\Delta z}{\Delta x}$	$\dfrac{\Delta z}{\Delta x} + \dfrac{\Delta z}{\Delta y} \cdot \dfrac{\Delta y}{\Delta x}$	
− 0.2	− 0.3	1.60						
			− 4.5	− 0.5	2	− 5.5	− 5.5	
− 0.1	− 0.1	1.05						
			− 0.5	− 0.0	2	− 0.5	− 0.5	
0.0	0.1	1.00						
			− 0.5	− 0.5	2	− 1.5	− 1.5	
0.1	0.3	0.85						
			− 4.5	− 2.0	2	− 8.5	− 8.5	
0.2	0.5	0.00						

The numerical demonstration of the total derivative of z with respect to x is given in table 14.7a. The function used for this demonstration is

$$z = 1 - 50\,x^2\,y,$$

and the path along which the derivative is taken is

$$y = 2\,x + 0.1.$$

Almost all the values given in that table are reproduced from table 14.6b where the total increment Δz of the same function and along the same path is shown. The result given in the last two columns of table 14.7a demonstrates the validity of equation (2).

The meaning of the total derivative of z with respect to y can be similarly shown. However, the numerical demonstration is omitted from the text and is left to the reader as an exercise.

There is no mystery about the differentiation of z with respect to x along a given path. This practice simply changes z into a function of x only. Along the path

$$y = 2x + 0.1,$$

the function

$$z = 1 - 50x^2 y$$

becomes

$$z = 1 - 50x^2(2x + 0.1) = 1 - 100x^3 - 5x^2$$

which is a function of x only. The derivative of this function, which is called the total derivative of z with respect to x, is (equations 3 and 4, section 5.7)

$$\frac{\Delta z}{\Delta x} = -100\left[3(\bar{x})^2 + \frac{1}{4}(\Delta x)^2\right] - 5(2\bar{x})$$

$$= -300(\bar{x})^2 - 10\bar{x} - 25(\Delta x)^2.$$

For the x-values

$$-0.2 \qquad -0.1 \qquad 0.0 \qquad 0.1 \qquad 0.2$$

given in table 14.7a, the mid-points $\bar{x}$ are:

$$-0.15 \qquad -0.05 \qquad 0.05 \qquad 0.15$$

At $\bar{x} = -0.15$, the derivative is equal to

$$\frac{\Delta z}{\Delta x} = -300(-0.15)^2 - 10(-0.15) - 25(0.1)^2 = -5.50.$$

At $\bar{x} = -0.05$, the derivative is equal to

$$\frac{\Delta z}{\Delta x} = -300(-0.05)^2 - 10(-0.05) - 25(0.1)^2 = -0.50.$$

At $\bar{x} = 0.05$, the derivative is equal to

$$\frac{\Delta z}{\Delta x} = -300(0.05)^2 - 10(0.05) - 25(0.1)^2 = -1.50.$$

At $\bar{x} = 0.15$, the derivative is equal to

$$\frac{\Delta z}{\Delta x} = -300(0.15)^2 - 10(0.15) - 25(0.1)^2 = -8.50.$$

These are the same values of the derivative given in table 14.7a.

Now the difference between a partial derivative and a total derivative is clear. The partial derivative of

$$z = f(x, y)$$

with respect to x is the derivative of z with respect to x, while the variable y is being held constant. The function being differentiated is

$$z = f(x, C)$$

which is a function of x only, and the path of differentiation is the horizontal line

$$y = C.$$

In contrast, the total derivative of z with respect to x is the derivative of z with respect to x along the path

$$y = g(x)$$

and the function being differentiated is

$$z = f[x, g(x)]$$

which is a function of x only.

The limiting form of the total derivative of z with respect to x can be obtained from equation (2). When all the increments approach zero, that equation becomes

$$\frac{dz}{dx} = \frac{\partial z}{\partial x} + \frac{\partial z}{\partial y} \cdot \frac{dy}{dx} \tag{4}$$

which is the total derivative of z with respect to x. Similarly, equation (3) becomes

$$\frac{dz}{dy} = \frac{\partial z}{\partial x} \cdot \frac{dx}{dy} + \frac{\partial z}{\partial y} \tag{5}$$

which is the total derivative of z with respect to y. For the function

$$z = 1 - 50\,x^2\,y$$

along the path

$$y = x^2,$$

the total derivative of z with respect to x is

$$\frac{dz}{dx} = -100\,x\,y + (-50\,x^2)(2\,x)$$

$$= -100\,x(x^2) - 100\,x^3$$

$$= -200\,x^3$$

and that of z with respect to y is

$$\frac{dz}{dy} = (-100\,x\,y)\left(\frac{1}{2\,x}\right) - 50\,x^2$$

$$= -50\,y - 50\,y$$

$$= -100\,y\,.$$

However, when z is expressed as a function of only one variable along the given path $y = x^2$, the function becomes

$$z = 1 - 50\,x^2\,y = 1 - 50\,x^4$$

or

$$z = 1 - 50\,x^2\,y = 1 - 50\,y^2$$

whose derivatives are

$$\frac{dz}{dx} = -50(4\,x^3) = -200\,x^3$$

and

$$\frac{dz}{dy} = -50(2\,y) = -100\,y$$

respectively. These total derivatives of z have the same expressions as those obtained through the partial derivatives of z.

The function $z = f(x, y)$ can be differentiated with respect to a new variable t, if x and y are both functions of t. When equation (1) is divided by Δt, the resulting equation is

$$\frac{\Delta z}{\Delta t} = \frac{\Delta z}{\Delta x} \cdot \frac{\Delta x}{\Delta t} + \frac{\Delta z}{\Delta y} \cdot \frac{\Delta y}{\Delta t}\,. \tag{6}$$

When all increments approach zero, the limiting equation is

$$\frac{dz}{dt} = \frac{\partial z}{\partial x} \cdot \frac{dx}{dt} + \frac{\partial z}{\partial y} \cdot \frac{dy}{dt} \tag{7}$$

which is the total derivative of z with respect to t.

Equation (7) may be applied to the problems of related rates (section 6.7). For example, one may be interested in the instantaneous rate of expansion of the volume of a cylinder whose length is 10 inches and expanding at the rate of 0.2 inch per hour and whose radius is 2 inches and expanding at the rate of 0.1 inch per hour. For this problem, the function to be differentiated is

$$z = \pi x^2 y$$

where z is the volume, x the radius and y the length of the cylinder. At the point

$$(x, y) = (2, 10),$$

the rates of expansion are given as

$$\frac{dx}{dt} = 0.1$$

and

$$\frac{dy}{dt} = 0.2.$$

The problem is to find the instantaneous rate of change of the volume z. To solve this problem, one obtains

$$\frac{dz}{dt} = 2\pi x y \frac{dx}{dt} + \pi x^2 \frac{dy}{dt}$$

from equation (7). When the given values are substituted into the above equation, the rate of change of the volume of the cylinder becomes

$$\frac{dz}{dt} = 2\pi(2)(10)(0.1) + \pi(2)^2(0.2) = 4.8\pi = 15.1$$

cubic inches per hour.

Table 14.7b

Rate of Change of Volume of Cylinder with One-hour Interval

t	x	y	z	$\frac{\Delta x}{\Delta t}$	$\frac{\Delta y}{\Delta t}$	$\frac{\Delta z}{\Delta t}$
0	2.0	10.0	125.66			
				0.1	0.2	15.66
1	2.1	10.2	141.32			

This problem can also be solved numerically. The details of computation are given in table 14.7b. In that table, the values 0 and 1 are assigned to the variable t. Thus the period of time is 1 hour. From the given information

$$(x, y) = (2, 10)$$

$$\frac{\Delta x}{\Delta t} = 0.1$$

and

$$\frac{\Delta y}{\Delta t} = 0.2,$$

one can deduce that the coordinates of the second point are

$$(x + \Delta x, y + \Delta y) = (2.1, 10.2).$$

Then the volumes of the cylinder at the two points can be computed through the formula

$$z = \pi x^2 y.$$

The result shows that the rate of expansion of the volume of the cylinder is 15.7 cubic inches per hour which is higher than 15.1 obtained through the differentiation of z with respect to t. However, if one is not satisfied with this accuracy, a shorter interval of time may be chosen.

TABLE 14.7c

RATE OF CHANGE OF VOLUME OF CYLINDER WITH SIX-MINUTE INTERVAL

t	x	y	z	$\frac{\Delta x}{\Delta t}$	$\frac{\Delta y}{\Delta t}$	$\frac{\Delta z}{\Delta t}$
0.0	2.00	10.00	125.664			
				0.1	0.2	15.13
0.1	2.01	10.02	127.177			

The same problem is solved in table 14.7c with a shorter period of time. This table is identical to table 14.7b except that the time interval is reduced from 1.0 to 0.1 hour or six minutes. For this length of period, 0.0 and 0.1 are assigned to the variable t. To conform with the given information

$$\frac{\Delta x}{\Delta t} = 0.1$$

and

$$\frac{\Delta y}{\Delta t} = 0.2,$$

the coordinates (2.01, 10.02) are assigned to the second point. The resulting rate of expansion of the volume of cylinder is 15.1 cubic inches per hour which is the same rate obtained through differentiation.

The example of expanding cylinder demonstrates once again that the difference between the instantaneous rate of change dz/dt and the average rate of change $\Delta z/\Delta t$ exists only as a mathematical concept (section 6.8). The final, numerical answers are the same if a sufficiently small Δt is used in the computation. For all practical purposes, the differential dt may be regarded as a small increment Δt.

EXERCISES

1. Make a table of values for the function

$$z = f(x, y) = x y^2$$

at $x = 0.1, 0.2, 0.3, 0.4, 0.5$ and $y = 1, 3, 5, 7, 9$. This table is similar in appearance to table 14.1b and will be used in several exercises of this chapter.

2. Find the partial derivative of $z = x y^2$ with respect to y by formula, and then evaluate the derivative at $x = 0.1$ and $x = 0.2$. Thus two equations for $\partial z/\partial y$ are obtained. Now substitute the same values of x into z to obtain two functions of y. Then differentiate these two functions with respect to y. These two derivatives should be equal to the partial derivative $\partial z/\partial y$ evaluated at $x = 0.1$ and $x = 0.2$. The purpose of this exercise is to show that the substitutions may be made either before or after the partial differentiation.

3. Repeat exercise 2 by the numerical process through the table of z-values of exercise 1. Make a table of values of $\Delta z/\Delta y$, and make another table for $\partial z/\partial y$ at the same points. These two tables should be identical.

4. Show that the equation

$$\frac{\partial^2 z}{\partial x\,\partial y} = \frac{\partial^2 z}{\partial y\,\partial x}$$

is true by differentiating the function $z = x\,y^2$ by formula. Repeat the operations numerically through the table of z-values obtained in exercise 1.

5. Find the maxima and minima of the function $z = x\,y^2$.

6. Find the maxima and minima of the function

$$z = x^2 + y^2 - 2x + 4y + 10.$$

7. Fit a straight line to the points (1, 4), (2, 9), (3, 12) and (4, 13) by the method of least squares. What is the equation of the line? What is the minimum sum of squares of the deviations of the points from the line?

8. Fit a straight line to the following data by the method of least squares:

x	1	1	2	2	3	3	4	4	5	5
y	4.0	4.2	6.8	6.4	8.9	9.3	11.8	11.4	14.0	14.2

9. From table 14.6b find the total derivative of the function

$$z = 1 - 50\,x^2\,y$$

with respect to y along the path

$$y = 2x + 0.1,$$

and thus verify equation (3) of section 14.7.

10. Find the total differential of the function

$$z = x\,y^2$$

with respect to x along the path

$$y = 20x - 1$$

through partial differentiation by formula as well as by numerical process. Use the table of z-values of exercise 1.

11. Find the total derivative of the function

$$z = x y^2$$

with respect to y along the path

$$y = 20 x - 1$$

through partial differentiation, and then express the derivative as a function of y. Now express z as a function of y first, and then differentiate this function with respect to y. The results thus obtained should be identical.

12. Find the instantaneous rate of expansion of the volume of a block with a square base when the base is 10 inches wide and changing at the rate of 0.2 inch per hour and the height is 20 inches long and changing at the rate of 0.3 inch per hour. Solve the problem by the formulas of differentiation. Then repeat the solution by a numerical process, but choose Δt sufficiently small so that the solutions obtained by the two methods would agree to three significant figures.

CHAPTER 15

MULTIPLE INTEGRATION

The integration of the function $f(x, y)$ with respect to x and y is discussed in this chapter. Besides integration by formula, the standard method and Simpson's rule are also included. These numerical methods are legitimate methods in their own right, but they are used in this chapter mainly for the purpose of explaining the physical meaning of multiple integration.

15.1 Partial Integral

The *partial integral* of $f(x, y)$ is the integral of that function with respect to one independent variable, while the other one is being held constant. For example, the partial integral of the function

$$z = 1 - 50 x^2 y$$

with respect to x, from $x = -0.25$ to $x = 0.25$, is

$$g(y) = \int_{-0.25}^{0.25} (1 - 50 x^2 y) \, \partial x$$

$$= \left[x - \frac{50}{3} x^3 y \right]_{-0.25}^{0.25}$$

$$= \frac{1}{3}(1.5 - 1.5625 y) \tag{1}$$

which is a function of y. This is the reason why the integral is designated by $g(y)$. The numerical values of this function for various values of y are given in table 15.1a. The other values given in that table will be explained later.

The partial integration is a short cut to replace many integrations. The values of $g(y)$ given in table 15.1a can be obtained by nine integrations. At $y = -0.3$, the function

$$z = 1 - 50 x^2 y$$

becomes

$$z = 1 + 15 x^2$$

TABLE 15.1a

PARTIAL INTEGRAL OF $z = 1 - 50\,x^2\,y$ WITH RESPECT TO x

i	y	$g(y)$	$(T_i.)\Delta x$	$\dfrac{y}{48}$
1	− 0.3	0.656250	0.65	− 0.006250
2	− 0.2	0.604167	0.60	− 0.004167
3	− 0.1	0.552083	0.55	− 0.002083
4	0.0	0.500000	0.50	0.000000
5	0.1	0.447917	0.45	0.002083
6	0.2	0.395833	0.40	0.004167
7	0.3	0.343750	0.35	0.006250
8	0.4	0.291667	0.30	0.008333
9	0.5	0.239583	0.25	0.010417

which is a function of x only. The definite integral of this function for the given limits is equal to

$$\int_{-0.25}^{0.25}(1 + 15\,x^2)\,dx = \left[x + 5\,x^3\right]_{-0.25}^{0.25} = 0.656250\,.$$

At $y = -0.2$, the definite integral is equal to

$$\int_{-0.25}^{0.25}(1 + 10\,x^2)\,dx = \left[x + \frac{10}{3}x^3\right]_{-0.25}^{0.25} = 0.604167\,.$$

These are the values of $g(y)$ given in table 15.1a. After nine integrations of z with respect to x, the complete set of values of $g(y)$ is obtained. Now the same job is done by partial integration where y is being retained as a symbol, and the values of $g(y)$ are obtained after the single integration is completed. By this change of order of operations, a number of integrations can be eliminated. This is the advantage of partial integration.

The meaning of the partial integral of $f(x, y)$ with respect to x can be demonstrated numerically. The function used for the demonstration is

$$z = f(x, y) = 1 - 50\,x^2\,y\,.$$

The numerical values of this function are given in table 14.1b as a 9×5 matrix. For the convenience of reference, a system of notations is devised to identify each number given in that table. A value of x is designated by x_j or the five x-values

$$-0.2 \quad -0.1 \quad 0.0 \quad 0.1 \quad 0.2$$

given in that table are identified by

$$x_1 \qquad x_2 \qquad x_3 \qquad x_4 \qquad x_5$$

respectively. Similarly, a value of y is designated by y_i or the nine y-values

$$-0.3 \quad -0.2 \quad -0.1 \quad 0.0 \quad 0.1 \quad 0.2 \quad 0.3 \quad 0.4 \quad 0.5$$

given in that table are identified by

$$y_1 \quad y_2 \quad y_3 \quad y_4 \quad y_5 \quad y_6 \quad y_7 \quad y_8 \quad y_9$$

respectively. It follows from the definitions of x_i and y_i that the z-value in the ith row and jth column must be equal to

$$z_{ij} = f(x_j, y_i).$$

Thus z_{12} is equal to

$$f(-0.1, -0.3) = 1.15;$$

z_{21} is equal to

$$f(-0.2, -0.2) = 1.40;$$

and z_{75} is equal to

$$f(0.2, 0.3) = 0.40.$$

The marginal totals and the grand total of the z-values given in table 14.1b can also be identified by symbols. The total of the z-values given in the ith row is designated by $T_{i.}$ or the nine row totals

$$6.50 \quad 6.00 \quad 5.50 \quad \cdots \quad 2.50$$

given in that table are identified by

$$T_{1.} \qquad T_{2.} \qquad T_{3.} \qquad \cdots \qquad T_{9.}$$

respectively. The total of the z-values given in the jth column is designated by $T_{.j}$ or the five column totals

$$7.20 \quad 8.55 \quad 9.00 \quad 8.55 \quad 7.20$$

given in that table are identified by

$$T_{.1} \qquad T_{.2} \qquad T_{.3} \qquad T_{.4} \qquad T_{.5}$$

respectively. The grand total, which is the total of all the z-values in that table, is designated by the letter T without subscripts. Thus the value of T is 40.50 as shown in table 14.1b.

The symbols of the totals can be expressed in terms of

$$z_{ij} = f(x_j, y_i)$$

which is the z-value located in the ith row and the jth column. For example, the total of the z-values given in the ith row of table 14.1b can be expressed as

$$T_{i.} = \sum_{j=1}^{5} z_{ij} = z_{i1} + z_{i2} + \cdots + z_{i5} \qquad i = 1, 2, \cdots, 9,$$

and that of the z-values given in the jth column as

$$T_{.j} = \sum_{i=1}^{9} z_{ij} = z_{1j} + z_{2j} + \cdots + z_{9j} \qquad j = 1, 2, \cdots, 5.$$

The grand total can be expressed in three different ways. In terms of the example given in table 14.1b, the grand total is equal to

$$T = \sum_{i=1}^{9} \sum_{j=1}^{5} z_{ij} = \sum_{j=1}^{5} \sum_{i=1}^{9} z_{ij}$$

which is to say that the grand total is the sum of all the z-values in that table. The grand total is also equal to

$$T = \sum_{i=1}^{9} T_{i.}$$

which is to say that the grand total is the sum of the nine row totals. The same quantity T can also be expressed as

$$T = \sum_{j=1}^{5} T_{.j}$$

which is to say that the grand total is the sum of the five column totals.

With the aid of this system of notations, the meaning of the partial integration can be clarified. The partial definite integral of the function

$$z = f(x, y) = 1 - 50 x^2 y$$

with respect to x is the sequence of row totals of z_{ij} multiplied by Δx. The row totals of table 14.1b multiplied by 0.1 are listed in table 15.1a as $(T_{i.})\Delta x$. These values are approximately equal to those of $g(y)$ given in that table. The reason for this is obvious, if one recalls the standard method of integration (section 8.5). When the x-values

$$-0.2 \qquad -0.1 \qquad 0.0 \qquad 0.1 \qquad 0.2$$

are considered the mid-points $\bar{x}$, the integral of the first row is

$$\sum_{-0.25}^{0.25} f(\bar{x}, -0.3)\, \Delta x = (6.50)(0.1) = 0.65$$

and that of the second row is

$$\sum_{-0.25}^{0.25} f(\bar{x}, -0.2)\, \Delta x = (6.00)(0.1) = 0.60$$

and so forth.

The discrepancy between $g(y)$ and $(T_{i.})\Delta x$ given in table 15.1a stems from the difference between dx and Δx. With infinitesimal intervals, the integral is equal to

$$g(y) = \int_{-0.25}^{0.25}(1 - 50\, x^2\, y)\, \partial x$$

$$= \left[x - \frac{50}{3}\, x^3\, y \right]_{-0.25}^{0.25}. \tag{2}$$

With finite intervals, the integral is equal to (equation 7, section 7.7)

$$\sum_{-0.25}^{0.25}[1 - 50(\bar{x})^2 y]\, \Delta x = \left[x - \frac{50}{3}\left\{ x^3 - \frac{x}{4}(\Delta x)^2 \right\} y \right]_{-0.25}^{0.25}. \tag{3}$$

Thus the discrepancy between them as shown in equations (2) and (3) is

$$\left[\frac{-50}{3}\left\{ -\frac{x}{4}(\Delta x)^2 y \right\} \right]_{-0.25}^{0.25} = \frac{y}{48} \tag{4}$$

because Δx is equal to 0.1 as shown in table 14.1b. However, it should be noted that the limit of this discrepancy is zero as Δx approaches zero.

The values of this discrepancy for various values of y are given in table 15.1a. The numbers in that table show that the equation

$$g(y) + \frac{y}{48} = (T_i.)\Delta x \tag{5}$$

holds for every value of y.

There is no mystery about the partial integration. In this operation, the function $f(x, y)$ is broken down into a sequence of functions of x by assigning different values of y to $f(x, y)$ and then each function of x is integrated with respect to x in the usual way. This is what the partial integration amounts to. However, the short cut that one integration replaces a number of integrations does create the impression that a new kind of integration has been introduced.

The partial integral of $f(x, y)$ with respect to y is defined in a similar way. It is the integral of

$$z = f(x, y)$$

with respect to y, while x is being treated as a constant. For the function

$$z = 1 - 50 x^2 y,$$

the definite partial integral of z, from $y = -0.35$ to $y = 0.55$, is equal to

$$h(x) = \int_{-0.35}^{0.55} (1 - 50 x^2 y) \, \partial y$$

$$= \left[y - 25 x^2 y^2 \right]_{-0.35}^{0.55}$$

$$= 0.9 - 4.5 x^2 \tag{6}$$

which is a function of x. The numerical values of this function for various values of x are given in table 15.1b. The other numbers given in that table will be explained later.

TABLE 15.1b

PARTIAL INTEGRAL OF $z = 1 - 50 x^2 y$ WITH RESPECT TO y

j	1	2	3	4	5
x	-0.2	-0.1	0.0	0.1	0.2
$h(x)$	0.720	0.855	0.900	0.855	0.720
$(T_j)\Delta y$	0.720	0.855	0.900	0.855	0.720

Numerically this partial integral $h(x)$ is the sequence of column totals of table 14.1b multiplied by Δy. These values are listed in table 15.1b as $(T._j)\Delta y$. They are identical to the values of the partial integral $h(x)$ given in that table.

In contrast to a definite integral with constant limits being a constant, the partial definite integral with constant limits is either a function of x or that of y. For example, the definite integral

$$\int_0^1 2x\,dx \;=\; \left[x^2\right]_0^1 \;=\; 1$$

is a constant and not a function of x. However, a partial definite integral with constant limits is a different story. The partial definite integral

$$\int_a^b f(x,y)\,\partial x \;=\; g(y)$$

is a function of y, and the partial definite integral

$$\int_c^d f(x,y)\,\partial y \;=\; h(x)$$

is a function of x. This can be seen from table 14.1b. A row total, which is obtained by integrating (x,y) with respect to x, changes with y; and a column total, which is obtained by integrating $f(x,y)$ with respect to y, changes with x. Of course, it is entirely possible that $g(y)$ and $h(x)$ may be constants on occasions. But, in general, $g(y)$ is a function of y, and $h(x)$ is that of x.

15.2 Multiple Integral

The *multiple integral* of the function $f(x,y)$ may be expressed as

$$\int_c^d \int_a^b f(x,y)\,\partial x\,dy \;=\; \int_c^d g(y)\,dy. \tag{1}$$

For example, the partial integral of the function

$$z \;=\; f(x,y) \;=\; 1 \,-\, 50\,x^2\,y$$

with respect to x, from $a = -0.25$ to $b = 0.25$, is equal to (equation 1, section 15.1)

$$g(y) \;=\; \frac{1}{3}(1.5 \,-\, 1.5625\,y) \tag{2}$$

and the multiple integral of z, from $c = -0.35$ to $d = 0.55$, is equal to

$$\int_{-0.35}^{0.55} g(y)\, dy = \frac{1}{3} \left[1.5\, y - \frac{1.5625}{2} y^2 \right]_{-0.35}^{0.55}$$

$$= 0.403125 . \tag{3}$$

In a multiple integral with constant limits, the order of integration is immaterial; that is,

$$\int_c^d \int_a^b f(x, y)\, \partial x\, dy = \int_a^b \int_c^d f(x, y)\, \partial y\, dx \tag{4}$$

or

$$\int_c^d g(y)\, dy = \int_a^b h(x)\, dx . \tag{5}$$

This can be illustrated by the same function

$$z = f(x, y) = 1 - 50\, x^2\, y .$$

The partial integral of z with respect to y is equal to (equation 6, section 15.1)

$$h(x) = 0.9 - 4.5\, x^2 , \tag{6}$$

and the multiple integral of $f(x, y)$ must be equal to

$$\int_a^b h(x)\, dx = \int_{-0.25}^{0.25} (0.9 - 4.5\, x^2)\, dx$$

$$= \left[0.9\, x - 1.5\, x^3 \right]_{-0.25}^{0.25}$$

$$= 0.403125 \tag{7}$$

which is the same value given in equation (3). Thus equations (3) and (7) jointly demonstrate

$$\int_{-0.35}^{0.55} \int_{-0.25}^{0.25} (1 - 50\, x^2\, y)\, \partial x\, dy = \int_{-0.25}^{0.25} \int_{-0.35}^{0.55} (1 - 50\, x^2\, y)\, \partial y\, dx \tag{8}$$

which illustrates equation (4).

The physical meaning of the multiple integral of $f(x, y)$ can be clarified through table 14.1b which shows the numerical values of the function

$$z = f(x, y) = 1 - 50\, x^2\, y .$$

The multiple integral given in equation (8) is approximately equal to

$$T(\Delta x)(\Delta y) \;=\; 40.50(0.1)(0.1) \;=\; 0.4050 \tag{9}$$

where T is the grand total of the z-values. The reason for this is obvious. The partial integral $g(y)$ is approximately equal to

$$(T_{i.})\Delta x \qquad i = 1, 2, \cdots, 9$$

as shown in table 15.1a. Then, according to the standard method of integration, the multiple integral (equation 3)

$$\int_{-0.35}^{0.55} g(y)\,dy \;=\; 0.403125 \tag{10}$$

is approximately equal to

$$\sum_{i=1}^{9}(T_{i.}\Delta x)\,\Delta y \;=\; T(\Delta x)(\Delta y) \;=\; 0.4050 \,. \tag{11}$$

This is the reason why the multiple integral of z is approximately equal to the grand total of z_{ij} multiplied by $(\Delta x)(\Delta y)$.

The discrepancy between equations (10) and (11)

$$0.4050 - 0.403125 \;=\; 0.001875 \tag{12}$$

stems from the difference between Δx and dx. For the given Δx, a row total multiplied by Δx is equal to (equation 5, section 15.1)

$$(T_{i.})\Delta x \;=\; g(y) + \frac{y}{48}$$

and the integral of $y/48$ is

$$\int_{-0.35}^{0.55}\frac{y}{48}\,dy \;=\; \left[\frac{y^2}{96}\right]_{-0.35}^{0.55} \;=\; \frac{0.18}{96} \;=\; 0.001875 \tag{13}$$

which is the discrepancy given in equation (12).

One may look at the same multiple integral at a different angle. The partial integral $h(x)$ is equal to

$$(T_{.j})\Delta y \qquad j = 1, 2, \cdots, 5$$

as shown in table 15.1b. Then the multiple integral (equation 6)

$$\int_{-0.25}^{0.25} h(x)\,dx \;=\; \int_{-0.25}^{0.25}(0.9 - 4.5\,x^2)\,dx \;=\; 0.403125 \tag{14}$$

must be approximately equal to

$$\sum_{j=1}^{5} (T._{j}\Delta y)\,\Delta x \;=\; T(\Delta x)(\Delta y) \;=\; 0.4050 . \tag{15}$$

The discrepancy between equations (14) and (15)

$$0.4050 - 0.403125 \;=\; 0.001875 \tag{16}$$

comes from the difference between Δx and dx. With finite intervals, the integral of x^2 is (equation 6, section 7.6)

$$\sum(\bar{x})^2\Delta x \;=\; \frac{1}{3}x^3 \;-\; \frac{x}{12}(\Delta x)^2 . \tag{17}$$

With infinitesimal intervals, the integral of the same function is equal to

$$\int x^2\,dx \;=\; \frac{1}{3}x^3 . \tag{18}$$

Then, from equations (14), (17) and (18), it can be seen that the discrepancy must be

$$\left[-4.5\left\{ -\frac{x}{12}\,(\Delta x)^2\right\} \right]_{-0.25}^{0.25} \;=\; 0.001875 \tag{19}$$

which is the same value given in equation (16).

It should be emphasized that 0.001875 is the magnitude of the discrepancy when Δx is equal to 0.1. It can be seen from equation (19) that the discrepancy diminishes when Δx becomes smaller. As Δx approaches zero, the discrepancy vanishes completely.

A multiple integral of $f(x, y)$ is a function of its limits. When the limits are constants, the integral is a constant and not a function of x and y. For example, the multiple integral

$$\int_0^1 \int_0^1 4\,x\,y\,\partial x\,dy \;=\; \int_0^1 \Big[2\,x^2\,y\Big]_0^1 dy$$

$$=\; \int_0^1 2\,y\,dy$$

$$=\; \Big[y^2\Big]_0^1$$

$$=\; 1$$

is a constant. In contrast, the integral

$$\int_0^t \int_0^1 4\,x\,y\,\partial x\,dy \;=\; \int_0^t 2\,y\,dy \;=\; t^2$$

is a function of t because the upper limit of y is the variable t. When one wishes to know whether a multiple integral is a function or a constant, he should look at the limits rather than the integrand.

The physical meaning of the partial and multiple integration of the function

$$z = f(x, y)$$

may be summarized as follows:

(1) A matrix of values of z is computed with different values of x as the columns and those of y as the rows. An example of such a matrix is given in table 14.1b.

(2) The partial integration of z with respect to x is to find a row total multiplied by Δx. The partial integral $g(y)$ is a function of y. This is to say that the value of a row total changes with the row.

(3) The partial integration of z with respect to y is to find a column total multiplied by Δy. The partial integral $h(x)$ is a function of x. This is to say that the value of a column total changes with the column.

(4) The multiple integral of z is the grand total multiplied by $(\Delta x)(\Delta y)$.

The z-values, row totals, column totals and grand total are functions of different numbers of independent variables. A z-value is a function of *two* variables x and y. A row total is a function of *one* variable y. A column total is a function of *one* variable x. The grand total being a constant is a function of *zero* variable.

The table of z-values reveals several additional characteristics of multiple integration with constant limits. The fact that the multiple integral is a constant is indicated by the existence of only one grand total. The fact that the multiple integral can be obtained by integrating z with respect to either x or y first is indicated by the fact that the grand total can be obtained through either the row totals or the column totals.

15.3 Geometric Interpretation

In the preceding sections, the partial and multiple integrals of the function

$$z = f(x, y)$$

are explained in terms of a table of values of z. Now, a geometric interpretation of the same integrals is given in this section.

The geometric interpretation of a function

$$z = f(x, y)$$

is given in section 14.1. When the intervals Δx and Δy are finite, the function can be represented by a three-dimensional model which consists of a forest of blocks as shown in figures 14.1a and 14.1b. As both Δx and Δy approach zero, the top of the blocks of a given model becomes a smooth surface.

To make the geometric interpretation specific, the function

$$z = f(x, y) = 1 - 50\,x^2\,y$$

is used as an illustration in this section. The numerical values of this function is given in table 14.1b and the three-dimensional model is shown in figure 14.1b.

When both Δx and Δy are finite, the multiple integral is the total volume of the blocks of the three-dimensional model. The height of a block is equal to z, and the area of the base is equal to $(\Delta x)(\Delta y)$. Thus the volume of a block is equal to $z(\Delta x)(\Delta y)$, and the total volume of all blocks is equal to the grand total of z multiplied by $(\Delta x)(\Delta y)$. Hence the multiple integral of the function

$$z = f(x, y)$$

with constant limits is the total volume of the blocks of the three-dimensional model which represents the function.

It follows from this interpretation that, as Δx and Δy both approach zero, the multiple integral

$$\int_c^d \int_a^b f(x, y)\,\partial x\,dy = \int_a^b \int_c^d f(x, y)\,\partial y\,dx$$

represents the volume under the surface $z = f(x, y)$. When z is positive, this volume is like that of a building. When it is negative, the volume is that of a rectangular excavation in the ground.

The whole model shown in figure 14.1b may be visualized as one building which has a roof, a floor and four walls. The top of the blocks is the roof which is irregular-shaped. The floor is the xy-plane, which is the plane where the axes of both x and y are located. The east and west walls are marked on the floor by the vertical lines

$$x = -0.25$$

and

$$x = 0.25$$

and the north and south walls by the horizontal lines

$$y = -0.35$$

and

$$y = 0.55 .$$

These walls are the limits of the multiple integral. Thus, in terms of this interpretation, the multiple integral with constant limits is the volume of the whole building. As Δx and Δy both approach zero, the interpretation remains the same. The only difference is that the rough edges on the roof have been smoothed out. As a result, the volume of the building will change.

By the same analogy, the partial integral of $f(x, y)$ is the area of a wall or a partition parallel to a wall. As an illustration, the model in figure 14.1b is regarded a building. If a partition is built inside the structure and parallel to the walls located at

$$y = -0.35$$

and

$$y = 0.55 ,$$

the partial integral of $f(x, y)$ with respect to x is the area of that partition. However, the area of the partition depends on where it is built between the two walls. This is due to the fact that the roof is not flat or z is not a constant. In mathematical terms, this is to say that the partial integral of $f(x, y)$ with respect to x is a function of y.

By the same analogy, the partial integration of $f(x, y)$ with respect to y is the area of a partition built parallel to the walls located at

$$x = -0.25$$

and

$$x = 0.25 .$$

Of course, the area of the partition depends on where it is built between these two walls. That is to say that the partial integral of $f(x, y)$ with respect to y is a function of x.

In reality, a partition inside a building may not be parallel to a wall. In fact, the partition may even be curved rather than flat. To find the area of such a partition calls for *line integral* which is not discussed in this text.

No applications of the partial and multiple integrals are given in this text. However, if one can visualize his problem as a table of numbers or as a geometric figure, he should be able to apply these technics to his problem.

15.4 Domain of Integration

The area of the xy-plane bounded by the limits of the multiple integral of the function

$$z = f(x, y)$$

is called the *domain of integration*. For example, the domain of the multiple integral (equation 3, section 15.2)

$$\int_{-0.35}^{0.55} \int_{-0.25}^{0.25} (1 - 50\,x^2\,y)\,\partial x\,dy = 0.403125$$

is the rectangular area bounded by the vertical lines

$$x = -0.25$$

and

$$x = 0.25$$

and the horizontal lines

$$y = -0.35$$

and

$$y = 0.55$$

as shown in figure 15.4a. If one visualizes the three-dimensional model of the given function as a building with an irregular-shaped roof, the domain of this integral is the entire floor of the structure. As long as all the four limits of a multiple integral are constants, the shape of the domain is rectangular.

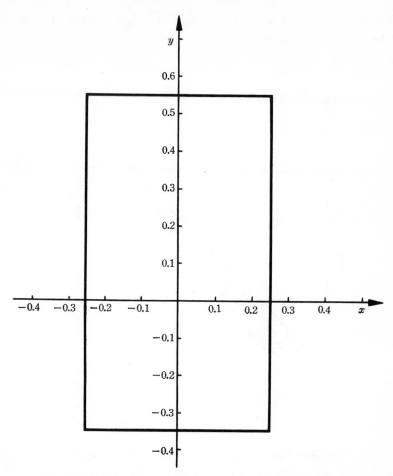

Fɪɢ. 15.4a.   Domain of multiple integral with constant limits.

The domain of integration can be of any shape. It is an area enclosed by one or more curves on the xy-plane. For example, the function

$$z = 2xy$$

may be integrated over the domain bounded by the straight line

$$y = x$$

and the curve

$$y = x^2.$$

This domain is the shaded area shown in figure 15.4b. The points of intersection of the two curves are $(0, 0)$ and $(1, 1)$.

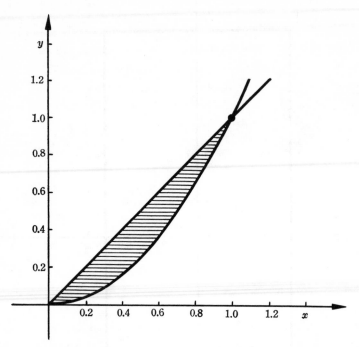

Fɪɢ. 15.4b. Domain bounded by $y = x$ and $y = x^2$.

The multiple integral may be evaluated by integrating z with respect to y first. The upper limit of y is the straight line

$$y = x$$

and the lower limit of y is the curve

$$y = x^2$$

as shown in figure 15.4b. Then the partial integral of $z = 2\,x\,y$ with respect to y is equal to

$$\int_{x^2}^{x} 2\,x\,y\,\partial y \ = \ \Big[x\,y^2 \Big]_{x^2}^{x} \ = \ x^3 - x^5,$$

and the multiple integral of z is equal to

$$\int_0^1 (x^3 - x^5)\,dx \ = \ \left[\frac{x^4}{4} - \frac{x^6}{6} \right]_0^1 \ = \ \frac{1}{12}. \tag{1}$$

The same multiple integral can also be evaluated by integrating z with respect to x first. The upper limit of x is the curve

$$x = \sqrt{y}$$

and the lower limit of x is the straight line

$$x = y$$

as shown in figure 15.4b. Then the partial integral of z with respect to x is equal to

$$\int_y^{\sqrt{y}} 2 x y\, \partial x = \left[x^2 y \right]_y^{\sqrt{y}} = y^2 - y^3 \, ,$$

and the multiple integral of z is equal to

$$\int_0^1 (y^2 - y^3)\, dx = \left[\frac{y^3}{3} - \frac{y^4}{4} \right]_0^1 = \frac{1}{3} - \frac{1}{4} = \frac{1}{12} \tag{2}$$

which is the same value given in equation (1).

This example illustrates two points in multiple integration. One is that the limits of a multiple integral are not necessarily all constants. The other is that the order of integration with respect to x and y cannot be interchanged without modifying the limits, if the limits are not all constants. For example, the multiple integral (equation 1)

$$\int_0^1 \int_{x^2}^x 2 x y\, \partial y\, dx = \frac{1}{12}$$

is not equal to

$$\int_{x^2}^x \int_0^1 2 x y\, \partial x\, dy = \int_{x^2}^x y\, dy = \frac{1}{2}(x^2 - x^4)$$

but equal to (equation 2)

$$\int_0^1 \int_y^{\sqrt{y}} 2 x y\, \partial x\, dy = \frac{1}{12}$$

whose limits are formulated anew from the given domain of integration. Even the limits 0 and 1 for both integrals cannot be taken for granted. The points of intersection of the given curves are

$$(x_1, y_1) = (0, 0)$$

and

$$(x_2, y_2) = (1, 1) .$$

The limits for x are x_1 and x_2, and those for y are y_1 and y_2. These two pairs of limits happen to be equal in this example.

Geometrically, the domain shown in figure 15.4b is the shape of the floor of a structure. The curves which enclose the domain constitute the perimeter of the floor where the walls are erected. The roof of this structure is the surface

$$z = 2 x y .$$

The multiple integral of z is the volume of the structure. However, the partial integral cannot be used in finding the area of a wall. These walls call for line integral which is not discussed in this text.

To find the volume of a structure, the multiple integration is useful only if the structure is of an irregular shape. For a box-like structure, the volume is the product of the length, width and depth of the box. Even in multiple integration the basic element is still $z(\Delta x)(\Delta y)$, and the multiple integral is the sum of a number of such elements.

The basic idea of multiple integration can be illustrated by the volume of a potato. The volume of such an object cannot be found by the multiplication of the length, width and depth of the object, because a potato is not box-shaped. However, a potato can be cut into shoe strings with rectangular cross-sections. Now the volume of each strip can be found by the multiplication of its length and the area of its cross section. When the volumes of all strips cut from the same potato are added together, the total volume is approximately equal to that of the whole potato. This is the basic idea of multiple integration. The length of a strip of potato is z, and the area of its cross section is $(\Delta x)(\Delta y)$. The idea of Δx and Δy approaching zero means that the potato is cut into extra fine strips. The domain of integration is the cross section of the thickest part of the potato.

The domain of integration can also be explained in terms of a table of numerical values of

$$z = f(x, y) .$$

In a numerical integration, the domain is the instructions which specify the values of i and j in the multiple integral

$$\sum \sum z_{ij}(\Delta x)(\Delta y) = \sum \sum f(x_j, y_i)(\Delta x)(\Delta y) .$$

For example, the domain of integration of the function

$$z = 1 - 50\,x^2\,y$$

may be the triangle shown in figure 15.4c.   The equation of the horizontal side of the triangle is

$$y = 0.25 ,$$

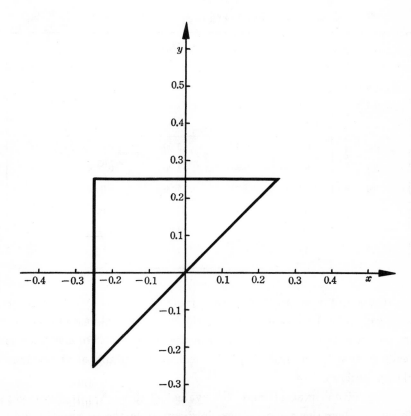

FIG. 15.4c.   Domain of integration of $z = 1 - 50\,x^2\,y$.

and that of the vertical side is

$$x = -0.25 .$$

The equation of the hypotenuse is

$$y = x .$$

When this domain is superimposed on a table of z-values as shown in table 15.4, the z-values to be added are specified. The quantity $\sum\sum z_{ij}$ is the sum of all z-values completely inside the triangle plus one half of the sum of the z-values lying on the hypotenuse. Thus the multiple integral over the given domain is

$$11.85(\Delta x)(\Delta y) = 0.1185 . \qquad (3)$$

TABLE 15.4

DOMAIN OF INTEGRATION OF $z = 1 - 50\, x^2 y$

y \ x	-0.2	-0.1	0.0	0.1	0.2
0.5	0.00	0.75	1.00	0.75	0.00
0.4	0.20	0.80	1.00	0.80	0.20
0.3	0.40	0.85	1.00	0.85	0.40
0.2	0.60	0.90	1.00	0.90	0.60
0.1	0.80	0.95	1.00	0.95	0.80
0.0	1.00	1.00	1.00	1.00	1.00
-0.1	1.20	1.05	1.00	1.05	1.20
-0.2	1.40	1.10	1.00	1.10	1.40
-0.3	1.60	1.15	1.00	1.15	1.60

Table 15.4 is reproduced from table 14.1b. The only difference between these two tables is that the value of y increases upwards in the new table and downwards in the old one. The new table is made so that its orientation is identical to the graph of the domain shown in figure 15.4c.

The given integral may be evaluated through integration by formula. Over the domain given in figure 15.4c, the multiple integral is equal to

$$\int_{-0.25}^{0.25} \int_{-0.25}^{y} (1 - 50\, x^2\, y)\, \partial x\, dy$$

$$= \int_{-0.25}^{0.25} \left[x - \frac{50}{3} x^3 y \right]_{-0.25}^{y} dy$$

$$= \int_{-0.25}^{0.25} \left(0.25 + \frac{2.21875}{3} y - \frac{50}{3} y^4 \right) dy$$

$$= \left[0.25\, y + \frac{2.21875}{6} y^2 - \frac{10}{3} y^5 \right]_{-0.25}^{0.25}$$

$$= \frac{0.35546875}{3}$$

$$= 0.11848958 . \tag{4}$$

This value is remarkably close to 0.1185 which is obtained numerically and given in equation (3).

The same integral can also be obtained by integrating z with respect to y first. Over the domain given in figure 15.4c, the multiple integral is equal to

$$\int_{-0.25}^{0.25} \int_{x}^{0.25} (1 - 50\, x^2\, y)\, \partial y\, dx$$

$$= \int_{-0.25}^{0.25} \left[y - 25\, x^2\, y^2 \right]_{x}^{0.25} dx$$

$$= \int_{-0.25}^{0.25} (0.25 - x - 1.5625\, x^2 + 25\, x^4)\, dx$$

$$= \left[0.25\, x - \frac{x^2}{2} - \frac{1.5625}{3} x^3 + 5\, x^5 \right]_{-0.25}^{0.25}$$

$$= \frac{0.35546875}{3}$$

$$= 0.11848958 \tag{5}$$

which is exactly equal to the value given in equation (4) and approximately equal to that given in equation (3).

15.5   Simpson's Rule for Multiple Integration

Simpson's rule of integration is described in section 8.7. It differs from the standard method of integration in several respects. By Simpson's rule, the definite integral of $f(x)$ from $x = a$ to $x = b$ is equal to

$$\frac{\Delta x}{3} \sum_{j=1}^{p+1} W_j\, f(x_j) \;=\; \frac{\Delta x}{3}\,[f(x_1) + 4f(x_2) + \cdots + f(x_{p+1})] \qquad (1)$$

with the lower limit of the integral being

$$a \;=\; x_1$$

and the upper limit being

$$b \;=\; x_{p+1}$$

where p is an even integer. The x-values $x_1, x_2, \cdots, x_{p+1}$ are the end-points of the p intervals. In contrast, the same integral by the standard method is equal to

$$\Delta x \sum_{j=1}^{p} f(\bar{x}_j) \;=\; \Delta x\,[f(\bar{x}_1) + f(\bar{x}_2) + \cdots + f(\bar{x}_p)] \qquad (2)$$

where $\bar{x}_1, \bar{x}_2, \cdots, \bar{x}_p$ are the mid-points of the p intervals. The lower limit of this integral is not $\bar{x}_1$ but

$$a \;=\; \bar{x}_1 - \frac{1}{2}\Delta x \;=\; x_1$$

and the upper limit is not $\bar{x}_p$ but

$$b \;=\; \bar{x}_p + \frac{1}{2}\Delta x \;=\; x_{p+1}.$$

The differences between these two methods are summarized in their algebraic expressions for the definite integral given in equations (1) and (2). But, for emphasis, the differences are enumerated one by one. First, Simpson's rule requires $p+1$ points for the p intervals because x_j is an end-point of an interval; while the standard method requires p points because $\bar{x}_j$ is the mid-point of an interval. Second, the limits of the integral in Simpson's rule are the smallest and the largest given values of x; while in the standard method, the limits extend beyond the range of the given value of x because a value of x in this method is considered the mid-point $\bar{x}$ of an interval. Third, the sum of $f(x_j)$ in Simpson's rule is a weighted one with W_j

$$1 \quad 4 \quad 2 \quad 4 \quad 2 \quad 4 \quad \cdots \quad 4 \quad 1$$

as the weights; while in the standard method, the sum of $f(\bar{x}_j)$ is the unweighted one or the straight total. Fourth, the multiplier of the weighted sum of $f(x_j)$ in Simpson's rule is $\Delta x/3$; while in the standard method, the corresponding multiplier is the lone Δx. With these differences in mind and the experience of using the standard method in multiple integration in section 15.1, one can develope the procedure for Simpson's rule for the same operation.

The multiple integral of $f(x, y)$ with constant limits can be evaluated by Simpson's rule only when the values of x and y are both equally spaced and the numbers of intervals for both variables are even. The first step of the method is to compute a matrix of values of

$$z_{ij} = f(x_j, y_i)$$

from the given integrand

$$z = f(x, y).$$

The second step is to find the weighted sum

$$S_{i.} = \sum_j W_j z_{ij} \tag{3}$$

for each row of the z-values with the weights W_j being

$$1 \quad 4 \quad 2 \quad 4 \quad \cdots \quad 4 \quad 1.$$

The third step is to find the quantity

$$S = \sum_i W_i S_{i.} = \sum_i \sum_j W_i W_j z_{ij} \tag{4}$$

which is the weighted sum of the weighted sums of the rows of the z-values with the weights W_i being

$$1 \quad 4 \quad 2 \quad 4 \quad \cdots \quad 4 \quad 1.$$

The fourth and the last step is to multiply S by $(\Delta x)(\Delta y)$ and divide the product by 9. The resulting quantity

$$\frac{1}{9}(S)(\Delta x)(\Delta y) = \frac{(\Delta x)(\Delta y)}{9} \sum_i \sum_j W_i W_j z_{ij} \tag{5}$$

is the value of the multiple integral.

The notations used in this section are similar to those introduced in section 15.1 where the standard method of integration is discussed. The unweighted total $T_{i.}$ of the ith row is now replaced by the weighted sum $S_{i.}$ of that row. The unweighted total $T_{.j}$ of the jth column is replaced by the weighted sum $S_{.j}$ of that column. The grand total T, which is the total of the marginal totals, is replaced by S, which is the weighted sum of the weighted sums. The complications introduced here are the weights, which are the same ones used in integrating a function of one independent variable.

As an illustration of the method, the integral (equation 3, section 15.2)

$$\int_{-0.35}^{0.55} \int_{-0.25}^{0.25} (1 - 50\, x^2\, y)\, \partial x\, dy = 0.403125 \tag{6}$$

is evaluated by Simpson's rule. First, the values of

$$z = 1 - 50\, x^2\, y$$

are computed and shown in table 15.5a. The values of x used in that table are

$$- 0.25 \qquad 0.00 \qquad 0.25\,,$$

and those of y are

$$- 0.35 \quad - 0.20 \quad - 0.05 \quad 0.10 \quad 0.25 \quad 0.40 \quad 0.55\,.$$

Thus both x and y are equally spaced. The value of Δx is 0.25, and that of Δy is 0.15. Furthermore, the numbers of intervals of both variables are even. The weight W_j for a row of z-values are

$$1 \qquad 4 \qquad 1$$

because x has two intervals. The weights W_i for a column of z-values are

$$1 \quad 4 \quad 2 \quad 4 \quad 2 \quad 4 \quad 1$$

because y has six intervals.

The contrast between table 14.1b and table 15.5a reveals some of the differences between the standard method of integration and Simpson's rule. Both tables contain the values of the function

$$z = f(x, y) = 1 - 50\, x^2\, y\,,$$

and both tables are used in evaluating the multiple integral of z with limits being equal to

$$- 0.25 \leqq x \leqq 0.25$$

and

$$- 0.35 \leqq y \leqq 0.55\,.$$

TABLE 15.5a

MULTIPLE INTEGRATION OF $z = 1 - 50\,x^2\,y$ BY SIMPSON'S RULE

y \ x	-0.25	0.0	0.25	$S_i.$	W_i
-0.35	2.09375	1.00000	2.09375	8.18750	1
-0.20	1.62500	1.00000	1.62500	7.25000	4
-0.05	1.15625	1.00000	1.15625	6.31250	2
0.10	0.68750	1.00000	0.68750	5.37500	4
0.25	0.21875	1.00000	0.21875	4.43750	2
0.40	-0.25000	1.00000	-0.25000	3.50000	4
0.55	-0.71875	1.00000	-0.71875	2.56250	1
W_j	1	4	1		

$$\frac{1}{9}(S)(\Delta x)(\Delta y) = \frac{1}{9}(96.75)(0.25)(0.15) = 0.403125$$

Yet the values of x and y used in the two tables are different. This is due to the fact that the values of x and y are the mid-points of the intervals in table 14.1b which is used in connection with the standard method of integration and those in table 15.5a which is used in connection with Simpson's rule are the end-points of the intervals. Furthermore, table 14.1b has five intervals for x and seven intervals for y, and table 15.5a has two intervals for x and six intervals for y. This is done because Simpson's rule requires even numbers of intervals for both x and y, and the standard method is not subject to such restrictions.

The second step of Simpson's rule is to find the weighted sum of each row of z-values given in table 15.5a. For example, the weighted sum of the first row is

$$S_1. = 1(2.09375) + 4(1.00000) + 1(2.09375) = 8.18750,$$

and that of the second row is

$$S_2. = 1(1.62500) + 4(1.00000) + 1(1.62500) = 7.25000.$$

The weighted sum of each row is obtained in the same way, and the weighted sums for the seven rows are listed as $S_i.$ in a column of table 15.5a.

The third step is to find the weighted sum of the weighted sums just obtained, using W_i as the weights. This is the sum of the products of the corresponding numbers listed in the last two columns of table 15.5a. The resulting quantity is

$$S = 1(8.18750) + 4(7.25000) + \cdots + 1(2.56250) = 96.75000. \qquad (7)$$

The fourth and the last step is to find the multiple integral itself. When the weighted sum of the weighted sums is multiplied by $(\Delta x)(\Delta y)$ and divided by 9, the resulting quantity

$$\frac{1}{9}(S)(\Delta x)(\Delta y) = \frac{1}{9}(96.75)(0.25)(0.15) = 0.403125 \qquad (8)$$

is the value of the multiple integral. This is the same value given in equation (6).

The computation of the weighted sum of a row of z-values given in table 15.5a is an intermediate step in integrating z with respect to x. By Simpson's rule, the integral of the ith row is equal to

$$\frac{\Delta x}{3}(z_{i1} + 4z_{i2} + z_{i3}) = \frac{\Delta x}{3} S_i. \qquad i = 1, 2, \cdots, 7. \qquad (9)$$

The corresponding partial integral obtained by formulas of integration is

$$g(y) = \int_{-0.25}^{0.25}(1 - 50\,x^2\,y)\,\partial x = \frac{1}{3}(1.5 - 1.5625\,y). \qquad (10)$$

These two functions of y should be equal.

To demonstrate the equation

$$g(y) = \frac{\Delta x}{3} S_i. \qquad i = 1, 2, \cdots, 7, \qquad (11)$$

the values of y and the weighted sums of the seven rows given in table 15.5a are reproduced in table 15.5b. From the given values of y, those of $g(y)$ are found from equation (10) and are listed in table 15.5b. From the weighted sums, the integral by Simpson's rule are found from equation (9) and are listed in the same table. The numbers in that table show that equation (11) holds for every value of y.

Table 15.5b

Partial Integral of $z = 1 - 50 x^2 y$ with Respect to x

i	y	$S_{i.}$	$\dfrac{\Delta x}{3} S_{i.}$	$g(y)$
1	-0.35	8.1875	2.046875/3	2.046875/3
2	-0.20	7.2500	1.812500/3	1.812500/3
3	-0.05	6.3125	1.578125/3	1.578125/3
4	0.10	5.3750	1.343750/3	1.343750/3
5	0.25	4.4375	1.109375/3	1.109375/3
6	0.40	3.5000	0.875000/3	0.875000/3
7	0.55	2.5625	0.640625/3	0.640625/3

The computation of the weighted sum of the weighted sums is an intermediate step in integrating $g(y)$ with respect to y. By Simpson's rule, the integral of $g(y)$ with respect to y is equal to

$$\frac{\Delta y}{3} [g(y_1) + 4g(y_2) + \cdots + g(y_7)] = \frac{\Delta y}{3} \sum_{i=1}^{7} W_i\, g(y_i) \cdot \qquad (12)$$

But, on account of equation (11), one may work with the weighted sums and temporarily leave out the factor $\Delta x/3$ which is common to all values of $g(y)$. In so doing, the integral of $g(y)$ with respect to y becomes

$$\frac{\Delta y}{3} \sum_{i=1}^{7} W_i \left(\frac{\Delta x}{3} S_{i.} \right) = \frac{1}{9} S(\Delta x)(\Delta y) \qquad (13)$$

which is the multiple integral of z by Simpson's rule. This is why Simpson's rule for multiple integration works the way it does.

The key to Simpson's rule for multiple integration is the weighted sum of the weighted sums. But there are several ways of finding this quantity besides the one described above. The most obvious one is to find the weighted sums of the columns by means of W_i and then the weighted sum of the weighted sums by means of W_j. This modification of Simpson's rule is equivalent to the interchange of the order of integrations of z with respect to x and y.

The modified Simpson's rule may be illustrated by the data given in table 15.5a. The z-values are listed in three columns, and their weights W_i are given in the last column of that table. The weighted sums $S._j$ are equal to

$$12.37500 \qquad 18.00000 \qquad 12.37500$$

for the three columns. Then, by means of the weights W_j

$$1 \qquad\qquad 4 \qquad\qquad 1,$$

the weighted sum of the weighted sums

$$S = \sum_{j=1}^{3} W_j S._j \qquad\qquad (14)$$

can be computed. Its numerical value is

$$S = 1(12.37500) + 4(18.00000) + 1(12.37500) = 96.75000 \qquad (15)$$

which is the same value given in equation (7). This modified method may be used as a checking device on computation.

The computation of the weighted sums for the three columns of table 15.5a is an intermediate step of partial integration of z with respect to y. When these weighted sums are multiplied by

$$\frac{\Delta y}{3} = \frac{0.15}{3} = 0.05,$$

the resulting quantities

$$0.61875 \qquad 0.90000 \qquad 0.61875$$

are the values of the partial integral (equation 6, section 15.1)

$$h(x) = \int_{-0.35}^{0.55} (1 - 50 x^2 y) \, \partial y = 0.9 - 4.5 x^2$$

evaluated at the given x-values

$$-0.25 \qquad 0.00 \qquad 0.25 \,.$$

For example, at $x = -0.25$, the value of $h(x)$ is

$$h(-0.25) = 0.9 - 4.5(-0.25)^2 = 0.9 - 0.28125 = 0.61875$$

which is the same value obtained by the multiplication of the weighted sum 12.375 of the first column and

$$\frac{\Delta y}{3} = \frac{0.15}{3} = 0.05 \,.$$

It is no coincidence that the value of the multiple integral

$$\int_{-0.35}^{0.55} \int_{-0.25}^{0.25} (1 - 50\, x^2 y)\partial x\, dy = 0.403125$$

obtained by formulas of integration and that obtained by Simpson's rule are identical. The integrand

$$z = 1 - 50\, x^2 y$$

is a second-degree polynomial in x and a first-degree polynomial in y, and Simpson's rule always yields an exact integral even if the degree of the polynomial is as high as three. Hence, for the given integrand, the two methods should yield identical results. As a consequence, the number of intervals of y given in table 15.5a need not be six. Two intervals with the y-values being

$$-0.35 \qquad 0.10 \qquad 0.55$$

should be sufficient. It is only for the purpose of demonstrating the general computing procedure of Simpson's rule that six intervals are given to the independent variable y.

15.6 Matrix and Simpson's Rule

Matrices can be brought into Simpson's rule. In fact, they are vividly shown in table 15.5a which is the example used in illustrating Simpson's rule for multiple integration. For example, the z-values in that table constitute a 7×3 matrix which may be designated by $[z_{ij}]$. The weights W_i listed in the last column of that table constitute a 7×1 matrix which may be designated by $[W_i]$. The weights W_j given at the bottom of the table constitute a 1×3 matrix which may be designated by $[W_j]$. The weighted sums $S_i.$ for the seven rows constitute a 7×1 matrix which may be designated by $[S_i.]$. The discussion in this section centers around these matrices.

The weighted sum of the weighted sums can be expressed as the product of three matrices (section 3.3). The transpose of the 7×1 matrix $[W_i]$ given in the last column of table 15.5a is the 1×7 matrix

$$[W_i'] = [1 \quad 4 \quad 2 \quad 4 \quad 2 \quad 4 \quad 1]. \tag{1}$$

The z-values given in that table constitute the 7×3 matrix $[z_{ij}]$.

The transpose of the 1×3 matrix $[W_j]$ given at the bottom of that table is the 3×1 matrix

$$[W'_j] = \begin{bmatrix} 1 \\ 4 \\ 1 \end{bmatrix}. \qquad (2)$$

When these three matrices are multiplied together, the product is the 1×1 matrix

$$S = [W'_i][z_{ij}][W'_j] \qquad (3)$$

which is the weighted sum of the weighted sums. Thus the multiple integral by Simpson's rule may be expressed as

$$\frac{1}{9} S(\Delta x)(\Delta y) = \frac{(\Delta x)(\Delta y)}{9} [W'_i][z_{ij}][W'_j]. \qquad (4)$$

The multiplication of the three matrices given in equation (3) may be carried out in two different ways. The product of three matrices may be regarded either as (equation 13, section 3.4)

$$ABC = (AB)C \qquad (5)$$

or as

$$ABC = A(BC). \qquad (6)$$

By the former way of multiplication, the product of the left and the middle matrices of equation (3) is the 1×3 matrix

$$[S_{.j}] = [W'_i][z_{ij}] \qquad j = 1, 2, 3 \qquad (7)$$

whose elements are the weighted sums for the three columns. This is to say that the function $f(x, y)$ is integrated with respect to y first. On the other hand, if the latter method of multiplication is used, the product of the middle and the right matrices is the 7×1 matrix $[S_{i.}]$ given in table 15.5a whose elements are the weighted sums for the seven rows. This is to say that the function $f(x, y)$ is integrated with respect to x first.

The interchange of the order of integrations of $f(x, y)$ with respect to x and y may also be interpreted as the transpose of the product of three matrices. This can be shown by transposing both sides of equation (3). The transpose of S is S itself, because S is a

1×1 matrix. The transpose of the product of three matrices on the right side of the equation must be equal to (equation 23, section 3.4)

$$S = [W_j][z'_{ij}][W_i] \qquad (8)$$

where $[W_j]$ is a 1×3 matrix, $[z'_{ij}]$ a 3×7 matrix, and $[W_i]$ a 7×1 matrix. If the multiplication of three matrices is consistently done according to the order

$$ABC = (AB)C,$$

equation (3) means that the function $f(x, y)$ is integrated with respect to y first, and equation (8) means that the function is integrated with respect to x first.

It is absolutely unnecessary to bring matrices into Simpson's rule. But it is deliberately done at the very end of this book to demonstrate several relevant points in mathematics. First, mathematics is not a collection of independent branches of learning such as algebra, geometry and analysis. It is because of convenience of teaching that the subject matter is divided into seemingly disconnected courses. In reality, all branches of mathematics are related to one another in some ways. The linkage of matrix and multiple integration is used here as an example. Second, a change in notation does not necessarily mean a corresponding change in computing method. Whether the weighted sum of the weighted sums is expressed in matrix notation or not, it is still computed in the same way. The third and perhaps the most important point is that a simplified notation does not imply a short cut in computation. The weighted sum of the weighted sums takes the same amount of time to compute whether the quantity is denoted by the lone letter S or by the product of three matrices.

EXERCISES

1. Evaluate, by formula, the multiple integral

$$\int_{1.0}^{2.0} \int_{0.0}^{0.5} 240\, x\, y^2\, dx\, dy .$$

2. Evaluate the integral given in exercise 1 by the standard method with Δx being equal to 0.1 and Δy equal to 0.2. Account for the discrepancy between the values obtained in exercises 1 and 2.

3. Evaluate the multiple integral given in exercise 1 by Simpson's rule with both Δx and Δy being equal to 0.25. Note that the value thus obtained is exactly equal to that obtained through the formulas of integration.

4. Repeat exercise 3, but use only two intervals for both x and y. Note that the value of the integral remains the same, despite the change in Δy.

5. Find the multiple integral of the function

$$z = f(x, y) = 240\, x\, y^2$$

by formulas of integration over the triangular domain bounded by the straight lines

$$y = 1.0$$

$$x = 0.5$$

and

$$y = 2x + 1.$$

Integrate z with respect to x first and then with respect to y first to show that the results thus obtained are the same. Then check the value of the integral just obtained by adding the appropriate values of z obtained in exercise 2, but do not expect an exact agreement.

6. Integrate the function

$$z = f(x, y) = 240\, x\, y^2$$

by formula over the domain bounded by the curves

$$y = x^2$$

and

$$y = x^4.$$

Integrate z with respect to x first, and then with respect to y first. The results thus obtained should be the same.

7. Find the multiple integral for the function

$$z = f(x, y) = 100\, e^{x+y}$$

by the formulas of integration over the rectangular domain

$$0.0 \leq x \leq 0.4$$

and

$$1.0 \leq y \leq 1.6.$$

8. Repeat exercise 7 by the standard method of integration. Use 0.1 for both Δx and Δy. Do not expect the integral obtained in this exercise to be exactly equal to that obtained in exercise 7.

9. Repeat exercise 7 by Simpson's rule. Use 0.1 for both Δx and Δy. Do not expect the integral obtained in this exercise to be exactly equal to that obtained in exercise 7, but Simpson's rule should give a closer approximation than the standard method.

10. Integrate the function

$$z = f(x, y) = 100\, e^{x+y}$$

by formula over the triangular domain bounded by the straight lines

$$y = x$$
$$y = 2x$$

and

$$x = 1.$$

APPENDIX

TABLE 1

COMMON LOGARITHMS

The detailed explanation

of

this table

is given in

section 9.3.

1.000 to 1.499

N	0	1	2	3	4	5	6	7	8	9
100	00 000	00 043	00 087	00 130	00 173	00 217	00 260	00 303	00 346	00 389
101	432	475	518	561	604	647	689	732	775	817
102	860	903	945	988	01 030	01 072	01 115	01 157	01 199	01 242
103	01 284	01 326	01 368	01 410	452	494	536	578	620	662
104	703	745	787	828	870	912	953	995	02 036	02 078
105	02 119	02 160	02 202	02 243	02 284	02 325	02 366	02 407	02 449	02 490
106	531	572	612	653	694	735	776	816	857	898
107	938	979	03 019	03 060	03 100	03 141	03 181	03 222	03 262	03 302
108	03 342	03 383	423	463	503	543	583	623	663	703
109	743	782	822	862	902	941	981	04 021	04 060	04 100
110	04 139	04 179	04 218	04 258	04 297	04 336	04 376	04 415	04 454	04 493
111	532	571	610	650	689	727	766	805	844	883
112	922	961	999	05 038	05 077	05 115	05 154	05 192	05 231	05 269
113	05 308	05 346	05 385	423	461	500	538	576	614	652
114	690	729	767	805	843	881	918	956	994	06 032
115	06 070	06 108	06 145	06 183	06 221	06 258	06 296	06 333	06 371	06 408
116	446	483	521	558	595	633	670	707	744	781
117	819	856	893	930	967	07 004	07 041	07 078	07 115	07 151
118	07 188	07 225	07 262	07 298	07 335	372	408	445	482	518
119	555	591	628	664	700	737	773	809	846	882
120	07 918	07 954	07 990	08 027	08 063	08 099	08 135	08 171	08 207	08 243
121	08 279	08 314	08 350	386	422	458	493	529	565	600
122	636	672	707	743	778	814	849	884	920	955
123	991	09 026	09 061	09 096	09 132	09 167	09 202	09 237	09 272	09 307
124	09 342	377	412	447	482	517	552	587	621	656
125	09 691	09 726	09 760	09 795	09 830	09 864	09 899	09 934	09 968	10 003
126	10 037	10 072	10 106	10 140	10 175	10 209	10 243	10 278	10 312	346
127	380	415	449	483	517	551	585	619	653	687
128	721	755	789	823	857	890	924	958	992	11 025
129	11 059	11 093	11 126	11 160	11 193	11 227	11 261	11 294	11 327	361
130	11 394	11 428	11 461	11 494	11 528	11 561	11 594	11 628	11 661	11 694
131	727	760	793	826	860	893	926	959	992	12 024
132	12 057	12 090	12 123	12 156	12 189	12 222	12 254	12 287	12 320	352
133	385	418	450	483	516	548	581	613	646	678
134	710	743	775	808	840	872	905	937	969	13 001
135	13 033	13 066	13 098	13 130	13 162	13 194	13 226	13 258	13 290	13 322
136	354	386	418	450	481	513	545	577	609	640
137	672	704	735	767	799	830	862	893	925	956
138	988	14 019	14 051	14 082	14 114	14 145	14 176	14 208	14 239	14 270
139	14 301	333	364	395	426	457	489	520	551	582
140	14 613	14 644	14 675	14 706	14 737	14 768	14 799	14 829	14 860	14 891
141	922	953	983	15 014	15 045	15 076	15 106	15 137	15 168	15 198
142	15 229	15 259	15 290	320	351	381	412	442	473	503
143	534	564	594	625	655	685	715	746	776	806
144	836	866	897	927	957	987	16 017	16 047	16 077	16 107
145	16 137	16 167	16 197	16 227	16 256	16 286	16 316	16 346	16 376	16 406
146	435	465	495	524	554	584	613	643	673	702
147	732	761	791	820	850	879	909	938	967	997
148	17 026	17 056	17 085	17 114	17 143	17 173	17 202	17 231	17 260	17 289
149	319	348	377	406	435	464	493	522	551	580

Table 1   COMMON LOGARITHMS   555

1.500 to 1.999

N	0	1	2	3	4	5	6	7	8	9
150	17 609	17 638	17 667	17 696	17 725	17 754	17 782	17 811	17 840	17 869
151	898	926	955	984	18 013	18 041	18 070	18 099	18 127	18 156
152	18 184	18 213	18 241	18 270	298	327	355	384	412	441
153	469	498	526	554	583	611	639	667	696	724
154	752	780	808	837	865	893	921	949	977	19 005
155	19 033	19 061	19 089	19 117	19 145	19 173	19 201	19 229	19 257	19 285
156	312	340	368	396	424	451	479	507	535	562
157	590	618	645	673	700	728	756	783	811	838
158	866	893	921	948	976	20 003	20 030	20 058	20 085	20 112
159	20 140	20 167	20 194	20 222	20 249	276	303	330	358	385
160	20 412	20 439	20 466	20 493	20 520	20 548	20 575	20 602	20 629	20 656
161	683	710	737	763	790	817	844	871	898	925
162	952	978	21 005	21 032	21 059	21 085	21 112	21 139	21 165	21 192
163	21 219	21 245	272	299	325	352	378	405	431	458
164	484	511	537	564	590	617	643	669	696	722
165	21 748	21 775	21 801	21 827	21 854	21 880	21 906	21 932	21 958	21 985
166	22 011	22 037	22 063	22 089	22 115	22 141	22 167	22 194	22 220	22 246
167	272	298	324	350	376	401	427	453	479	505
168	531	557	583	608	634	660	686	712	737	763
169	789	814	840	866	891	917	943	968	994	23 019
170	23 045	23 070	23 096	23 121	23 147	23 172	23 198	23 223	23 249	23 274
171	300	325	350	376	401	426	452	477	502	528
172	553	578	603	629	654	679	704	729	754	779
173	805	830	855	880	905	930	955	980	24 005	24 030
174	24 055	24 080	24 105	24 130	24 155	24 180	24 204	24 229	254	279
175	24 304	24 329	24 353	24 378	24 403	24 428	24 452	24 477	24 502	24 527
176	551	576	601	625	650	674	699	724	748	773
177	797	822	846	871	895	920	944	969	993	25 018
178	25 042	25 066	25 091	25 115	25 139	25 164	25 188	25 212	25 237	261
179	285	310	334	358	382	406	431	455	479	503
180	25 527	25 551	25 575	25 600	25 624	25 648	25 672	25 696	25 720	25 744
181	768	792	816	840	864	888	912	935	959	983
182	26 007	26 031	26 055	26 079	26 102	26 126	26 150	26 174	26 198	26 221
183	245	269	293	316	340	364	387	411	435	458
184	482	505	529	553	576	600	623	647	670	694
185	26 717	26 741	26 764	26 788	26 811	26 834	26 858	26 881	26 905	26 928
186	951	975	998	27 021	27 045	27 068	27 091	27 114	27 138	27 161
187	27 184	27 207	27 231	254	277	300	323	346	370	393
188	416	439	462	485	508	531	554	577	600	623
189	646	669	692	715	738	761	784	807	830	852
190	27 875	27 898	27 921	27 944	27 967	27 989	28 012	28 035	28 058	28 081
191	28 103	28 126	28 149	28 171	28 194	28 217	240	262	285	307
192	330	353	375	398	421	443	466	488	511	533
193	556	578	601	623	646	668	691	713	735	758
194	780	803	825	847	870	892	914	937	959	981
195	29 003	29 026	29 048	29 070	29 092	29 115	29 137	29 159	29 181	29 203
196	226	248	270	292	314	336	358	380	403	425
197	447	469	491	513	535	557	579	601	623	645
198	667	688	710	732	754	776	798	820	842	863
199	885	907	929	951	973	994	30 016	30 038	30 060	30 081

2.000 to 2.499

N	0	1	2	3	4	5	6	7	8	9
200	30 103	30 125	30 146	30 168	30 190	30 211	30 233	30 255	30 276	30 298
201	320	341	363	384	406	428	449	471	492	514
202	535	557	578	600	621	643	664	685	707	728
203	750	771	792	814	835	856	878	899	920	942
204	963	984	31 006	31 027	31 048	31 069	31 091	31 112	31 133	31 154
205	31 175	31 197	31 218	31 239	31 260	31 281	31 302	31 323	31 345	31 366
206	387	408	429	450	471	492	513	534	555	576
207	597	618	639	660	681	702	723	744	765	785
208	806	827	848	869	890	911	931	952	973	994
209	32 015	32 035	32 056	32 077	32 098	32 118	32 139	32 160	32 181	32 201
210	32 222	32 243	32 263	32 284	32 305	32 325	32 346	32 366	32 387	32 408
211	428	449	469	490	510	531	552	572	593	613
212	634	654	675	695	715	736	756	777	797	818
213	838	858	879	899	919	940	960	980	33 001	33 021
214	33 041	33 062	33 082	33 102	33 122	33 143	33 163	33 183	203	224
215	33 244	33 264	33 284	33 304	33 325	33 345	33 365	33 385	33 405	33 425
216	445	465	486	506	526	546	566	586	606	626
217	646	666	686	706	726	746	766	786	806	826
218	846	866	885	905	925	945	965	985	34 005	34 025
219	34 044	34 064	34 084	34 104	34 124	34 143	34 163	34 183	203	223
220	34 242	34 262	34 282	34 301	34 321	34 341	34 361	34 380	34 400	34 420
221	439	459	479	498	518	537	557	577	596	616
222	635	655	674	694	713	733	753	772	792	811
223	830	850	869	889	908	928	947	967	986	35 005
224	35 025	35 044	35 064	35 083	35 102	35 122	35 141	35 160	35 180	199
225	35 218	35 238	35 257	35 276	35 295	35 315	35 334	35 353	35 372	35 392
226	411	430	449	468	488	507	526	545	564	583
227	603	622	641	660	679	698	717	736	755	774
228	793	813	832	851	870	889	908	927	946	965
229	984	36 003	36 021	36 040	36 059	36 078	36 097	36 116	36 135	36 154
230	36 173	36 192	36 211	36 229	36 248	36 267	36 286	36 305	36 324	36 342
231	361	380	399	418	436	455	474	493	511	530
232	549	568	586	605	624	642	661	680	698	717
233	736	754	773	791	810	829	847	866	884	903
234	922	940	959	977	996	37 014	37 033	37 051	37 070	37 088
235	37 107	37 125	37 144	37 162	37 181	37 199	37 218	37 236	37 254	37 273
236	291	310	328	346	365	383	401	420	438	457
237	475	493	511	530	548	566	585	603	621	639
238	658	676	694	712	731	749	767	785	803	822
239	840	858	876	894	912	931	949	967	985	38 003
240	38 021	38 039	38 057	38 075	38 093	38 112	38 130	38 148	38 166	38 184
241	202	220	238	256	274	292	310	328	346	364
242	382	399	417	435	453	471	489	507	525	543
243	561	578	596	614	632	650	668	686	703	721
244	739	757	775	792	810	828	846	863	881	899
245	38 917	38 934	38 952	38 970	38 987	39 005	39 023	39 041	39 058	39 076
246	39 094	39 111	39 129	39 146	39 164	182	199	217	235	252
247	270	287	305	322	340	358	375	393	410	428
248	445	463	480	498	515	533	550	568	585	602
249	620	637	655	672	690	707	724	742	759	777

Table 1 COMMON LOGARITHMS 557

2.500 to 2.999

N	0	1	2	3	4	5	6	7	8	9
250	39 794	39 811	39 829	39 846	39 863	39 881	39 898	39 915	39 933	39 950
251	967	985	40 002	40 019	40 037	40 054	40 071	40 088	40 106	40 123
252	40 140	40 157	175	192	209	226	243	261	278	295
253	312	329	346	364	381	398	415	432	449	466
254	483	500	518	535	552	569	586	603	620	637
255	40 654	40 671	40 688	40 705	40 722	40 739	40 756	40 773	40 790	40 807
256	824	841	858	875	892	909	926	943	960	976
257	993	41 010	41 027	41 044	41 061	41 078	41 095	41 111	41 128	41 145
258	41 162	179	196	212	229	246	263	280	296	313
259	330	347	363	380	397	414	430	447	464	481
260	41 497	41 514	41 531	41 547	41 564	41 581	41 597	41 614	41 631	41 647
261	664	681	697	714	731	747	764	780	797	814
262	830	847	863	880	896	913	929	946	963	979
263	996	42 012	42 029	42 045	42 062	42 078	42 095	42 111	42 127	42 144
264	42 160	177	193	210	226	243	259	275	292	308
265	42 325	42 341	42 357	42 374	42 390	42 406	42 423	42 439	42 455	42 472
266	488	504	521	537	553	570	586	602	619	635
267	651	667	684	700	716	732	749	765	781	797
268	813	830	846	862	878	894	911	927	943	959
269	975	991	43 008	43 024	43 040	43 056	43 072	43 088	43 104	43 120
270	43 136	43 152	43 169	43 185	43 201	43 217	43 233	43 249	43 265	43 281
271	297	313	329	345	361	377	393	409	425	441
272	457	473	489	505	521	537	553	569	584	600
273	616	632	648	664	680	696	712	727	743	759
274	775	791	807	823	838	854	870	886	902	917
275	43 933	43 949	43 965	43 981	43 996	44 012	44 028	44 044	44 059	44 075
276	44 091	44 107	44 122	44 138	44 154	170	185	201	217	232
277	248	264	279	295	311	326	342	358	373	389
278	404	420	436	451	467	483	498	514	529	545
279	560	576	592	607	623	638	654	669	685	700
280	44 716	44 731	44 747	44 762	44 778	44 793	44 809	44 824	44 840	44 855
281	871	886	902	917	932	948	963	979	994	45 010
282	45 025	45 040	45 056	45 071	45 086	45 102	45 117	45 133	45 148	163
283	179	194	209	225	240	255	271	286	301	317
284	332	347	362	378	393	408	423	439	454	469
285	45 484	45 500	45 515	45 530	45 545	45 561	45 576	45 591	45 606	45 621
286	637	652	667	682	697	712	728	743	758	773
287	788	803	818	834	849	864	879	894	909	924
288	939	954	969	984	46 000	46 015	46 030	46 045	46 060	46 075
289	46 090	46 105	46 120	46 135	150	165	180	195	210	225
290	46 240	46 255	46 270	46 285	46 300	46 315	46 330	46 345	46 359	46 374
291	389	404	419	434	449	464	479	494	509	523
292	538	553	568	583	598	613	627	642	657	672
293	687	702	716	731	746	761	776	790	805	820
294	835	850	864	879	894	909	923	938	953	967
295	46 982	46 997	47 012	47 026	47 041	47 056	47 070	47 085	47 100	47 114
296	47 129	47 144	159	173	188	202	217	232	246	261
297	276	290	305	319	334	349	363	378	392	407
298	422	436	451	465	480	494	509	524	538	553
299	567	582	596	611	625	640	654	669	683	698

3.000 to 3.499

N	0	1	2	3	4	5	6	7	8	9
300	47 712	47 727	47 741	47 756	47 770	47 784	47 799	47 813	47 828	47 842
301	857	871	885	900	914	929	943	958	972	986
302	48 001	48 015	48 029	48 044	48 058	48 073	48 087	48 101	48 116	48 130
303	144	159	173	187	202	216	230	244	259	273
304	287	302	316	330	344	359	373	387	401	416
305	48 430	48 444	48 458	48 473	48 487	48 501	48 515	48 530	48 544	48 558
306	572	586	601	615	629	643	657	671	686	700
307	714	728	742	756	770	785	799	813	827	841
308	855	869	883	897	911	926	940	954	968	982
309	996	49 010	49 024	49 038	49 052	49 066	49 080	49 094	49 108	49 122
310	49 136	49 150	49 164	49 178	49 192	49 206	49 220	49 234	49 248	49 262
311	276	290	304	318	332	346	360	374	388	402
312	415	429	443	457	471	485	499	513	527	541
313	554	568	582	596	610	624	638	651	665	679
314	693	707	721	734	748	762	776	790	803	817
315	49 831	49 845	49 859	49 872	49 886	49 900	49 914	49 927	49 941	49 955
316	969	982	996	50 010	50 024	50 037	50 051	50 065	50 079	50 092
317	50 106	50 120	50 133	147	161	174	188	202	215	229
318	243	256	270	284	297	311	325	338	352	365
319	379	393	406	420	433	447	461	474	488	501
320	50 515	50 529	50 542	50 556	50 569	50 583	50 596	50 610	50 623	50 637
321	651	664	678	691	705	718	732	745	759	772
322	786	799	813	826	840	853	866	880	893	907
323	920	934	947	961	974	987	51 001	51 014	51 028	51 041
324	51 055	51 068	51 081	51 095	51 108	51 121	135	148	162	175
325	51 188	51 202	51 215	51 228	51 242	51 255	51 268	51 282	51 295	51 308
326	322	335	348	362	375	388	402	415	428	441
327	455	468	481	495	508	521	534	548	561	574
328	587	601	614	627	640	654	667	680	693	706
329	720	733	746	759	772	786	799	812	825	838
330	51 851	51 865	51 878	51 891	51 904	51 917	51 930	51 943	51 957	51 970
331	983	996	52 009	52 022	52 035	52 048	52 061	52 075	52 088	52 101
332	52 114	52 127	140	153	166	179	192	205	218	231
333	244	257	270	284	297	310	323	336	349	362
334	375	388	401	414	427	440	453	466	479	492
335	52 504	52 517	52 530	52 543	52 556	52 569	52 582	52 595	52 608	52 621
336	634	647	660	673	686	699	711	724	737	750
337	763	776	789	802	815	827	840	853	866	879
338	892	905	917	930	943	956	969	982	994	53 007
339	53 020	53 033	53 046	53 058	53 071	53 084	53 097	53 110	53 122	135
340	53 148	53 161	53 173	53 186	53 199	53 212	53 224	53 237	53 250	53 263
341	275	288	301	314	326	339	352	364	377	390
342	403	415	428	441	453	466	479	491	504	517
343	529	542	555	567	580	593	605	618	631	643
344	656	668	681	694	706	719	732	744	757	769
345	53 782	53 794	53 807	53 820	53 832	53 845	53 857	53 870	53 882	53 895
346	908	920	933	945	958	970	983	995	54 008	54 020
347	54 033	54 045	54 058	54 070	54 083	54 095	54 108	54 120	133	145
348	158	170	183	195	208	220	233	245	258	270
349	283	295	307	320	332	345	357	370	382	394

3.500 to 3.999

N	0	1	2	3	4	5	6	7	8	9
350	54 407	54 419	54 432	54 444	54 456	54 469	54 481	54 494	54 506	54 518
351	531	543	555	568	580	593	605	617	630	642
352	654	667	679	691	704	716	728	741	753	765
353	777	790	802	814	827	839	851	864	876	888
354	900	913	925	937	949	962	974	986	998	55 011
355	55 023	55 035	55 047	55 060	55 072	55 084	55 096	55 108	55 121	55 133
356	145	157	169	182	194	206	218	230	242	255
357	267	279	291	303	315	328	340	352	364	376
358	388	400	413	425	437	449	461	473	485	497
359	509	522	534	546	558	570	582	594	606	618
360	55 630	55 642	55 654	55 666	55 678	55 691	55 703	55 715	55 727	55 739
361	751	763	775	787	799	811	823	835	847	859
362	871	883	895	907	919	931	943	955	967	979
363	991	56 003	56 015	56 027	56 038	56 050	56 062	56 074	56 086	56 098
364	56 110	122	134	146	158	170	182	194	205	217
365	56 229	56 241	56 253	56 265	56 277	56 289	56 301	56 312	56 324	56 336
366	348	360	372	384	396	407	419	431	443	455
367	467	478	490	502	514	526	538	549	561	573
368	585	597	608	620	632	644	656	667	679	691
369	703	714	726	738	750	761	773	785	797	808
370	56 820	56 832	56 844	56 855	56 867	56 879	56 891	56 902	56 914	56 926
371	937	949	961	972	984	996	57 008	57 019	57 031	57 043
372	57 054	57 066	57 078	57 089	57 101	57 113	124	136	148	159
373	171	183	194	206	217	229	241	252	264	276
374	287	299	310	322	334	345	357	368	380	392
375	57 403	57 415	57 426	57 438	57 449	57 461	57 473	57 484	57 496	57 507
376	519	530	542	553	565	576	588	600	611	623
377	634	646	657	669	680	692	703	715	726	738
378	749	761	772	784	795	807	818	830	841	852
379	864	875	887	898	910	921	933	944	955	967
380	57 978	57 990	58 001	58 013	58 024	58 035	58 047	58 058	58 070	58 081
381	58 092	58 104	115	127	138	149	161	172	184	195
382	206	218	229	240	252	263	274	286	297	309
383	320	331	343	354	365	377	388	399	410	422
384	433	444	456	467	478	490	501	512	524	535
385	58 546	58 557	58 569	58 580	58 591	58 602	58 614	58 625	58 636	58 647
386	659	670	681	692	704	715	726	737	749	760
387	771	782	794	805	816	827	838	850	861	872
388	883	894	906	917	928	939	950	961	973	984
389	995	59 006	59 017	59 028	59 040	59 051	59 062	59 073	59 084	59 095
390	59 106	59 118	59 129	59 140	59 151	59 162	59 173	59 184	59 195	59 207
391	218	229	240	251	262	273	284	295	306	318
392	329	340	351	362	373	384	395	406	417	428
393	439	450	461	472	483	494	506	517	528	539
394	550	561	572	583	594	605	616	627	638	649
395	59 660	59 671	59 682	59 693	59 704	59 715	59 726	59 737	59 748	59 759
396	770	780	791	802	813	824	835	846	857	868
397	879	890	901	912	923	934	945	956	966	977
398	988	999	60 010	60 021	60 032	60 043	60 054	60 065	60 076	60 086
399	60 097	60 108	119	130	141	152	163	173	184	195

APPENDIX

4.000 to 4.499

N	0	1	2	3	4	5	6	7	8	9
400	60 206	60 217	60 228	60 239	60 249	60 260	60 271	60 282	60 293	60 304
401	314	325	336	347	358	369	379	390	401	412
402	423	433	444	455	466	477	487	498	509	520
403	531	541	552	563	574	584	595	606	617	627
404	638	649	660	670	681	692	703	713	724	735
405	60 746	60 756	60 767	60 778	60 788	60 799	60 810	60 821	60 831	60 842
406	853	863	874	885	895	906	917	927	938	949
407	959	970	981	991	61 002	61 013	61 023	61 034	61 045	61 055
408	61 066	61 077	61 087	61 098	109	119	130	140	151	162
409	172	183	194	204	215	225	236	247	257	268
410	61 278	61 289	61 300	61 310	61 321	61 331	61 342	61 352	61 363	61 374
411	384	395	405	416	426	437	448	458	469	479
412	490	500	511	521	532	542	553	563	574	584
413	595	606	616	627	637	648	658	669	679	690
414	700	711	721	731	742	752	763	773	784	794
415	61 805	61 815	61 826	61 836	61 847	61 857	61 868	61 878	61 888	61 899
416	909	920	930	941	951	962	972	982	993	62 003
417	62 014	62 024	62 034	62 045	62 055	62 066	62 076	62 086	62 097	107
418	118	128	138	149	159	170	180	190	201	211
419	221	232	242	252	263	273	284	294	304	315
420	62 325	62 335	62 346	62 356	62 366	62 377	62 387	62 397	62 408	62 418
421	428	439	449	459	469	480	490	500	511	521
422	531	542	552	562	572	583	593	603	613	624
423	634	644	655	665	675	685	696	706	716	726
424	737	747	757	767	778	788	798	808	818	829
425	62 839	62 849	62 859	62 870	62 880	62 890	62 900	62 910	62 921	62 931
426	941	951	961	972	982	992	63 002	63 012	63 022	63 033
427	63 043	63 053	63 063	63 073	63 083	63 094	104	114	124	134
428	144	155	165	175	185	195	205	215	225	236
429	246	256	266	276	286	296	306	317	327	337
430	63 347	63 357	63 367	63 377	63 387	63 397	63 407	63 417	63 428	63 438
431	448	458	468	478	488	498	508	518	528	538
432	548	558	568	579	589	599	609	619	629	639
433	649	659	669	679	689	699	709	719	729	739
434	749	759	769	779	789	799	809	819	829	839
435	63 849	63 859	63 869	63 879	63 889	63 899	63 909	63 919	63 929	63 939
436	949	959	969	979	988	998	64 008	64 018	64 028	64 038
437	64 048	64 058	64 068	64 078	64 088	64 098	108	118	128	137
438	147	157	167	177	187	197	207	217	227	237
439	246	256	266	276	286	296	306	316	326	335
440	64 345	64 355	64 365	64 375	64 385	64 395	64 404	64 414	64 424	64 434
441	444	454	464	473	483	493	503	513	523	532
442	542	552	562	572	582	591	601	611	621	631
443	640	650	660	670	680	689	699	709	719	729
444	738	748	758	768	777	787	797	807	816	826
445	64 836	64 846	64 856	64 865	64 875	64 885	64 895	64 904	64 914	64 924
446	933	943	953	963	972	982	992	65 002	65 011	65 021
447	65 031	65 040	65 050	65 060	65 070	65 079	65 089	099	108	118
448	128	137	147	157	167	176	186	196	205	215
449	225	234	244	254	263	273	283	292	302	312

Table 1   COMMON LOGARITHMS   561

4.500 to 4.999

N	0	1	2	3	4	5	6	7	8	9
450	65 321	65 331	65 341	65 350	65 360	65 369	65 379	65 389	65 398	65 408
451	418	427	437	447	456	466	475	485	495	504
452	514	523	533	543	552	562	571	581	591	600
453	610	619	629	639	648	658	667	677	686	696
454	706	715	725	734	744	753	763	772	782	792
455	65 801	65 811	65 820	65 830	65 839	65 849	65 858	65 868	65 877	65 887
456	896	906	916	925	935	944	954	963	973	982
457	992	66 001	66 011	66 020	66 030	66 039	66 049	66 058	66 068	66 077
458	66 087	096	106	115	124	134	143	153	162	172
459	181	191	200	210	219	229	238	247	257	266
460	66 276	66 285	66 295	66 304	66 314	66 323	66 332	66 342	66 351	66 361
461	370	380	389	398	408	417	427	436	445	455
462	464	474	483	492	502	511	521	530	539	549
463	558	567	577	586	596	605	614	624	633	642
464	652	661	671	680	689	699	708	717	727	736
465	66 745	66 755	66 764	66 773	66 783	66 792	66 801	66 811	66 820	66 829
466	839	848	857	867	876	885	894	904	913	922
467	932	941	950	960	969	978	987	997	67 006	67 015
468	67 025	67 034	67 043	67 052	67 062	67 071	67 080	67 089	099	108
469	117	127	136	145	154	164	173	182	191	201
470	67 210	67 219	67 228	67 237	67 247	67 256	67 265	67 274	67 284	67 293
471	302	311	321	330	339	348	357	367	376	385
472	394	403	413	422	431	440	449	459	468	477
473	486	495	504	514	523	532	541	550	560	569
474	578	587	596	605	614	624	633	642	651	660
475	67 669	67 679	67 688	67 697	67 706	67 715	67 724	67 733	67 742	67 752
476	761	770	779	788	797	806	815	825	834	843
477	852	861	870	879	888	897	906	916	925	934
478	943	952	961	970	979	988	997	68 006	68 015	68 024
479	68 034	68 043	68 052	68 061	68 070	68 079	68 088	097	106	115
480	68 124	68 133	68 142	68 151	68 160	68 169	68 178	68 187	68 196	68 205
481	215	224	233	242	251	260	269	278	287	296
482	305	314	323	332	341	350	359	368	377	386
483	395	404	413	422	431	440	449	458	467	476
484	485	494	502	511	520	529	538	547	556	565
485	68 574	68 583	68 592	68 601	68 610	68 619	68 628	68 637	68 646	68 655
486	664	673	681	690	699	708	717	726	735	744
487	753	762	771	780	789	797	806	815	824	833
488	842	851	860	869	878	886	895	904	913	922
489	931	940	949	958	966	975	984	993	69 002	69 011
490	69 020	69 028	69 037	69 046	69 055	69 064	69 073	69 082	69 090	69 099
491	108	117	126	135	144	152	161	170	179	188
492	197	205	214	223	232	241	249	258	267	276
493	285	294	302	311	320	329	338	346	355	364
494	373	381	390	399	408	417	425	434	443	452
495	69 461	69 469	69 478	69 487	69 496	69 504	69 513	69 522	69 531	69 539
496	548	557	566	574	583	592	601	609	618	627
497	636	644	653	662	671	679	688	697	705	714
498	723	732	740	749	758	767	775	784	793	801
499	810	819	827	836	845	854	862	871	880	888

5.000 to 5.499

N	0	1	2	3	4	5	6	7	8	9
500	69 897	69 906	69 914	69 923	69 932	69 940	69 949	69 958	69 966	69 975
501	984	992	70 001	70 010	70 018	70 027	70 036	70 044	70 053	70 062
502	70 070	70 079	088	096	105	114	122	131	140	148
503	157	165	174	183	191	200	209	217	226	234
504	243	252	260	269	278	286	295	303	312	321
505	70 329	70 338	70 346	70 355	70 364	70 372	70 381	70 389	70 398	70 406
506	415	424	432	441	449	458	467	475	484	492
507	501	509	518	526	535	544	552	561	569	578
508	586	595	603	612	621	629	638	646	655	663
509	672	680	689	697	706	714	723	731	740	749
510	70 757	70 766	70 774	70 783	70 791	70 800	70 808	70 817	70 825	70 834
511	842	851	859	868	876	885	893	902	910	919
512	927	935	944	952	961	969	978	986	995	71 003
513	71 012	71 020	71 029	71 037	71 046	71 054	71 063	71 071	71 079	088
514	096	105	113	122	130	139	147	155	164	172
515	71 181	71 189	71 198	71 206	71 214	71 223	71 231	71 240	71 248	71 257
516	265	273	282	290	299	307	315	324	332	341
517	349	357	366	374	383	391	399	408	416	425
518	433	441	450	458	466	475	483	492	500	508
519	517	525	533	542	550	559	567	575	584	592
520	71 600	71 609	71 617	71 625	71 634	71 642	71 650	71 659	71 667	71 675
521	684	692	700	709	717	725	734	742	750	759
522	767	775	784	792	800	809	817	825	834	842
523	850	858	867	875	883	892	900	908	917	925
524	933	941	950	958	966	975	983	991	999	72 008
525	72 016	72 024	72 032	72 041	72 049	72 057	72 066	72 074	72 082	72 090
526	099	107	115	123	132	140	148	156	165	173
527	181	189	198	206	214	222	230	239	247	255
528	263	272	280	288	296	304	313	321	329	337
529	346	354	362	370	378	387	395	403	411	419
530	72 428	72 436	72 444	72 452	72 460	72 469	72 477	72 485	72 493	72 501
531	509	518	526	534	542	550	558	567	575	583
532	591	599	607	616	624	632	640	648	656	665
533	673	681	689	697	705	713	722	730	738	746
534	754	762	770	779	787	795	803	811	819	827
535	72 835	72 843	72 852	72 860	72 868	72 876	72 884	72 892	72 900	72 908
536	916	925	933	941	949	957	965	973	981	989
537	997	73 006	73 014	73 022	73 030	73 038	73 046	73 054	73 062	73 070
538	73 078	086	094	102	111	119	127	135	143	151
539	159	167	175	183	191	199	207	215	223	231
540	73 239	73 247	73 255	73 263	73 272	73 280	73 288	73 296	73 304	73 312
541	320	328	336	344	352	360	368	376	384	392
542	400	408	416	424	432	440	448	456	464	472
543	480	488	496	504	512	520	528	536	544	552
544	560	568	576	584	592	600	608	616	624	632
545	73 640	73 648	73 656	73 664	73 672	73 679	73 687	73 695	73 703	73 711
546	719	727	735	743	751	759	767	775	783	791
547	799	807	815	823	830	838	846	854	862	870
548	878	886	894	902	910	918	926	933	941	949
549	957	965	973	981	989	997	74 005	74 013	74 020	74 028

Table 1 COMMON LOGARITHMS 563

5.500 to 5.999

N	0	1	2	3	4	5	6	7	8	9
550	74 036	74 044	74 052	74 060	74 068	74 076	74 084	74 092	74 099	74 107
551	115	123	131	139	147	155	162	170	178	186
552	194	202	210	218	225	233	241	249	257	265
553	273	280	288	296	304	312	320	327	335	343
554	351	359	367	374	382	390	398	406	414	421
555	74 429	74 437	74 445	74 453	74 461	74 468	74 476	74 484	74 492	74 500
556	507	515	523	531	539	547	554	562	570	578
557	586	593	601	609	617	624	632	640	648	656
558	663	671	679	687	695	702	710	718	726	733
559	741	749	757	764	772	780	788	796	803	811
560	74 819	74 827	74 834	74 842	74 850	74 858	74 865	74 873	74 881	74 889
561	896	904	912	920	927	935	943	950	958	966
562	974	981	989	997	75 005	75 012	75 020	75 028	75 035	75 043
563	75 051	75 059	75 066	75 074	082	089	097	105	113	120
564	128	136	143	151	159	166	174	182	189	197
565	75 205	75 213	75 220	75 228	75 236	75 243	75 251	75 259	75 266	75 274
566	282	289	297	305	312	320	328	335	343	351
567	358	366	374	381	389	397	404	412	420	427
568	435	442	450	458	465	473	481	488	496	504
569	511	519	526	534	542	549	557	565	572	580
570	75 587	75 595	75 603	75 610	75 618	75 626	75 633	75 641	75 648	75 656
571	664	671	679	686	694	702	709	717	724	732
572	740	747	755	762	770	778	785	793	800	808
573	815	823	831	838	846	853	861	868	876	884
574	891	899	906	914	921	929	937	944	952	959
575	75 967	75 974	75 982	75 989	75 997	76 005	76 012	76 020	76 027	76 035
576	76 042	76 050	76 057	76 065	76 072	080	087	095	103	110
577	118	125	133	140	148	155	163	170	178	185
578	193	200	208	215	223	230	238	245	253	260
579	268	275	283	290	298	305	313	320	328	335
580	76 343	76 350	76 358	76 365	76 373	76 380	76 388	76 395	76 403	76 410
581	418	425	433	440	448	455	462	470	477	485
582	492	500	507	515	522	530	537	545	552	559
583	567	574	582	589	597	604	612	619	626	634
584	641	649	656	664	671	678	686	693	701	708
585	76 716	76 723	76 730	76 738	76 745	76 753	76 760	76 768	76 775	76 782
586	790	797	805	812	819	827	834	842	849	856
587	864	871	879	886	893	901	908	916	923	930
588	938	945	953	960	967	975	982	989	997	77 004
589	77 012	77 019	77 026	77 034	77 041	77 048	77 056	77 063	77 070	078
590	77 085	77 093	77 100	77 107	77 115	77 122	77 129	77 137	77 144	77 151
591	159	166	173	181	188	195	203	210	217	225
592	232	240	247	254	262	269	276	283	291	298
593	305	313	320	327	335	342	349	357	364	371
594	379	386	393	401	408	415	422	430	437	444
595	77 452	77 459	77 466	77 474	77 481	77 488	77 495	77 503	77 510	77 517
596	525	532	539	546	554	561	568	576	583	590
597	597	605	612	619	627	634	641	648	656	663
598	670	677	685	692	699	706	714	721	728	735
599	743	750	757	764	772	779	786	793	801	808

6.000 to 6.499

N	0	1	2	3	4	5	6	7	8	9
600	77 815	77 822	77 830	77 837	77 844	77 851	77 859	77 866	77 873	77 880
601	887	895	902	909	916	924	931	938	945	952
602	960	967	974	981	988	996	78 003	78 010	78 017	78 025
603	78 032	78 039	78 046	78 053	78 061	78 068	075	082	089	097
604	104	111	118	125	132	140	147	154	161	168
605	78 176	78 183	78 190	78 197	78 204	78 211	78 219	78 226	78 233	78 240
606	247	254	262	269	276	283	290	297	305	312
607	319	326	333	340	347	355	362	369	376	383
608	390	398	405	412	419	426	433	440	447	455
609	462	469	476	483	490	497	504	512	519	526
610	78 533	78 540	78 547	78 554	78 561	78 569	78 576	78 583	78 590	78 597
611	604	611	618	625	633	640	647	654	661	668
612	675	682	689	696	704	711	718	725	732	739
613	746	753	760	767	774	781	789	796	803	810
614	817	824	831	838	845	852	859	866	873	880
615	78 888	78 895	78 902	78 909	78 916	78 923	78 930	78 937	78 944	78 951
616	958	965	972	979	986	993	79 000	79 007	79 014	79 021
617	79 029	79 036	79 043	79 050	79 057	79 064	071	078	085	092
618	099	106	113	120	127	134	141	148	155	162
619	169	176	183	190	197	204	211	218	225	232
620	79 239	79 246	79 253	79 260	79 267	79 274	79 281	79 288	79 295	79 302
621	309	316	323	330	337	344	351	358	365	372
622	379	386	393	400	407	414	421	428	435	442
623	449	456	463	470	477	484	491	498	505	511
624	518	525	532	539	546	553	560	567	574	581
625	79 588	79 595	79 602	79 609	79 616	79 623	79 630	79 637	79 644	79 650
626	657	664	671	678	685	692	699	706	713	720
627	727	734	741	748	754	761	768	775	782	789
628	796	803	810	817	824	831	837	844	851	858
629	865	872	879	886	893	900	906	913	920	927
630	79 934	79 941	79 948	79 955	79 962	79 969	79 975	79 982	79 989	79 996
631	80 003	80 010	80 017	80 024	80 030	80 037	80 044	80 051	80 058	80 065
632	072	079	085	092	099	106	113	120	127	134
633	140	147	154	161	168	175	182	188	195	202
634	209	216	223	229	236	243	250	257	264	271
635	80 277	80 284	80 291	80 298	80 305	80 312	80 318	80 325	80 332	80 339
636	346	353	359	366	373	380	387	393	400	407
637	414	421	428	434	441	448	455	462	468	475
638	482	489	496	502	509	516	523	530	536	543
639	550	557	564	570	577	584	591	598	604	611
640	80 618	80 625	80 632	80 638	80 645	80 652	80 659	80 665	80 672	80 679
641	686	693	699	706	713	720	726	733	740	747
642	754	760	767	774	781	787	794	801	808	814
643	821	828	835	841	848	855	862	868	875	882
644	889	895	902	909	916	922	929	936	943	949
645	80 956	80 963	80 969	80 976	80 983	80 990	80 996	81 003	81 010	81 017
646	81 023	81 030	81 037	81 043	81 050	81 057	81 064	070	077	084
647	090	097	104	111	117	124	131	137	144	151
648	158	164	171	178	184	191	198	204	211	218
649	224	231	238	245	251	258	265	271	278	285

6.500 to 6.999

N	0	1	2	3	4	5	6	7	8	9
650	81 291	81 298	81 305	81 311	81 318	81 325	81 331	81 338	81 345	81 351
651	358	365	371	378	385	391	398	405	411	418
652	425	431	438	445	451	458	465	471	478	485
653	491	498	505	511	518	525	531	538	544	551
654	558	564	571	578	584	591	598	604	611	617
655	81 624	81 631	81 637	81 644	81 651	81 657	81 664	81 671	81 677	81 684
656	690	697	704	710	717	723	730	737	743	750
657	757	763	770	776	783	790	796	803	809	816
658	823	829	836	842	849	856	862	869	875	882
659	889	895	902	908	915	921	928	935	941	948
660	81 954	81 961	81 968	81 974	81 981	81 987	81 994	82 000	82 007	82 014
661	82 020	82 027	82 033	82 040	82 046	82 053	82 060	066	073	079
662	086	092	099	105	112	119	125	132	138	145
663	151	158	164	171	178	184	191	197	204	210
664	217	223	230	236	243	249	256	263	269	276
665	82 282	82 289	82 295	82 302	82 308	82 315	82 321	82 328	82 334	82 341
666	347	354	360	367	373	380	387	393	400	406
667	413	419	426	432	439	445	452	458	465	471
668	478	484	491	497	504	510	517	523	530	536
669	543	549	556	562	569	575	582	588	595	601
670	82 607	82 614	82 620	82 627	82 633	82 640	82 646	82 653	82 659	82 666
671	672	679	685	692	698	705	711	718	724	730
672	737	743	750	756	763	769	776	782	789	795
673	802	808	814	821	827	834	840	847	853	860
674	866	872	879	885	892	898	905	911	918	924
675	82 930	82 937	82 943	82 950	82 956	82 963	82 969	82 975	82 982	82 988
676	995	83 001	83 008	83 014	83 020	83 027	83 033	83 040	83 046	83 052
677	83 059	065	072	078	085	091	097	104	110	117
678	123	129	136	142	149	155	161	168	174	181
679	187	193	200	206	213	219	225	232	238	245
680	83 251	83 257	83 264	83 270	83 276	83 283	83 289	83 296	83 302	83 308
681	315	321	327	334	340	347	353	359	366	372
682	378	385	391	398	404	410	417	423	429	436
683	442	448	455	461	467	474	480	487	493	499
684	506	512	518	525	531	537	544	550	556	563
685	83 569	83 575	83 582	83 588	83 594	83 601	83 607	83 613	83 620	83 626
686	632	639	645	651	658	664	670	677	683	689
687	696	702	708	715	721	727	734	740	746	753
688	759	765	771	778	784	790	797	803	809	816
689	822	828	835	841	847	853	860	866	872	879
690	83 885	83 891	83 897	83 904	83 910	83 916	83 923	83 929	83 935	83 942
691	948	954	960	967	973	979	985	992	998	84 004
692	84 011	84 017	84 023	84 029	84 036	84 042	84 048	84 055	84 061	067
693	073	080	086	092	098	105	111	117	123	130
694	136	142	148	155	161	167	173	180	186	192
695	84 198	84 205	84 211	84 217	84 223	84 230	84 236	84 242	84 248	84 255
696	261	267	273	280	286	292	298	305	311	317
697	323	330	336	342	348	354	361	367	373	379
698	386	392	398	404	410	417	423	429	435	442
699	448	454	460	466	473	479	485	491	497	504

7.000 to 7.499

N	0	1	2	3	4	5	6	7	8	9
700	84 510	84 516	84 522	84 528	84 535	84 541	84 547	84 553	84 559	84 566
701	572	578	584	590	597	603	609	615	621	628
702	634	640	646	652	658	665	671	677	683	689
703	696	702	708	714	720	726	733	739	745	751
704	757	763	770	776	782	788	794	800	807	813
705	84 819	84 825	84 831	84 837	84 844	84 850	84 856	84 862	84 868	84 874
706	880	887	893	899	905	911	917	924	930	936
707	942	948	954	960	967	973	979	985	991	997
708	85 003	85 009	85 016	85 022	85 028	85 034	85 040	85 046	85 052	85 058
709	065	071	077	083	089	095	101	107	114	120
710	85 126	85 132	85 138	85 144	85 150	85 156	85 163	85 169	85 175	85 181
711	187	193	199	205	211	217	224	230	236	242
712	248	254	260	266	272	278	285	291	297	303
713	309	315	321	327	333	339	345	352	358	364
714	370	376	382	388	394	400	406	412	418	425
715	85 431	85 437	85 443	85 449	85 455	85 461	85 467	85 473	85 479	85 485
716	491	497	503	509	516	522	528	534	540	546
717	552	558	564	570	576	582	588	594	600	606
718	612	618	625	631	637	643	649	655	661	667
719	673	679	685	691	697	703	709	715	721	727
720	85 733	85 739	85 745	85 751	85 757	85 763	85 769	85 775	85 781	85 788
721	794	800	806	812	818	824	830	836	842	848
722	854	860	866	872	878	884	890	896	902	908
723	914	920	926	932	938	944	950	956	962	968
724	974	980	986	992	998	86 004	86 010	86 016	86 022	86 028
725	86 034	86 040	86 046	86 052	86 058	86 064	86 070	86 076	86 082	86 088
726	094	100	106	112	118	124	130	136	141	147
727	153	159	165	171	177	183	189	195	201	207
728	213	219	225	231	237	243	249	255	261	267
729	273	279	285	291	297	303	308	314	320	326
730	86 332	86 338	86 344	86 350	86 356	86 362	86 368	86 374	86 380	86 386
731	392	398	404	410	415	421	427	433	439	445
732	451	457	463	469	475	481	487	493	499	504
733	510	516	522	528	534	540	546	552	558	564
734	570	576	581	587	593	599	605	611	617	623
735	86 629	86 635	86 641	86 646	86 652	86 658	86 664	86 670	86 676	86 682
736	688	694	700	705	711	717	723	729	735	741
737	747	753	759	764	770	776	782	788	794	800
738	806	812	817	823	829	835	841	847	853	859
739	864	870	876	882	888	894	900	906	911	917
740	86 923	86 929	86 935	86 941	86 947	86 953	86 958	86 964	86 970	86 976
741	982	988	994	999	87 005	87 011	87 017	87 023	87 029	87 035
742	87 040	87 046	87 052	87 058	064	070	075	081	087	093
743	099	105	111	116	122	128	134	140	146	151
744	157	163	169	175	181	186	192	198	204	210
745	87 216	87 221	87 227	87 233	87 239	87 245	87 251	87 256	87 262	87 268
746	274	280	286	291	297	303	309	315	320	326
747	332	338	344	349	355	361	367	373	379	384
748	390	396	402	408	413	419	425	431	437	442
749	448	454	460	466	471	477	483	489	495	500

Table 1   COMMON LOGARITHMS   567

7.500 to 7.999

N	0	1	2	3	4	5	6	7	8	9
750	87 506	87 512	87 518	87 523	87 529	87 535	87 541	87 547	87 552	87 558
751	564	570	576	581	587	593	599	604	610	616
752	622	628	633	639	645	651	656	662	668	674
753	679	685	691	697	703	708	714	720	726	731
754	737	743	749	754	760	766	772	777	783	789
755	87 795	87 800	87 806	87 812	87 818	87 823	87 829	87 835	87 841	87 846
756	852	858	864	869	875	881	887	892	898	904
757	910	915	921	927	933	938	944	950	955	961
758	967	973	978	984	990	996	88 001	88 007	88 013	88 018
759	88 024	88 030	88 036	88 041	88 047	88 053	058	064	070	076
760	88 081	88 087	88 093	88 098	88 104	88 110	88 116	88 121	88 127	88 133
761	138	144	150	156	161	167	173	178	184	190
762	195	201	207	213	218	224	230	235	241	247
763	252	258	264	270	275	281	287	292	298	304
764	309	315	321	326	332	338	343	349	355	360
765	88 366	88 372	88 377	88 383	88 389	88 395	88 400	88 406	88 412	88 417
766	423	429	434	440	446	451	457	463	468	474
767	480	485	491	497	502	508	513	519	525	530
768	536	542	547	553	559	564	570	576	581	587
769	593	598	604	610	615	621	627	632	638	643
770	88 649	88 655	88 660	88 666	88 672	88 677	88 683	88 689	88 694	88 700
771	705	711	717	722	728	734	739	745	750	756
772	762	767	773	779	784	790	795	801	807	812
773	818	824	829	835	840	846	852	857	863	868
774	874	880	885	891	897	902	908	913	919	925
775	88 930	88 936	88 941	88 947	88 953	88 958	88 964	88 969	88 975	88 981
776	986	992	997	89 003	89 009	89 014	89 020	89 025	89 031	89 037
777	89 042	89 048	89 053	059	064	070	076	081	087	092
778	098	104	109	115	120	126	131	137	143	148
779	154	159	165	170	176	182	187	193	198	204
780	89 209	89 215	89 221	89 226	89 232	89 237	89 243	89 248	89 254	89 260
781	265	271	276	282	287	293	298	304	310	315
782	321	326	332	337	343	348	354	360	365	371
783	376	382	387	393	398	404	409	415	421	426
784	432	437	443	448	454	459	465	470	476	481
785	89 487	89 492	89 498	89 504	89 509	89 515	89 520	89 526	89 531	89 537
786	542	548	553	559	564	570	575	581	586	592
787	597	603	609	614	620	625	631	636	642	647
788	653	658	664	669	675	680	686	691	697	702
789	708	713	719	724	730	735	741	746	752	757
790	89 763	89 768	89 774	89 779	89 785	89 790	89 796	89 801	89 807	89 812
791	818	823	829	834	840	845	851	856	862	867
792	873	878	883	889	894	900	905	911	916	922
793	927	933	938	944	949	955	960	966	971	977
794	982	988	993	998	90 004	90 009	90 015	90 020	90 026	90 031
795	90 037	90 042	90 048	90 053	90 059	90 064	90 069	90 075	90 080	90 086
796	091	097	102	108	113	119	124	129	135	140
797	146	151	157	162	168	173	179	184	189	195
798	200	206	211	217	222	227	233	238	244	249
799	255	260	266	271	276	282	287	293	298	304

8.000 to 8.499

N	0	1	2	3	4	5	6	7	8	9
800	90 309	90 314	90 320	90 325	90 331	90 336	90 342	90 347	90 352	90 358
801	363	369	374	380	385	390	396	401	407	412
802	417	423	428	434	439	445	450	455	461	466
803	472	477	482	488	493	499	504	509	515	520
804	526	531	536	542	547	553	558	563	569	574
805	90 580	90 585	90 590	90 596	90 601	90 607	90 612	90 617	90 623	90 628
806	634	639	644	650	655	660	666	671	677	682
807	687	693	698	703	709	714	720	725	730	736
808	741	747	752	757	763	768	773	779	784	789
809	795	800	806	811	816	822	827	832	838	843
810	90 849	90 854	90 859	90 865	90 870	90 875	90 881	90 886	90 891	90 897
811	902	907	913	918	924	929	934	940	945	950
812	956	961	966	972	977	982	988	993	998	91 004
813	91 009	91 014	91 020	91 025	91 030	91 036	91 041	91 046	91 052	057
814	062	068	073	078	084	089	094	100	105	110
815	91 116	91 121	91 126	91 132	91 137	91 142	91 148	91 153	91 158	91 164
816	169	174	180	185	190	196	201	206	212	217
817	222	228	233	238	243	249	254	259	265	270
818	275	281	286	291	297	302	307	312	318	323
819	328	334	339	344	350	355	360	365	371	376
820	91 381	91 387	91 392	91 397	91 403	91 408	91 413	91 418	91 424	91 429
821	434	440	445	450	455	461	466	471	477	482
822	487	492	498	503	508	514	519	524	529	535
823	540	545	551	556	561	566	572	577	582	587
824	593	598	603	609	614	619	624	630	635	640
825	91 645	91 651	91 656	91 661	91 666	91 672	91 677	91 682	91 687	91 693
826	698	703	709	714	719	724	730	735	740	745
827	751	756	761	766	772	777	782	787	793	798
828	803	808	814	819	824	829	834	840	845	850
829	855	861	866	871	876	882	887	892	897	903
830	91 908	91 913	91 918	91 924	91 929	91 934	91 939	91 944	91 950	91 955
831	960	965	971	976	981	986	991	997	92 002	92 007
832	92 012	92 018	92 023	92 028	92 033	92 038	92 044	92 049	054	059
833	065	070	075	080	085	091	096	101	106	111
834	117	122	127	132	137	143	148	153	158	163
835	92 169	92 174	92 179	92 184	92 189	92 195	92 200	92 205	92 210	92 215
836	221	226	231	236	241	247	252	257	262	267
837	273	278	283	288	293	298	304	309	314	319
838	324	330	335	340	345	350	355	361	366	371
839	376	381	387	392	397	402	407	412	418	423
840	92 428	92 433	92 438	92 443	92 449	92 454	92 459	92 464	92 469	92 474
841	480	485	490	495	500	505	511	516	521	526
842	531	536	542	547	552	557	562	567	572	578
843	583	588	593	598	603	609	614	619	624	629
844	634	639	645	650	655	660	665	670	675	681
845	92 686	92 691	92 696	92 701	92 706	92 711	92 716	92 722	92 727	92 732
846	737	742	747	752	758	763	768	773	778	783
847	788	793	799	804	809	814	819	824	829	834
848	840	845	850	855	860	865	870	875	881	886
849	891	896	901	906	911	916	921	927	932	937

8.500 to 8.999

N	0	1	2	3	4	5	6	7	8	9
850	92 942	92 947	92 952	92 957	92 962	92 967	92 973	92 978	92 983	92 988
851	993	998	93 003	93 008	93 013	93 018	93 024	93 029	93 034	93 039
852	93 044	93 049	054	059	064	069	075	080	085	090
853	095	100	105	110	115	120	125	131	136	141
854	146	151	156	161	166	171	176	181	186	192
855	93 197	93 202	93 207	93 212	93 217	93 222	93 227	93 232	93 237	93 242
856	247	252	258	263	268	273	278	283	288	293
857	298	303	308	313	318	323	328	334	339	344
858	349	354	359	364	369	374	379	384	389	394
859	399	404	409	414	420	425	430	435	440	445
860	93 450	93 455	93 460	93 465	93 470	93 475	93 480	93 485	93 490	93 495
861	500	505	510	515	520	526	531	536	541	546
862	551	556	561	566	571	576	581	586	591	596
863	601	606	611	616	621	626	631	636	641	646
864	651	656	661	666	671	676	682	687	692	697
865	93 702	93 707	93 712	93 717	93 722	93 727	93 732	93 737	93 742	93 747
866	752	757	762	767	772	777	782	787	792	797
867	802	807	812	817	822	827	832	837	842	847
868	852	857	862	867	872	877	882	887	892	897
869	902	907	912	917	922	927	932	937	942	947
870	93 952	93 957	93 962	93 967	93 972	93 977	93 982	93 987	93 992	93 997
871	94 002	94 007	94 012	94 017	94 022	94 027	94 032	94 037	94 042	94 047
872	052	057	062	067	072	077	082	086	091	096
873	101	106	111	116	121	126	131	136	141	146
874	151	156	161	166	171	176	181	186	191	196
875	94 201	94 206	94 211	94 216	94 221	94 226	94 231	94 236	94 240	94 245
876	250	255	260	265	270	275	280	285	290	295
877	300	305	310	315	320	325	330	335	340	345
878	349	354	359	364	369	374	379	384	389	394
879	399	404	409	414	419	424	429	433	438	443
880	94 448	94 453	94 458	94 463	94 468	94 473	94 478	94 483	94 488	94 493
881	498	503	507	512	517	522	527	532	537	542
882	547	552	557	562	567	571	576	581	586	591
883	596	601	606	611	616	621	626	630	635	640
884	645	650	655	660	665	670	675	680	685	689
885	94 694	94 699	94 704	94 709	94 714	94 719	94 724	94 729	94 734	94 738
886	743	748	753	758	763	768	773	778	783	787
887	792	797	802	807	812	817	822	827	832	836
888	841	846	851	856	861	866	871	876	880	885
889	890	895	900	905	910	915	919	924	929	934
890	94 939	94 944	94 949	94 954	94 959	94 963	94 968	94 973	94 978	94 983
891	988	993	998	95 002	95 007	95 012	95 017	95 022	95 027	95 032
892	95 036	95 041	95 046	051	056	061	066	071	075	080
893	085	090	095	100	105	109	114	119	124	129
894	134	139	143	148	153	158	163	168	173	177
895	95 182	95 187	95 192	95 197	95 202	95 207	95 211	95 216	95 221	95 226
896	231	236	240	245	250	255	260	265	270	274
897	279	284	289	294	299	303	308	313	318	323
898	328	332	337	342	347	352	357	361	366	371
899	376	381	386	390	395	400	405	410	415	419

9.000 to 9.499

N	0	1	2	3	4	5	6	7	8	9
900	95 424	95 429	95 434	95 439	95 444	95 448	95 453	95 458	95 463	95 468
901	472	477	482	487	492	497	501	506	511	516
902	521	525	530	535	540	545	550	554	559	564
903	569	574	578	583	588	593	598	602	607	612
904	617	622	626	631	636	641	646	650	655	660
905	95 665	95 670	95 674	95 679	95 684	95 689	95 694	95 698	95 703	95 708
906	713	718	722	727	732	737	742	746	751	756
907	761	766	770	775	780	785	789	794	799	804
908	809	813	818	823	828	832	837	842	847	852
909	856	861	866	871	875	880	885	890	895	899
910	95 904	95 909	95 914	95 918	95 923	95 928	95 933	95 938	95 942	95 947
911	952	957	961	966	971	976	980	985	990	995
912	999	96 004	96 009	96 014	96 019	96 023	96 028	96 033	96 038	96 042
913	96 047	052	057	061	066	071	076	080	085	090
914	095	099	104	109	114	118	123	128	133	137
915	96 142	96 147	96 152	96 156	96 161	96 166	96 171	96 175	96 180	96 185
916	190	194	199	204	209	213	218	223	227	232
917	237	242	246	251	256	261	265	270	275	280
918	284	289	294	298	303	308	313	317	322	327
919	332	336	341	346	350	355	360	365	369	374
920	96 379	96 384	96 388	96 393	96 398	96 402	96 407	96 412	96 417	96 421
921	426	431	435	440	445	450	454	459	464	468
922	473	478	483	487	492	497	501	506	511	515
923	520	525	530	534	539	544	548	553	558	562
924	567	572	577	581	586	591	595	600	605	609
925	96 614	96 619	96 624	96 628	96 633	96 638	96 642	96 647	96 652	96 656
926	661	666	670	675	680	685	689	694	699	703
927	708	713	717	722	727	731	736	741	745	750
928	755	759	764	769	774	778	783	788	792	797
929	802	806	811	816	820	825	830	834	839	844
930	96 848	96 853	96 858	96 862	96 867	96 872	96 876	96 881	96 886	96 890
931	895	900	904	909	914	918	923	928	932	937
932	942	946	951	956	960	965	970	974	979	984
933	988	993	997	97 002	97 007	97 011	97 016	97 021	97 025	97 030
934	97 035	97 039	97 044	049	053	058	063	067	072	077
935	97 081	97 086	97 090	97 095	97 100	97 104	97 109	97 114	97 118	97 123
936	128	132	137	142	146	151	155	160	165	169
937	174	179	183	188	192	197	202	206	211	216
938	220	225	230	234	239	243	248	253	257	262
939	267	271	276	280	285	290	294	299	304	308
940	97 313	97 317	97 322	97 327	97 331	97 336	97 340	97 345	97 350	97 354
941	359	364	368	373	377	382	387	391	396	400
942	405	410	414	419	424	428	433	437	442	447
943	451	456	460	465	470	474	479	483	488	493
944	497	502	506	511	516	520	525	529	534	539
945	97 543	97 548	97 552	97 557	97 562	97 566	97 571	97 575	97 580	97 585
946	589	594	598	603	607	612	617	621	626	630
947	635	640	644	649	653	658	663	667	672	676
948	681	685	690	695	699	704	708	713	717	722
949	727	731	736	740	745	749	754	759	763	768

Table 1   COMMON LOGARITHMS   571

9.500 to 9.999

N	0	1	2	3	4	5	6	7	8	9
950	97 772	97 777	97 782	97 786	97 791	97 795	97 800	97 804	97 809	97 813
951	818	823	827	832	836	841	845	850	855	859
952	864	868	873	877	882	886	891	896	900	905
953	909	914	918	923	928	932	937	941	946	950
954	955	959	964	968	973	978	982	987	991	996
955	98 000	98 005	98 009	98 014	98 019	98 023	98 028	98 032	98 037	98 041
956	046	050	055	059	064	068	073	078	082	087
957	091	096	100	105	109	114	118	123	127	132
958	137	141	146	150	155	159	164	168	173	177
959	182	186	191	195	200	204	209	214	218	223
960	98 227	98 232	98 236	98 241	98 245	98 250	98 254	98 259	98 263	98 268
961	272	277	281	286	290	295	299	304	308	313
962	318	322	327	331	336	340	345	349	354	358
963	363	367	372	376	381	385	390	394	399	403
964	408	412	417	421	426	430	435	439	444	448
965	98 453	98 457	98 462	98 466	98 471	98 475	98 480	98 484	98 489	98 493
966	498	502	507	511	516	520	525	529	534	538
967	543	547	552	556	561	565	570	574	579	583
968	588	592	597	601	605	610	614	619	623	628
969	632	637	641	646	650	655	659	664	668	673
970	98 677	98 682	98 686	98 691	98 695	98 700	98 704	98 709	98 713	98 717
971	722	726	731	735	740	744	749	753	758	762
972	767	771	776	780	784	789	793	798	802	807
973	811	816	820	825	829	834	838	843	847	851
974	856	860	865	869	874	878	883	887	892	896
975	98 900	98 905	98 909	98 914	98 918	98 923	98 927	98 932	98 936	98 941
976	945	949	954	958	963	967	972	976	981	985
977	989	994	998	99 003	99 007	99 012	99 016	99 021	99 025	99 029
978	99 034	99 038	99 043	047	052	056	061	065	069	074
979	078	083	087	092	096	100	105	109	114	118
980	99 123	99 127	99 131	99 136	99 140	99 145	99 149	99 154	99 158	99 162
981	167	171	176	180	185	189	193	198	202	207
982	211	216	220	224	229	233	238	242	247	251
983	255	260	264	269	273	277	282	286	291	295
984	300	304	308	313	317	322	326	330	335	339
985	99 344	99 348	99 352	99 357	99 361	99 366	99 370	99 374	99 379	99 383
986	388	392	396	401	405	410	414	419	423	427
987	432	436	441	445	449	454	458	463	467	471
988	476	480	484	489	493	498	502	506	511	515
989	520	524	528	533	537	542	546	550	555	559
990	99 564	99 568	99 572	99 577	99 581	99 585	99 590	99 594	99 599	99 603
991	607	612	616	621	625	629	634	638	642	647
992	651	656	660	664	669	673	677	682	686	691
993	695	699	704	708	712	717	721	726	730	734
994	739	743	747	752	756	760	765	769	774	778
995	99 782	99 787	99 791	99 795	99 800	99 804	99 808	99 813	99 817	99 822
996	826	830	835	839	843	848	852	856	861	865
997	870	874	878	883	887	891	896	900	904	909
998	913	917	922	926	930	935	939	944	948	952
999	957	961	965	970	974	978	983	987	991	996

APPENDIX

TABLE 2

EXPONENTIAL FUNCTIONS

x	e^x	e^{-x}	x	e^x	e^{-x}
0.0	1.0000	1.00000	3.0	20.086	0.04979
0.1	1.1052	0.90484	3.1	22.198	0.04505
0.2	1.2214	0.81873	3.2	24.533	0.04076
0.3	1.3499	0.74082	3.3	27.113	0.03688
0.4	1.4918	0.67032	3.4	29.964	0.03337
0.5	1.6487	0.60653	3.5	33.115	0.03020
0.6	1.8221	0.54881	3.6	36.598	0.02732
0.7	2.0138	0.49659	3.7	40.447	0.02472
0.8	2.2255	0.44933	3.8	44.701	0.02237
0.9	2.4596	0.40657	3.9	49.402	0.02024
1.0	2.7183	0.36788	4.0	54.598	0.01832
1.1	3.0042	0.33287	4.1	60.340	0.01657
1.2	3.3201	0.30119	4.2	66.686	0.01500
1.3	3.6693	0.27253	4.3	73.700	0.01357
1.4	4.0552	0.24660	4.4	81.451	0.01228
1.5	4.4817	0.22313	4.5	90.017	0.01111
1.6	4.9530	0.20190	4.6	99.484	0.01005
1.7	5.4739	0.18268	4.7	109.950	0.00910
1.8	6.0496	0.16530	4.8	121.510	0.00823
1.9	6.6859	0.14957	4.9	134.290	0.00745
2.0	7.3891	0.13534	5.0	148.410	0.00674
2.1	8.1662	0.12246	5.1	164.020	0.00610
2.2	9.0250	0.11080	5.2	181.270	0.00552
2.3	9.9742	0.10026	5.3	200.340	0.00499
2.4	11.0230	0.09072	5.4	221.410	0.00452
2.5	12.1820	0.08208	5.5	244.690	0.00409
2.6	13.4640	0.07427	5.6	270.430	0.00370
2.7	14.8800	0.06721	5.7	298.870	0.00335
2.8	16.4450	0.06081	5.8	330.300	0.00303
2.9	18.1740	0.05502	5.9	365.040	0.00274

Table 3   NATURAL LOGARITHMS   573

TABLE 3

NATURAL LOGARITHMS

N	0	1	2	3	4	5	6	7	8	9
1.0	0.00000	0.00995	0.01980	0.02956	0.03922	0.04879	0.05827	0.06766	0.07696	0.08618
1.1	0.09531	0.10436	0.11333	0.12222	0.13103	0.13976	0.14842	0.15700	0.16551	0.17395
1.2	0.18232	0.19062	0.19885	0.20701	0.21511	0.22314	0.23111	0.23902	0.24686	0.25464
1.3	0.26236	0.27003	0.27763	0.28518	0.29267	0.30010	0.30748	0.31481	0.32208	0.32930
1.4	0.33647	0.34359	0.35066	0.35767	0.36464	0.37156	0.37844	0.38526	0.39204	0.39878
1.5	0.40547	0.41211	0.41871	0.42527	0.43178	0.43825	0.44469	0.45108	0.45742	0.46373
1.6	0.47000	0.47623	0.48243	0.48858	0.49470	0.50078	0.50682	0.51282	0.51879	0.52473
1.7	0.53063	0.53649	0.54232	0.54812	0.55389	0.55962	0.56531	0.57098	0.57661	0.58222
1.8	0.58779	0.59333	0.59884	0.60432	0.60977	0.61519	0.62058	0.62594	0.63127	0.63658
1.9	0.64185	0.64710	0.65233	0.65752	0.66269	0.66783	0.67294	0.67803	0.68310	0.68813
2.0	0.69315	0.69813	0.70310	0.70804	0.71295	0.71784	0.72271	0.72755	0.73237	0.73716
2.1	0.74194	0.74669	0.75142	0.75612	0.76081	0.76547	0.77011	0.77473	0.77932	0.78390
2.2	0.78846	0.79299	0.79751	0.80200	0.80648	0.81093	0.81536	0.81978	0.82418	0.82855
2.3	0.83291	0.83725	0.84157	0.84587	0.85015	0.85442	0.85866	0.86289	0.86710	0.87129
2.4	0.87547	0.87963	0.88377	0.88789	0.89200	0.89609	0.90016	0.90422	0.90826	0.91228
2.5	0.91629	0.92028	0.92426	0.92822	0.93216	0.93609	0.94001	0.94391	0.94779	0.95166
2.6	0.95551	0.95935	0.96317	0.96698	0.97078	0.97456	0.97833	0.98208	0.98582	0.98954
2.7	0.99325	0.99695	1.00063	1.00430	1.00796	1.01160	1.01523	1.01885	1.02245	1.02604
2.8	1.02962	1.03318	1.03674	1.04028	1.04380	1.04732	1.05082	1.05431	1.05779	1.06126
2.9	1.06471	1.06815	1.07158	1.07500	1.07841	1.08181	1.08519	1.08856	1.09192	1.09527
3.0	1.09861	1.10194	1.10526	1.10856	1.11186	1.11514	1.11841	1.12168	1.12493	1.12817
3.1	1.13140	1.13462	1.13783	1.14103	1.14422	1.14740	1.15057	1.15373	1.15688	1.16002
3.2	1.16315	1.16627	1.16938	1.17248	1.17557	1.17865	1.18173	1.18479	1.18784	1.19089
3.3	1.19392	1.19695	1.19996	1.20297	1.20597	1.20896	1.21194	1.21491	1.21788	1.22083
3.4	1.22378	1.22671	1.22964	1.23256	1.23547	1.23837	1.24127	1.24415	1.24703	1.24990
3.5	1.25276	1.25562	1.25846	1.26130	1.26413	1.26695	1.26976	1.27257	1.27536	1.27815
3.6	1.28093	1.28371	1.28647	1.28923	1.29198	1.29473	1.29746	1.30019	1.30291	1.30563
3.7	1.30833	1.31103	1.31372	1.31641	1.31909	1.32176	1.32442	1.32708	1.32972	1.33237
3.8	1.33500	1.33763	1.34025	1.34286	1.34547	1.34807	1.35067	1.35325	1.35584	1.35841
3.9	1.36098	1.36354	1.36609	1.36864	1.37118	1.37372	1.37624	1.37877	1.38128	1.38379
4.0	1.38629	1.38879	1.39128	1.39377	1.39624	1.39872	1.40118	1.40364	1.40610	1.40854
4.1	1.41099	1.41342	1.41585	1.41828	1.42070	1.42311	1.42552	1.42792	1.43031	1.43270
4.2	1.43508	1.43746	1.43984	1.44220	1.44456	1.44692	1.44927	1.45161	1.45395	1.45629
4.3	1.45862	1.46094	1.46326	1.46557	1.46787	1.47018	1.47247	1.47476	1.47705	1.47933
4.4	1.48160	1.48387	1.48614	1.48840	1.49065	1.49290	1.49515	1.49739	1.49962	1.50185
4.5	1.50408	1.50630	1.50851	1.51072	1.51293	1.51513	1.51732	1.51951	1.52170	1.52388
4.6	1.52606	1.52823	1.53039	1.53256	1.53471	1.53687	1.53902	1.54116	1.54330	1.54543
4.7	1.54756	1.54969	1.55181	1.55393	1.55604	1.55814	1.56025	1.56235	1.56444	1.56653
4.8	1.56862	1.57070	1.57277	1.57485	1.57691	1.57898	1.58104	1.58309	1.58515	1.58719
4.9	1.58924	1.59127	1.59331	1.59534	1.59737	1.59939	1.60141	1.60342	1.60543	1.60744
5.0	1.60944	1.61144	1.61343	1.61542	1.61741	1.61939	1.62137	1.62334	1.62531	1.62728
5.1	1.62924	1.63120	1.63315	1.63511	1.63705	1.63900	1.64094	1.64287	1.64481	1.64673
5.2	1.64866	1.65058	1.65250	1.65441	1.65632	1.65823	1.66013	1.66203	1.66393	1.66582
5.3	1.66771	1.66959	1.67147	1.67335	1.67523	1.67710	1.67896	1.68083	1.68269	1.68455
5.4	1.68640	1.68825	1.69010	1.69194	1.69378	1.69562	1.69745	1.69928	1.70111	1.70293

TABLE 3 (*continued*)

NATURAL LOGARITHMS

N	0	1	2	3	4	5	6	7	8	9
5.5	1.70475	1.70656	1.70838	1.71019	1.71199	1.71380	1.71560	1.71740	1.71919	1.72098
5.6	1.72277	1.72455	1.72633	1.72811	1.72988	1.73166	1.73342	1.73519	1.73695	1.73871
5.7	1.74047	1.74222	1.74397	1.74572	1.74746	1.74920	1.75094	1.75267	1.75440	1.75613
5.8	1.75786	1.75958	1.76130	1.76302	1.76473	1.76644	1.76815	1.76985	1.77156	1.77326
5.9	1.77495	1.77665	1.77834	1.78002	1.78171	1.78339	1.78507	1.78675	1.78842	1.79009
6.0	1.79176	1.79342	1.79509	1.79675	1.79840	1.80006	1.80171	1.80336	1.80500	1.80665
6.1	1.80829	1.80993	1.81156	1.81319	1.81482	1.81645	1.81808	1.81970	1.82132	1.82294
6.2	1.82455	1.82616	1.82777	1.82938	1.83098	1.83258	1.83418	1.83578	1.83737	1.83896
6.3	1.84055	1.84214	1.84372	1.84530	1.84688	1.84845	1.85003	1.85160	1.85317	1.85473
6.4	1.85630	1.85786	1.85942	1.86097	1.86253	1.86408	1.86563	1.86718	1.86872	1.87026
6.5	1.87180	1.87334	1.87487	1.87641	1.87794	1.87947	1.88099	1.88251	1.88403	1.88555
6.6	1.88707	1.88858	1.89010	1.89160	1.89311	1.89462	1.89612	1.89762	1.89912	1.90061
6.7	1.90211	1.90360	1.90509	1.90658	1.90806	1.90954	1.91102	1.91250	1.91398	1.91545
6.8	1.91692	1.91839	1.91986	1.92132	1.92279	1.92425	1.92571	1.92716	1.92862	1.93007
6.9	1.93152	1.93297	1.93442	1.93586	1.93730	1.93874	1.94018	1.94162	1.94305	1.94448
7.0	1.94591	1.94734	1.94876	1.95019	1.95161	1.95303	1.95445	1.95586	1.95727	1.95869
7.1	1.96009	1.96150	1.96291	1.96431	1.96571	1.96711	1.96851	1.96991	1.97130	1.97269
7 2	1.97408	1.97547	1.97685	1.97824	1.97962	1.98100	1.98238	1.98376	1.98513	1.98650
7.3	1.98787	1.98924	1.99061	1.99198	1.99334	1.99470	1.99606	1.99742	1.99877	2.00013
7.4	2.00148	2.00283	2.00418	2.00553	2.00687	2.00821	2.00956	2.01089	2.01223	2.01357
7.5	2.01490	2.01624	2.01757	2.01890	2.02022	2.02155	2.02287	2.02419	2.02551	2.02683
7.6	2.02815	2.02946	2.03078	2.03209	2.03340	2.03471	2.03601	2.03732	2.03862	2.03992
7.7	2.04122	2.04252	2.04381	2.04511	2.04640	2.04769	2.04898	2.05027	2.05156	2.05284
7.8	2.05412	2.05540	2.05668	2.05796	2.05924	2.06051	2.06179	2.06306	2.06433	2.06560
7.9	2.06686	2.06813	2.06939	2.07065	2.07191	2.07317	2.07443	2.07568	2.07694	2.07819
8.0	2.07944	2.08069	2.08194	2.08318	2.08443	2.08567	2.08691	2.08815	2.08939	2.09063
8.1	2.09186	2.09310	2.09433	2.09556	2.09679	2.09802	2.09924	2.10047	2.10169	2.10291
8.2	2.10413	2.10535	2.10657	2.10779	2.10900	2.11021	2.11142	2.11263	2.11384	2.11505
8.3	2.11626	2.11746	2.11866	2.11986	2.12106	2.12226	2.12346	2.12465	2.12585	2.12704
8.4	2.12823	2.12942	2.13061	2.13180	2.13298	2.13417	2.13535	2.13653	2.13771	2.13889
8.5	2.14007	2.14124	2.14242	2.14359	2.14476	2.14593	2.14710	2.14827	2.14943	2.15060
8.6	2.15176	2.15292	2.15409	2.15524	2.15640	2.15756	2.15871	2.15987	2.16102	2.16217
8.7	2.16332	2.16447	2.16562	2.16677	2.16791	2.16905	2.17020	2.17134	2.17248	2.17361
8.8	2.17475	2.17589	2.17702	2.17816	2.17929	2.18042	2.18155	2.18267	2.18380	2.18493
8.9	2.18605	2.18717	2.18830	2.18942	2.19054	2.19165	2.19277	2.19389	2.19500	2.19611
9.0	2.19722	2.19834	2.19944	2.20055	2.20166	2.20276	2.20387	2.20497	2.20607	2.20717
9.1	2.20827	2.20937	2.21047	2.21157	2.21266	2.21375	2.21485	2.21594	2.21703	2.21812
9.2	2.21920	2.22029	2.22138	2.22246	2.22354	2.22462	2.22570	2.22678	2.22786	2.22894
9.3	2.23001	2.23109	2.23216	2.23324	2.23431	2.23538	2.23645	2.23751	2.23858	2.23965
9.4	2.24071	2.24177	2.24284	2.24390	2.24496	2.24601	2.24707	2.24813	2.24918	2.25024
9.5	2.25129	2.25234	2.25339	2.25444	2.25549	2.25654	2.25759	2.25863	2.25968	2.26072
9.6	2.26176	2.26280	2.26384	2.26488	2.26592	2.26696	2.26799	2.26903	2.27006	2.27109
9.7	2.27213	2.27316	2.27419	2.27521	2.27624	2.27727	2.27829	2.27932	2.28034	2.28136
9.8	2.28238	2.28340	2.28442	2.28544	2.28646	2.28747	2.28849	2.28950	2.29051	2.29152
9.9	2.29253	2.29354	2.29455	2.29556	2.29657	2.29757	2.29858	2.29958	2.30058	2.30158
10.0	2.30259	2.30358	2.30458	2.30558	2.30658	2.30757	2.30857	2.30956	2.31055	2.31154

Table 4

Trigonometric Functions

The detailed explanation

of

this table

is given in

section 11.1

APPENDIX

0°

′	sin	cos	tan	cot	′
0	.00000	1.0000	.00000	—	60
1	029	000	029	3437.7	59
2	058	000	058	1718.9	58
3	087	000	087	1145.9	57
4	116	000	116	859.44	56
5	.00145	1.0000	.00145	687.55	55
6	175	000	175	572.96	54
7	204	000	204	491.11	53
8	233	000	233	429.72	52
9	262	000	262	381.97	51
10	.00291	1.0000	.00291	343.77	50
11	320	.99999	320	312.52	49
12	349	999	349	286.48	48
13	378	999	378	264.44	47
14	407	999	407	245.55	46
15	.00436	.99999	.00436	229.18	45
16	465	999	465	214.86	44
17	495	999	495	202.22	43
18	524	999	524	190.98	42
19	553	998	553	180.93	41
20	.00582	.99998	.00582	171.89	40
21	611	998	611	163.70	39
22	640	998	640	156.26	38
23	669	998	669	149.47	37
24	698	998	698	143.24	36
25	.00727	.99997	.00727	137.51	35
26	756	997	756	132.22	34
27	785	997	785	127.32	33
28	814	997	815	122.77	32
29	844	996	844	118.54	31
30	.00873	.99996	.00873	114.59	30
31	902	996	902	110.89	29
32	931	996	931	107.43	28
33	960	995	960	104.17	27
34	.00989	995	.00989	101.11	26
35	.01018	.99995	.01018	98.218	25
36	047	995	047	95.489	24
37	076	994	076	92.908	23
38	105	994	105	90.463	22
39	134	994	135	88.144	21
40	.01164	.99993	.01164	85.940	20
41	193	993	193	83.844	19
42	222	993	222	81.847	18
43	251	992	251	79.943	17
44	280	992	280	78.126	16
45	.01309	.99991	.01309	76.390	15
46	338	991	338	74.729	14
47	367	991	367	73.139	13
48	396	990	396	71.615	12
49	425	990	425	70.153	11
50	.01454	.99989	.01455	68.750	10
51	483	989	484	67.402	9
52	513	989	513	66.105	8
53	542	988	542	64.858	7
54	571	988	571	63.657	6
55	.01600	.99987	.01600	62.499	5
56	629	987	629	61.383	4
57	658	986	658	60.306	3
58	687	986	687	59.266	2
59	716	985	716	58.261	1
60	.01745	.99985	.01746	57.290	0
′	cos	sin	cot	tan	′

89°

1°

′	sin	cos	tan	cot	′
0	.01745	.99985	.01746	57.290	60
1	774	984	775	56.351	59
2	803	984	804	55.442	58
3	832	983	833	54.561	57
4	862	983	862	53.709	56
5	.01891	.99982	.01891	52.882	55
6	920	982	920	52.081	54
7	949	981	949	51.303	53
8	.01978	980	.01978	50.549	52
9	.02007	980	.02007	49.816	51
10	.02036	.99979	.02036	49.104	50
11	065	979	066	48.412	49
12	094	978	095	47.740	48
13	123	977	124	47.085	47
14	152	977	153	46.449	46
15	.02181	.99976	.02182	45.829	45
16	211	976	211	45.226	44
17	240	975	240	44.639	43
18	269	974	269	44.066	42
19	298	974	298	43.508	41
20	.02327	.99973	.02328	42.964	40
21	356	972	357	42.433	39
22	385	972	386	41.916	38
23	414	971	415	41.411	37
24	443	970	444	40.917	36
25	.02472	.99969	.02473	40.436	35
26	501	969	502	39.965	34
27	530	968	531	39.506	33
28	560	967	560	39.057	32
29	589	966	589	38.618	31
30	.02618	.99966	.02619	38.188	30
31	647	965	648	37.769	29
32	676	964	677	37.358	28
33	705	963	706	36.956	27
34	734	963	735	36.563	26
35	.02763	.99962	.02764	36.178	25
36	792	961	793	35.801	24
37	821	960	822	35.431	23
38	850	959	851	35.070	22
39	879	959	881	34.715	21
40	.02908	.99958	.02910	34.368	20
41	938	957	939	34.027	19
42	967	956	968	33.694	18
43	.02996	955	.02997	33.366	17
44	.03025	954	.03026	33.045	16
45	.03054	.99953	.03055	32.730	15
46	083	952	084	32.421	14
47	112	952	114	32.118	13
48	141	951	143	31.821	12
49	170	950	172	31.528	11
50	.03199	.99949	.03201	31.242	10
51	228	948	230	30.960	9
52	257	947	259	30.683	8
53	286	946	288	30.412	7
54	316	945	317	30.145	6
55	.03345	.99944	.03346	29.882	5
56	374	943	376	29.624	4
57	403	942	405	29.371	3
58	432	941	434	29.122	2
59	461	940	463	28.877	1
60	.03490	.99939	.03492	28.636	0
′	cos	sin	cot	tan	′

88°

2°

′	sin	cos	tan	cot	′
0	.03490	.99939	.03492	28.636	60
1	519	938	521	.399	59
2	548	937	550	28.166	58
3	577	936	579	27.937	57
4	606	935	609	.712	56
5	.03635	.99934	.03638	27.490	55
6	664	933	667	.271	54
7	693	932	696	27.057	53
8	723	931	725	26.845	52
9	752	930	754	.637	51
10	.03781	.99929	.03783	26.432	50
11	810	927	812	.230	49
12	839	926	842	26.031	48
13	868	925	871	25.835	47
14	897	924	900	.642	46
15	.03926	.99923	.03929	25.452	45
16	955	922	958	.264	44
17	.03984	921	.03987	25.080	43
18	.04013	919	.04016	24.898	42
19	042	918	046	.719	41
20	.04071	.99917	.04075	24.542	40
21	100	916	104	.368	39
22	129	915	133	.196	38
23	159	913	162	24.026	37
24	188	912	191	23.859	36
25	.04217	.99911	.04220	23.695	35
26	246	910	250	.532	34
27	275	909	279	.372	33
28	304	907	308	.214	32
29	333	906	337	23.058	31
30	.04362	.99905	.04366	22.904	30
31	391	904	395	.752	29
32	420	902	424	.602	28
33	449	901	454	.454	27
34	478	900	483	.308	26
35	.04507	.99898	.04512	22.164	25
36	536	897	541	22.022	24
37	565	896	570	21.881	23
38	594	894	599	.743	22
39	623	893	628	.606	21
40	.04653	.99892	.04658	21.470	20
41	682	890	687	.337	19
42	711	889	716	.205	18
43	740	888	745	21.075	17
44	769	886	774	20.946	16
45	.04798	.99885	.04803	20.819	15
46	827	883	833	.693	14
47	856	882	862	.569	13
48	885	881	891	.446	12
49	914	879	920	.325	11
50	.04943	.99878	.04949	20.206	10
51	.04972	876	.04978	20.087	9
52	.05001	875	.05007	19.970	8
53	030	873	037	.855	7
54	059	872	066	.740	6
55	.05088	.99870	.05095	19.627	5
56	117	869	124	.516	4
57	146	867	153	.405	3
58	175	866	182	.296	2
59	205	864	212	.188	1
60	.05234	.99863	.05241	19.081	0
′	cos	sin	cot	tan	′

87°

Table 4   TRIGONOMETRIC FUNCTIONS   579

3°

′	sin	cos	tan	cot	′
0	.05234	.99863	.05241	19.081	60
1	263	861	270	18.976	59
2	292	860	299	.871	58
3	321	858	328	.768	57
4	350	857	357	.666	56
5	.05379	.99855	.05387	18.564	55
6	408	854	416	.464	54
7	437	852	445	.366	53
8	466	851	474	.268	52
9	495	849	503	.171	51
10	.05524	.99847	.05533	18.075	50
11	553	846	562	17.980	49
12	582	844	591	.886	48
13	611	842	620	.793	47
14	640	841	649	.702	46
15	.05669	.99839	.05678	17.611	45
16	698	838	708	.521	44
17	727	836	737	.431	43
18	756	834	766	.343	42
19	785	833	795	.256	41
20	.05814	.99831	.05824	17.169	40
21	844	829	854	17.084	39
22	873	827	883	16.999	38
23	902	826	912	.915	37
24	931	824	941	.832	36
25	.05960	.99822	.05970	16.750	35
26	.05989	821	.05999	.668	34
27	.06018	819	.06029	.587	33
28	047	817	058	.507	32
29	076	815	087	.428	31
30	.06105	.99813	.06116	16.350	30
31	134	812	145	.272	29
32	163	810	175	.195	28
33	192	808	204	.119	27
34	221	806	233	16.043	26
35	.06250	.99804	.06262	15.969	25
36	279	803	291	.895	24
37	308	801	321	.821	23
38	337	799	350	.748	22
39	366	797	379	.676	21
40	.06395	.99795	.06408	15.605	20
41	424	793	438	.534	19
42	453	792	467	.464	18
43	482	790	496	.394	17
44	511	788	525	.325	16
45	.06540	.99786	.06554	15.257	15
46	569	784	584	.189	14
47	598	782	613	.122	13
48	627	780	642	15.056	12
49	656	778	671	14.990	11
50	.06685	.99776	.06700	14.924	10
51	714	774	730	.860	9
52	743	772	759	.795	8
53	773	770	788	.732	7
54	802	768	817	.669	6
55	.06831	.99766	.06847	14.606	5
56	860	764	876	.544	4
57	889	762	905	.482	3
58	918	760	934	.421	2
59	947	758	963	.361	1
60	.06976	.99756	.06993	14.301	0
′	cos	sin	cot	tan	′

86°

APPENDIX

4°

′	sin	cos	tan	cot	′
0	.06976	.99756	.06993	14.301	60
1	.07005	754	.07022	.241	59
2	034	752	051	.182	58
3	063	750	080	.124	57
4	092	748	110	.065	56
5	.07121	.99746	.07139	14.008	55
6	150	744	168	13.951	54
7	179	742	197	.894	53
8	208	740	227	.838	52
9	237	738	256	.782	51
10	.07266	.99736	.07285	13.727	50
11	295	734	314	.672	49
12	324	731	344	.617	48
13	353	729	373	.563	47
14	382	727	402	.510	46
15	.07411	.99725	.07431	13.457	45
16	440	723	461	.404	44
17	469	721	490	.352	43
18	498	719	519	.300	42
19	527	716	548	.248	41
20	.07556	.99714	.07578	13.197	40
21	585	712	607	.146	39
22	614	710	636	.096	38
23	643	708	665	13.046	37
24	672	705	695	12.996	36
25	.07701	.99703	.07724	12.947	35
26	730	701	753	.898	34
27	759	699	782	.850	33
28	788	696	812	.801	32
29	817	694	841	.754	31
30	.07846	.99692	.07870	12.706	30
31	875	689	899	.659	29
32	904	687	929	.612	28
33	933	685	958	.566	27
34	962	683	.07987	.520	26
35	.07991	.99680	.08017	12.474	25
36	.08020	678	046	.429	24
37	049	676	075	.384	23
38	078	673	104	.339	22
39	107	671	134	.295	21
40	.08136	.99668	.08163	12.251	20
41	165	666	192	.207	19
42	194	664	221	.163	18
43	223	661	251	.120	17
44	252	659	280	.077	16
45	.08281	.99657	.08309	12.035	15
46	310	654	339	11.992	14
47	339	652	368	.950	13
48	368	649	397	.909	12
49	397	647	427	.867	11
50	.08426	.99644	.08456	11.826	10
51	455	642	485	.785	9
52	484	639	514	.745	8
53	513	637	544	.705	7
54	542	635	573	.664	6
55	.08571	.99632	.08602	11.625	5
56	600	630	632	.585	4
57	629	627	661	.546	3
58	658	625	690	.507	2
59	687	622	720	.468	1
60	.08716	.99619	.08749	11.430	0
′	cos	sin	cot	tan	′

85°

Table 4 TRIGONOMETRIC FUNCTIONS 581

5°

′	sin	cos	tan	cot	′
0	.08716	.99619	.08749	11.430	60
1	745	617	778	.392	59
2	774	614	807	.354	58
3	803	612	837	.316	57
4	831	609	866	.279	56
5	.08860	.99607	.08895	11.242	55
6	889	604	925	.205	54
7	918	602	954	.168	53
8	947	599	.08983	.132	52
9	.08976	596	.09013	.095	51
10	.09005	.99594	.09042	11.059	50
11	034	591	071	11.024	49
12	063	588	101	10.988	48
13	092	586	130	.953	47
14	121	583	159	.918	46
15	.09150	.99580	.09189	10.883	45
16	179	578	218	.848	44
17	208	575	247	.814	43
18	237	572	277	.780	42
19	266	570	306	.746	41
20	.09295	.99567	.09335	10.712	40
21	324	564	365	.678	39
22	353	562	394	.645	38
23	382	559	423	.612	37
24	411	556	453	.579	36
25	.09440	.99553	.09482	10.546	35
26	469	551	511	.514	34
27	498	548	541	.481	33
28	527	545	570	.449	32
29	556	542	600	.417	31
30	.09585	.99540	.09629	10.385	30
31	614	537	658	.354	29
32	642	534	688	.322	28
33	671	531	717	.291	27
34	700	528	746	.260	26
35	.09729	.99526	.09776	10.229	25
36	758	523	805	.199	24
37	787	520	834	.168	23
38	816	517	864	.138	22
39	845	514	893	.108	21
40	.09874	.99511	.09923	10.078	20
41	903	508	952	.048	19
42	932	506	.09981	10.019	18
43	961	503	.10011	9.9893	17
44	.09990	500	040	.9601	16
45	.10019	.99497	.10069	9.9310	15
46	048	494	099	.9021	14
47	077	491	128	.8734	13
48	106	488	158	.8448	12
49	135	485	187	.8164	11
50	.10164	.99482	.10216	9.7882	10
51	192	479	246	.7601	9
52	221	476	275	.7322	8
53	250	473	305	.7044	7
54	279	470	334	.6768	6
55	.10308	.99467	.10363	9.6493	5
56	337	464	393	.6220	4
57	366	461	422	.5949	3
58	395	458	452	.5679	2
59	424	455	481	.5411	1
60	.10453	.99452	.10510	9.5144	0
′	cos	sin	cot	tan	′

84°

6°

'	sin	cos	tan	cot	'
0	.10453	.99452	.10510	9.5144	60
1	482	449	540	.4878	59
2	511	446	569	.4614	58
3	540	443	599	.4352	57
4	569	440	628	.4090	56
5	.10597	.99437	.10657	9.3831	55
6	626	434	687	.3572	54
7	655	431	716	.3315	53
8	684	428	746	.3060	52
9	713	424	775	.2806	51
10	.10742	.99421	.10805	9.2553	50
11	771	418	834	.2302	49
12	800	415	863	.2052	48
13	829	412	893	.1803	47
14	858	409	922	.1555	46
15	.10887	.99406	.10952	9.1309	45
16	916	402	981	.1065	44
17	945	399	.11011	.0821	43
18	.10973	396	040	.0579	42
19	.11002	393	070	.0338	41
20	.11031	.99390	.11099	9.0098	40
21	060	386	128	8.9860	39
22	089	383	158	.9623	38
23	118	380	187	.9387	37
24	147	377	217	.9152	36
25	.11176	.99374	.11246	8.8919	35
26	205	370	276	.8686	34
27	234	367	305	.8455	33
28	263	364	335	.8225	32
29	291	360	364	.7996	31
30	.11320	.99357	.11394	8.7769	30
31	349	354	423	.7542	29
32	378	351	452	.7317	28
33	407	347	482	.7093	27
34	436	344	511	.6870	26
35	.11465	.99341	.11541	8.6648	25
36	494	337	570	.6427	24
37	523	334	600	.6208	23
38	552	331	629	.5989	22
39	580	327	659	.5772	21
40	.11609	.99324	.11688	8.5555	20
41	638	320	718	.5340	19
42	667	317	747	.5126	18
43	696	314	777	.4913	17
44	725	310	806	.4701	16
45	.11754	.99307	.11836	8.4490	15
46	783	303	865	.4280	14
47	812	300	895	.4071	13
48	840	297	924	.3863	12
49	869	293	954	.3656	11
50	.11898	.99290	.11983	8.3450	10
51	927	286	.12013	.3245	9
52	956	283	042	.3041	8
53	.11985	279	072	.2838	7
54	.12014	276	101	.2636	6
55	.12043	.99272	.12131	8.2434	5
56	071	269	160	.2234	4
57	100	265	190	.2035	3
58	129	262	219	.1837	2
59	158	258	249	.1640	1
60	.12187	.99255	.12278	8.1443	0
'	cos	sin	cot	tan	'

83°

7°

′	sin	cos	tan	cot	′
0	.12187	.99255	.12278	8.1443	60
1	216	251	308	.1248	59
2	245	248	338	.1054	58
3	274	244	367	.0860	57
4	302	240	397	.0667	56
5	.12331	.99237	.12426	8.0476	55
6	360	233	456	.0285	54
7	389	230	485	8.0095	53
8	418	226	515	7.9906	52
9	447	222	544	.9718	51
10	.12476	.99219	.12574	7.9530	50
11	504	215	603	.9344	49
12	533	211	633	.9158	48
13	562	208	662	.8973	47
14	591	204	692	.8789	46
15	.12620	.99200	.12722	7.8606	45
16	649	197	751	.8424	44
17	678	193	781	.8243	43
18	706	189	810	.8062	42
19	735	186	840	.7882	41
20	.12764	.99182	.12869	7.7704	40
21	793	178	899	.7525	39
22	822	175	929	.7348	38
23	851	171	958	.7171	37
24	880	167	.12988	.6996	36
25	.12908	.99163	.13017	7.6821	35
26	937	160	047	.6647	34
27	966	156	076	.6473	33
28	.12995	152	106	.6301	32
29	.13024	148	136	.6129	31
30	.13053	.99144	.13165	7.5958	30
31	081	141	195	.5787	29
32	110	137	224	.5618	28
33	139	133	254	.5449	27
34	168	129	284	.5281	26
35	.13197	.99125	.13313	7.5113	25
36	226	122	343	.4947	24
37	254	118	372	.4781	23
38	283	114	402	.4615	22
39	312	110	432	.4451	21
40	.13341	.99106	.13461	7.4287	20
41	370	102	491	.4124	19
42	399	098	521	.3962	18
43	427	094	550	.3800	17
44	456	091	580	.3639	16
45	.13485	.99087	.13609	7.3479	15
46	514	083	639	.3319	14
47	543	079	669	.3160	13
48	572	075	698	.3002	12
49	600	071	728	.2844	11
50	.13629	.99067	.13758	7.2687	10
51	658	063	787	.2531	9
52	687	059	817	.2375	8
53	716	055	846	.2220	7
54	744	051	876	.2066	6
55	.13773	.99047	.13906	7.1912	5
56	802	043	935	.1759	4
57	831	039	965	.1607	3
58	860	035	.13995	.1455	2
59	889	031	.14024	.1304	1
60	.13917	.99027	.14054	7.1154	0
′	cos	sin	cot	tan	′

82°

8°

′	sin	cos	tan	cot	′
0	.13917	.99027	.14054	7.1154	60
1	946	023	084	.1004	59
2	.13975	019	113	.0855	58
3	.14004	015	143	.0706	57
4	033	011	173	.0558	56
5	.14061	.99006	.14202	7.0410	55
6	090	.99002	232	.0264	54
7	119	.98998	262	7.0117	53
8	148	994	291	6.9972	52
9	177	990	321	.9827	51
10	.14205	.98986	.14351	6.9682	50
11	234	982	381	.9538	49
12	263	978	410	.9395	48
13	292	973	440	.9252	47
14	320	969	470	.9110	46
15	.14349	.98965	.14499	6.8969	45
16	378	961	529	.8828	44
17	407	957	559	.8687	43
18	436	953	588	.8548	42
19	464	948	618	.8408	41
20	.14493	.98944	.14648	6.8269	40
21	522	940	678	.8131	39
22	551	936	707	.7994	38
23	580	931	737	.7856	37
24	608	927	767	.7720	36
25	.14637	.98923	.14796	6.7584	35
26	666	919	826	.7448	34
27	695	914	856	.7313	33
28	723	910	886	.7179	32
29	752	906	915	.7045	31
30	.14781	.98902	.14945	6.6912	30
31	810	897	.14975	.6779	29
32	838	893	.15005	.6646	28
33	867	889	034	.6514	27
34	896	884	064	.6383	26
35	.14925	.98880	.15094	6.6252	25
36	954	876	124	.6122	24
37	.14982	871	153	.5992	23
38	.15011	867	183	.5863	22
39	040	863	213	.5734	21
40	.15069	.98858	.15243	6.5606	20
41	097	854	272	.5478	19
42	126	849	302	.5350	18
43	155	845	332	.5223	17
44	184	841	362	.5097	16
45	.15212	.98836	.15391	6.4971	15
46	241	832	421	.4846	14
47	270	827	451	.4721	13
48	299	823	481	.4596	12
49	327	818	511	.4472	11
50	.15356	.98814	.15540	6.4348	10
51	385	809	570	.4225	9
52	414	805	600	.4103	8
53	442	800	630	.3980	7
54	471	796	660	.3859	6
55	.15500	.98791	.15689	6.3737	5
56	529	787	719	.3617	4
57	557	782	749	.3496	3
58	586	778	779	.3376	2
59	615	773	809	.3257	1
60	.15643	.98769	.15838	6.3138	0
′	cos	sin	cot	tan	′

81°

Table 4   TRIGONOMETRIC FUNCTIONS   585

9°

′	sin	cos	tan	cot	′
0	.15643	.98769	.15838	6.3138	60
1	672	764	868	.3019	59
2	701	760	898	.2901	58
3	730	755	928	.2783	57
4	758	751	958	.2666	56
5	.15787	.98746	.15988	6.2549	55
6	816	741	.16017	.2432	54
7	845	737	047	.2316	53
8	873	732	077	.2200	52
9	902	728	107	.2085	51
10	.15931	.98723	.16137	6.1970	50
11	959	718	167	.1856	49
12	.15988	714	196	.1742	48
13	.16017	709	226	.1628	47
14	046	704	256	.1515	46
15	.16074	.98700	.16286	6.1402	45
16	103	695	316	.1290	44
17	132	690	346	.1178	43
18	160	686	376	.1066	42
19	189	681	405	.0955	41
20	.16218	.98676	.16435	6.0844	40
21	246	671	465	.0734	39
22	275	667	495	.0624	38
23	304	662	525	.0514	37
24	333	657	555	.0405	36
25	.16361	.98652	.16585	6.0296	35
26	390	648	615	.0188	34
27	419	643	645	6.0080	33
28	447	638	674	5.9972	32
29	476	633	704	.9865	31
30	.16505	.98629	.16734	5.9758	30
31	533	624	764	.9651	29
32	562	619	794	.9545	28
33	591	614	824	.9439	27
34	620	609	854	.9333	26
35	.16648	.98604	.16884	5.9228	25
36	677	600	914	.9124	24
37	706	595	944	.9019	23
38	734	590	.16974	.8915	22
39	763	585	.17004	.8811	21
40	.16792	.98580	.17033	5.8708	20
41	820	575	063	.8605	19
42	849	570	093	.8502	18
43	878	565	123	.8400	17
44	906	561	153	.8298	16
45	.16935	.98556	.17183	5.8197	15
46	964	551	213	.8095	14
47	.16992	546	243	.7994	13
48	.17021	541	273	.7894	12
49	050	536	303	.7794	11
50	.17078	.98531	.17333	5.7694	10
51	107	526	363	.7594	9
52	136	521	393	.7495	8
53	164	516	423	.7396	7
54	193	511	453	.7297	6
55	.17222	.98506	.17483	5.7199	5
56	250	501	513	.7101	4
57	279	496	543	.7004	3
58	308	491	573	.6906	2
59	336	486	603	.6809	1
60	.17365	.98481	.17633	5.6713	0
′	cos	sin	cot	tan	′

80°

10°

′	sin	cos	tan	cot	′
0	.17365	.98481	.17633	5.6713	60
1	393	476	663	.6617	59
2	422	471	693	.6521	58
3	451	466	723	.6425	57
4	479	461	753	.6329	56
5	.17508	.98455	.17783	5.6234	55
6	537	450	813	.6140	54
7	565	445	843	.6045	53
8	594	440	873	.5951	52
9	623	435	903	.5857	51
10	.17651	.98430	.17933	5.5764	50
11	680	425	963	.5671	49
12	708	420	.17993	.5578	48
13	737	414	.18023	.5485	47
14	766	409	053	.5393	46
15	.17794	.98404	.18083	5.5301	45
16	823	399	113	.5209	44
17	852	394	143	.5118	43
18	880	389	173	.5026	42
19	909	383	203	.4936	41
20	.17937	.98378	.18233	5.4845	40
21	966	373	263	.4755	39
22	.17995	368	293	.4665	38
23	.18023	362	323	.4575	37
24	052	357	353	.4486	36
25	.18081	.98352	.18384	5.4397	35
26	109	347	414	.4308	34
27	138	341	444	.4219	33
28	166	336	474	.4131	32
29	195	331	504	.4043	31
30	.18224	.98325	.18534	5.3955	30
31	252	320	564	.3868	29
32	281	315	594	.3781	28
33	309	310	624	.3694	27
34	338	304	654	.3607	26
35	.18367	.98299	.18684	5.3521	25
36	395	294	714	.3435	24
37	424	288	745	.3349	23
38	452	283	775	.3263	22
39	481	277	805	.3178	21
40	.18509	.98272	.18835	5.3093	20
41	538	267	865	.3008	19
42	567	261	895	.2924	18
43	595	256	925	.2839	17
44	624	250	955	.2755	16
45	.18652	.98245	.18986	5.2672	15
46	681	240	.19016	.2588	14
47	710	234	046	.2505	13
48	738	229	076	.2422	12
49	767	223	106	.2339	11
50	.18795	.98218	.19136	5.2257	10
51	824	212	166	.2174	9
52	852	207	197	.2092	8
53	881	201	227	.2011	7
54	910	196	257	.1929	6
55	.18938	.98190	.19287	5.1848	5
56	967	185	317	.1767	4
57	.18995	179	347	.1686	3
58	.19024	174	378	.1606	2
59	052	168	408	.1526	1
60	.19081	.98163	.19438	5.1446	0
′	cos	sin	cot	tan	′

79°

11°

′	sin	cos	tan	cot	′
0	.19081	.98163	.19438	5.1446	60
1	109	157	468	.1366	59
2	138	152	498	.1286	58
3	167	146	529	.1207	57
4	195	140	559	.1128	56
5	.19224	.98135	.19589	5.1049	55
6	252	129	619	.0970	54
7	281	124	649	.0892	53
8	309	118	680	.0814	52
9	338	112	710	.0736	51
10	.19366	.98107	.19740	5.0658	50
11	395	101	770	.0581	49
12	423	096	801	.0504	48
13	452	090	831	.0427	47
14	481	084	861	.0350	46
15	.19509	.98079	.19891	5.0273	45
16	538	073	921	.0197	44
17	566	067	952	.0121	43
18	595	061	.19982	5.0045	42
19	623	056	.20012	4.9969	41
20	.19652	.98050	.20042	4.9894	40
21	680	044	073	.9819	39
22	709	039	103	.9744	38
23	737	033	133	.9669	37
24	766	027	164	.9594	36
25	.19794	.98021	.20194	4.9520	35
26	823	016	224	.9446	34
27	851	010	254	.9372	33
28	880	.98004	285	.9298	32
29	908	.97998	315	.9225	31
30	.19937	.97992	.20345	4.9152	30
31	965	987	376	.9078	29
32	.19994	981	406	.9006	28
33	.20022	975	436	.8933	27
34	051	969	466	.8860	26
35	.20079	.97963	.20497	4.8788	25
36	108	958	527	.8716	24
37	136	952	557	.8644	23
38	165	946	588	.8573	22
39	193	940	618	.8501	21
40	.20222	.97934	.20648	4.8430	20
41	250	928	679	.8359	19
42	279	922	709	.8288	18
43	307	916	739	.8218	17
44	336	910	770	.8147	16
45	.20364	.97905	.20800	4.8077	15
46	393	899	830	.8007	14
47	421	893	861	.7937	13
48	450	887	891	.7867	12
49	478	881	921	.7798	11
50	.20507	.97875	.20952	4.7729	10
51	535	869	.20982	.7659	9
52	563	863	.21013	.7591	8
53	592	857	043	.7522	7
54	620	851	073	.7453	6
55	.20649	.97845	.21104	4.7385	5
56	677	839	134	.7317	4
57	706	833	164	.7249	3
58	734	827	195	.7181	2
59	763	821	225	.7114	1
60	.20791	.97815	.21256	4.7046	0
′	cos	sin	cot	tan	′

78°

APPENDIX

12°

′	sin	cos	tan	cot	′
0	.20791	.97815	.21256	4.7046	60
1	820	809	286	.6979	59
2	848	803	316	.6912	58
3	877	797	347	.6845	57
4	905	791	377	.6779	56
5	.20933	.97784	.21408	4.6712	55
6	962	778	438	.6646	54
7	.20990	772	469	.6580	53
8	.21019	766	499	.6514	52
9	047	760	529	.6448	51
10	.21076	.97754	.21560	4.6382	50
11	104	748	590	.6317	49
12	132	742	621	.6252	48
13	161	735	651	.6187	47
14	189	729	682	.6122	46
15	.21218	.97723	.21712	4.6057	45
16	246	717	743	.5993	44
17	275	711	773	.5928	43
18	303	705	804	.5864	42
19	331	698	834	.5800	41
20	.21360	.97692	.21864	4.5736	40
21	388	686	895	.5673	39
22	417	680	925	.5609	38
23	445	673	956	.5546	37
24	474	667	.21986	.5483	36
25	.21502	.97661	.22017	4.5420	35
26	530	655	047	.5357	34
27	559	648	078	.5294	33
28	587	642	108	.5232	32
29	616	636	139	.5169	31
30	.21644	.97630	.22169	4.5107	30
31	672	623	200	.5045	29
32	701	617	231	.4983	28
33	729	611	261	.4922	27
34	758	604	292	.4860	26
35	.21786	.97598	.22322	4.4799	25
36	814	592	353	.4737	24
37	843	585	383	.4676	23
38	871	579	414	.4615	22
39	899	573	444	.4555	21
40	.21928	.97566	.22475	4.4494	20
41	956	560	505	.4434	19
42	.21985	553	536	.4373	18
43	.22013	547	567	.4313	17
44	041	541	597	.4253	16
45	.22070	.97534	.22628	4.4194	15
46	098	528	658	.4134	14
47	126	521	689	.4075	13
48	155	515	719	.4015	12
49	183	508	750	.3956	11
50	.22212	.97502	.22781	4.3897	10
51	240	496	811	.3838	9
52	268	489	842	.3779	8
53	297	483	872	.3721	7
54	325	476	903	.3662	6
55	.22353	.97470	.22934	4.3604	5
56	382	463	964	.3546	4
57	410	457	.22995	.3488	3
58	438	450	.23026	.3430	2
59	467	444	056	.3372	1
60	.22495	.97437	.23087	4.3315	0
′	cos	sin	cot	tan	′

77°

13°

′	sin	cos	tan	cot	′
0	.22495	.97437	.23087	4.3315	60
1	523	430	117	.3257	59
2	552	424	148	.3200	58
3	580	417	179	.3143	57
4	608	411	209	.3086	56
5	.22637	.97404	.23240	4.3029	55
6	665	398	271	.2972	54
7	693	391	301	.2916	53
8	722	384	332	.2859	52
9	750	378	363	.2803	51
10	.22778	.97371	.23393	4.2747	50
11	807	365	424	.2691	49
12	835	358	455	.2635	48
13	863	351	485	.2580	47
14	892	345	516	.2524	46
15	.22920	.97338	.23547	4.2468	45
16	948	331	578	.2413	44
17	.22977	325	608	.2358	43
18	.23005	318	639	.2303	42
19	033	311	670	.2248	41
20	.23062	.97304	.23700	4.2193	40
21	090	298	731	.2139	39
22	118	291	762	.2084	38
23	146	284	793	.2030	37
24	175	278	823	.1976	36
25	.23203	.97271	.23854	4.1922	35
26	231	264	885	.1868	34
27	260	257	916	.1814	33
28	288	251	946	.1760	32
29	316	244	.23977	.1706	31
30	.23345	.97237	.24008	4.1653	30
31	373	230	039	.1600	29
32	401	223	069	.1547	28
33	429	217	100	.1493	27
34	458	210	131	.1441	26
35	.23486	.97203	.24162	4.1388	25
36	514	196	193	.1335	24
37	542	189	223	.1282	23
38	571	182	254	.1230	22
39	599	176	285	.1178	21
40	.23627	.97169	.24316	4.1126	20
41	656	162	347	.1074	19
42	684	155	377	.1022	18
43	712	148	408	.0970	17
44	740	141	439	.0918	16
45	.23769	.97134	.24470	4.0867	15
46	797	127	501	.0815	14
47	825	120	532	.0764	13
48	853	113	562	.0713	12
49	882	106	593	.0662	11
50	.23910	.97100	.24624	4.0611	10
51	938	093	655	.0560	9
52	966	086	686	.0509	8
53	.23995	079	717	.0459	7
54	.24023	072	747	.0408	6
55	.24051	.97065	.24778	4.0358	5
56	079	058	809	.0308	4
57	108	051	840	.0257	3
58	136	044	871	.0207	2
59	164	037	902	.0158	1
60	.24192	.97030	.24933	4.0108	0
′	cos	sin	cot	tan	′

14°

′	sin	cos	tan	cot	′
0	.24192	.97030	.24933	4.0108	60
1	220	023	964	.0058	59
2	249	015	.24995	4.0009	58
3	277	008	.25026	3.9959	57
4	305	.97001	056	.9910	56
5	.24333	.96994	.25087	3.9861	55
6	362	987	118	.9812	54
7	390	980	149	.9763	53
8	418	973	180	.9714	52
9	446	966	211	.9665	51
10	.24474	.96959	.25242	3.9617	50
11	503	952	273	.9568	49
12	531	945	304	.9520	48
13	559	937	335	.9471	47
14	587	930	366	.9423	46
15	.24615	.96923	.25397	3.9375	45
16	644	916	428	.9327	44
17	672	909	459	.9279	43
18	700	902	490	.9232	42
19	728	894	521	.9184	41
20	.24756	.96887	.25552	3.9136	40
21	784	880	583	.9089	39
22	813	873	614	.9042	38
23	841	866	645	.8995	37
24	869	858	676	.8947	36
25	.24897	.96851	.25707	3.8900	35
26	925	844	738	.8854	34
27	954	837	769	.8807	33
28	.24982	829	800	.8760	32
29	.25010	822	831	.8714	31
30	.25038	.96815	.25862	3.8667	30
31	066	807	893	.8621	29
32	094	800	924	.8575	28
33	122	793	955	.8528	27
34	151	786	.25986	.8482	26
35	.25179	.96778	.26017	3.8436	25
36	207	771	048	.8391	24
37	235	764	079	.8345	23
38	263	756	110	.8299	22
39	291	749	141	.8254	21
40	.25320	.96742	.26172	3.8208	20
41	348	734	203	.8163	19
42	376	727	235	.8118	18
43	404	719	266	.8073	17
44	432	712	297	.8028	16
45	.25460	.96705	.26328	3.7983	15
46	488	697	359	.7938	14
47	516	690	390	.7893	13
48	545	682	421	.7848	12
49	573	675	452	.7804	11
50	.25601	.96667	.26483	3.7760	10
51	629	660	515	.7715	9
52	657	653	546	.7671	8
53	685	645	577	.7627	7
54	713	638	608	.7583	6
55	.25741	.96630	.26639	3.7539	5
56	769	623	670	.7495	4
57	798	615	701	.7451	3
58	826	608	733	.7408	2
59	854	600	764	.7364	1
60	.25882	.96593	.26795	3.7321	0
′	cos	sin	cot	tan	′

75°

Table 4   TRIGONOMETRIC FUNCTIONS   591

15°

′	sin	cos	tan	cot	′
0	.25882	.96593	.26795	3.7321	60
1	910	585	826	.7277	59
2	938	578	857	.7234	58
3	966	570	888	.7191	57
4	.25994	562	920	.7148	56
5	.26022	.96555	.26951	3.7105	55
6	050	547	.26982	.7062	54
7	079	540	.27013	.7019	53
8	107	532	044	.6976	52
9	135	524	076	.6933	51
10	.26163	.96517	.27107	3.6891	50
11	191	509	138	.6848	49
12	219	502	169	.6806	48
13	247	494	201	.6764	47
14	275	486	232	.6722	46
15	.26303	.96479	.27263	3.6680	45
16	331	471	294	.6638	44
17	359	463	326	.6596	43
18	387	456	357	.6554	42
19	415	448	388	.6512	41
20	.26443	.96440	.27419	3.6470	40
21	471	433	451	.6429	39
22	500	425	482	.6387	38
23	528	417	513	.6346	37
24	556	410	545	.6305	36
25	.26584	.96402	.27576	3.6264	35
26	612	394	607	.6222	34
27	640	386	638	.6181	33
28	668	379	670	.6140	32
29	696	371	701	.6100	31
30	.26724	.96363	.27732	3.6059	30
31	752	355	764	.6018	29
32	780	347	795	.5978	28
33	808	340	826	.5937	27
34	836	332	858	.5897	26
35	.26864	.96324	.27889	3.5856	25
36	892	316	921	.5816	24
37	920	308	952	.5776	23
38	948	301	.27983	.5736	22
39	.26976	293	.28015	.5696	21
40	.27004	.96285	.28046	3.5656	20
41	032	277	077	.5616	19
42	060	269	109	.5576	18
43	088	261	140	.5536	17
44	116	253	172	.5497	16
45	.27144	.96246	.28203	3.5457	15
46	172	238	234	.5418	14
47	200	230	266	.5379	13
48	228	222	297	.5339	12
49	256	214	329	.5300	11
50	.27284	.96206	.28360	3.5261	10
51	312	198	391	.5222	9
52	340	190	423	.5183	8
53	368	182	454	.5144	7
54	396	174	486	.5105	6
55	.27424	.96166	.28517	3.5067	5
56	452	158	549	.5028	4
57	480	150	580	.4989	3
58	508	142	612	.4951	2
59	536	134	643	.4912	1
60	.27564	.96126	.28675	3.4874	0
′	cos	sin	cot	tan	′

74°

16°

'	sin	cos	tan	cot	'
0	.27564	.96126	.28675	3.4874	60
1	592	118	706	.4836	59
2	620	110	738	.4798	58
3	648	102	769	.4760	57
4	676	094	801	.4722	56
5	.27704	.96086	.28832	3.4684	55
6	731	078	864	.4646	54
7	759	070	895	.4608	53
8	787	062	927	.4570	52
9	815	054	958	.4533	51
10	.27843	.96046	.28990	3.4495	50
11	871	037	.29021	.4458	49
12	899	029	053	.4420	48
13	927	021	084	.4383	47
14	955	013	116	.4346	46
15	.27983	.96005	.29147	3.4308	45
16	.28011	.95997	179	.4271	44
17	039	989	210	.4234	43
18	067	981	242	.4197	42
19	095	972	274	.4160	41
20	.28123	.95964	.29305	3.4124	40
21	150	956	337	.4087	39
22	178	948	368	.4050	38
23	206	940	400	.4014	37
24	234	931	432	.3977	36
25	.28262	.95923	.29463	3.3941	35
26	290	915	495	.3904	34
27	318	907	526	.3868	33
28	346	898	558	.3832	32
29	374	890	590	.3796	31
30	.28402	.95882	.29621	3.3759	30
31	429	874	653	.3723	29
32	457	865	685	.3687	28
33	485	857	716	.3652	27
34	513	849	748	.3616	26
35	.28541	.95841	.29780	3.3580	25
36	569	832	811	.3544	24
37	597	824	843	.3509	23
38	625	816	875	.3473	22
39	652	807	906	.3438	21
40	.28680	.95799	.29938	3.3402	20
41	708	791	.29970	.3367	19
42	736	782	.30001	.3332	18
43	764	774	033	.3297	17
44	792	766	065	.3261	16
45	.28820	.95757	.30097	3.3226	15
46	847	749	128	.3191	14
47	875	740	160	.3156	13
48	903	732	192	.3122	12
49	931	724	224	.3087	11
50	.28959	.95715	.30255	3.3052	10
51	.28987	707	287	.3017	9
52	.29015	698	319	.2983	8
53	042	690	351	.2948	7
54	070	681	382	.2914	6
55	.29098	.95673	.30414	3.2879	5
56	126	664	446	.2845	4
57	154	656	478	.2811	3
58	182	647	509	.2777	2
59	209	639	541	.2743	1
60	.29237	.95630	.30573	3.2709	0
'	cos	sin	cot	tan	'

73°

17°

′	sin	cos	tan	cot	′
0	.29237	.95630	.30573	3.2709	60
1	265	622	605	.2675	59
2	293	613	637	.2641	58
3	321	605	669	.2607	57
4	348	596	700	.2573	56
5	.29376	.95588	.30732	3.2539	55
6	404	579	764	.2506	54
7	432	571	796	.2472	53
8	460	562	828	.2438	52
9	487	554	860	.2405	51
10	.29515	.95545	.30891	3.2371	50
11	543	536	923	.2338	49
12	571	528	955	.2305	48
13	599	519	.30987	.2272	47
14	626	511	.31019	.2238	46
15	.29654	.95502	.31051	3.2205	45
16	682	493	083	.2172	44
17	710	485	115	.2139	43
18	737	476	147	.2106	42
19	765	467	178	.2073	41
20	.29793	.95459	.31210	3.2041	40
21	821	450	242	.2008	39
22	849	441	274	.1975	38
23	876	433	306	.1943	37
24	904	424	338	.1910	36
25	.29932	.95415	.31370	3.1878	35
26	960	407	402	.1845	34
27	.29987	398	434	.1813	33
28	.30015	389	466	.1780	32
29	043	380	498	.1748	31
30	.30071	.95372	.31530	3.1716	30
31	098	363	562	.1684	29
32	126	354	594	.1652	28
33	154	345	626	.1620	27
34	182	337	658	.1588	26
35	.30209	.95328	.31690	3.1556	25
36	237	319	722	.1524	24
37	265	310	754	.1492	23
38	292	301	786	.1460	22
39	320	293	818	.1429	21
40	.30348	.95284	.31850	3.1397	20
41	376	275	882	.1366	19
42	403	266	914	.1334	18
43	431	257	946	.1303	17
44	459	248	.31978	.1271	16
45	.30486	.95240	.32010	3.1240	15
46	514	231	042	.1209	14
47	542	222	074	.1178	13
48	570	213	106	.1146	12
49	597	204	139	.1115	11
50	.30625	.95195	.32171	3.1084	10
51	653	186	203	.1053	9
52	680	177	235	.1022	8
53	708	168	267	.0991	7
54	736	159	299	.0961	6
55	.30763	.95150	.32331	3.0930	5
56	791	142	363	.0899	4
57	819	133	396	.0868	3
58	846	124	428	.0838	2
59	874	115	460	.0807	1
60	.30902	.95106	.32492	3.0777	0
′	cos	sin	cot	tan	′

72°

594 APPENDIX

18°

'	sin	cos	tan	cot	'
0	.30902	.95106	.32492	3.0777	60
1	929	097	524	.0746	59
2	957	088	556	.0716	58
3	.30985	079	588	.0686	57
4	.31012	070	621	.0655	56
5	.31040	.95061	.32653	3.0625	55
6	068	052	685	.0595	54
7	095	043	717	.0565	53
8	123	033	749	.0535	52
9	151	024	782	.0505	51
10	.31178	.95015	.32814	3.0475	50
11	206	.95006	846	.0445	49
12	233	.94997	878	.0415	48
13	261	988	911	.0385	47
14	289	979	943	.0356	46
15	.31316	.94970	.32975	3.0326	45
16	344	961	.33007	.0296	44
17	372	952	040	.0267	43
18	399	943	072	.0237	42
19	427	933	104	.0208	41
20	.31454	.94924	.33136	3.0178	40
21	482	915	169	.0149	39
22	510	906	201	.0120	38
23	537	897	233	.0090	37
24	565	888	266	.0061	36
25	.31593	.94878	.33298	3.0032	35
26	620	869	330	3.0003	34
27	648	860	363	2.9974	33
28	675	851	395	.9945	32
29	703	842	427	.9916	31
30	.31730	.94832	.33460	2.9887	30
31	758	823	492	.9858	29
32	786	814	524	.9829	28
33	813	805	557	.9800	27
34	841	795	589	.9772	26
35	.31868	.94786	.33621	2.9743	25
36	896	777	654	.9714	24
37	923	768	686	.9686	23
38	951	758	718	.9657	22
39	.31979	749	751	.9629	21
40	.32006	.94740	.33783	2.9600	20
41	034	730	816	.9572	19
42	061	721	848	.9544	18
43	089	712	881	.9515	17
44	116	702	913	.9487	16
45	.32144	.94693	.33945	2.9459	15
46	171	684	.33978	.9431	14
47	199	674	.34010	.9403	13
48	227	665	043	.9375	12
49	254	656	075	.9347	11
50	.32282	.94646	.34108	2.9319	10
51	309	637	140	.9291	9
52	337	627	173	.9263	8
53	364	618	205	.9235	7
54	392	609	238	.9208	6
55	.32419	.94599	.34270	2.9180	5
56	447	590	303	.9152	4
57	474	580	335	.9125	3
58	502	571	368	.9097	2
59	529	561	400	.9070	1
60	.32557	.94552	.34433	2.9042	0

| ' | cos | sin | cot | tan | ' |

71°

Table 4   TRIGONOMETRIC FUNCTIONS   595

19°

′	sin	cos	tan	cot	′
0	.32557	.94552	.34433	2.9042	60
1	584	542	465	.9015	59
2	612	533	498	.8987	58
3	639	523	530	.8960	57
4	667	514	563	.8933	56
5	.32694	.94504	.34596	2.8905	55
6	722	495	628	.8878	54
7	749	485	661	.8851	53
8	777	476	693	.8824	52
9	804	466	726	.8797	51
10	.32832	.94457	.34758	2.8770	50
11	859	447	791	.8743	49
12	887	438	824	.8716	48
13	914	428	856	.8689	47
14	942	418	889	.8662	46
15	.32969	.94409	.34922	2.8636	45
16	.32997	399	954	.8609	44
17	.33024	390	.34987	.8582	43
18	051	380	.35020	.8556	42
19	079	370	052	.8529	41
20	.33106	.94361	.35085	2.8502	40
21	134	351	118	.8476	39
22	161	342	150	.8449	38
23	189	332	183	.8423	37
24	216	322	216	.8397	36
25	.33244	.94313	.35248	2.8370	35
26	271	303	281	.8344	34
27	298	293	314	.8318	33
28	326	284	346	.8291	32
29	353	274	379	.8265	31
30	.33381	.94264	.35412	2.8239	30
31	408	254	445	.8213	29
32	436	245	477	.8187	28
33	463	235	510	.8161	27
34	490	225	543	.8135	26
35	.33518	.94215	.35576	2.8109	25
36	545	206	608	.8083	24
37	573	196	641	.8057	23
38	600	186	674	.8032	22
39	627	176	707	.8006	21
40	.33655	.94167	.35740	2.7980	20
41	682	157	772	.7955	19
42	710	147	805	.7929	18
43	737	137	838	.7903	17
44	764	127	871	.7878	16
45	.33792	.94118	.35904	2.7852	15
46	819	108	937	.7827	14
47	846	098	.35969	.7801	13
48	874	088	.36002	.7776	12
49	901	078	035	.7751	11
50	.33929	.94068	.36068	2.7725	10
51	956	058	101	.7700	9
52	.33983	049	134	.7675	8
53	.34011	039	167	.7650	7
54	038	029	199	.7625	6
55	.34065	.94019	.36232	2.7600	5
56	093	.94009	265	.7575	4
57	120	.93999	298	.7550	3
58	147	989	331	.7525	2
59	175	979	364	.7500	1
60	.34202	.93969	.36397	2.7475	0
′	cos	sin	cot	tan	′

70°

20°

′	sin	cos	tan	cot	′
0	.34202	.93969	.36397	2.7475	60
1	229	959	430	.7450	59
2	257	949	463	.7425	58
3	284	939	496	.7400	57
4	311	929	529	.7376	56
5	.34339	.93919	.36562	2.7351	55
6	366	909	595	.7326	54
7	393	899	628	.7302	53
8	421	889	661	.7277	52
9	448	879	694	.7253	51
10	.34475	.93869	.36727	2.7228	50
11	503	859	760	.7204	49
12	530	849	793	.7179	48
13	557	839	826	.7155	47
14	584	829	859	.7130	46
15	.34612	.93819	.36892	2.7106	45
16	639	809	925	.7082	44
17	666	799	958	.7058	43
18	694	789	.36991	.7034	42
19	721	779	.37024	.7009	41
20	.34748	.93769	.37057	2.6985	40
21	775	759	090	.6961	39
22	803	748	123	.6937	38
23	830	738	157	.6913	37
24	857	728	190	.6889	36
25	.34884	.93718	.37223	2.6865	35
26	912	708	256	.6841	34
27	939	698	289	.6818	33
28	966	688	322	.6794	32
29	.34993	677	355	.6770	31
30	.35021	.93667	.37388	2.6746	30
31	048	657	422	.6723	29
32	075	647	455	.6699	28
33	102	637	488	.6675	27
34	130	626	521	.6652	26
35	.35157	.93616	.37554	2.6628	25
36	184	606	588	.6605	24
37	211	596	621	.6581	23
38	239	585	654	.6558	22
39	266	575	687	.6534	21
40	.35293	.93565	.37720	2.6511	20
41	320	555	754	.6488	19
42	347	544	787	.6464	18
43	375	534	820	.6441	17
44	402	524	853	.6418	16
45	.35429	.93514	.37887	2.6395	15
46	456	503	920	.6371	14
47	484	493	953	.6348	13
48	511	483	.37986	.6325	12
49	538	472	.38020	.6302	11
50	.35565	.93462	.38053	2.6279	10
51	592	452	086	.6256	9
52	619	441	120	.6233	8
53	647	431	153	.6210	7
54	674	420	186	.6187	6
55	.35701	.93410	.38220	2.6165	5
56	728	400	253	.6142	4
57	755	389	286	.6119	3
58	782	379	320	.6096	2
59	810	368	353	.6074	1
60	.35837	.93358	.38386	2.6051	0
′	cos	sin	cot	tan	′

69°

Table 4 TRIGONOMETRIC FUNCTIONS 597

21°

′	sin	cos	tan	cot	′
0	.35837	.93358	.38386	2.6051	60
1	864	348	420	.6028	59
2	891	337	453	.6006	58
3	918	327	487	.5983	57
4	945	316	520	.5961	56
5	.35973	.93306	.38553	2.5938	55
6	.36000	295	587	.5916	54
7	027	285	620	.5893	53
8	054	274	654	.5871	52
9	081	264	687	.5848	51
10	.36108	.93253	.38721	2.5826	50
11	135	243	754	.5804	49
12	162	232	787	.5782	48
13	190	222	821	.5759	47
14	217	211	854	.5737	46
15	.36244	.93201	.38888	2.5715	45
16	271	190	921	.5693	44
17	298	180	955	.5671	43
18	325	169	.38988	.5649	42
19	352	159	.39022	.5627	41
20	.36379	.93148	.39055	2.5605	40
21	406	137	089	.5583	39
22	434	127	122	.5561	38
23	461	116	156	.5539	37
24	488	106	190	.5517	36
25	.36515	.93095	.39223	2.5495	35
26	542	084	257	.5473	34
27	569	074	290	.5452	33
28	596	063	324	.5430	32
29	623	052	357	.5408	31
30	.36650	.93042	.39391	2.5386	30
31	677	031	425	.5365	29
32	704	020	458	.5343	28
33	731	.93010	492	.5322	27
34	758	.92999	526	.5300	26
35	.36785	.92988	.39559	2.5279	25
36	812	978	593	.5257	24
37	839	967	626	.5236	23
38	867	956	660	.5214	22
39	894	945	694	.5193	21
40	.36921	.92935	.39727	2.5172	20
41	948	924	761	.5150	19
42	.36975	913	795	.5129	18
43	.37002	902	829	.5108	17
44	029	892	862	.5086	16
45	.37056	.92881	.39896	2.5065	15
46	083	870	930	.5044	14
47	110	859	963	.5023	13
48	137	849	.39997	.5002	12
49	164	838	.40031	.4981	11
50	.37191	.92827	.40065	2.4960	10
51	218	816	098	.4939	9
52	245	805	132	.4918	8
53	272	794	166	.4897	7
54	299	784	200	.4876	6
55	.37326	.92773	.40234	2.4855	5
56	353	762	267	.4834	4
57	380	751	301	.4813	3
58	407	740	335	.4792	2
59	434	729	369	.4772	1
60	.37461	.92718	.40403	2.4751	0
′	cos	sin	cot	tan	′

68°

22°

′	sin	cos	tan	cot	′
0	.37461	.92718	.40403	2.4751	60
1	488	707	436	.4730	59
2	515	697	470	.4709	58
3	542	686	504	.4689	57
4	569	675	538	.4668	56
5	.37595	.92664	.40572	2.4648	55
6	622	653	606	.4627	54
7	649	642	640	.4606	53
8	676	631	674	.4586	52
9	703	620	707	.4566	51
10	.37730	.92609	.40741	2.4545	50
11	757	598	775	.4525	49
12	784	587	809	.4504	48
13	811	576	843	.4484	47
14	838	565	877	.4464	46
15	.37865	.92554	.40911	2.4443	45
16	892	543	945	.4423	44
17	919	532	.40979	.4403	43
18	946	521	.41013	.4383	42
19	973	510	047	.4362	41
20	.37999	.92499	.41081	2.4342	40
21	.38026	488	115	.4322	39
22	053	477	149	.4302	38
23	080	466	183	.4282	37
24	107	455	217	.4262	36
25	.38134	.92444	.41251	2.4242	35
26	161	432	285	.4222	34
27	188	421	319	.4202	33
28	215	410	353	.4182	32
29	241	399	387	.4162	31
30	.38268	.92388	.41421	2.4142	30
31	295	377	455	.4122	29
32	322	366	490	.4102	28
33	349	355	524	.4083	27
34	376	343	558	.4063	26
35	.38403	.92332	.41592	2.4043	25
36	430	321	626	.4023	24
37	456	310	660	.4004	23
38	483	299	694	.3984	22
39	510	287	728	.3964	21
40	.38537	.92276	.41763	2.3945	20
41	564	265	797	.3925	19
42	591	254	831	.3906	18
43	617	243	865	.3886	17
44	644	231	899	.3867	16
45	.38671	.92220	.41933	2.3847	15
46	698	209	.41968	.3828	14
47	725	198	.42002	.3808	13
48	752	186	036	.3789	12
49	778	175	070	.3770	11
50	.38805	.92164	.42105	2.3750	10
51	832	152	139	.3731	9
52	859	141	173	.3712	8
53	886	130	207	.3693	7
54	912	119	242	.3673	6
55	.38939	.92107	.42276	2.3654	5
56	966	096	310	.3635	4
57	.38993	085	345	.3616	3
58	.39020	073	379	.3597	2
59	046	062	413	.3578	1
60	.39073	.92050	.42447	2.3559	0
′	cos	sin	cot	tan	′

67°

Table 4 TRIGONOMETRIC FUNCTIONS 599

23°

′	sin	cos	tan	cot	′
0	.39073	.92050	.42447	2.3559	60
1	100	039	482	.3539	59
2	127	028	516	.3520	58
3	153	016	551	.3501	57
4	180	.92005	585	.3483	56
5	.39207	.91994	.42619	2.3464	55
6	234	982	654	.3445	54
7	260	971	688	.3426	53
8	287	959	722	.3407	52
9	314	948	757	.3388	51
10	.39341	.91936	.42791	2.3369	50
11	367	925	826	.3351	49
12	394	914	860	.3332	48
13	421	902	894	.3313	47
14	448	891	929	.3294	46
15	.39474	.91879	.42963	2.3276	45
16	501	868	.42998	.3257	44
17	528	856	.43032	.3238	43
18	555	845	067	.3220	42
19	581	833	101	.3201	41
20	.39608	.91822	.43136	2.3183	40
21	635	810	170	.3164	39
22	661	799	205	.3146	38
23	688	787	239	.3127	37
24	715	775	274	.3109	36
25	.39741	.91764	.43308	2.3090	35
26	768	752	343	.3072	34
27	795	741	378	.3053	33
28	822	729	412	.3035	32
29	848	718	447	.3017	31
30	.39875	.91706	.43481	2.2998	30
31	902	694	516	.2980	29
32	928	683	550	.2962	28
33	955	671	585	.2944	27
34	.39982	660	620	.2925	26
35	.40008	.91648	.43654	2.2907	25
36	035	636	689	.2889	24
37	062	625	724	.2871	23
38	088	613	758	.2853	22
39	115	601	793	.2835	21
40	.40141	.91590	.43828	2.2817	20
41	168	578	862	.2799	19
42	195	566	897	.2781	18
43	221	555	932	.2763	17
44	248	543	.43966	.2745	16
45	.40275	.91531	.44001	2.2727	15
46	301	519	036	.2709	14
47	328	508	071	.2691	13
48	355	496	105	.2673	12
49	381	484	140	.2655	11
50	.40408	.91472	.44175	2.2637	10
51	434	461	210	.2620	9
52	461	449	244	.2602	8
53	488	437	279	.2584	7
54	514	425	314	.2566	6
55	.40541	.91414	.44349	2.2549	5
56	567	402	384	.2531	4
57	594	390	418	.2513	3
58	621	378	453	.2496	2
59	647	366	488	.2478	1
60	.40674	.91355	.44523	2.2460	0

′	cos	sin	cot	tan	′

66°

24°

′	sin	cos	tan	cot	′
0	.40674	.91355	.44523	2.2460	60
1	700	343	558	.2443	59
2	727	331	593	.2425	58
3	753	319	627	.2408	57
4	780	307	662	.2390	56
5	.40806	.91295	.44697	2.2373	55
6	833	283	732	.2355	54
7	860	272	767	.2338	53
8	886	260	802	.2320	52
9	913	248	837	.2303	51
10	.40939	.91236	.44872	2.2286	50
11	966	224	907	.2268	49
12	.40992	212	942	.2251	48
13	.41019	200	.44977	.2234	47
14	045	188	.45012	.2216	46
15	.41072	.91176	.45047	2.2199	45
16	098	164	082	.2182	44
17	125	152	117	.2165	43
18	151	140	152	.2148	42
19	178	128	187	.2130	41
20	.41204	.91116	.45222	2.2113	40
21	231	104	257	.2096	39
22	257	092	292	.2079	38
23	284	080	327	.2062	37
24	310	068	362	.2045	36
25	.41337	.91056	.45397	2.2028	35
26	363	044	432	.2011	34
27	390	032	467	.1994	33
28	416	020	502	.1977	32
29	443	.91008	538	.1960	31
30	.41469	.90996	.45573	2.1943	30
31	496	984	608	.1926	29
32	522	972	643	.1909	28
33	549	960	678	.1892	27
34	575	948	713	.1876	26
35	.41602	.90936	.45748	2.1859	25
36	628	924	784	.1842	24
37	655	911	819	.1825	23
38	681	899	854	.1808	22
39	707	887	889	.1792	21
40	.41734	.90875	.45924	2.1775	20
41	760	863	960	.1758	19
42	787	851	.45995	.1742	18
43	813	839	.46030	.1725	17
44	840	826	065	.1708	16
45	.41866	.90814	.46101	2.1692	15
46	892	802	136	.1675	14
47	919	790	171	.1659	13
48	945	778	206	.1642	12
49	972	766	242	.1625	11
50	.41998	.90753	.46277	2.1609	10
51	.42024	741	312	.1592	9
52	051	729	348	.1576	8
53	077	717	383	.1560	7
54	104	704	418	.1543	6
55	.42130	.90692	.46454	2.1527	5
56	156	680	489	.1510	4
57	183	668	525	.1494	3
58	209	655	560	.1478	2
59	235	643	595	.1461	1
60	.42262	.90631	.46631	2.1445	0
′	cos	sin	cot	tan	′

65°

Table 4   TRIGONOMETRIC FUNCTIONS   601

25°

′	sin	cos	tan	cot	′
0	.42262	.90631	.46631	2.1445	60
1	288	618	666	.1429	59
2	315	606	702	.1413	58
3	341	594	737	.1396	57
4	367	582	772	.1380	56
5	.42394	.90569	.46808	2.1364	55
6	420	557	843	.1348	54
7	446	545	879	.1332	53
8	473	532	914	.1315	52
9	499	520	950	.1299	51
10	.42525	.90507	.46985	2.1283	50
11	552	495	.47021	.1267	49
12	578	483	056	.1251	48
13	604	470	092	.1235	47
14	631	458	128	.1219	46
15	.42657	.90446	.47163	2.1203	45
16	683	433	199	.1187	44
17	709	421	234	.1171	43
18	736	408	270	.1155	42
19	762	396	305	.1139	41
20	.42788	.90383	.47341	2.1123	40
21	815	371	377	.1107	39
22	841	358	412	.1092	38
23	867	346	448	.1076	37
24	894	334	483	.1060	36
25	.42920	.90321	.47519	2.1044	35
26	946	309	555	.1028	34
27	972	296	590	.1013	33
28	.42999	284	626	.0997	32
29	.43025	271	662	.0981	31
30	.43051	.90259	.47698	2.0965	30
31	077	246	733	.0950	29
32	104	233	769	.0934	28
33	130	221	805	.0918	27
34	156	208	840	.0903	26
35	.43182	.90196	.47876	2.0887	25
36	209	183	912	.0872	24
37	235	171	948	.0856	23
38	261	158	.47984	.0840	22
39	287	146	.48019	.0825	21
40	.43313	.90133	.48055	2.0809	20
41	340	120	091	.0794	19
42	366	108	127	.0778	18
43	392	095	163	.0763	17
44	418	082	198	.0748	16
45	.43445	.90070	.48234	2.0732	15
46	471	057	270	.0717	14
47	497	045	306	.0701	13
48	523	032	342	.0686	12
49	549	019	378	.0671	11
50	.43575	.90007	.48414	2.0655	10
51	602	.89994	450	.0640	9
52	628	981	486	.0625	8
53	654	968	521	.0609	7
54	680	956	557	.0594	6
55	.43706	.89943	.48593	2.0579	5
56	733	930	629	.0564	4
57	759	918	665	.0549	3
58	785	905	701	.0533	2
59	811	892	737	.0518	1
60	.43837	.89879	.48773	2.0503	0
′	cos	sin	cot	tan	′

64°

26°

′	sin	cos	tan	cot	′
0	.43837	.89879	.48773	2.0503	60
1	863	867	809	.0488	59
2	889	854	845	.0473	58
3	916	841	881	.0458	57
4	942	828	917	.0443	56
5	.43968	.89816	.48953	2.0428	55
6	.43994	803	.48989	.0413	54
7	.44020	790	.49026	.0398	53
8	046	777	062	.0383	52
9	072	764	098	.0368	51
10	.44098	.89752	.49134	2.0353	50
11	124	739	170	.0338	49
12	151	726	206	.0323	48
13	177	713	242	.0308	47
14	203	700	278	.0293	46
15	.44229	.89687	.49315	2.0278	45
16	255	674	351	.0263	44
17	281	662	387	.0248	43
18	307	649	423	.0233	42
19	333	636	459	.0219	41
20	.44359	.89623	.49495	2.0204	40
21	385	610	532	.0189	39
22	411	597	568	.0174	38
23	437	584	604	.0160	37
24	464	571	640	.0145	36
25	.44490	.89558	.49677	2.0130	35
26	516	545	713	.0115	34
27	542	532	749	.0101	33
28	568	519	786	.0086	32
29	594	506	822	.0072	31
30	.44620	.89493	.49858	2.0057	30
31	646	480	894	.0042	29
32	672	467	931	.0028	28
33	698	454	.49967	2.0013	27
34	724	441	.50004	1.9999	26
35	.44750	.89428	.50040	1.9984	25
36	776	415	076	.9970	24
37	802	402	113	.9955	23
38	828	389	149	.9941	22
39	854	376	185	.9926	21
40	.44880	.89363	.50222	1.9912	20
41	906	350	258	.9897	19
42	932	337	295	.9883	18
43	958	324	331	.9868	17
44	.44984	311	368	.9854	16
45	.45010	.89298	.50404	1.9840	15
46	036	285	441	.9825	14
47	062	272	477	.9811	13
48	088	259	514	.9797	12
49	114	245	550	.9782	11
50	.45140	.89232	.50587	1.9768	10
51	166	219	623	.9754	9
52	192	206	660	.9740	8
53	218	193	696	.9725	7
54	243	180	733	.9711	6
55	.45269	.89167	.50769	1.9697	5
56	295	153	806	.9683	4
57	321	140	843	.9669	3
58	347	127	879	.9654	2
59	373	114	916	.9640	1
60	.45399	.89101	.50953	1.9626	0
′	cos	sin	cot	tan	′

63°

Table 4 TRIGONOMETRIC FUNCTIONS 603

27°

′	sin	cos	tan	cot	′
0	.45399	.89101	.50953	1.9626	60
1	425	087	.50989	.9612	59
2	451	074	.51026	.9598	58
3	477	061	063	.9584	57
4	503	048	099	.9570	56
5	.45529	.89035	.51136	1.9556	55
6	554	021	173	.9542	54
7	580	.89008	209	.9528	53
8	606	.88995	246	.9514	52
9	632	981	283	.9500	51
10	.45658	.88968	.51319	1.9486	50
11	684	955	356	.9472	49
12	710	942	393	.9458	48
13	736	928	430	.9444	47
14	762	915	467	.9430	46
15	.45787	.88902	.51503	1.9416	45
16	813	888	540	.9402	44
17	839	875	577	.9388	43
18	865	862	614	.9375	42
19	891	848	651	.9361	41
20	.45917	.88835	.51688	1.9347	40
21	942	822	724	.9333	39
22	968	808	761	.9319	38
23	.45994	795	798	.9306	37
24	.46020	782	835	.9292	36
25	.46046	.88768	.51872	1.9278	35
26	072	755	909	.9265	34
27	097	741	946	.9251	33
28	123	728	.51983	.9237	32
29	149	715	.52020	.9223	31
30	.46175	.88701	.52057	1.9210	30
31	201	688	094	.9196	29
32	226	674	131	.9183	28
33	252	661	168	.9169	27
34	278	647	205	.9155	26
35	.46304	.88634	.52242	1.9142	25
36	330	620	279	.9128	24
37	355	607	316	.9115	23
38	381	593	353	.9101	22
39	407	580	390	.9088	21
40	.46433	.88566	.52427	1.9074	20
41	458	553	464	.9061	19
42	484	539	501	.9047	18
43	510	526	538	.9034	17
44	536	512	575	.9020	16
45	.46561	.88499	.52613	1.9007	15
46	587	485	650	.8993	14
47	613	472	687	.8980	13
48	639	458	724	.8967	12
49	664	445	761	.8953	11
50	.46690	.88431	.52798	1.8940	10
51	716	417	836	.8927	9
52	742	404	873	.8913	8
53	767	390	910	.8900	7
54	793	377	947	.8887	6
55	.46819	.88363	.52985	1.8873	5
56	844	349	.53022	.8860	4
57	870	336	059	.8847	3
58	896	322	096	.8834	2
59	921	308	134	.8820	1
60	.46947	.88295	.53171	1.8807	0
′	cos	sin	cot	tan	′

62°

28°

′	sin	cos	tan	cot	′
0	.46947	.88295	.53171	1.8807	60
1	973	281	208	.8794	59
2	.46999	267	246	.8781	58
3	.47024	254	283	.8768	57
4	050	240	320	.8755	56
5	.47076	.88226	.53358	1.8741	55
6	101	213	395	.8728	54
7	127	199	432	.8715	53
8	153	185	470	.8702	52
9	178	172	507	.8689	51
10	.47204	.88158	.53545	1.8676	50
11	229	144	582	.8663	49
12	255	130	620	.8650	48
13	281	117	657	.8637	47
14	306	103	694	.8624	46
15	.47332	.88089	.53732	1.8611	45
16	358	075	769	.8598	44
17	383	062	807	.8585	43
18	409	048	844	.8572	42
19	434	034	882	.8559	41
20	.47460	.88020	.53920	1.8546	40
21	486	.88006	957	.8533	39
22	511	.87993	.53995	.8520	38
23	537	979	.54032	.8507	37
24	562	965	070	.8495	36
25	.47588	.87951	.54107	1.8482	35
26	614	937	145	.8469	34
27	639	923	183	.8456	33
28	665	909	220	.8443	32
29	690	896	258	.8430	31
30	.47716	.87882	.54296	1.8418	30
31	741	868	333	.8405	29
32	767	854	371	.8392	28
33	793	840	409	.8379	27
34	818	826	446	.8367	26
35	.47844	.87812	.54484	1.8354	25
36	869	798	522	.8341	24
37	895	784	560	.8329	23
38	920	770	597	.8316	22
39	946	756	635	.8303	21
40	.47971	.87743	.54673	1.8291	20
41	.47997	729	711	.8278	19
42	.48022	715	748	.8265	18
43	048	701	786	.8253	17
44	073	687	824	.8240	16
45	.48099	.87673	.54862	1.8228	15
46	124	659	900	.8215	14
47	150	645	938	.8202	13
48	175	631	.54975	.8190	12
49	201	617	.55013	.8177	11
50	.48226	.87603	.55051	1.8165	10
51	252	589	089	.8152	9
52	277	575	127	.8140	8
53	303	561	165	.8127	7
54	328	546	203	.8115	6
55	.48354	.87532	.55241	1.8103	5
56	379	518	279	.8090	4
57	405	504	317	.8078	3
58	430	490	355	.8065	2
59	456	476	393	.8053	1
60	.48481	.87462	.55431	1.8040	0
′	cos	sin	cot	tan	′

61°

Table 4　　TRIGONOMETRIC FUNCTIONS　　605

29°

′	sin	cos	tan	cot	′
0	.48481	.87462	.55431	1.8040	60
1	506	448	469	.8028	59
2	532	434	507	.8016	58
3	557	420	545	.8003	57
4	583	406	583	.7991	56
5	.48608	.87391	.55621	1.7979	55
6	634	377	659	.7966	54
7	659	363	697	.7954	53
8	684	349	736	.7942	52
9	710	335	774	.7930	51
10	.48735	.87321	.55812	1.7917	50
11	761	306	850	.7905	49
12	786	292	888	.7893	48
13	811	278	926	.7881	47
14	837	264	.55964	.7868	46
15	.48862	.87250	.56003	1.7856	45
16	888	235	041	.7844	44
17	913	221	079	.7832	43
18	938	207	117	.7820	42
19	964	193	156	.7808	41
20	.48989	.87178	.56194	1.7796	40
21	.49014	164	232	.7783	39
22	040	150	270	.7771	38
23	065	136	309	.7759	37
24	090	121	347	.7747	36
25	.49116	.87107	.56385	1.7735	35
26	141	093	424	.7723	34
27	166	079	462	.7711	33
28	192	064	501	.7699	32
29	217	050	539	.7687	31
30	.49242	.87036	.56577	1.7675	30
31	268	021	616	.7663	29
32	293	.87007	654	.7651	28
33	318	.86993	693	.7639	27
34	344	978	731	.7627	26
35	.49369	.86964	.56769	1.7615	25
36	394	949	808	.7603	24
37	419	935	846	.7591	23
38	445	921	885	.7579	22
39	470	906	923	.7567	21
40	.49495	.86892	.56962	1.7556	20
41	521	878	.57000	.7544	19
42	546	863	039	.7532	18
43	571	849	078	.7520	17
44	596	834	116	.7508	16
45	.49622	.86820	.57155	1.7496	15
46	647	805	193	.7485	14
47	672	791	232	.7473	13
48	697	777	271	.7461	12
49	723	762	309	.7449	11
50	.49748	.86748	.57348	1.7437	10
51	773	733	386	.7426	9
52	798	719	425	.7414	8
53	824	704	464	.7402	7
54	849	690	503	.7391	6
55	.49874	.86675	.57541	1.7379	5
56	899	661	580	.7367	4
57	924	646	619	.7355	3
58	950	632	657	.7344	2
59	.49975	617	696	.7332	1
60	.50000	.86603	.57735	1.7321	0
′	cos	sin	cot	tan	′

60°

30°

′	sin	cos	tan	cot	′
0	.50000	.86603	.57735	1.7321	60
1	025	588	774	.7309	59
2	050	573	813	.7297	58
3	076	559	851	.7286	57
4	101	544	890	.7274	56
5	.50126	.86530	.57929	1.7262	55
6	151	515	.57968	.7251	54
7	176	501	.58007	.7239	53
8	201	486	046	.7228	52
9	227	471	085	.7216	51
10	.50252	.86457	.58124	1.7205	50
11	277	442	162	.7193	49
12	302	427	201	.7182	48
13	327	413	240	.7170	47
14	352	398	279	.7159	46
15	.50377	.86384	.58318	1.7147	45
16	403	369	357	.7136	44
17	428	354	396	.7124	43
18	453	340	435	.7113	42
19	478	325	474	.7102	41
20	.50503	.86310	.58513	1.7090	40
21	528	295	552	.7079	39
22	553	281	591	.7067	38
23	578	266	631	.7056	37
24	603	251	670	.7045	36
25	.50628	.86237	.58709	1.7033	35
26	654	222	748	.7022	34
27	679	207	787	.7011	33
28	704	192	826	.6999	32
29	729	178	865	.6988	31
30	.50754	.86163	.58905	1.6977	30
31	779	148	944	.6965	29
32	804	133	.58983	.6954	28
33	829	119	.59022	.6943	27
34	854	104	061	.6932	26
35	.50879	.86089	.59101	1.6920	25
36	904	074	140	.6909	24
37	929	059	179	.6898	23
38	954	045	218	.6887	22
39	.50979	030	258	.6875	21
40	.51004	.86015	.59297	1.6864	20
41	029	.86000	336	.6853	19
42	054	.85985	376	.6842	18
43	079	970	415	.6831	17
44	104	956	454	.6820	16
45	.51129	.85941	.59494	1.6808	15
46	154	926	533	.6797	14
47	179	911	573	.6786	13
48	204	896	612	.6775	12
49	229	881	651	.6764	11
50	.51254	.85866	.59691	1.6753	10
51	279	851	730	.6742	9
52	304	836	770	.6731	8
53	329	821	809	.6720	7
54	354	806	849	.6709	6
55	.51379	.85792	.59888	1.6698	5
56	404	777	928	.6687	4
57	429	762	.59967	.6676	3
58	454	747	.60007	.6665	2
59	479	732	046	.6654	1
60	.51504	.85717	.60086	1.6643	0
′	cos	sin	cot	tan	′

59°

31°

′	sin	cos	tan	cot	′
0	.51504	.85717	.60086	1.6643	60
1	529	702	126	.6632	59
2	554	687	165	.6621	58
3	579	672	205	.6610	57
4	604	657	245	.6599	56
5	.51628	.85642	.60284	1.6588	55
6	653	627	324	.6577	54
7	678	612	364	.6566	53
8	703	597	403	.6555	52
9	728	582	443	.6545	51
10	.51753	.85567	.60483	1.6534	50
11	778	551	522	.6523	49
12	803	536	562	.6512	48
13	828	521	602	.6501	47
14	852	506	642	.6490	46
15	.51877	.85491	.60681	1.6479	45
16	902	476	721	.6469	44
17	927	461	761	.6458	43
18	952	446	801	.6447	42
19	.51977	431	841	.6436	41
20	.52002	.85416	.60881	1.6426	40
21	026	401	921	.6415	39
22	051	385	.60960	.6404	38
23	076	370	.61000	.6393	37
24	101	355	040	.6383	36
25	.52126	.85340	.61080	1.6372	35
26	151	325	120	.6361	34
27	175	310	160	.6351	33
28	200	294	200	.6340	32
29	225	279	240	.6329	31
30	.52250	.85264	.61280	1.6319	30
31	275	249	320	.6308	29
32	299	234	360	.6297	28
33	324	218	400	.6287	27
34	349	203	440	.6276	26
35	.52374	.85188	.61480	1.6265	25
36	399	173	520	.6255	24
37	423	157	561	.6244	23
38	448	142	601	.6234	22
39	473	127	641	.6223	21
40	.52498	.85112	.61681	1.6212	20
41	522	096	721	.6202	19
42	547	081	761	.6191	18
43	572	066	801	.6181	17
44	597	051	842	.6170	16
45	.52621	.85035	.61882	1.6160	15
46	646	020	922	.6149	14
47	671	.85005	.61962	.6139	13
48	696	.84989	.62003	.6128	12
49	720	974	043	.6118	11
50	.52745	.84959	.62083	1.6107	10
51	770	943	124	.6097	9
52	794	928	164	.6087	8
53	819	913	204	.6076	7
54	844	897	245	.6066	6
55	.52869	.84882	.62285	1.6055	5
56	893	866	325	.6045	4
57	918	851	366	.6034	3
58	943	836	406	.6024	2
59	967	820	446	.6014	1
60	.52992	.84805	.62487	1.6003	0
′	cos	sin	cot	tan	′

58°

32°

′	sin	cos	tan	cot	′
0	.52992	.84805	.62487	1.6003	60
1	.53017	789	527	.5993	59
2	041	774	568	.5983	58
3	066	759	608	.5972	57
4	091	743	649	.5962	56
5	.53115	.84728	.62689	1.5952	55
6	140	712	730	.5941	54
7	164	697	770	.5931	53
8	189	681	811	.5921	52
9	214	666	852	.5911	51
10	.53238	.84650	.62892	1.5900	50
11	263	635	933	.5890	49
12	288	619	.62973	.5880	48
13	312	604	.63014	.5869	47
14	337	588	055	.5859	46
15	.53361	.84573	.63095	1.5849	45
16	386	557	136	.5839	44
17	411	542	177	.5829	43
18	435	526	217	.5818	42
19	460	511	258	.5808	41
20	.53484	.84495	.63299	1.5798	40
21	509	480	340	.5788	39
22	534	464	380	.5778	38
23	558	448	421	.5768	37
24	583	433	462	.5757	36
25	.53607	.84417	.63503	1.5747	35
26	632	402	544	.5737	34
27	656	386	584	.5727	33
28	681	370	625	.5717	32
29	705	355	666	.5707	31
30	.53730	.84339	.63707	1.5697	30
31	754	324	748	.5687	29
32	779	308	789	.5677	28
33	804	292	830	.5667	27
34	828	277	871	.5657	26
35	.53853	.84261	.63912	1.5647	25
36	877	245	953	.5637	24
37	902	230	.63994	.5627	23
38	926	214	.64035	.5617	22
39	951	198	076	.5607	21
40	.53975	.84182	.64117	1.5597	20
41	.54000	167	158	.5587	19
42	024	151	199	.5577	18
43	049	135	240	.5567	17
44	073	120	281	.5557	16
45	.54097	.84104	.64322	1.5547	15
46	122	088	363	.5537	14
47	146	072	404	.5527	13
48	171	057	446	.5517	12
49	195	041	487	.5507	11
50	.54220	.84025	.64528	1.5497	10
51	244	.84009	569	.5487	9
52	269	.83994	610	.5477	8
53	293	978	652	.5468	7
54	317	962	693	.5458	6
55	.54342	.83946	.64734	1.5448	5
56	366	930	775	.5438	4
57	391	915	817	.5428	3
58	415	899	858	.5418	2
59	440	883	899	.5408	1
60	.54464	.83867	.64941	1.5399	0

′	cos	sin	cot	tan	′

57°

Table 4　　TRIGONOMETRIC FUNCTIONS　　609

33°

′	sin	cos	tan	cot	′
0	.54464	.83867	.64941	1.5399	60
1	488	851	.64982	.5389	59
2	513	835	.65024	.5379	58
3	537	819	065	.5369	57
4	561	804	106	.5359	56
5	.54586	.83788	.65148	1.5350	55
6	610	772	189	.5340	54
7	635	756	231	.5330	53
8	659	740	272	.5320	52
9	683	724	314	.5311	51
10	.54708	.83708	.65355	1.5301	50
11	732	692	397	.5291	49
12	756	676	438	.5282	48
13	781	660	480	.5272	47
14	805	645	521	.5262	46
15	.54829	.83629	.65563	1.5253	45
16	854	613	604	.5243	44
17	878	597	646	.5233	43
18	902	581	688	.5224	42
19	927	565	729	.5214	41
20	.54951	.83549	.65771	1.5204	40
21	975	533	813	.5195	39
22	.54999	517	854	.5185	38
23	.55024	501	896	.5175	37
24	048	485	938	.5166	36
25	.55072	.83469	.65980	1.5156	35
26	097	453	.66021	.5147	34
27	121	437	063	.5137	33
28	145	421	105	.5127	32
29	169	405	147	.5118	31
30	.55194	.83389	.66189	1.5108	30
31	218	373	230	.5099	29
32	242	356	272	.5089	28
33	266	340	314	.5080	27
34	291	324	356	.5070	26
35	.55315	.83308	.66398	1.5061	25
36	339	292	440	.5051	24
37	363	276	482	.5042	23
38	388	260	524	.5032	22
39	412	244	566	.5023	21
40	.55436	.83228	.66608	1.5013	20
41	460	212	650	.5004	19
42	484	195	692	.4994	18
43	509	179	734	.4985	17
44	533	163	776	.4975	16
45	.55557	.83147	.66818	1.4966	15
46	581	131	860	.4957	14
47	605	115	902	.4947	13
48	630	098	944	.4938	12
49	654	082	.66986	.4928	11
50	.55678	.83066	.67028	1.4919	10
51	702	050	071	.4910	9
52	726	034	113	.4900	8
53	750	017	155	.4891	7
54	775	.83001	197	.4882	6
55	.55799	.82985	.67239	1.4872	5
56	823	969	282	.4863	4
57	847	953	324	.4854	3
58	871	936	366	.4844	2
59	895	920	409	.4835	1
60	.55919	.82904	.67451	1.4826	0

′	cos	sin	cot	tan	′

56°

APPENDIX

34°

′	sin	cos	tan	cot	′
0	.55919	.82904	.67451	1.4826	60
1	943	887	493	.4816	59
2	968	871	536	.4807	58
3	.55992	855	578	.4798	57
4	.56016	839	620	.4788	56
5	.56040	.82822	.67663	1.4779	55
6	064	806	705	.4770	54
7	088	790	748	.4761	53
8	112	773	790	.4751	52
9	136	757	832	.4742	51
10	.56160	.82741	.67875	1.4733	50
11	184	724	917	.4724	49
12	208	708	.67960	.4715	48
13	232	692	.68002	.4705	47
14	256	675	045	.4696	46
15	.56280	.82659	.68088	1.4687	45
16	305	643	130	.4678	44
17	329	626	173	.4669	43
18	353	610	215	.4659	42
19	377	593	258	.4650	41
20	.56401	.82577	.68301	1.4641	40
21	425	561	343	.4632	39
22	449	544	386	.4623	38
23	473	528	429	.4614	37
24	497	511	471	.4605	36
25	.56521	.82495	.68514	1.4596	35
26	545	478	557	.4586	34
27	569	462	600	.4577	33
28	593	446	642	.4568	32
29	617	429	685	.4559	31
30	.56641	.82413	.68728	1.4550	30
31	665	396	771	.4541	29
32	689	380	814	.4532	28
33	713	363	857	.4523	27
34	736	347	900	.4514	26
35	.56760	.82330	.68942	1.4505	25
36	784	314	.68985	.4496	24
37	808	297	.69028	.4487	23
38	832	281	071	.4478	22
39	856	264	114	.4469	21
40	.56880	.82248	.69157	1.4460	20
41	904	231	200	.4451	19
42	928	214	243	.4442	18
43	952	198	286	.4433	17
44	.56976	181	329	.4424	16
45	.57000	.82165	.69372	1.4415	15
46	024	148	416	.4406	14
47	047	132	459	.4397	13
48	071	115	502	.4388	12
49	095	098	545	.4379	11
50	.57119	.82082	.69588	1.4370	10
51	143	065	631	.4361	9
52	167	048	675	.4352	8
53	191	032	718	.4344	7
54	215	.82015	761	.4335	6
55	.57238	.81999	.69804	1.4326	5
56	262	982	847	.4317	4
57	286	965	891	.4308	3
58	310	949	934	.4299	2
59	334	932	.69977	.4290	1
60	.57358	.81915	.70021	1.4281	0
′	cos	sin	cot	tan	′

55°

Table 4 TRIGONOMETRIC FUNCTIONS 611

35°

′	sin	cos	tan	cot	′
0	.57358	.81915	.70021	1.4281	60
1	381	899	064	.4273	59
2	405	882	107	.4264	58
3	429	865	151	.4255	57
4	453	848	194	.4246	56
5	.57477	.81832	.70238	1.4237	55
6	501	815	281	.4229	54
7	524	798	325	.4220	53
8	548	782	368	.4211	52
9	572	765	412	.4202	51
10	.57596	.81748	.70455	1.4193	50
11	619	731	499	.4185	49
12	643	714	542	.4176	48
13	667	698	586	.4167	47
14	691	681	629	.4158	46
15	.57715	.81664	.70673	1.4150	45
16	738	647	717	.4141	44
17	762	631	760	.4132	43
18	786	614	804	.4124	42
19	810	597	848	.4115	41
20	.57833	.81580	.70891	1.4106	40
21	857	563	935	.4097	39
22	881	546	.70979	.4089	38
23	904	530	.71023	.4080	37
24	928	513	066	.4071	36
25	.57952	.81496	.71110	1.4063	35
26	976	479	154	.4054	34
27	.57999	462	198	.4045	33
28	.58023	445	242	.4037	32
29	047	428	285	.4028	31
30	.58070	.81412	.71329	1.4019	30
31	094	395	373	.4011	29
32	118	378	417	.4002	28
33	141	361	461	.3994	27
34	165	344	505	.3985	26
35	.58189	.81327	.71549	1.3976	25
36	212	310	593	.3968	24
37	236	293	637	.3959	23
38	260	276	681	.3951	22
39	283	259	725	.3942	21
40	.58307	.81242	.71769	1.3934	20
41	330	225	813	.3925	19
42	354	208	857	.3916	18
43	378	191	901	.3908	17
44	401	174	946	.3899	16
45	.58425	.81157	.71990	1.3891	15
46	449	140	.72034	.3882	14
47	472	123	078	.3874	13
48	496	106	122	.3865	12
49	519	089	167	.3857	11
50	.58543	.81072	.72211	1.3848	10
51	567	055	255	.3840	9
52	590	038	299	.3831	8
53	614	021	344	.3823	7
54	637	.81004	388	.3814	6
55	.58661	.80987	.72432	1.3806	5
56	684	970	477	.3798	4
57	708	953	521	.3789	3
58	731	936	565	.3781	2
59	755	919	610	.3772	1
60	.58779	.80902	.72654	1.3764	0
′	cos	sin	cot	tan	′

54°

APPENDIX

36°

'	sin	cos	tan	cot	'
0	.58779	.80902	.72654	1.3764	60
1	802	885	699	.3755	59
2	826	867	743	.3747	58
3	849	850	788	.3739	57
4	873	833	832	.3730	56
5	.58896	.80816	.72877	1.3722	55
6	920	799	921	.3713	54
7	943	782	.72966	.3705	53
8	967	765	.73010	.3697	52
9	.58990	748	055	.3688	51
10	.59014	.80730	.73100	1.3680	50
11	037	713	144	.3672	49
12	061	696	189	.3663	48
13	084	679	234	.3655	47
14	108	662	278	.3647	46
15	.59131	.80644	.73323	1.3638	45
16	154	627	368	.3630	44
17	178	610	413	.3622	43
18	201	593	457	.3613	42
19	225	576	502	.3605	41
20	.59248	.80558	.73547	1.3597	40
21	272	541	592	.3588	39
22	295	524	637	.3580	38
23	318	507	681	.3572	37
24	342	489	726	.3564	36
25	.59365	.80472	.73771	1.3555	35
26	389	455	816	.3547	34
27	412	438	861	.3539	33
28	436	420	906	.3531	32
29	459	403	951	.3522	31
30	.59482	.80386	.73996	1.3514	30
31	506	368	.74041	.3506	29
32	529	351	086	.3498	28
33	552	334	131	.3490	27
34	576	316	176	.3481	26
35	.59599	.80299	.74221	1.3473	25
36	622	282	267	.3465	24
37	646	264	312	.3457	23
38	669	247	357	.3449	22
39	693	230	402	.3440	21
40	.59716	.80212	.74447	1.3432	20
41	739	195	492	.3424	19
42	763	178	538	.3416	18
43	786	160	583	.3408	17
44	809	143	628	.3400	16
45	.59832	.80125	.74674	1.3392	15
46	856	108	719	.3384	14
47	879	091	764	.3375	13
48	902	073	810	.3367	12
49	926	056	855	.3359	11
50	.59949	.80038	.74900	1.3351	10
51	972	021	946	.3343	9
52	.59995	.80003	.74991	.3335	8
53	.60019	.79986	.75037	.3327	7
54	042	968	082	.3319	6
55	.60065	.79951	.75128	1.3311	5
56	089	934	173	.3303	4
57	112	916	219	.3295	3
58	135	899	264	.3287	2
59	158	881	310	.3278	1
60	.60182	.79864	.75355	1.3270	0
'	cos	sin	cot	tan	'

53°

Table 4 TRIGONOMETRIC FUNCTIONS 613

37°

′	sin	cos	tan	cot	′
0	.60182	.79864	.75355	1.3270	60
1	205	846	401	.3262	59
2	228	829	447	.3254	58
3	251	811	492	.3246	57
4	274	793	538	.3238	56
5	.60298	.79776	.75584	1.3230	55
6	321	758	629	.3222	54
7	344	741	675	.3214	53
8	367	723	721	.3206	52
9	390	706	767	.3198	51
10	.60414	.79688	.75812	1.3190	50
11	437	671	858	.3182	49
12	460	653	904	.3175	48
13	483	635	950	.3167	47
14	506	618	.75996	.3159	46
15	.60529	.79600	.76042	1.3151	45
16	553	583	088	.3143	44
17	576	565	134	.3135	43
18	599	547	180	.3127	42
19	622	530	226	.3119	41
20	.60645	.79512	.76272	1.3111	40
21	668	494	318	.3103	39
22	691	477	364	.3095	38
23	714	459	410	.3087	37
24	738	441	456	.3079	36
25	.60761	.79424	.76502	1.3072	35
26	784	406	548	.3064	34
27	807	388	594	.3056	33
28	830	371	640	.3048	32
29	853	353	686	.3040	31
30	.60876	.79335	.76733	1.3032	30
31	899	318	779	.3024	29
32	922	300	825	.3017	28
33	945	282	871	.3009	27
34	968	264	918	.3001	26
35	.60991	.79247	.76964	1.2993	25
36	.61015	229	.77010	.2985	24
37	038	211	057	.2977	23
38	061	193	103	.2970	22
39	084	176	149	.2962	21
40	.61107	.79158	.77196	1.2954	20
41	130	140	242	.2946	19
42	153	122	289	.2938	18
43	176	105	335	.2931	17
44	199	087	382	.2923	16
45	.61222	.79069	.77428	1.2915	15
46	245	051	475	.2907	14
47	268	033	521	.2900	13
48	291	.79016	568	.2892	12
49	314	.78998	615	.2884	11
50	.61337	.78980	.77661	1.2876	10
51	360	962	708	.2869	9
52	383	944	754	.2861	8
53	406	926	801	.2853	7
54	429	908	848	.2846	6
55	.61451	.78891	.77895	1.2838	5
56	474	873	941	.2830	4
57	497	855	.77988	.2822	3
58	520	837	.78035	.2815	2
59	543	819	082	.2807	1
60	.61566	.78801	.78129	1.2799	0
′	cos	sin	cot	tan	′

52°

APPENDIX

38°

′	sin	cos	tan	cot	′
0	.61566	.78801	.78129	1.2799	60
1	589	783	175	.2792	59
2	612	765	222	.2784	58
3	635	747	269	.2776	57
4	658	729	316	.2769	56
5	.61681	.78711	.78363	1.2761	55
6	704	694	410	.2753	54
7	726	676	457	.2746	53
8	749	658	504	.2738	52
9	772	640	551	.2731	51
10	.61795	.78622	.78598	1.2723	50
11	818	604	645	.2715	49
12	841	586	692	.2708	48
13	864	568	739	.2700	47
14	887	550	786	.2693	46
15	.61909	.78532	.78834	1.2685	45
16	932	514	881	.2677	44
17	955	496	928	.2670	43
18	.61978	478	.78975	.2662	42
19	.62001	460	.79022	.2655	41
20	.62024	.78442	.79070	1.2647	40
21	046	424	117	.2640	39
22	069	405	164	.2632	38
23	092	387	212	.2624	37
24	115	369	259	.2617	36
25	.62138	.78351	.79306	1.2609	35
26	160	333	354	.2602	34
27	183	315	401	.2594	33
28	206	297	449	.2587	32
29	229	279	496	.2579	31
30	.62251	.78261	.79544	1.2572	30
31	274	243	591	.2564	29
32	297	225	639	.2557	28
33	320	206	686	.2549	27
34	342	188	734	.2542	26
35	.62365	.78170	.79781	1.2534	25
36	388	152	829	.2527	24
37	411	134	877	.2519	23
38	433	116	924	.2512	22
39	456	098	.79972	.2504	21
40	.62479	.78079	.80020	1.2497	20
41	502	061	067	.2489	19
42	524	043	115	.2482	18
43	547	025	163	.2475	17
44	570	.78007	211	.2467	16
45	.62592	.77988	.80258	1.2460	15
46	615	970	306	.2452	14
47	638	952	354	.2445	13
48	660	934	402	.2437	12
49	683	916	450	.2430	11
50	.62706	.77897	.80498	1.2423	10
51	728	879	546	.2415	9
52	751	861	594	.2408	8
53	774	843	642	.2401	7
54	796	824	690	.2393	6
55	.62819	.77806	.80738	1.2386	5
56	842	788	786	.2378	4
57	864	769	834	.2371	3
58	887	751	882	.2364	2
59	909	733	930	.2356	1
60	.62932	.77715	.80978	1.2349	0
′	cos	sin	cot	tan	′

51°

39°

′	sin	cos	tan	cot	′
0	.62932	.77715	.80978	1.2349	60
1	955	696	.81027	.2342	59
2	.62977	678	075	.2334	58
3	.63000	660	123	.2327	57
4	022	641	171	.2320	56
5	.63045	.77623	.81220	1.2312	55
6	068	605	268	.2305	54
7	090	586	316	.2298	53
8	113	568	364	.2290	52
9	135	550	413	.2283	51
10	.63158	.77531	.81461	1.2276	50
11	180	513	510	.2268	49
12	203	494	558	.2261	48
13	225	476	606	.2254	47
14	248	458	655	.2247	46
15	.63271	.77439	.81703	1.2239	45
16	293	421	752	.2232	44
17	316	402	800	.2225	43
18	338	384	849	.2218	42
19	361	366	898	.2210	41
20	.63383	.77347	.81946	1.2203	40
21	406	329	.81995	.2196	39
22	428	310	.82044	.2189	38
23	451	292	092	.2181	37
24	473	273	141	.2174	36
25	.63496	.77255	.82190	1.2167	35
26	518	236	238	.2160	34
27	540	218	287	.2153	33
28	563	199	336	.2145	32
29	585	181	385	.2138	31
30	.63608	.77162	.82434	1.2131	30
31	630	144	483	.2124	29
32	653	125	531	.2117	28
33	675	107	580	.2109	27
34	698	088	629	.2102	26
35	.63720	.77070	.82678	1.2095	25
36	742	051	727	.2088	24
37	765	033	776	.2081	23
38	787	.77014	825	.2074	22
39	810	.76996	874	.2066	21
40	.63832	.76977	.82923	1.2059	20
41	854	959	.82972	.2052	19
42	877	940	.83022	.2045	18
43	899	921	071	.2038	17
44	922	903	120	.2031	16
45	.63944	.76884	.83169	1.2024	15
46	966	866	218	.2017	14
47	.63989	847	268	.2009	13
48	.64011	828	317	.2002	12
49	033	810	366	.1995	11
50	.64056	.76791	.83415	1.1988	10
51	078	772	465	.1981	9
52	100	754	514	.1974	8
53	123	735	564	.1967	7
54	145	717	613	.1960	6
55	.64167	.76698	.83662	1.1953	5
56	190	679	712	.1946	4
57	212	661	761	.1939	3
58	234	642	811	.1932	2
59	256	623	860	.1925	1
60	.64279	.76604	.83910	1.1918	0
′	cos	sin	cot	tan	′

50°

APPENDIX

40°

′	sin	cos	tan	cot	′
0	.64279	.76604	.83910	1.1918	60
1	301	586	.83960	.1910	59
2	323	567	.84009	.1903	58
3	346	548	059	.1896	57
4	368	530	108	.1889	56
5	.64390	.76511	.84158	1.1882	55
6	412	492	208	.1875	54
7	435	473	258	.1868	53
8	457	455	307	.1861	52
9	479	436	357	.1854	51
10	.64501	.76417	.84407	1.1847	50
11	524	398	457	.1840	49
12	546	380	507	.1833	48
13	568	361	556	.1826	47
14	590	342	606	.1819	46
15	.64612	.76323	.84656	1.1812	45
16	635	304	706	.1806	44
17	657	286	756	.1799	43
18	679	267	806	.1792	42
19	701	248	856	.1785	41
20	.64723	.76229	.84906	1.1778	40
21	746	210	.84956	.1771	39
22	768	192	.85006	.1764	38
23	790	173	057	.1757	37
24	812	154	107	.1750	36
25	.64834	.76135	.85157	1.1743	35
26	856	116	207	.1736	34
27	878	097	257	.1729	33
28	901	078	308	.1722	32
29	923	059	358	.1715	31
30	.64945	.76041	.85408	1.1708	30
31	967	022	458	.1702	29
32	.64989	.76003	509	.1695	28
33	.65011	.75984	559	.1688	27
34	033	965	609	.1681	26
35	.65055	.75946	.85660	1.1674	25
36	077	927	710	.1667	24
37	100	908	761	.1660	23
38	122	889	811	.1653	22
39	144	870	862	.1647	21
40	.65166	.75851	.85912	1.1640	20
41	188	832	.85963	.1633	19
42	210	813	.86014	.1626	18
43	232	794	064	.1619	17
44	254	775	115	.1612	16
45	.65276	.75756	.86166	1.1606	15
46	298	738	216	.1599	14
47	320	719	267	.1592	13
48	342	700	318	.1585	12
49	364	680	368	.1578	11
50	.65386	.75661	.86419	1.1571	10
51	408	642	470	.1565	9
52	430	623	521	.1558	8
53	452	604	572	.1551	7
54	474	585	623	.1544	6
55	.65496	.75566	.86674	1.1538	5
56	518	547	725	.1531	4
57	540	528	776	.1524	3
58	562	509	827	.1517	2
59	584	490	878	.1510	1
60	.65606	.75471	.86929	1.1504	0
′	cos	sin	cot	tan	′

49°

41°

′	sin	cos	tan	cot	′
0	.65606	.75471	.86929	1.1504	60
1	628	452	.86980	.1497	59
2	650	433	.87031	.1490	58
3	672	414	082	.1483	57
4	694	395	133	.1477	56
5	.65716	.75375	.87184	1.1470	55
6	738	356	236	.1463	54
7	759	337	287	.1456	53
8	781	318	338	.1450	52
9	803	299	389	.1443	51
10	.65825	.75280	.87441	1.1436	50
11	847	261	492	.1430	49
12	869	241	543	.1423	48
13	891	222	595	.1416	47
14	913	203	646	.1410	46
15	.65935	.75184	.87698	1.1403	45
16	956	165	749	.1396	44
17	.65978	146	801	.1389	43
18	.66000	126	852	.1383	42
19	022	107	904	.1376	41
20	.66044	.75088	.87955	1.1369	40
21	066	069	.88007	.1363	39
22	088	050	059	.1356	38
23	109	030	110	.1349	37
24	131	.75011	162	.1343	36
25	.66153	.74992	.88214	1.1336	35
26	175	973	265	.1329	34
27	197	953	317	.1323	33
28	218	934	369	.1316	32
29	240	915	421	.1310	31
30	.66262	.74896	.88473	1.1303	30
31	284	876	524	.1296	29
32	306	857	576	.1290	28
33	327	838	628	.1283	27
34	349	818	680	.1276	26
35	.66371	.74799	.88732	1.1270	25
36	393	780	784	.1263	24
37	414	760	836	.1257	23
38	436	741	888	.1250	22
39	458	722	940	.1243	21
40	.66480	.74703	.88992	1.1237	20
41	501	683	.89045	.1230	19
42	523	664	097	.1224	18
43	545	644	149	.1217	17
44	566	625	201	.1211	16
45	.66588	.74606	.89253	1.1204	15
46	610	586	306	.1197	14
47	632	567	358	.1191	13
48	653	548	410	.1184	12
49	675	528	463	.1178	11
50	.66697	.74509	.89515	1.1171	10
51	718	489	567	.1165	9
52	740	470	620	.1158	8
53	762	451	672	.1152	7
54	783	431	725	.1145	6
55	.66805	.74412	.89777	1.1139	5
56	827	392	830	.1132	4
57	848	373	883	.1126	3
58	870	353	935	.1119	2
59	891	334	.89988	.1113	1
60	.66913	.74314	.90040	1.1106	0
′	cos	sin	cot	tan	′

48°

42°

′	sin	cos	tan	cot	′
0	.66913	.74314	.90040	1.1106	60
1	935	295	093	.1100	59
2	956	276	146	.1093	58
3	978	256	199	.1087	57
4	.66999	237	251	.1080	56
5	.67021	.74217	.90304	1.1074	55
6	043	198	357	.1067	54
7	064	178	410	.1061	53
8	086	159	463	.1054	52
9	107	139	516	.1048	51
10	.67129	.74120	.90569	1.1041	50
11	151	100	621	.1035	49
12	172	080	674	.1028	48
13	194	061	727	.1022	47
14	215	041	781	.1016	46
15	.67237	.74022	.90834	1.1009	45
16	258	.74002	887	.1003	44
17	280	.73983	940	.0996	43
18	301	963	.90993	.0990	42
19	323	944	.91046	.0983	41
20	.67344	.73924	.91099	1.0977	40
21	366	904	153	.0971	39
22	387	885	206	.0964	38
23	409	865	259	.0958	37
24	430	846	313	.0951	36
25	.67452	.73826	.91366	1.0945	35
26	473	806	419	.0939	34
27	495	787	473	.0932	33
28	516	767	526	.0926	32
29	538	747	580	.0919	31
30	.67559	.73728	.91633	1.0913	30
31	580	708	687	.0907	29
32	602	688	740	.0900	28
33	623	669	794	.0894	27
34	645	649	847	.0888	26
35	.67666	.73629	.91901	1.0881	25
36	688	610	.91955	.0875	24
37	709	590	.92008	.0869	23
38	730	570	062	.0862	22
39	752	551	116	.0856	21
40	.67773	.73531	.92170	1.0850	20
41	795	511	224	.0843	19
42	816	491	277	.0837	18
43	837	472	331	.0831	17
44	859	452	385	.0824	16
45	.67880	.73432	.92439	1.0818	15
46	901	413	493	.0812	14
47	923	393	547	.0805	13
48	944	373	601	.0799	12
49	965	353	655	.0793	11
50	.67987	.73333	.92709	1.0786	10
51	.68008	314	763	.0780	9
52	029	294	817	.0774	8
53	051	274	872	.0768	7
54	072	254	926	.0761	6
55	.68093	.73234	.92980	1.0755	5
56	115	215	.93034	.0749	4
57	136	195	088	.0742	3
58	157	175	143	.0736	2
59	179	155	197	.0730	1
60	.68200	.73135	.93252	1.0724	0
′	cos	sin	cot	tan	′

47°

43°

′	sin	cos	tan	cot	′
0	.68200	.73135	.93252	1.0724	60
1	221	116	306	.0717	59
2	242	096	360	.0711	58
3	264	076	415	.0705	57
4	285	056	469	.0699	56
5	.68306	.73036	.93524	1.0692	55
6	327	.73016	578	.0686	54
7	349	.72996	633	.0680	53
8	370	976	688	.0674	52
9	391	957	742	.0668	51
10	.68412	.72937	.93797	1.0661	50
11	434	917	852	.0655	49
12	455	897	906	.0649	48
13	476	877	.93961	.0643	47
14	497	857	.94016	.0637	46
15	.68518	.72837	.94071	1.0630	45
16	539	817	125	.0624	44
17	561	797	180	.0618	43
18	582	777	235	.0612	42
19	603	757	290	.0606	41
20	.68624	.72737	.94345	1.0599	40
21	645	717	400	.0593	39
22	666	697	455	.0587	38
23	688	677	510	.0581	37
24	709	657	565	.0575	36
25	.68730	.72637	.94620	1.0569	35
26	751	617	676	.0562	34
27	772	597	731	.0556	33
28	793	577	786	.0550	32
29	814	557	841	.0544	31
30	.68835	.72537	.94896	1.0538	30
31	857	517	.94952	.0532	29
32	878	497	.95007	.0526	28
33	899	477	062	.0519	27
34	920	457	118	.0513	26
35	.68941	.72437	.95173	1.0507	25
36	962	417	229	.0501	24
37	.68983	397	284	.0495	23
38	.69004	377	340	.0489	22
39	025	357	395	.0483	21
40	.69046	.72337	.95451	1.0477	20
41	067	317	506	.0470	19
42	088	297	562	.0464	18
43	109	277	618	.0458	17
44	130	257	673	.0452	16
45	.69151	.72236	.95729	1.0446	15
46	172	216	785	.0440	14
47	193	196	841	.0434	13
48	214	176	897	.0428	12
49	235	156	.95952	.0422	11
50	.69256	.72136	.96008	1.0416	10
51	277	116	064	.0410	9
52	298	095	120	.0404	8
53	319	075	176	.0398	7
54	340	055	232	.0392	6
55	.69361	.72035	.96288	1.0385	5
56	382	.72015	344	.0379	4
57	403	.71995	400	.0373	3
58	424	974	457	.0367	2
59	445	954	513	.0361	1
60	.69466	.71934	.96569	1.0355	0
′	cos	sin	cot	tan	′

46°

44°

'	sin	cos	tan	cot	'
0	.69466	.71934	.96569	1.0355	60
1	487	914	625	.0349	59
2	508	894	681	.0343	58
3	529	873	738	.0337	57
4	549	853	794	.0331	56
5	.69570	.71833	.96850	1.0325	55
6	591	813	907	.0319	54
7	612	792	.96963	.0313	53
8	633	772	.97020	.0307	52
9	654	752	076	.0301	51
10	.69675	.71732	.97133	1.0295	50
11	696	711	189	.0289	49
12	717	691	246	.0283	48
13	737	671	302	.0277	47
14	758	650	359	.0271	46
15	.69779	.71630	.97416	1.0265	45
16	800	610	472	.0259	44
17	821	590	529	.0253	43
18	842	569	586	.0247	42
19	862	549	643	.0241	41
20	.69883	.71529	.97700	1.0235	40
21	904	508	756	.0230	39
22	925	488	813	.0224	38
23	946	468	870	.0218	37
24	966	447	927	.0212	36
25	.69987	.71427	.97984	1.0206	35
26	.70008	407	.98041	.0200	34
27	029	386	098	.0194	33
28	049	366	155	.0188	32
29	070	345	213	.0182	31
30	.70091	.71325	.98270	1.0176	30
31	112	305	327	.0170	29
32	132	284	384	.0164	28
33	153	264	441	.0158	27
34	174	243	499	.0152	26
35	.70195	.71223	.98556	1.0147	25
36	215	203	613	.0141	24
37	236	182	671	.0135	23
38	257	162	728	.0129	22
39	277	141	786	.0123	21
40	.70298	.71121	.98843	1.0117	20
41	319	100	901	.0111	19
42	339	080	.98958	.0105	18
43	360	059	.99016	.0099	17
44	381	039	073	.0094	16
45	.70401	.71019	.99131	1.0088	15
46	422	.70998	189	.0082	14
47	443	978	247	.0076	13
48	463	957	304	.0070	12
49	484	937	362	.0064	11
50	.70505	.70916	.99420	1.0058	10
51	525	896	478	.0052	9
52	546	875	536	.0047	8
53	567	855	594	.0041	7
54	587	834	652	.0035	6
55	.70608	.70813	.99710	1.0029	5
56	628	793	768	.0023	4
57	649	772	826	.0017	3
58	670	752	884	.0012	2
59	690	731	.99942	.0006	1
60	.70711	.70711	1.0000	1.0000	0
'	cos	sin	cot	tan	'

45°

SOLUTION TO PROBLEMS

CHAPTER 2

1. (a)   19,227 feet

   (b) $m = 8$ $x = 3$ $i = 1, 2, \cdots, 8$ $a_2 = 941$ $a_3 x = 2{,}526$

   $\sum a_i = 6{,}409$ $\sum a_i x = 19{,}227$ $x \sum a_i = 19{,}227$

2. (a)   20.7 hours

   (b) $m = 4$ $a_1 = 4$ $b_2 = 30$ $x = 1$ $y = 1/60$

   $\sum a_i = 19$ $\sum b_i = 102$ $\sum (a_i x + b_i y) = 20.7$

   (c) $x_1 = 1$ $x_2 = 1/60$ $m = 4$ $n = 2$ $c_{12} = 15$ $c_{21} = 5$

   $\sum c_{i1} = 19$ $\sum c_{i2} = 102$ $\sum x_j \sum c_{ij} = 20.7$

3. 19,005   21,733   24,589   27,573

4.

   (a) $\displaystyle\sum_{i=1}^{3} \frac{a_i}{b_i}$ (b) $\displaystyle\sum_{i=1}^{4} \frac{a_i}{a_{i+1}}$

   (c) $\displaystyle\sum_{i=1}^{4} a_i b_i$ (d) $\displaystyle\sum_{i=1}^{3} x_i x_{i+1}$

   (e) $\displaystyle\sum_{i=1}^{5} x_i^2$ (f) $\displaystyle\sum_{i=1}^{3} x_i y_i$

5. $16 w + 10 x - 2 y - 2 z$

6.

   (a) $\displaystyle\sum_{i=1}^{2}\sum_{j=2}^{3} c_{ij}$ (b) $\displaystyle\sum_{i=1}^{2} c_{i,\, i+1}$ (c) $\displaystyle\sum_{i=1}^{2} c_{i+2,\, i}$

   (d) $\displaystyle\sum_{i=1}^{2}\sum_{j=1}^{2} c_{ij}$ $i \neq j$ (e) $\displaystyle\sum_{i=1}^{3}\sum_{j=1}^{3} c_{ij}$ $i + j = 4$

7. (a) $c_{13} + c_{22} + c_{31}$

   (b) $c_{41} + c_{32} + c_{23}$

   (c) $c_{21} + c_{31} + c_{41} + c_{32} + c_{42} + c_{43}$

   (d) $c_{21} + c_{22} + c_{23}$

   (e) $c_{13} + c_{23} + c_{33} + c_{43}$

CHAPTER 3

1. (a) $[u \quad v \quad w] = [-1 \quad 4 \quad 12]$

   (b) $[x_1 \quad x_2 \quad x_3] = [\ 2 \quad -5 \quad 7]$

   (c) $[b_1 \quad b_2 \quad b_3] = [-2 \quad 3 \quad 1]$

2.

(a) $\begin{bmatrix} 5 & 7 \\ -29 & -1 \end{bmatrix}$ (b) $\begin{bmatrix} 23 & 30 & 37 \\ 11 & 14 & 17 \end{bmatrix}$ (c) 68   (d) $\begin{bmatrix} 32 \\ 42 \end{bmatrix}$

(e) $x_1^2 + x_2^2 + x_3^2$ or $\sum x_i^2$ $i = 1, 2, 3$

(f) $b_1 x_1 + b_2 x_2$ or $\sum b_i s_i$ $i = 1, 2$

(g) $\begin{bmatrix} a_{11}b_{11} + a_{12}b_{21} + a_{13}b_{31} + a_{14}b_{41} & a_{11}b_{12} + a_{12}b_{22} + a_{13}b_{32} + a_{14}b_{42} \\ a_{21}b_{11} + a_{22}b_{21} + a_{23}b_{31} + a_{24}b_{41} & a_{21}b_{12} + a_{22}b_{22} + a_{23}b_{32} + a_{24}b_{42} \\ a_{31}b_{11} + a_{32}b_{21} + a_{33}b_{31} + a_{34}b_{41} & a_{31}b_{12} + a_{32}b_{22} + a_{33}b_{32} + a_{34}b_{42} \end{bmatrix}$

3.

(a) $\begin{bmatrix} 20 & 10 & 1 \\ 5 & 2 & 4 \\ 2 & -1 & 1 \end{bmatrix} \begin{bmatrix} u \\ v \\ w \end{bmatrix} = \begin{bmatrix} 32 \\ 51 \\ 6 \end{bmatrix}$

(b) $\begin{bmatrix} 20 & 4 & -15 \\ 16 & 3 & -10 \\ 4 & 2 & -8 \end{bmatrix} \begin{bmatrix} x_1 \\ x_2 \\ x_3 \end{bmatrix} = \begin{bmatrix} -85 \\ -53 \\ -58 \end{bmatrix}$

(c) $\begin{bmatrix} 5 & 6 & -3 \\ 2 & -5 & 2 \\ 4 & 2 & -5 \end{bmatrix} \begin{bmatrix} b_1 \\ b_2 \\ b_3 \end{bmatrix} = \begin{bmatrix} 5 \\ -17 \\ -7 \end{bmatrix}$

5.

(a) $141\,A^{-1} = \begin{bmatrix} 6 & -11 & 38 \\ 3 & 18 & -75 \\ -9 & 40 & -10 \end{bmatrix}$

(b) $28\,A^{-1} = \begin{bmatrix} 4 & -2 & -5 \\ -88 & 100 & 40 \\ -20 & 24 & 4 \end{bmatrix}$

(c) $141\,A^{-1} = \begin{bmatrix} 21 & 24 & -3 \\ 18 & -13 & -16 \\ 24 & 14 & -37 \end{bmatrix}$

7.

$[a_1 \ \ a_2 \ \ a_3] = [c_1 \ \ c_2 \ \ c_3] \begin{bmatrix} b_{11} & b_{21} & b_{31} \\ b_{12} & b_{22} & b_{32} \\ b_{13} & b_{23} & b_{33} \end{bmatrix}$

8. Use the procedure demonstrated in equations (5) and (6) of section 3.3 and equations (3) to (8) of section 3.5.

9.

$$\begin{bmatrix} \dfrac{d}{a\,d\,-\,b\,c} & \dfrac{-\,b}{a\,d\,-\,b\,c} \\[2ex] \dfrac{-\,c}{a\,d\,-\,b\,c} & \dfrac{a}{a\,d\,-\,b\,c} \end{bmatrix}$$

CHAPTER 4

1. (a) $\sqrt{320} = 17.89$ (b) $\sqrt{244} = 15.62$
   (c) $\sqrt{142.74} = 119.47$

2. (a) 2   (b) -1.2 (c) 1.24

3. (a) $y = 2x + 1$ (b) $y = -1.2x + 8.4$
   (c) $y = 1.24x + 2.516$

7. (a) 7.25   (b) 431.25
   (c) $y = 4.75 + 0.25x$ $x = 1, 2, 3, \cdots$
      or
      $y = 5.00 + 0.25x$ $x = 0, 1, 2, \cdots$

8. (a) 65   (b) 975
   (c) $y = 105 - 5x$ $x = 1, 2, 3, \cdots$
      or
      $y = 100 - 5x$ $x = 0, 1, 2, \cdots$

10. (a) $y = \dfrac{10}{3}x - \dfrac{5}{9}x^2$

   (b) $y = \dfrac{1}{6}(18 + 53x - 45x^2 + 10x^3)$

11. $x_0 = 3.25$

12. At $x = 4.688$, both $g(x)$ and $h(x)$ are equal to 148.

CHAPTER 5

3.

$\bar{x}$	0.1	0.3	0.5	0.7	0.9	1.1
$\dfrac{\Delta y}{\Delta x}$	-0.92	-0.44	0.52	1.96	3.88	6.28

$$\frac{\Delta y}{\Delta x} = 6(\bar{x})^2 - 0.98$$

5.

$\bar{x}$	3	5	7	9
$\dfrac{\Delta y}{\Delta x}$	1.55	0.75	4.65	-3.95

10. (a)

$\bar{x}$	-3	-1	1	3
$\dfrac{\Delta y}{\Delta x}$	-20	-8	4	16

$$\frac{\Delta y}{\Delta x} = 6\bar{x} - 2$$

(b)

$\bar{x}$	-3	-1	1	3
$\dfrac{\Delta y}{\Delta x}$	-126	-10	10	126

$$\frac{\Delta y}{\Delta x} = 4(\bar{x})^3 + 6\bar{x}$$

CHAPTER 6

1.

Δx	0.1	0.01	0.001	0.0001
$\dfrac{\Delta}{\Delta x}\,4x^2$	80.4	80.04	80.004	80.0004

2.

$\bar{x}$	1.1	1.3	1.5	1.7	1.9
$\dfrac{\Delta y}{\Delta x}$	8.2	8.6	9.0	9.4	9.8

$$\frac{dy}{dx} = 2(x + 3) \qquad \frac{\Delta y}{\Delta x} = 2(\bar{x} + 3)$$

3.

$\bar{x}$	1.1	1.3	1.5	1.7	1.9
$\dfrac{\Delta y}{\Delta x}$	50.44	55.48	60.76	66.28	72.04
$\dfrac{dy}{dx}$	50.43	55.47	60.75	66.27	72.03

$$\frac{\Delta y}{\Delta x} - \frac{dy}{dx} = \frac{1}{4}(\Delta x)^2 = 0.01$$

4.

$\bar{x}$	$\dfrac{\Delta y}{\Delta x}$	$\dfrac{dy}{dx}$	x	$\dfrac{\Delta^2 y}{(\Delta x)^2}$	$\dfrac{d^2 y}{dx^2}$
11	88	88			
			12	8	8
13	104	104			
			14	8	8
15	120	120			
			16	8	8
17	136	136			
			18	8	8
19	152	152			

$$\frac{\Delta y}{\Delta x} = \frac{dy}{dx} = 8\,\bar{x} \qquad\qquad \frac{\Delta^2 y}{(\Delta x)^2} = \frac{d^2 y}{dx^2} = 8$$

5. Minimum located at $(0, 0)$.

6. Minimum located at $(0, 0)$.

7. Maximum located at $(0, 4)$.

8. Maximum located at $(0.5, 103.5)$, and minimum at $(2.5, 87.5)$.

9. (a) $\dfrac{dy}{dx} = 0$ at any point.

(b) $\dfrac{dy}{dx} = 5$ at any point.

(c) $\dfrac{dy}{dx} = 14\,x = 140$ at $x = 10$.

(d) $\dfrac{dy}{dx} = 27\,x^2 = 2{,}700$ at $x = 10$.

(e) $\dfrac{dy}{dx} = 8\,x^3 + 8\,x + 6 = 8{,}086$ at $x = 10$.

(f) $\dfrac{dy}{dx} = 5\,x^4 + 3\,x^2 + 10\,x = 50{,}400$ at $x = 10$.

(g) $\dfrac{dy}{dx} = \dfrac{-3}{x^4} = -0.0003$ at $x = 10$.

(h) $\dfrac{dy}{dx} = \dfrac{x(2 - x^3)}{(x^3 + 1)^2} = \dfrac{-9{,}980}{1{,}002{,}001} = -0.009960$ at $x = 10$.

(i) $\dfrac{dy}{dx} = \dfrac{6 - x^2}{(6 + x^2)^2} = \dfrac{-94}{11{,}236} = -0.008366$ at $x = 10$.

(j) $\dfrac{dy}{dx} = \dfrac{x^2(24 - 5x^4)}{(5x^4 + 8)^2} = \dfrac{-4{,}997{,}600}{2{,}500{,}800{,}064} = -0.0019984$ at $x = 10$.

10. The minimum value of y is 40 which is located at $a = b = 5$.

11. The maximum capacity of the box is reached when the height is 5 inches and the base is 10 inches squared. The maximum capacity is 500 cubic inches.

12. Six square inches per minute.

CHAPTER 7

1. (a)

x	0.9	1.1	1.3	1.5	1.7	1.9	2.1
$F(x)$	0.0	1.6	3.6	4.4	3.4	2.8	5.2

The integral is $F(x) + C$ where C is an unknown constant.

(b) (i) 1.2   (ii) 4.4

(d) (i) −0.8   (ii) 0.8   (iii) 3.4   (iv) 0.0

2. (a)

x	5	15	25	35	45	55	65	75	85	95
$F(x)$	0	90	130	100	30	40	120	230	410	660

The integral is $F(x) + C$ where C is an unknown constant.

(b) 140

(d) (i) 130   (ii) 120   (iii) 310   (iv) − 50

3. (b) $\frac{1}{2}x^2 + 2x + C$ (c) 144

4. (b) $\frac{5}{3}(x^3 - 4x) + C$ (c) 6,640

5. (b) $\frac{1}{4}x^4 - 2x^2 + C$ (c) 15,840

6. (b) $\frac{1}{12}(3x^4 - 20x^3 - 18x^2 + 104x) + C$ (c) 9,344

10. $\frac{1}{3}m(m+1)(4m-1)$

CHAPTER 8

2. (a) C (b) $x+C$ (c) $\frac{1}{2}x^2+C$ (d) $\frac{1}{2}x^2+x+C$

3. (a) $\frac{x^3}{3}$ (b) $\frac{y^3}{3}$ (c) $\frac{t^3}{3}$ (d) 9   (e) 63

4. (a) 10.4   (b) 75.75
5. 960
6. $-32/3$
7. 4/15
10. When Δx is equal to 1, the integral is equal to 972. When Δx is equal to 0.5, the integral is equal to 963. When Δx is infinitesimal, the integral is equal to 960 which is called the true area in the problem.

CHAPTER 9

1. (a) 0   (b) 1   (c) 6   (d) -2
2. (a) 2   (b) 5
3. (a) 2.505   (b) 3.21   (c) 12.18   (d) 2
4. (a) 8,000   (b) 0.006944
5. (a) 0.91629   (b) 4.60518   (c) -0.69315 (d) -2.30259
6. (a) 1,250   6,250   (b) 7,810
7. (a) 1,024   512   256   128   64   32   (b) 2,016
8. First term = 3.01030; common difference = -0.30103.
9. First term = 1; common ratio = 10.
10. (a) $267.65   (b) $269.37   (c) $269.77   (d) $269.98
This degree of accuracy may not be obtainable through the five-place table of common logarithms.
11. Approximately 7 %.
12. (a) 2.727   (b) 10

CHAPTER 10

1. $y = 64\left(\frac{1}{2}\right)^x$ $x = 0, 1, 2, 3, 4, 5$.

$$\frac{\Delta y}{\Delta x} = 64\left(\frac{1}{2}\right)^x\left(\frac{1}{2}-1\right) = -32\left(\frac{1}{2}\right)^x \qquad x = 0, 1, 2, 3, 4.$$

2. $\frac{\Delta}{\Delta x} 4^x = 2(4^x)$.

3. For the six intervals of x, the values of

$$\frac{\Delta}{\Delta x} e^{2x} = 2 e^{2\bar{x}}$$

are 0.67, 0.81, 0.99, 1.2, 1.5 and 1.8.

5. $\frac{dy}{dx} = \frac{2}{2x+1}$.

6. $\dfrac{dy}{dx} = \dfrac{2 \log_{10} e}{2x + 1} = \dfrac{0.43429}{x + 0.5}$.

10. The integral evaluated by either method is equal to 6.3067.

12. The integral evaluated by either method is equal to 0.07421.

13. $\dfrac{dy}{dx} = \dfrac{x}{\sqrt{x^2 + 1}}$

15. The definite integral is equal to 0.4 when evaluated by formula, and equal to 0.4005 when evaluated by Simpson's rule.

16. (a) $\dfrac{1}{2}$ (b) $\dfrac{1}{2}$ (c) $\dfrac{1}{\log_e 2} = 1.443$

17. (a) $x^2\, 2^x\, (x \log_e 2 + 3)$

    (b) $x(1 + 2 \log_e x)$

    (c) $(1 - 2x)\, e^{-2x}$

    (d) $\dfrac{x^2 + 4}{x + 1} + 2x \log_e(x + 1)$

18. (a) 0.4055   (b) 1.7274

CHAPTER 11

1.

Angle	sin	cos	tan	cot	sec	csc
15° 16′	0.26331	0.96471	0.27294	3.6638	1.0366	3.7978
42° 14′	0.67215	0.74041	0.90781	1.1016	1.3506	1.4878
63° 15′	0.89298	0.45010	1.9840	0.50404	2.2217	1.1198
74° 39′	0.96433	0.26471	3.6429	0.27451	3.7777	1.0370

2. $\sin 45° = \cos 45° = \dfrac{1}{\sqrt{2}} = \dfrac{1}{1.4142136} = 0.70711$

   $\tan 45° = \cot 45° = \dfrac{1}{1} = 1.0000$

3.

Angle	sin	cos	tan	cot	sec	csc
125° 16′	0.81647	−0.57738	−1.4141	−0.70717	−1.7320	1.2248
170° 25′	0.16648	−0.98604	−0.16884	−5.9228	−1.0142	6.0067
220° 40′	−0.65166	−0.75851	0.85912	1.1640	−1.3184	−1.5345
249° 42′	−0.93789	−0.34694	2.7034	0.36991	−2.8823	−1.0662
340° 26′	−0.33490	0.94225	−0.35543	−2.8135	1.0613	−2.9860
310° 48′	−0.75700	0.65342	−1.1585	−0.86318	1.5304	−1.3210

4. (a) 0.6959   (b) 0.9468   (c) 1.2259
   (d) 1.3872   (e) 1.8913   (f) 1.7267
5. (a) 30°   (b) 45°   (c) 60°
   (d) 270°   (e) 300°   (f) 150°
7. (a) $0.2\pi, 0.8\pi$ (b) $0.1\pi, 1.9\pi$
   (c) $0.3\pi, 1.3\pi$ (d) $0.4\pi, 1.4\pi$
9. 45°, 135°, 225°, 315°
10. 60°, 300°

CHAPTER 12

2. The definite integrals by standard method are as follows:
   (a) 0.0274   (b) 0.0446   (c) 0.0321
   (d) 0.0855   (e) 0.0614   (f) 0.100
3. The definite integrals obtained by trapezoidal rule and those obtained by formula are equal to those of exercise 2.
4. The definite integrals obtained by Simpson's rule and those obtained by formula are equal to those of exercise 2.
5. Maximum located at $(\pi/2, 1)$, and minimum at $(3\pi/2, -1)$.
6. The area is equal to 4.
7. Maxima located at $x = \pi/6, 5\pi/6$ and $9\pi/6$ where y is equal to 2. Minima located at $x = 3\pi/6, 7\pi/6$ and $11\pi/6$ where y is equal to -2.
8. The area is equal to 8.

CHAPTER 13

1. (a) 1   (b) 1/2
2. (a) 120   (b) 5,040   (c) 20   (d) 0.2
3. (a) $\dfrac{9!}{6!}$ (b) 4!   (c) $\dfrac{n!}{(n-3)!}$ (d) $\dfrac{(n+k+1)!}{(n+k-1)!}$

CHAPTER 14

2. $\dfrac{\partial z}{\partial y} = 0.2\,y$ at $x = 0.1$ $\dfrac{\partial z}{\partial y} = 0.4\,y$ at $x = 0.2$
3. Same as exercise 2.
4. $\dfrac{\partial^2 z}{\partial x \partial y} = 2\,y$
5. No maximum or minimum.

6. Minimum of z is located at $(x, y) = (1, -2)$ where z is equal to 5.

7. $y = 3x + 2$

8. $y = 2.5x + 1.6$

10. $\dfrac{dz}{dx} = 1{,}200\,x^2 - 80\,x + 1$

11. $\dfrac{dz}{dy} = \dfrac{3\,y^2 + 2\,y}{20}$

12. Volume expands at the rate of 110 cubic inches per hour.

CHAPTER 15

1. 70	2. 69.9	3. 70	4. 70	5. 39
6. 30/7	7. 109.92	8. 109.82	9. 109.91	10. 316.7

INDEXES

INDEX TO TABLES

INDEX TO TABLES (*continued*)

INDEX TO FIGURES

INDEX TO SUBJECT MATTER